The Sirt Food Diet Cookbook

~1001~

Fuss Free, Fast and Healthy New Year Sirt Food Diet Recipes for Whole Family

Lindsay Hoffman

Table of Contents

DINNER 110

SNACKS 187

INTRODUCTION

The Sirt diet uses powerful superfoods—known as Sirtfoods—to activate what doctors in nutritional medicine refer to as the 'skinny gene.' This skinny gene is a natural biological process that is naturally activated when a person practices exercise, fasting, and now the Sirt diet. We can enable this process, as the top Sirtfoods contain a natural organic chemical known as polyphenols. When consumed, these polyphenols react to the cells in a way that mimics the same process that occurs when we exercise and fast. This is a powerful ability. It allows us to directly tap into weight loss mechanisms, even when we aren't exercising or fasting, resulting in dramatic weight loss without the loss of valuable muscle tone. There are many polyphenol-rich plant foods, but the tip twenty—such as dark chocolate, kale, and red wine—are known as Sirtfoods. These are the twenty foods that you will consume daily on the Sirt diet and other plant foods and protein to maintain a well-rounded and balanced diet. Scientists have long known that these foods are powerful health foods that can affect health, aging mood, weight loss, and more. But it has only more recently been discovered that these benefits originate from the commonly shared polyphenols, also known as sirtuins that they contain, classifying them as Sirtfoods.

Along with providing weight loss while maintaining muscle tone, Sirtfoods are also known to increase health, boost memory, and better control blood sugar. Along with preventing muscle loss, some people can build muscle tone when on the Sirt diet! This is important because even if you don't want to be a bodybuilder, lean muscle tone is vital for every human to maintain health and everyday strength.

Specific plants contain polyphenols, the plant-form of sirtuins, as these plants require a sophisticated network of nutrients to protect themselves. While animals can protect themselves with teeth and claws, plants are stationary and need specific natural compounds to protect themselves from wildlife. These compounds are part of an elaborate stress-response system, which helps the plants to thrive in a wild environment better. But, when we eat these plants, we consume the compounds and benefit ourselves.

All plants have stress-response systems of their own, to a certain extent. Only certain plants have developed sophisticated polyphenols that can activate the natural sirtuin receptors in human biology. It is these foods that are known as sirtfoods and have powerful effects on weight loss and health. Including them into your regular diet can allow you to gain the health and weight loss benefits you want, even without strict exercise and fasting regimens. Even if you don't adopt a full Sirt diet, you can still benefit from including more sirtfoods in your everyday life. After all, by eating many of these plant polyphenols in sirtfoods, you can gain many diets and health benefits, even if you don't pair it with the calorie reduction that is part of the Sirt diet. Of course, if you want to lose a lot of weight, it is generally suggested to try to full Sirt diet, as you can only experience some of the weight loss benefits with Sirtfoods alone. They are more powerful when they work together with calorie reduction, as they are more easily able to help you lose weight, rather than just maintaining weight.

While many foods contain polyphenols, a lot of these only contain them in small quantities. The Sirtfood diet focuses on the top twenty Sirtfoods that contain the most polyphenol, as the more polyphenols you consume, the more effective your weight loss will be. Remember, while many people believe the Sirt diet only includes these foods that is not the case. You eat a balanced diet, complete with other fruits, vegetables, and proteins, along with these Sirtfoods in large quantities.

Along with eating an abundance of these delicious Sirtfoods, the Sirt diet plan has two phases: weight loss and weight maintenance and refuel. In both phases, you are encouraged to drink plenty of the Sirtfood green juice, a freshly made juice containing powerful sirtuins. These are juiced, rather than eating them whole, as it allows you to drink a quick boost of sirtuins to ensure you are consuming enough.

The green juice is full of fresh kale, arugula, parsley, celery, green apple, lemon, matcha green tea powder, and lovage. While matcha is becoming more popular, you can even purchase matcha lattes at Starbucks, many people don't stock their kitchen with it or know where to buy it. While you could purchase matcha at a health food store, you can also find it readily online. Similarly, many people outside of the United Kingdom aren't familiar with lovage. This is a green herb, much like parsley, that is fresh-tasting and powerfully healthy. But you can't simply purchase the herb in American grocery stores. If you are not from the United Kingdom and looking for lovage, you can buy seeds online. These seeds can easily be planted in small pots that you can grow in a brightly lit windowsill in your home, on a balcony, or in your yard. It is incredibly easy to grow, no matter how little space you have. Of course, it doesn't grow instantly. While it will grow quickly, if you want to get started on the Sirt diet right away before you have lovage on your hand, you can replace it with extra parsley in your green juice.

BREAKFAST

1. Sirt Muesli

Preparation time: 5 minutes
Cooking time: 5 minutes
Servings: 2

Ingredients:

- 10g buckwheat puffs
- 20g buckwheat flakes
- 15g coconut flakes or desiccated coconut
- 15g walnuts, chopped
- 40g Medjool dates, pitted and chopped
- 100g strawberries, hulled and chopped
- 10g cocoa nibs
- 100g plain Fresh Greek yoghurt (or vegan alternative, such as coconut or soy yoghurt)

Directions:

1. Mix all of the ingredients together, then add the yoghurt and strawberries before serving, if made in bulk.

Nutrition: Calories: 460 kcal Protein: 13.47 g Fat: 16.88 g Carbohydrates: 71.56 g

2. Apple Pancakes With Blackcurrant Compote

Preparation time: 5 minutes
Cooking time: 20 minutes
Servings: 4

Ingredients:

- 75g porridge oats
- 125g plain flour
- 1 tsp. baking powder
- 2 tbsp. caster sugar
- Pinch of salt
- Two apples, peeled and cut into small
- 300ml semi-skimmed milk
- Two egg whites
- 2 tsp. light olive oil
- For the compote:
- 120g blackcurrants washed and stalks removed
- 2 tbsp. caster sugar
- 3 tbsp. water

Directions:

1. Make the compote, first. Put sugar, blackcurrants, and water in a small saucepan. Bring to a simmer and cook for around 10-15 minutes.
2. In a large bowl, add flour, the oats, baking powder, caster sugar, and salt, then mix well. Stir in the apple and whisk a little at a time in the milk until you have a smooth blend. Whisk the egg whites with a blender to form stiff peaks, then fold into the batter for the pancake. Pour the batter to a jug.
3. Heat 1/2 tsp. Oil in a nonstick frying pan on medium-high heat and pour in approximately one-quarter of the batter. Cook until golden brown, on both sides. Remove and repeat to make more pancakes.
4. Serve the pancakes drizzled over with blackcurrant compote.

Nutrition: Calories: 1054 kcal Protein: 39.85 g Fat: 22.29 g Carbohydrates: 204.08 g

3. Raspberry And Blackcurrant Jelly

Preparation time: 5 minutes
Cooking time: 15 minutes + setting time
Servings: 2

Ingredients:

- 100g raspberries washed
- Two leaves gelatin
- 100g blackcurrants washed and stalks removed
- 2 tbsps. granulated sugar
- 300ml water

Directions:

1. Set the raspberries in two dishes/glasses/molds. Put the gelatine leaves in a bowl filled with cold water for softening.
2. Place the blackcurrants with the sugar and 100ml water in a small saucepan and bring to a boil. Simmer hard for 5 minutes, then remove from heat. Leave for 2 minutes.
3. Squeeze the gelatine leaves out of the excess water and add to the saucepan. Stir until they are completely dissolved, then stir in the remaining water. Pour the liquid into the dishes and set aside to cool. The jellies should be ready overnight or in about 3-4 hours.

Nutrition: Calories: 224 kcal Protein: 10.58 g Fat: 7.06 g Carbohydrates: 33.14 g

4. Gluten-Free Puffed Buckwheat Toasted Muesli

Preparation time: 10 minutes
Cooking time: 35 minutes
Servings: 11

Ingredients:

- 2 cups puffed buckwheat
- 1 1/2 cups raw seeds and nuts, any combination
- 1 cup buckwheat flakes
- 1/3 cup rice malt syrup (or another liquid sweetener)
- 1/4 cup coconut oil (60-70 mL)
- 1 tbsp. ground cinnamon
- 1 tbsp. vanilla extract
- 1/2 tsp fine salt

Directions:

1. Preheat oven to 150 C and then take a large baking tray (or two small trays) and line with baking paper.
2. Combine the buckwheat, coconut, seed, cinnamon, and salt into a large bowl.
3. Add the coconut oil, rice malt syrup and vanilla then melt together in a small pan, so it gets nice and runny and removes from the heat. Pour the liquid in a dry mixture and thoroughly combine, so that all the dry ingredients are coated well.
4. Spread the prepared mixture evenly on the baking tray. Bake for about 25 minutes and gently turn over the mixture, about every 7-10 minutes, to avoid it to burn around the edges.
5. Pull out the dish from the oven and let it cool completely; the muesli will crisp up a lot as it cools down.
6. Store in an airtight container (it should last about one month). You can also add to the mixture a handful of your favorite dried fruit after cooking if you like.

Nutrition: Calories: 2647 kcal Protein: 74.19 g Fat: 171.86 g Carbohydrates: 228.57 g

5. Sirtfood Diet Shakshuka

Preparation time: 10 minutes
Cooking time: 40 minutes
Servings: 1

Ingredients:

- 1 tsp. extra virgin olive oil
- 40 g Red onion, finely chopped
- 1 Garlic clove, finely chopped
- 1 Bird's eye chili, finely chopped
- 30 g Celery, finely chopped
- 1 tsp. Ground turmeric
- 1 tsp. Paprika
- 400 g Tinned chopped tomatoes
- 1 tsp. ground cumin
- 1 tbsp. Chopped parsley
- 30 g Kale, stems removed and chopped roughly
- 2 Medium eggs

Directions:

1. Heat a small, deep-sided frying pan over medium-low heat. Then add the oil and 1-2 minutes fry the onion, garlic, celery, chili, and spices.
2. Add the tomatoes, and simmer the sauce gently, occasionally stirring for 20 minutes.
3. Stir the kale and cook for another 5 minutes. If you feel that your sauce is getting way too thick, add a bit of water. Stir in the parsley, when your sauce has a nice rich consistency.
4. Make two small little wells in the sauce and crack each egg into them. Reduce heat to its lowest setting and use a lid or foil to cover the pan. Leave the eggs for 10–12 minutes to cook, where the whites should be firm while the yolks are still runny. Cook for an additional 3–4 minutes, if you prefer firm yolks. Serve right away-ideally straight from the pan.

Nutrition: Calories: 351 kcal Protein: 25.22 g Fat: 18.38 g Carbohydrates: 25.31 g

6. Date And Walnut Porridge

Preparation time: 5 minutes
Cooking time: 10 minutes
Servings: 1

Ingredients:

- 200 ml Milk or dairy-free alternative
- 1 Medjool date, chopped
- 35 g Buckwheat flakes
- 1 tsp. Walnut butter or four chopped walnut halves
- 50 g Strawberries, hulled

Directions:

1. Place the milk and date in a saucepan, heat gently, then add the buckwheat flakes and cook until the porridge is the consistency you want.
2. Stir in the walnut butter or walnuts, top with the strawberries and serve.

Nutrition: Calories: 230 kcal Protein: 8.39 g Fat: 10.28 g Carbohydrates: 28.81 g

7. Mushroom Scramble Eggs

Preparation time: 5 minutes
Cooking time: 15 minutes
Servings: 1

Ingredients:

- 2 eggs
- 1 tsp. ground turmeric
- 1 tsp. mild curry powder
- 20g kale, roughly chopped
- 5g parsley, finely chopped
- 1 tsp. extra virgin olive oil
- A handful of button mushrooms, thinly sliced
- ½ bird's eye chili, thinly sliced

Optional

- Add Rooster Sauce for flavor and seed mixture as a topper.

Directions:

1. Mix the curry and turmeric powder, then add a little water until a light paste is formed.
2. Steam up the kale for 2–3 minutes.
3. Get the oil heated on medium heat in a frying pan and fry the chilli and mushrooms for 2–3 minutes until they are brown and are softened.
4. Add the eggs and spice paste and cook over medium heat, then add the kale and continue to cook over medium heat for a further minute Finally, add the parsley, mix well, and serve.

Nutrition: Calories: 304 kcal Protein: 19.53 g Fat: 21.8 g Carbohydrates: 7.23 g

8. Smoked Salmon Omelet

Preparation time: 5 minutes
Cooking time: 10 minutes
Servings: 1

Ingredients:

- 2 Medium eggs
- 100 g Smoked salmon, sliced
- 1/2 tsp. Capers
- 10 g Rocket, chopped
- 1 tsp. Parsley, chopped
- 1 tsp. extra virgin olive oil

Directions:

1. Crack the eggs and whisk well in a bowl. Add the salmon, capers, parsley, and rocket.
2. In a nonstick frying pan, heat the olive oil until hot but not smoking. Add the egg mixture and move the mixture around the pan, using a spatula or fish slice until it is even. Reduce heat and let the omelet cook thoroughly. Slide the spatula around the edges of the pan and roll the omelet up or fold in half to serve.

Nutrition: Calories: 400 kcal Protein: 40.7 g Fat: 24.64 g Carbohydrates: 0.72 g

9. Moroccan Spiced Eggs

Preparation time: 5 minutes
Cooking time: 50 minutes
Servings: 2

Ingredients:

- 1 tsp. olive oil
- 1 shallot, peeled and finely chopped
- 1 red bellpepper, deseeded and well chopped
- 1 garlic clove, peeled and finely chopped
- 1 courgette (zucchini), peeled and finely chopped
- 1 tbsp. tomato puree (paste)
- ½ tsp. mild chili powder
- ¼ tsp. ground cinnamon
- ¼ tsp. ground cumin
- ½ tsp. salt
- 1 × 400g (14oz) can chopped tomatoes
- 1 x 400g (14oz) canned chickpeas in water
- A small handful of flat-leaf parsley (10g (1/3oz)), chopped
- 4 medium eggs at room temperature

Directions:

1. Heat oil in a saucepan, add the shallot and red pepper (bell), and fry gently for 5 minutes. Stir in the garlic and courgette (zucchini) and cook for a minute or two. Add the tomato puree (paste), salt, and spices and stir in.

2. Stir in the chopped tomatoes and chickpeas (soaking liquor and all) and heat up to medium. Simmer the sauce for 30 minutes with the lid off the pan – make sure it bubbles gently throughout, and allow it to reduce by about one-third in volume.
3. Remove from the heat and then add in the chopped parsley.
4. Preheat the oven to 200C.
5. Bring the tomato sauce to a simmer when you are ready to cook the eggs and transfer it to a small ovenproof dish.
6. Crack eggs on the side of the platter, and gently lower them into the stew. Cover with the foil, and bake for 10-15 minutes in the oven. Serve the concoction with the eggs floating on top in individual bowls.

Nutrition: Calories: 473 kcal Protein: 34.58 g Fat: 29 g Carbohydrates: 20.94 g

10. Savory Turmeric Pancakes With Lemon Yogurt Sauce

Preparation time: 10 minutes
Cooking time: 40 minutes
Servings: 8
Ingredients:

- For The Yogurt Sauce
- 1 cup plain Greek yoghurt
- 1 garlic clove, minced
- ¼ teaspoon ground turmeric
- Ten fresh mint leaves, minced
- 1-2 tablespoons lemon juice, to taste
- 2 teaspoons lemon zest (from 1 lemon)
- For the Pancakes
- 2 teaspoons ground turmeric
- 1½ teaspoons ground cumin
- 1 teaspoon salt
- 1 teaspoon ground coriander
- ½ teaspoon garlic powder
- ½ teaspoon freshly ground black pepper
- 1 head broccoli, cut into florets
- 3 large eggs, lightly beaten
- 2tablespoons plain unsweetened almond milk
- 1 cup almond flour
- 4teaspoons coconut oil

Directions:

1. Make the sauce with yoghurt. In a bowl, Put the yoghurt, garlic, lemon juice, turmeric, mint, and zest. Where needed, taste, and season with more lemon juice. Refrigerate or set aside until ready to serve.
2. Make the pancakes. In a bowl, combine the turmeric, cumin, salt, coriander, garlic, and pepper.
3. Add the broccoli in a food processor and pulse into small pieces until the florets are broken. Transfer the broccoli to a bowl, add in the eggs, almond milk, and almond flour. Stir in the spice mix and mix well.
4. Heat 1 teaspoon of coconut oil over medium to low heat in a nonstick pan. Pour 1/4 batter into your skillet. Cook the pancake until there are small bubbles on the surface, and the bottom is golden brown, 2 to 3 minutes. Flip over and cook the pancake for another 2 to 3 minutes. Transfer the cooked pancakes to an oven-safe dish, and place them in a 200 ° F oven to keep them warm.
5. Continue making the remaining three pancakes, using the remaining oil and batter.

Nutrition: Calories: 94 kcal Protein: 3.18 g Fat: 7.47 g Carbohydrates: 4.25 g

11. Turkey Breakfast Sausages

Preparation time: 10 minutes
Cooking time: 20 minutes
Servings: 4
Ingredients:

- 1 lb. extra lean ground turkey
- 1 tbsp. EVOO 9 Extra Virgin Olive Oil), and a little more to coat pan
- 1 tbsp. fennel seeds
- 2 teaspoons smoked paprika
- 1 teaspoon red pepper flakes
- 1 teaspoon peppermint
- 1 teaspoon chicken seasoning A couple of shredded cheddar cheese
- A couple of chives, finely chopped A few shakes garlic and onion powder
- 2 spins of pepper and salt

Directions:

1. Preheat oven to 350 F.
2. Utilize a little EVOO to grease a miniature muffin pan.
3. Combine all ingredients and blend thoroughly.
4. Fill each pit on top of the pan and then cook for approximately 15-20 minutes. Each toaster differs; therefore, when muffin temperature is 165, then remove.

Nutrition: Calories: 41 kcal Total Fat: 1.91 g Saturated Fat: 0.559 g Cholesterol: 16 mg Sodium: 137 mg Total Carbs: 0 g Fiber: 0 g Sugar: 0 g Protein: 5.53 g

12. Banana Pecan Muffins

Preparation time: 10 minutes
Cooking time: 50 minutes
Servings: 4
Ingredients:

- 3 tbsp. butter softened
- 4 ripe bananas
- 1 tbsp. honey
- ⅛ Cup OJ
- 1 teaspoon cinnamon
- 2 cups all-purpose flour
- 2 capsules
- A couple of pecans, sliced
- 1 tbsp. vanilla

Directions:

1. Preheat the oven to 180°c.
2. Lightly grease the bottom and each sides of the muffin tin, and then dust with flour.
3. Dust the surfaces of the tin gently with flour then tap to eradicate any excess.
4. Peel and insert the batter to a mixing bowl and with a fork, mash the carrots; therefore that you've got a combination of chunky and smooth, and then put aside.
5. Insert the orange juice, melted butter, eggs, vanilla, and spices and stir to combine.
6. Roughly chop the pecans onto a chopping board, when using, then fold throughout the mix.
7. Spoon at the batter 3/4 full and bake in the oven for approximately 40 minutes, or until golden and cooked through

Nutrition: Calories: 286.8 kcal Total Fat: 14.6 g Saturated Fat: 6.5 g Cholesterol: 61.9 mg Sodium: 143 mg Total Carbs: 192.6 g Fiber: 1.9 g Sugar: 19.2 g Protein: 4.4 g

13. Banana And Blueberry Muffins

Preparation time: 10 minutes

Cooking time: 30 minutes
Servings: 4
Ingredients:

- 4 large ripe bananas, peeled and mashed
- 3/4 cup of sugar
- 1 egg, lightly crushed
- 1/2 cup of butter, melted (and a little extra to dust the interiors of this muffin tin)
- 2 cups of blueberries (if they are frozen, do not defrost them.Simply pop them into the batter as is)
- 1 teaspoon baking powder
- 1 teaspoon baking soda
- 1/2 teaspoon salt
- 1 cup of coconut bread
- 1/2 cup of flour (or 1-1; two cup bread)
- 1/2 cup applesauce
- Dash of cinnamon

Directions:

1. Add mashed banana to a large mixing bowl.
2. Add sugar & egg and mix well.
3. Add butter and strawberries.
4. Sift all the dry ingredients together, then add the dry ingredients into the wet mix and mix together lightly.
5. Set into 12 greased muffin cups
6. Bake for 20-30min in 180c or 350 f.

Nutrition: Calories: 183 kcal Total Fat: 5 g Saturated Fat: 3 g Cholesterol: 26 mg Sodium: 209 mg Total Carbs: 30 g Fiber: 3 g Sugar: 0 g Protein: 3 g

14. Morning Meal Sausage Gravy

Preparation time: 5 minutes
Cooking time: 10 minutes
Servings: 4
Ingredients:

- 1 lb. sausage
- 2 cups 2% milk (whole milk is great also)
- 1/4 cup whole wheat flour
- Salt and a lot of pepper to flavor

Directions:

1. Cook sausage from skillet.
2. Add flour and blend cook for about a minute.
3. Insert two cups of milk.
4. Whisk while gravy thickens and bubbles.
5. Add pepper and salt and to taste until perfect.
6. Let stand a minute or so to scrape it over the desired foods.

Nutrition: Calories: 1008 kcal Total Fat: 58 g Saturated Fat: 28 g Cholesterol: 20 mg Sodium: 3262 mg Total Carbs: 144 g Fiber: 2 g Sugar: 6 g Protein: 19 g

15. Easy Egg-White Muffins

Preparation time: 10 minutes
Cooking time: 1 hour and 10 minutes
Servings: 4
Ingredients:

- English muffin - I enjoy Ezekiel 7 grain
- Egg-whites - 6 tbsp. or two large egg whites
- Turkey bacon or bacon sausage
- Sharp cheddar cheese or Gouda
- Organic berry

Optional

- lettuce and hot sauce, hummus, flaxseeds, etc.

Directions:

1. Get a microwavable safe container, then spray entirely to stop the egg from adhering, then pour egg whites into the dish.
2. Lay turkey bacon or bacon sausage paper towel and then cook.
3. Subsequently, toast your muffin, if preferred.
4. Then put the egg dish in the microwave for 30 minutes. Afterward, with a spoon or fork, immediately flip egg within the dish and cook for another 30 minutes.
5. While the dish remains hot, sprinkle some cheese while preparing sausage.
6. The secret is to get a paste of some kind between each coating to put up the sandwich together, i.e. - a very small little bit of hummus or even cheese.

Nutrition: Calories: 24.8 kcal Total Fat: 0 g Saturated Fat: 0 g Cholesterol: 0.4 mg Sodium: 79.1 mg Total Carbs: 1.3 g Fiber: 0.3 g Sugar: 0.6 g Protein: 4.3 g

16. Kale Scramble

Preparation time: 10 minutes
Cooking time: 6 minutes
Servings: 2
Ingredients:

- 4 eggs
- 1/8 teaspoon ground turmeric
- Salt and ground black pepper, to taste
- 1 tablespoon water
- 2 teaspoons olive oil
- 1 cup fresh kale,chopped and ribs removed

Directions:

1. In a bowl, add the eggs, turmeric, salt, black pepper, and water and with a whisk, beat until foamy.
2. In a wok, heat the oil over medium heat.
3. Add the egg mixture and stir to combine.
4. Immediately, reduce the heat to medium-low and cook for about 1–2 minutes, stirring frequently.
5. Stir the kale and cook for about 3–4 minutes, stirring frequently.
6. Remove from the heat and serve immediately.

Nutrition: Calories: 183 kcal Total Fat: 13.4 g Saturated Fat: 0 g Cholesterol: 0 mg Sodium: 0 mg Total Carbs: 4.3 g Fiber: 0 g Sugar: 0 g Protein: 12.1 g

17. Buckwheat Porridge

Preparation time: 10 minutes
Cooking time: 15 minutes
Servings: 2
Ingredients:

- 1 cup buckwheat, rinsed
- 1 cup unsweetened almond milk
- 1 cup of water
- ½ teaspoon ground cinnamon
- ½ teaspoon vanilla extract
- 1–2 tablespoons raw honey
- ¼ cup fresh blueberries

Directions:

1. In a pan, place all the ingredients (except honey and blueberries) over medium-high heat and bring to a boil.
2. Now, reduce the heat to low and simmer, covered for about 10 minutes.
3. Stir in the honey and remove from the heat.
4. Set aside, covered, for about 5 minutes.
5. With a fork, fluff the mixture, and transfer into serving bowls.
6. Top with blueberries and serve.

Nutrition: Calories: 358 kcal Total Fat: 4.7 g Saturated Fat: 0 g Cholesterol: 0 mg Sodium: 0 mg Total Carbs: 3.7 g Fiber: 0 g Sugar: 0 g Protein: 12 g

18. Chocolate Granola

Preparation time: 10 minutes
Cooking time: 38 minutes
Servings: 8
Ingredients:

- ¼ cup cacao powder
- ¼ cup maple syrup
- 2 tablespoons coconut oil, melted
- ½ teaspoon vanilla extract
- 1/8 teaspoon salt
- 2 cups gluten-free rolled oats
- ¼ cup unsweetened coconut flakes
- 2 tablespoons chia seeds
- 2 tablespoons unsweetened dark chocolate, chopped finely

Directions:

1. Preheat the oven to 300°F and then line a medium baking sheet with parchment paper.
2. In a medium pan, add the cacao powder, maple syrup, coconut oil, vanilla extract, and salt, and mix well.
3. Now, place the pan over medium heat and cook for about 2–3 minutes, or until thick and syrupy, stirring continuously.
4. Remove from the heat and set aside.
5. In a large bowl, set the oats, coconut, and chia seeds, and mix well.
6. Add the syrup mixture and mix until well combined.
7. Transfer the granola mixture onto a prepared baking sheet and spread in an even layer.
8. Bake for about 35 minutes.
9. Remove from the oven and set aside for about 1 hour.
10. Add the chocolate pieces and stir to combine.
11. Serve immediately.

Nutrition: Calories: 193 kcal Total Fat: 9.1 g Saturated Fat: 0 g Cholesterol: 0 mg Sodium: 0 mg Total Carbs: 26.1 g Fiber: 0 g Sugar: 0 g Protein: 5g

19. Blueberry Muffins

Preparation time: 15 minutes
Cooking time: 20 minutes
Servings: 8
Ingredients:

- 1 cup buckwheat flour
- ¼ cup arrowroot starch
- 1½ teaspoons baking powder
- ¼ teaspoon of sea salt
- 2 eggs ½ cup unsweetened almond milk
- 2–3 tablespoons maple syrup
- 2 tablespoons coconut oil, melted
- 1 cup fresh blueberries

Directions:

1. Preheat the oven to 350°F.
2. Line 8 cups of a muffin tin.
3. In a bowl, place the buckwheat flour, arrowroot starch, baking powder, and salt, and mix well.
4. In a separate bowl, place the eggs, almond milk, maple syrup, and coconut oil, and beat until well combined.
5. Now, place the flour mixture and mix until just combined.
6. Gently, fold in the blueberries.
7. Transfer the mixture into prepared muffin cups evenly.
8. Bake for about 25 minutes or until a toothpick inserted in the center comes out clean.
9. Remove the muffin tin from the oven and place onto a wire rack to cool for about 10 minutes.
10. Carefully invert the muffins onto the wire rack to cool completely before serving.

Nutrition: Calories: 136 kcal Total Fat: 5.3 g Saturated Fat: 0 g Cholesterol: 0 mg Sodium: 0 mg Total Carbs20.7 0 g Fiber: 0 g Sugar: 0 g Protein: 3.5 g

20. Chocolate Waffles

Preparation time: 15 minutes
Cooking time: 24 minutes
Servings: 8
Ingredients:

- 2 cups unsweetened almond milk
- 1 tablespoon fresh lemon juice
- 1 cup buckwheat flour
- ½ cup cacao powder
- ¼ cup flaxseed meal
- 1 teaspoon baking soda
- 1 teaspoon baking powder
- ¼ teaspoons kosher salt
- 2 large eggs
- ½ cup coconut oil, melted
- ¼ cup dark brown sugar
- 2 teaspoons vanilla extract
- 2 ounces unsweetened dark chocolate, chopped roughly

Directions:

1. In a bowl, combine the almond milk and lemon juice and mix well.
2. Set aside for about 10 minutes.
3. In a bowl, place buckwheat flour, cacao powder, flaxseed meal, baking soda, baking powder, and salt, and mix well.
4. In the bowl of the almond milk mixture, place the eggs, coconut oil, brown sugar, and vanilla extract, and beat until smooth.
5. Now, place the flour mixture and beat until smooth.
6. Gently fold in the chocolate pieces.
7. Preheat the waffle iron and then grease it.
8. Place the desired amount of the mixture into the preheated waffle iron and cook for about 3 minutes, or until golden brown.
9. Repeat with the remaining mixture.

Nutrition: Calories 295 Fat 22.1 g Carbs 1.5 g Protein 6.3 g

21. Salmon & Kale Omelet

Preparation time: 10 minutes
Cooking time: 7 minutes
Servings: 4
Ingredients:

- 6 eggs
- 2 tablespoons unsweetened almond milk Salt and ground black pepper, to taste
- 2 tablespoons olive oil
- 4 ounces smoked salmon, cut into bite-sized chunks
- 2 cup fresh kale, tough ribs removed and chopped finely
- 4 scallions, chopped finely

Directions:

1. In a bowl, place the eggs, coconut milk, salt, and black pepper, and beat well. Set aside.
2. In a non-stick pan, heat the oil in medium heat.
3. Place the egg mixture evenly and cook for about 30 seconds without stirring.
4. Place the salmon kale and scallions on top of the egg mixture evenly.

5. Now, reduce heat to low.
6. With the lid, cover the pan and cook for about 4–5 minutes or until the omelet is done completely.
7. Uncover the pan and cook for around 1 minute.
8. Carefully transfer the omelet onto a serving plate and serve.

Nutrition: Calories: 210 kcal Total Fat: 0 14.9 Saturated Fat: 0 g Cholesterol: 0 mg Sodium: 0 mg Total Carbs: 5.2 g Fiber: 0 g Sugar: 0 g Protein: 14.8 g

22. Chilaquiles With Gochujang

Preparation time: 30 minutes
Cooking time: 20 minutes
Servings: 2

Ingredients:

- One dried ancho chile
- 2 cups of water
- 1 cup squashed tomatoes
- 2 cloves of garlic
- 1 teaspoon genuine salt
- 1/2 tablespoons gochujang
- 5 to 6 cups tortilla chips
- 3 enormous eggs
- 1 tablespoon olive oil

Directions:

1. Get the water to heat a pot. I cheated marginally and heated the water in an electric pot and emptied it into the pan. There's no sound unrivalled strategy here. Add the anchor Chile to the bubbled water and drench for 15 minutes to give it an opportunity to stout up.
2. When completed, use tongs or a spoon to extricate Chile. Make sure to spare the water for the sauce! Nonetheless, on the off chance that you incidentally dump the water, it's not the apocalypse.
3. Mix the doused Chile, 1 cup of saved high temp water, squashed tomatoes, garlic, salt and gochujang until smooth.
4. Empty sauce into a large dish and warmth over medium warmth for 4 to 5 minutes, mood killer the heat and include the tortilla chips. Mix the chips to cover with the sauce. In a different skillet, shower a teaspoon of oil and fry an egg on top, until the whites have settled. Plate the egg and cook the remainder of the eggs. If you are phenomenal at performing various tasks, you can likely sear the eggs while you heat the red sauce. I am not precisely so capable.
5. Top the chips with the seared eggs, cotija, hacked cilantro, jalapeños, onions and avocado. Serve right away.

Nutrition: Calories: 484 kcal Total Fat: 18.62 g Saturated Fat: 0 g Cholesterol: 0 mg Sodium: 0 mg Total Carbs: 64.04 g Fiber: 0 g Sugar: 0 g Protein: 14.55 g

23. Twice Baked Breakfast Potatoes

Preparation time: 1 hour and 10 minutes
Cooking time: 1 hour
Servings: 2

Ingredients:

- 2 medium reddish brown potatoes, cleaned and pricked with a fork everywhere
- 2 tablespoons unsalted spread
- 3 tablespoons overwhelming cream
- 4 rashers cooked bacon
- 4 huge eggs
- ½ cup destroyed cheddar daintily cut chives
- Salt and pepper to taste

Directions:

1. Preheat grill to 400°F.
2. Spot potatoes straightforwardly on stove rack in the focal point of the grill and prepare for 30 to 45 min.
3. Evacuate and permit potatoes to cool for around 15 minutes.
4. Cut every potato down the middle longwise and burrow every half out, scooping the potato substance into a blending bowl.
5. Gather margarine and cream to the potato and pound into a single unit until smooth — season with salt and pepper and mix.
6. Spread a portion of the potato blend into the base of each emptied potato skin and sprinkle with one tablespoon cheddar (you may make them remain pounded potato left to snack on).
7. Add one rasher bacon to every half and top with a raw egg.
8. Spot potatoes onto a heating sheet and come back to the appliance.
9. Lower broiler temperature to 375°F and heat potatoes until egg whites simply set and yolks are as yet runny.
10. Top every potato with a sprinkle of the rest of the cheddar, season with salt and pepper and finish with cut chives.

Nutrition: Calories: 647 kcal Total Fat: 55.79 g Saturated Fat: 0 g Cholesterol: 0 mg Sodium: 0 mg Total Carbs: 7.49 g Fiber: 0 g Sugar: 0 g Protein: 30.46 g

24. Exquisite Turmeric Pancakes With Lemon Yogurt Sauce

Preparation time: 45 minutes
Cooking time: 15 minutes
Servings: 8 hotcakes

Ingredients:

- For The Yogurt Sauce
- 1 cup plain Greek yogurt
- 1 garlic clove, minced
- 1 to 2 tablespoons lemon juice
- ¼ teaspoon ground turmeric
- 10 crisp mint leaves, minced
- 2 teaspoons lemon pizzazz (from 1 lemon)
- For The Pancakes
- 2 teaspoons ground turmeric
- 1½ teaspoons ground cumin
- 1 teaspoon salt
- 1 teaspoon ground coriander
- ½ teaspoon garlic powder
- ½ teaspoon naturally ground dark pepper
- 1 head broccoli, cut into florets
- 3 enormous eggs, gently beaten
- 2 tablespoons plain unsweetened almond milk
- 1 cup almond flour
- 4 teaspoons coconut oil

Directions:

1. Make the yogurt sauce. Join the yogurt, garlic, lemon juice, turmeric, mint, and pizzazz in a bowl. Taste and enjoy with more lemon juice, if possible. Keep in a safe spot or freeze until prepared to serve.
2. Make the flapjacks. In a little bowl, join the turmeric, cumin, salt, coriander, garlic, and pepper.
3. Spot the broccoli in a nourishment processor, and heartbeat until the florets are separated into little pieces. Move the broccoli to an enormous bowl and include the

eggs, almond milk, and almond flour. Mix in the flavor blend and consolidate well.

4. Heat 1 teaspoon of the coconut oil in a nonstick dish over medium-low heat. Empty ¼ cup player into the skillet. Cook the hotcake until little air pockets start to show up superficially, and the base is brilliant darker 2 to 3 minutes. Flip over and cook the hotcake for 2 to 3 minutes more. Keep warm, move the cooked hotcakes to a stove dish, and a spot in a 200°F oven.
5. Keep making the staying 3 hotcakes, utilizing the rest of the oil and player.

Nutrition: Calories: 262 kcal Total Fat: 19.28 g Saturated Fat: 0 g Cholesterol: 0 mg Sodium: 0 mg Total Carbs: 12.06 g Fiber: 0 g Sugar: 0 g Protein: 11.68 g

25. Strawberry Buckwheat Pancakes

Preparation time: 5 Minutes
Cooking time: 45 Minutes
Servings: 4

Ingredients:

- 3½oz strawberries, chopped
- 3½ oz. buckwheat flour
- 1 egg
- 8fl oz. milk
- 1 teaspoon olive oil
- 1 teaspoon olive oil for frying
- Freshly squeezed juice of 1 orange

Directions:

1. Put the milk into a bowl and mix in the egg and a teaspoon of olive oil. Sift in the flour to the liquid mixture until smooth and creamy. Allow it to rest for 15 minutes. Heat a little oil in a pan and pour in a quarter of the mixture or the size you prefer.
2. Sprinkle in a quarter of the strawberries into the batter. Cook for around 2 minutes on each side. Serve hot with a drizzle of orange juice. You could try experimenting with other berries such as blueberries and blackberries.

Nutrition: Calories: 180 kcal Total Fat: 7.5 g Saturated Fat: 0 g Cholesterol: 0 mg Sodium: 0 mg Total Carbs: 22.58 g Fiber: 0 g Sugar: 0 g Protein: 7.46 g

26. Avocado Toast With Egg

Preparation time: 5 minutes
Cooking time: 10 minutes
Servings: 4

Ingredients:

- 4 eggs
- 1 avocado, peeled, cooked & mashed
- 4 slices whole-wheat bread
- ¼ tsp salt
- ¼ tsp pepper
- 1 tbsp olive oil
- ½ cup fresh salsa

Directions:

1. Toast the bread.
2. In a pan, heat the oil in a medium to high heat.
3. Crack eggs into a pan and fry until cooked
4. Divide mashed avocado into 4 portions and spread onto toast, one piece per slice
5. Place 1 fried egg onto each slice of toast.
6. Sprinkle with salt and pepper
7. Drizzle each slice with salsa and serve

Nutritional Information : Calories: 247 Fat: 14.5g Protein: 11g Carbohydrate: 19g Fiber: 6g

27. King Prawn Fry Almond Noodles

Preparation time: 10 minutes
Cooking time:
30 minutes
Servings: 6

Ingredients:

- 300 grams Buckwheat / Soba Noodles When you try to get 100% buckwheat, you can
- 2 tablespoons extra virgin vegetable oil
- Cut1 purple onion sliced thin
- 2 celery chopped 2 Stick chopped
- 100g bananas approximately
- 100g green beans cut 33cm
- Ginger grated
- 3 garlic cloves grated or finely chopped
- 1 germander speedwell by removing chili seeds/membrane and finely chopped (or taste)
- 600 Gram Raja Prawns tablespoons parcel 2 tablespoons Tamari / Soybean cut 2(or if you like) " will get it!)

Directions:

1. Cook the noodles for about 3-5 minutes or until they are your liking. Drain, rinse in cold water. Drizzle over a touch of vegetable oil, mix and set aside.
2. While the noodles cooking, prep the remaining ingredients.
3. In a skillet or large fry pan, fry the purple onions and celery over a little vegetable oil over a light onion until softened for 3 minutes, then add the bananas and green beans and cook on medium-high heat for 3 minutes.
4. Heat again and add ginger, garlic, chili, and prawns. Fry for 2-3 minutes until the prawns hot all the way through.
5. Add the noodles, tamari/soy sauce, and cook for 1 more minute until the noodles hot again. Sprinkle with parsley and serve.

Nutrition: Calories: 2545 kcal Protein: 211.75 g Fat: 115.77 g Carbohydrates: 206.87 g

28. Sautéed Mushroom Gouda And Kale Potato Skins

Preparation time: 10 minutes
Cooking time: 30 minutes
Servings: 4

Ingredients

- 6 (or 3 as a hearty main) as a side mushrooms
- 1 tbsp. butter
- 1 tbsp. vegetable oil
- 1 small onion, finely chopped
- 8 white button (Ceremony) mushrooms,
- 1 clove Garlic, minced.
- 1 teaspoon thyme
- Wine cup wine or broth
- Salt and pepper taste
- Potatoes
- 6 red Idaho potatoes or 3 russet potatoes
- 2 tablespoons vegetable oil, split
- 1 tablespoon butter
- Cream
- Sour cup sour co cup parcels Grated gouda (or cheddar, gruyere, Or comet)
- Keel. Banana paste
- 1 bunch (approx. / Lb. / 226 gr), de-steamed and coarsely chopped

- 1 clove, peel
- ⅓ Cup nut
- Juice lemon
- 22 tbsp Parmesan-Reggiano cheese, grated
- 2 tbsp Romano cheese, grated tsp
- 3Spoon Extra-Virgin Vegetable Oil
- 1 oz. cup cooking water, plus if necessary

Directions:

Mushrooms

1. Melt butter with oil in a pan over medium-high heat. Add onion and sauce, until translucent, about 6 7 minutes.
2. Add garlic and thyme and fragrant for a few minutes.
3. Add chopped Ceremony mushrooms and sauté 'until they turn golden brown and begin caramel for about 10 minutes.
4. Add the wine (or broth), stir the pan, and cook until most of the liquid has evaporated about 3 minutes.
5. Season with salt and pepper, add parsley and take away from heat. Cancel.

Potato

6. Preheat the oven 400 ° F (200 ° C) and place a rack in the middle.
7. Gently rub the potatoes, but do not peel. Pierce several times with a fork.
8. Place on an external baking sheet and bake for 25 half an hour (40 minutes if you are using red potatoes).
9. When they handled cool enough, slice the potatoes in half, scoop out most of the meat but leave a touch attached the skin aid them to hold their shape (leave about ¼ inch of skin and potatoes.)
10. Melt butter and mix with vegetable oil. Brush the skin and outer part of the skin and bake the skin for an additional 5–10 minutes until it well and crispy.

Kale Pesto

11. Bring a heavy salty pot of water a boiling boil. Add garlic and banana (bound submerge it underwater) and blanch for 3 minutes.
12. Using a slotted spoonful of fish, take out the banana and, therefore, garlic from the water and transfer a colander. Allow cool slightly and squeeze several glasses of water on the back of the spoon (or use your hands if you dare).
13. Add walnuts a kitchen appliance; The lentils mixed until the mixture turns in a coarse meal.
14. Add fennel, garlic, and juice.
15. Pulse until choppy and almost smooth.
16. Employing the spatula, lowering the edges. Throat-in Parmesan Cheese, Romano Cheese, and Cayenne Flakes (if using). Pulse again, and while the kitchen appliance slowly moving, add water until the peaches a creamy consistency.
17. Transfer the black paste a bowl and employ a spoonful stirring within the vegetable oil until it is completely absorbed.
18. If the banana passbooks too thick, add more water (not oil) up a teaspoon at a time, until it reaches the specified consistency.
19. Gather the pot skins in a large bowl mash the Pota flesh until it forms a sticking mass. Add sour cream, cup gouda, banana pes (I used about 4 tablespoons), and season with salt and pepper.
20. Stuffing filling within prepared pot peels, top with mushrooms, and sprinkle with remaining oud cup gouda.
21. Pop in the oven for about 15 twenty minutes finish.

Nutrition: Calories: 1101 kcal Protein: 39.23 g Fat: 46.03 g Carbohydrates: 140.45 g

29. Steak And Balsamic Vinaigrette With Strawberry Arugula Salad

Preparation time: 10 minutes
Cooking time: 30 minutes
Servings: 4

Ingredients

- Steak
- 4 Steak of your choice (Beef Tenderloin picture)
- Steak Spice (Montreal Steak Spice was used in the photos)
- 1 Tbsp Oil
- Salad
- 6 Cups Arugula
- 6 oz Raspberry (1 cup)
- 6 oz Blueberries (1 cup)
- 1 cup strawberries (chopped)
- 1/2 cup feta cheese (crumbled)
- 1/4 cup diluted almonds
- Balsamic vinaigrette
- 1/4 cup balsamic vinegar
- 1/4 cup vegetable oil
- 3 tablespoons sugar
- 1 / 2 tablespoons Dijon mustard
- Salt and pepper.

Directions:

Steak:

1. Season steak and allow it to sit at temperature for 5-10 minutes.
2. Heat the oil during a cast-iron skeleton over medium-high heat. Wait until the oil boiling; it will flicker.
3. Add steak the pan, do not touch it. Cook for five minutes, flip over, and cook for 3 minutes or until the internal temperature reaches 130–135 ° F (for medium-rare).
4. Transfer the steak a plate and allow it to rest for five minutes before cutting in strips.

Salad

5. While the steak relaxes, combine all the salad ingredients during a large bowl.
6. Stir all the vinaigrette ingredients together during a small shaker, then add a salad and toss coat evenly.
7. Serve, but.
8. Divide salad in4 bowls and top with steak.

Nutrition: Calories: 827 kcal Protein: 43.31 g Fat: 56.36 g Carbohydrates: 37.64 g

30. Cobb Salad

Preparation time: 20 minutes
Cooking time: 0 minutes
Servings: 4

Ingredients:

- 4 slices bacon
- 4 eggs
- 1/4 cup blue (icing)
- 1/2 cup cherry tomatoes (leave whole)
- 2 cups cucumbers (chopped)
- 4 cups romaine lettuce (Washed, cracked, and dried)
- Red Wine Vinaigrette
- 2 tablespoons wine vinegar
- 2 tablespoons extra virgin vegetable oil
- 1 tbsp honey (or maple syrup; see low carb *)
- 1/4 teaspoon Dijon mustard
- Salt and pepper

- Optional - fresh
- Add 1 avocado (chopped)
- Green onion (chopped)

Directions:

1. Serve immediately.
2. While cooking the bacon inside a fry pan or oven. Keep aside cool and dig small pieces.
3. Cook eggs in a pot or on the stove. Let it cool. Peel and dig cubes.
4. Prep the wine vinaigrette and toss all the vegetables within the dressing.
5. Divide vegetables between four bowls. Hard-coded egg, blue, avocado, and chives if desired, with bacon.
6. Using for food,
7. a multi-compartment container keeps the veggies away from the dressing.
8. Keep in an air tight container in the refrigerator for 4 days.
9. Enjoy all the ingredients before serving!

Nutrition: Calories: 500 kcal Protein: 18.66 g Fat: 38.34 g Carbohydrates: 23 g

31. Western Wild Rice And Sweet Salad

Preparation time: 30 minutes
Cooking time: 10 minutes
Servings: 2
Ingredients:

- Roasted Sweet Potatoes
- 4 cups sweet potatoes (peeled and dug 1-inch cubes, roughly 1 big or 2 small sweet potatoes)
- 1 teaspoon vegetable oil
- Incense shade
- Salad
- 3/4 cup wild rice mixture (Uncooked)
- 1 carrot (peeled and grated)
- 1 celery (finely chopped)
- 1 red chili (diced)
- 1 yellow pepper (diced)
- 1/4 cup purple onion (finely chopped)
- 1/2 cup cilantro leaves (approx. Fully sliced; loosely packed).
- Vinaigrette
- 3tablespoons vegetable oil
- 3 tablespoons wine vinegar
- 2 teaspoons juice
- 1 teaspoon taste
- 2 teaspoons honey (maple syrup makes it vegetarian)
- 1 clove garlic (minced)
- 1/4 teaspoon salt

Directions:

1. Roasted sweet potato
2. Heat oven 425 ° F. Season with sweet protein vegetable oil, and salt and pepper. Arrange on a baking sheet.
3. Bake for quarter-hours, stirring, and still bake for 10–15 minutes until the fork easily comes the sweet potato.
4. Remove from the oven and set aside fresh.
5. The Salad
6. The Cook Rice package conforms to the instructions. You should only find yourself with 2 cups of cooked rice. Let the salad cool completely before assembling.
7. Combine cooled sweet potato, cooked rice, and remaining salad ingredients.
8. Stir all the vinaigrette ingredients together and toss the salad well.
9. Storage
10. If you are getting the salad, make-ahead, leave the cilantro until just before serving.
11. Flap for food - discard the cilantro and add a can of black beans. Sh2 cups in a food prep container and refrigerate for 4 days.

Nutrition: Calories: 697 kcal Protein: 18.99 g Fat: 27.14 g Carbohydrates: 99.62 g

32. Green Omelet

Preparation time: 10 min
Cooking time: 5 min
Servings: 1
Ingredients:

- 2 large eggs, at room temperature
- 1 shallot, peeled and chopped
- Handful arugula
- 3 sprigs of parsley, chopped
- 1 tsp extra virgin olive oil
- Salt and black pepper

Directions:

1. Ina small bowl, beat the egg and set aside. Sauté the shallot for 5 minutes with a bit of the oil, on low-medium heat. Pour the eggs in the pans, stirring the mixture for just a second.
2. The eggs on medium heat, and tip the pan just enough to let the loose egg run underneath after about one minute on the burner. Add the greens, herbs, and the seasonings to the top side as it is still soft. TIP: You do not even have to flip it, as you can just cook the egg slowly egg as is well (being careful not to burn).

TIP: Another option is to put it into an oven to broil for 3-5 minutes (checking to make sure it is only until it is golden but burned).

Nutrition: Calories: 236 kcal Protein: 12.82 g Fat: 17.19 g Carbohydrates: 7.55 g

33. Berry Oat Breakfast Cobbler

Preparation time: 40 min
Cooking time: 5 min
Servings: 2
Ingredients:

- 2 cups of oats/flakes that are ready without cooking
- 1 cup of blackcurrants without the stems
- 1 teaspoon of honey (or ¼ teaspoon of raw sugar)
- ½ cup of water (add more or less by testing the pan)
- 1 cup of plain yogurt (or soy or coconut)

Directions:

1. Boil the berries, honey and water and then turn it down on low. Put in a glass container in a refrigerator until it is cool and set (about 30 minutes or more)
2. When ready to eat, scoop the berries on top of the oats and yogurt. Serve immediately.

Nutrition: Calories: 442 kcal Protein: 27.18 g Fat: 13.74 g Carbohydrates: 88.44 g

34. Pancakes With Apples And Blackcurrants

Preparation time: 30 min
Cooking time: 10 min
Servings: 4
Ingredients:

- 2 apples, cut into small chunks
- 2 cups of quick-cooking oats
- 1 cup flour of your choice

- 1 tsp baking powder
- 2 tbsp. Raw sugar, coconut sugar, or 2 tbsp. honey that is warm and easy to distribute
- 3 egg whites
- ¼ cups of milk (or soy/rice/coconut)
- 2tsp extra virgin olive oil
- A dash of salt
- For the berry topping:
- 1 cup blackcurrants, washed and stalks removed
- 3 tbsp. water (may use less)
- 2 tbsp. sugar (see above for types)

Directions:

1. Place the ingredients for the topping in a small pot simmer, frequently stirring for about 10 minutes until it cooks down and the juices are released.
2. Take the dry ingredients and mix them in a bowl. After, add the apples and the milk a bit at a time (you may not use it all), until it is a batter. Stiffly whisk the egg whites and then gently mix them into the pancake batter. Set aside in the refrigerator.
3. Pour a one quarter of the oil onto a flat pan or flat griddle, and when hot, pour some of the batter into it in a pancake shape. When the pancakes start to have golden brown edges and form air bubbles, they may be ready to be gently flipped.
4. Test to be sure the bottom can live away from the pan before actually flipping. Repeat for the next three pancakes. Top each pancake with the berries.

Nutrition: Calories: 287 kcal Protein: 12.57 g Fat: 4.5 g Carbohydrates: 57.05 g

35. Summer Berry Smoothie

Preparation time: 30 min
Cooking time: 0 min
Servings: 1

Ingredients

- 50g (2oz) blueberries
- 50g (2oz) strawberries
- 25g (1oz) blackcurrants
- 25g (1oz) red grapes
- 1 carrot, peeled
- 1 orange, peeled
- Juice of 1 lime

Directions:

1. Combine all of the ingredients into a blender and cover them with water. Blitz until smooth. You can also add some crushed ice and a mint leaf to garnish.

Nutrition: Calories: 1202 kcal Protein: 17.13 g Fat: 107.03 g Carbohydrates: 49.65 g

36. Mango, Celery & Ginger Smoothie

Preparation time: 30 min
Cooking time: 0 min
Servings: 1

Ingredients:

- 1 stalk of celery
- 50g (2oz) kale
- 1 apple, cored
- 50g (2oz) mango, peeled, de-stoned and chopped
- 2.5cm (1 inch) chunk of fresh ginger root, peeled and chopped

Directions:

1. Put all the ingredients into a blender with some water and blitz until smooth. Add ice to make your smoothie really refreshing.

Nutrition: Calories: 234 kcal Protein: 9.54 g Fat: 7.06 g Carbohydrates: 37.5 g

37. Orange, Carrot & Kale Smoothie

Preparation time: 30 min
Cooking time: 0 min
Servings: 1

Ingredients

- 1 carrot, peeled
- 1 orange, peeled
- 1 stick of celery
- 1 apple, cored
- 50g (2oz) kale
- ½ teaspoon matcha powder

Directions:

1. Combine all of the ingredients into a blender and add in enough water to cover them. Process until smooth, serve and enjoy.

Nutrition: Calories: 226 kcal Protein: 9.58 g Fat: 6.98 g Carbohydrates: 35.36 g

38. Creamy Strawberry & Cherry Smoothie

Preparation time: 30 min
Cooking time: 0 min
Servings: 1

Ingredients

- 100g (3½ oz) strawberries
- 75g (3oz) frozen pitted cherries
- 1 tablespoon plain full-fat yogurt
- 175mls (6fl oz) unsweetened soya milk

Directions:

1. Combine all of the ingredients into a blender and process until smooth. Serve and enjoy.

Nutrition: Calories: 16183 kcal Protein: 1065.49 g Fat: 640.84 g Carbohydrates: 1557.96 g

39. Grape, Celery & Parsley Reviver

Preparation time: 30 min
Cooking time: 0 min
Servings: 1

Ingredients:

- 75g (3oz) red grapes
- sticks of celery
- 1 avocado, de-stoned and peeled
- 1 tablespoon fresh parsley
- ½ teaspoon matcha powder

Directions:

1. Combine all of the ingredients into a blender with enough water to cover them and blitz until smooth and creamy. Add crushed ice to make it even more refreshing.

Nutrition: Calories: 457 kcal Protein: 11.08 g Fat: 35.68 g Carbohydrates: 30.97 g

40. Strawberry & Citrus Blend

Preparation time: 30 min
Cooking time: 0 min
Servings: 1

Ingredients:

- 75g (3oz) strawberries
- 1 apple, cored

- 1 orange, peeled
- ½ avocado, peeled and de-stoned
- ½ teaspoon matcha powder
- Juice of 1 lime

Directions:

1. Combine all of the ingredients into a blender with enough water to cover them and process until smooth.

Nutrition: Calories: 373 kcal Protein: 9.57 g Fat: 21.36 g Carbohydrates: 43.18 g

41. Grapefruit & Celery Blast

Preparation time: 30 min
Cooking time: 0 min
Servings: 1

Ingredients:

- 1 grapefruit, peeled
- 2 stalks of celery
- 50g (2oz) kale
- ½ teaspoon matcha powder

Directions:

1. Set all the ingredients into a blender with enough water to cover them and blitz until smooth.

Nutrition: Calories: 112 kcal Protein: 8.78 g Fat: 6.58 g Carbohydrates: 5.39 g

42. Orange & Celery Crush

Preparation time: 30 min
Cooking time: 0 min
Servings: 1

Ingredients

- 1 carrot, peeled
- Stalks of celery
- 1 orange, peeled
- ½ teaspoon matcha powder
- Juice of 1 lime

Directions:

1. Combine all of the ingredients into a blender with enough water to cover them and blitz until smooth.

Nutrition: Calories: 121 kcal Protein: 7.27 g Fat: 6.27 g Carbohydrates: 10.06 g

43. Walnut & Spiced Apple Tonic

Preparation time: 30 min
Cooking time: 0 min
Servings: 1

Ingredients:

- walnuts halves
- 1 apple, cored
- 1 banana
- ½ teaspoon matcha powder
- ½ teaspoon cinnamon
- Pinch of ground nutmeg

Directions:

1. Combine all of the ingredients into a blender and add sufficient water to cover them. Blitz until smooth and creamy.

Nutrition: Calories: 366 kcal Protein: 11.25 g Fat: 24.91 g Carbohydrates: 30.08 g

44. Pineapple & Cucumber Smoothie

Preparation time: 30 min
Cooking time: 0 min
Servings: 1

Ingredients:

- 50g (2oz) cucumber
- 1 stalk of celery
- 2 slices of fresh pineapple
- 2 sprigs of parsley
- ½ teaspoon matcha powder
- Squeeze of lemon juice

Directions:

1. Combine all of the ingredients into a blender with enough water to cover them and blitz until smooth.

Nutrition: Calories: 160 kcal Protein: 7.47 g Fat: 6.35 g Carbohydrates: 20.52 g

45. Sweet Rocket (Arugula) Boost

Preparation time: 30 min
Cooking time: 0 min
Servings: 1

Ingredients:

- 25g (1oz) fresh rocket (arugula) leaves
- 75g (3oz) kale
- 1 apple
- 1 carrot
- 1 tablespoon fresh parsley
- Juice of 1 lime

Directions:

1. Combine all of the ingredients into a blender with enough water to cover and process until smooth.

Nutrition: Calories: 267 kcal Protein: 13.3 g Fat: 7.63 g Carbohydrates: 43.56 g

46. Power Balls

Preparation time: 15 minutes
Cooking time: 45 minutes
Servings: 4-6

Ingredients:

- 1 cup old fashion ginger, dried (I've used apple cinnamon-flavored oats also)
- 1/4 cup quinoa cooked using 3/4 cup orange juice
- 1/4 cup shredded unsweetened coconut
- 1/3 cup dried cranberry/raisin blend
- 1/3 cup dark chocolate chips
- 1/4 cup slivered almonds
- 1 Tbsp reduced-fat peanut butter

Direction:

1. Cook quinoa in orange juice. Bring to boil and simmer for approximately 1-2 minutes. Let cool.
2. Combine chilled quinoa and the remaining ingredients into a bowl.
3. With wet hands and combine ingredients and roll in golden ball sized chunks.
4. Set at a Tupperware and set in the refrigerator for two weeks until the firm.

Nutrition: Calories: 54 kcal Protein: 2.11 g Fat: 2.34 g Carbohydrates: 6.18 g

47. Cinnamon Crescent Rolls

Preparation time: 10 minutes
Cooking time: 20 minutes
Servings: 4

Ingredients:

- 2 cans refrigerated crescent rolls
- 1 stick butter, softened
- 1/2 cup brown or white sugar
- 1 tbsp cinnamon
- Glaze
- 1/2 cup powdered sugar

- 1 tsp vanilla
- 2 tbsp milk

Direction:

1. Heat oven to 350°F.
2. In a small bowl, put sugar, butter, and cinnamon; beat until smooth.
3. Separate dough into rectangles.
4. Spread each rectangle about two tbsp cinnamon butter mix.
5. Roll-up starting at the broadest side, as you'll ordinarily do to crescent rolls. Firmly press ends to seal.
6. Put each cinnamon filled crescent roll on a parchment lineup baking sheet. *Be sure that you line the cookie sheet, or that you might have a large mess after *
7. Allow it bake for 10 to 15 minutes or until it turns golden brown.
8. In a small bowl, combine all glaze ingredients, adding enough milk for desired drizzling consistency. Drizzle over hot rolls.

Nutrition: Calories: 447 kcal Protein: 4.26 g Fat: 25.49 g Carbohydrates: 52.06 g

48. Fresh Fruit Pizza

Preparation time: 10 minutes
Cooking time: 20 minutes
Servings: 4

Ingredients:

- 4 crescent rolls
- 2 spoonfuls of moderate Cream-cheese
- Inch teaspoon of sugar
- 1 teaspoon Vanilla extract
- Handful berries - chopped
- Sliced almonds

Direction:

1. Put crescent rolls in a non-stick pan and then poke a few times with a fork. Cook at 375°F for about 14 minutes. Let it cool.
2. In a bowl, combine cream, Vanilla infusion & sugar stir with a spoon.
3. Spread onto crescent rolls, then add almonds and fruit.
4. Sprinkled a bit of sugar at the top.

Nutrition: Calories: 145 kcal Protein: 5.81 g Fat: 3.25 g Carbohydrates: 21.93 g

49. Sirtfood Diet's Braised Puy Lentils

Preparation time: 10 minutes
Cooking time: 50 minutes
Servings: 1

Ingredients:

- 8 Cherries, halved
- Red onion, cut thinly (40 g)
- 2 Tsp. Virgin olive oil
- 40 g Carrots, peeled and sliced
- 1 clove of Garlic, finely chopped
- 1 tsp. of paprika
- 40 g Celery, fine-sliced;
- 75 g puy Lentils
- 1 Tsp. thyme (fresh or dry)
- 220 ml of Livestock
- 1 Tbsp. Parsley, chopped;
- 50 g Kale, cut;
- Rocket 20 g

Directions:

1. Heat the oven 120°C/gas ½. Place the tomatoes in a tiny roasting pan and roast for 35 to 45 minutes.
2. Heat a casserole over low-medium-pressure. Apply 1 tablespoon of olive oil with garlic, red onion, carrot and celery and fry until softened for 1 to 2 minutes. Add thyme and paprika and cook it for another minute.
3. Wash the lentils in a sieve and attach them to the order. Bring to boil, reduce the flame, and let it cook for about 20 minutes with a cover on the pan. Give the pan a swirl after 7 minutes, adding water if some amount fall too little.
4. Add kale and cook another 10 minutes. When baked, add in the parsley and roasted tomatoes. Serve with the rocket with the remaining olive oil tablespoon.

Nutrition: Calories: 241 kcal Protein: 8.85 g Fat: 15.67 g Carbohydrates: 17.79 g

50. Vanilla Protein Pancakes

Preparation Time: 20 minutes
Cooking Time: Cook: 15 minutes
Servings: 8

Ingredients:

- 1½ cups Pea protein isolate
- ½ cup Whole wheat flour
- 1½ cups Almond milk (can be substituted with water)
- 2 tsp. Baking powder
- 2 tsp. Vanilla extract
- Optional Toppings:
- Walnuts
- Blueberries (fresh or frozen)
- Shredded coconut

Directions:

1. Add all ingredients to a blender and blend until smooth, scraping down the sides of the mixer to prevent any lumps if necessary.
2. Bring a non-stick frying pan over medium heat.
3. Pour a large tablespoon of batter into the frying pan and bake until the edges are dry and bubbles form in the pancake.
4. Flip the pancake and bake the other side until it's lightly browned.
5. Repeat the process for the remaining pancake batter.
6. Serve the pancakes with the optional toppings and enjoy!
7. Store the pancakes in a fridge and consume within three days. Alternatively, store in the freezer for an of 30 days and thaw at room temperature. Use a microwave or non-stick frying pan to reheat the pancakes before serving.

Nutrition: Calories: 120 Carbs: 9.0 g. Fat: 2.2 g. Protein: 18.2 g. Fiber: 2.4 g. Sugar: 1.2

51. Choco Berry Pudding

Preparation Time: 5 minutes
Cooking Time: 0 minute
Servings: 2

Ingredients:

- Three bananas (peeled)
- Two scoops Soy protein isolate (chocolate flavor)
- ¼ cup Flaxseeds 1 cup Mixed berries (fresh or frozen) 3 cups Water
- Optional Toppings:
- Mint leaves Cocoa powder Coconut flakes

Directions:

1. Add all the ingredients to a blender and blend until smooth. Alternatively, blend the berries and two tablespoons of flaxseeds first, and half fill two glasses, bowls, or Mason jars with the berry mix.

2. Blend the remaining ingredients afterward, and top the berry mix with the banana protein mix.
3. Serve with the optional toppings and enjoy!
4. In the fridge, store the pudding in an airtight container and consume within two days. Alternately, store in the freezer for a maximum of 60 days and defrost at room temperature.

Nutrition: Calories: 407 Carbs: 53.3 g. Fat: 7.3 g. Protein: 32.3 g Fiber: 11.25 g. Sugar: 26.9 g.

52. Mango Choco Protein Pudding

Preparation Time: 5 minutes
Cooking Time: 0 minute
Servings: 2

Ingredients:

- 2 cups Mango cubes (fresh or frozen)
- 1 banana (peeled)
- Scoops Soy protein isolate (chocolate flavor) ¼ cup Flaxseeds 3 cups Water
- Optional Toppings: Blueberries Cocoa powder Kiwi slices

Directions:

1. Add all the ingredients to a blender and blend until smooth.
2. Alternatively, blend the banana, soy isolate, two tablespoons of flaxseeds, and the water first and divide half of the mixture between two glasses, bowls, or Mason jars.
3. Scoop out the remaining banana mixture into a glass or bowl and set it aside for now.
4. Blend the mango with the remaining flaxseeds. Divide the mango purée between the two glasses, bowls or Mason jars, and top with the remaining banana mix. Serve with the optional toppings and enjoy!
5. Store the pudding in an sealed container in the fridge, and consume within two days. Alternatively, store in the freezer for a maximum of 60 days and thaw at room temperature.

Nutrition: Calories: 343 Carbs: 39.1 g. Fat: 6.9 g. Protein: 31.1 g. Fiber: 7.9 g. Sugar: 25.9 g.

53. Chocolate Avocado Smoothie

Preparation Time: 5 minutes
Cooking Time: 0 minute
Servings: 2

Ingredients:

- 1 cup
- Spinach (fresh or frozen)
- 2 scoops Soy protein isolate (chocolate flavour)
- 2 bananas (peeled)
- 1 small Hass avocado (peeled, stoned)
- ¼ cup Flaxseeds
- 3 cups Water
- Optional Toppings:
- Lemon slices Mint leaves

Directions:

1. Add all the ingredients to a blender and blend until smooth.
2. Serve with the optional toppings and enjoy!
3. Store the smoothie in an airtight container in the fridge, and consume within two days. Alternatively, store in the freezer for a maximum of 60 days and thaw at room temperature.

Nutrition: Calories: 433 Carbs: 36.1 g Fat: 16.2. g. Protein: 35.6 g. Fiber: 12.9 g. Sugar: 15.8 g.

54. Gingerbread Smoothie

Preparation Time: 5 minutes
Cooking Time: 0 minute
Servings: 2

Ingredients:

- 2 scoops Soy protein isolate (chocolate flavour)
- 2 bananas (peeled)
- 1 medium Hass avocado (peeled, stoned) 2 tbsp. Chia seeds 2 tbsp.5-spice powder
- 3 cups Water
- Optional Toppings:
- Blueberries Shredded coconut Cocoa powder

Directions:

1. Add all the ingredients to a blender and blend until smooth.
2. Serve with the optional toppings and enjoy!

Nutrition: Calories: 392 Carbs: 36.4 g. Fat: 13.4 g. Protein: 31.2 g. Fiber: 10.2 g. Sugar: 14.4 g.

55. Breakfast Quesadillas With Bacon, Egg, And Cheese

Preparation time: 30 minutes
Cooking time: 30 minutes
Servings: 8

Ingredients:

- Cuts bacon
- Enormous eggs
- Salt and naturally dark pepper, to taste
- Ounces cheddar, grated or cut flimsy
- Enormous flour tortillas
- For serving
- Salsa, harsh cream and guacamole

Directions:

1. Warm a large skillet over medium heat.
2. Include the bacon cuts and cook, turning once, until fresh and darker (or to your inclination).
3. Evacuate to a paper towel-lined plate. Once cooled, cleave into pieces.
4. Crash a tad bit of the bacon oil from the dish.
5. Break the eggs into a bowl and include a sprinkle of water or milk. Speed until smooth.
6. Empty eggs into the skillet, season with salt and pepper, and scramble until cooked. Expel to a plate.
7. Spread one flour tortilla with a slim layer of destroyed cheddar.
8. Top with a portion of the fried eggs and some hacked bacon.
9. Top with some progressively destroyed cheddar and spot another flour tortilla on top.
10. Painstakingly set the quesadilla into the skillet over medium warmth. Cook until the cheddar starts to soften marginally, and the base tortilla is brilliant dark-colored.
11. Cautiously flip to the opposite side and cook for 1-2 additional minutes. Evacuate to a plate.
12. Cut and serve warm with salsa, harsh cream and guacamole, whenever wanted.

Nutrition: Calories: 126 Complete fat: 21g Cholesterol: 20 mg Sodium: 104 mg Potassium: 113 mg Starches: 2.1 g Salt: 19 mcg Calcium: 29 mg Magnesium: 16 mg

56. Classic French Toast

Preparation time: 10 minutes
Cooking time: 35 minutes
Servings: 8

Ingredients:

- Huge eggs

- 1/2 cup entire milk
- 1 teaspoon vanilla concentrate
- 1/2 teaspoons ground cinnamon partitioned
- 8 cuts Brioche bread

Directions:

1. On the off chance that is using an electric iron, preheat the frying pan to 350 degrees F.
2. Race until very much consolidated.
3. Plunge each side of the bread in the egg blend. Include the other portion of the cinnamon after you have plunged half of your bread cuts and blend once more. This will ensure the entirety of the cuts gets a decent measure of cinnamon.
4. Soften a little margarine on the hot frying pan or in a large skillet over medium warmth. Cook the French toast until brilliant dark-colored, around 2-3 minutes on each side.
5. Serve the French toast warm with maple syrup, powdered sugar, and berries, whenever wanted.
6. Note-to keeps the French toast warm, heat the stove to 200 degrees F. Spot a wire rack on a massive preparing sheet, and spot the French toast on the shelf. Keep warm in the grill for as long as 30 minutes.

Nutrition: Calories: 110 Complete fat: 11g Cholesterol: 12 mg Sodium: 10 mg Potassium: 13 mg Starches: 2.1 g Salt: 12mcg Calcium: 21 mg Magnesium: 10 mg

57. Avocado And Kale Omelet

Preparation time: 5 minutes
Cooking time: 5 minutes
Servings: 2

Ingredients:

- 2 enormous eggs
- 1 teaspoon low-fat milk
- Spot of salt
- 1 teaspoon extra-virgin olive oil, partitioned
- 1 cup cleaved kale
- 1 tablespoon lime juice
- 1 tablespoon cleaved new cilantro
- 1 teaspoon unsalted sunflower seeds
- Spot of squashed red pepper
- Spot of salt
- ¼ avocado cut

Directions:

1. Mix eggs with milk and salt in a little bowl.
2. Heat 1 teaspoon of oil in a little nonstick skillet over medium warmth.
3. Include the egg blend and cook until the base is set, and the inside is still somewhat runny 1 to 2 minutes. Flip the omelet over and cook until set, around 30 seconds more. Move to a plate.
4. Hurl kale with the one teaspoon oil, lime juice, cilantro, sunflower seeds, squashed red pepper, and a touch of salt. Top the omelet with the kale plate of mixed greens and avocado.

Nutrition: Calories: 339 Complete fat: 28.1 g Soaked fat: 5.8 g Cholesterol: 372 mg Sodium: 446 mg Potassium: 506 mg Starches: 8.6 g Fiber: 4.4 g Sugar: 2 g Protein: 15 g IU nutrient: 2343 Nutrient c: 29 mg Salt: 119 mcg Calcium: 97 mg Iron: 3 mg Magnesium: 40 mg

58. Avocado Eggs With Toast

Preparation time: 15 minutes
Cooking time: 15 minutes
Servings: 4

Ingredients:

- 1 avocado
- 4 cuts entire wheat sandwich bread
- 2 tablespoons avocado oil
- 4 medium eggs
- ¼ teaspoon salt, separated
- ¼ teaspoon ground pepper, separated
- 4 tablespoons salsa

Directions:

1. Preheat stove to 375 degrees F. Coat a huge rimmed preparing sheet with cooking splash.
2. Split avocado and strip. Cut the long way into 1/4-inch-thick cuts, so you have cut through the entire length of the avocado with the gap from the pit.
3. Separate the four cuts nearest to either side of the hole and the external cuts; put in a safe spot.
4. Utilizing a baked good brush, delicately cover the two sides of each cut of bread with oil. Cut a piece out of the focal point on bread, looking like an avocado cut.
5. Move the dough and slice out bread pieces to the readied heating sheet. Spot the external avocado cuts in the gaps of the bread.
6. Split an egg over every one of the avocado cuts in the dough. Sprinkle the eggs with 1/8 teaspoon salt and 1/8 teaspoon pepper.
7. Prepare until the toast has seared in spots, and the eggs are simply set 10 to 12 minutes. Top with salsa, whenever wanted. Present with the cut-out bread pieces.

Nutrition: Calories: 285 Absolute fat: 20.1 g Soaked fat: 3.6 g Cholesterol: 186 mg Sodium: 347 mg Potassium: 386 mg Starches: 16.7 g Fiber: 3.4 g Sugar: 2 g Protein: 10.8 g IU nutrient: 345 Nutrient c: 5 mg Salt: 76 mcg Calcium: 80 mg Iron: 2 mg Magnesium: 42 mg

59. Baked Oatmeal

Preparation time: 30 minutes
Cooking time: 55 minutes
Servings: 3

Ingredients:

- 2 cups old-fashioned oats
- ½ cup pecans, hacked
- 2 teaspoons ground cinnamon
- 1 teaspoon preparing powder
- ¾ teaspoon salt
- ¼ teaspoon ground nutmeg
- 1/8 tsp. ground cloves
- 2 cups unsweetened almond milk or 2% milk
- 1 cup low-fat plain Greek yogurt
- ¼ cup unadulterated maple syrup
- 2 tablespoons extra-virgin olive oil
- 1 teaspoon vanilla concentrate
- 2 pears, diced little
- ⅓ cup low-fat plain Greek yogurt

Directions:

1. Preheat stove to 375 degrees F.
2. Coat a 9-inch-square preparing dish with a cooking shower.
3. Blend the oats, pecans, cinnamon, heating powder, salt, nutmeg, and cloves in an enormous bowl.
4. Whisk the almond milk (or milk), 1 cup yogurt, maple syrup, oil, and vanilla in a medium bowl.
5. Empty the wet fixings into the dry fixings. Delicately blend in. Move the blend to the readied heating dish.
6. Cook for 45 to 55 minutes.

Nutrition: Calories: 311 Total fat: 14.8 g Immersed fat: 2.1 g Cholesterol: 4 mg Sodium: 449 mg Potassium: 338 mg Starches:

37.8 g Fiber: 5.1 g Sugar: 15 g Protein: 9.3 g IU nutrient: 256 Nutrient c: 2 mg Salt: 31 mcg Calcium: 310 mg Iron: 2 mg Magnesium: 59 mg

60. Yoghurt Parfait

Preparation time: 10 minutes
Cooking time: 10 minutes
Servings: 2

Ingredients:

- ¾ cup nonfat vanilla Greek yogurt
- ¼ cup part-skim ricotta
- ½ teaspoon lemon pizzazz
- ¼ cup raspberries
- 1 tablespoon fragmented almonds
- 1 teaspoon chia seeds

Directions:

1. Mix yogurt, ricotta, and lemon get-up-and-go in a bowl.
2. Top with raspberries, almonds, and chia seeds.

Nutrition: Calories: 272 All out fat: 9.6 g Soaked fat: 3.4 g Cholesterol: 24 mg Sodium: 119 mg Potassium: 398 mg Starches: 25.1 g Fiber: 5.1 g Sugar: 14 g Protein: 21.7 g IU nutrient: 251 Nutrient c: 9 mg Salt: 19 mcg Calcium: 385 mg Iron: 1 mg Magnesium: 46 mg

61. Vegetable & Nut Loaf

Preparation Time: 10 minutes
Cooking Time: 90 minutes
Servings: 4

Ingredients

- 175g (6oz) mushrooms, finely chopped
- 100g (3½ oz.) haricot beans
- 100g (3½ oz.) walnuts, finely chopped
- 100g (3½ oz.) peanuts, finely chopped
- 1 carrot, finely chopped
- 3 sticks celery, finely chopped
- 1 bird's-eye chili, finely chopped
- 1 red onion, finely chopped
- 1 egg, beaten
- 2 cloves of garlic, chopped
- 2 tablespoons olive oil
- 2 teaspoons turmeric powder
- 2 tablespoons soy sauce
- 4 tablespoons fresh parsley, chopped
- 100mls (3½ fl oz.) water
- 60mls (2fl oz.) red wine

Directions:

1. In a pan, heat the oil and put the garlic, chili, carrot, celery, onion, mushrooms and turmeric. Cook for 5 minutes. Place the haricot beans in a bowl and stir in nuts, vegetables, soy sauce, egg, parsley, red wine, and water. Grease and line a large loaf tin with greaseproof paper. Into a loaf tin, spoon the mixture and cover with foil and bake in the oven at 190C/375F for 60-90 minutes. Let it rest for 10 minutes then turn onto a serving plate.

Nutrition: Energy (calories): 315 kcal; Protein: 13.45 g; Fat: 27.86 g; Carbohydrates: 28.95 g

62. Dates & Parma Ham

Preparation Time: 10 minutes
Cooking Time: 0 minutes
Servings: 4

Ingredients:

- 12 medjool dates
- 2 slices of Parma ham, cut into strips

Directions:

1. Wrap each date with a strip of Parma ham. Can be served hot or cold.

Nutrition: Energy (calories): 645 kcal; Protein: 12.99 g; Fat: 2 g; Carbohydrates: 216.36 g

63. Braised Celery

Preparation time: 10 minutes
Cooking time: 15 minutes
Servings: 4

Ingredients

- 250g (9oz) celery, chopped
- 100mls (3½ fl oz) warm vegetable stock (broth)
- 1 red onion, chopped
- 1 clove of garlic, crushed
- 1 tablespoon fresh parsley, chopped
- 25g (1oz) butter
- Sea salt and freshly ground black pepper

Directions:

1. Place the celery, onion, stock (broth), garlic into a saucepan, bring it to the boil, and reduce the heat and simmer for 10 minutes. Mix in the parsley and butter and season with salt and pepper. Serve as an accompaniment to roast meat dishes.

Nutrition: Energy (calories): 269 kcal; Protein: 3.45 g; Fat: 20.86 g; Carbohydrates: 18.95 g

64. Cheesy Buckwheat Cakes

Preparation time: 10 minutes
Cooking time: 5 minutes
Servings: 2

Ingredients

- 100g (3½oz) buckwheat, cooked and cooled
- 1 large egg
- 25g (1oz) cheddar cheese, grated (shredded)
- 25g (1oz) wholemeal breadcrumbs
- 2 shallots, chopped
- 2 tablespoons fresh parsley, chopped
- 1 tablespoon olive oil

Directions:

1. Beat the egg into a bowl, whisk it, then set aside. In a separate bowl, combine all the buckwheat, cheese, shallots, and parsley and mix well. Pour in the beaten egg to the buckwheat mixture and stir well. Shape the mixture into patties. Scatter the breadcrumbs on a plate and roll the patties in them.
2. Put oil the a large frying pan and heat it, gently place the cakes in the oil. Cook for 3-4 minutes on either side until slightly golden.

Nutritional Value: Energy (calories): 352 kcal; Protein: 11.03 g; Fat: 21.7 g; Carbohydrates: 30.75 g

65. Red Chicory & Stilton Cheese Boats

Preparation time: 10 minutes
Cooking time: 4 minutes
Servings: 4

Ingredients

- 200g (7oz) stilton cheese, crumbled
- 200g (7oz) red chicory leaves (or if unavailable, use yellow)
- 2 tablespoon fresh parsley, chopped
- 1 tablespoon olive oil

Directions:

1. Place the red chicory leaves onto a baking sheet. Drizzle them with olive oil then sprinkle the cheese inside the leaves. Place them under a hot grill (broiler) for around 4

minutes until the cheese has melted. Sprinkle with chopped parsley and serve.

Nutritional Value: Energy (calories): 846 kcal; Protein: 35.85 g; Fat: 56.42 g; Carbohydrates: 52.96 g

66. Cherry Tomatoes Red Pesto Porridge

Preparation time: 5 minutes
Cooking time: 5-10 minutes
Servings: 1

Ingredients:

- Salt, pepper
- 1 tablespoon of hemp seed
- 1 tablespoon of pumpkin seed
- 2 tablespoon of nutritional yeast
- 1 tablespoon of sun-dried tomato-walnut pesto
- 1 teaspoon of tahini
- 1 scallion
- 1 cup of sliced cherry tomatoes
- 1 cup of chopped kale
- 1 teaspoon of dried basil
- 1, 5 teaspoons of dried oregano
- 5-2 cups of veggie stock (or water)
- ½ cup of couscous
- ½ cup of oats

Directions:

1. In a small cooking pot, add oats, oregano, vegetable stock, basil, couscous, pepper, and salt and cook for about 5 minutes on medium heat frequently stirring until porridge is creamy and soft.
2. Add chopped kale but reserve a bit for garnish, tomatoes, and sliced scallion. Cook for an additional 1 minute, mix in pesto, tahini, and nutritional yeast.
3. Top with the reserved kale, pumpkin and hemp seeds plus cherry tomatoes, Enjoy!

Nutrition: Calories: 188g Fat: 2.8g Fiber: 3.6g Carbs: 34.9g Protein: 5g

67. Blue Hawaii Smoothie

Preparation time: 5 minutes
Cooking time: 0 minutes
Servings: 1

Ingredients:

- 2 tablespoons rings or approximately 4-5 balls
- 1/2 cup frozen tomatoes
- Two tbsp ground flaxseed
- ⅛ cup tender coconut (unsweetened, organic)
- Few walnuts
- 1/2 cup fat-free yogurt
- 5-6 ice cubes
- Splash of water

Directions:

1. Throw all of the ingredients together and combine until smooth. You might need to shake it or put more water in the mix.

Nutrition: Calories: 304 kcal Protein: 19.31 g Fat: 18.6 g Carbohydrates: 16.15 g

68. Turkey Breakfast Sausages

Preparation time: 10 minutes
Cooking time: 15 minutes
Servings: 4

Ingredients:

- 1 lb. extra lean ground turkey
- 1 tbsp. EVOO 9 Extra Virgin Olive Oil), and a little more to coat pan
- 1 tbsp. fennel seeds
- 2 teaspoons smoked paprika
- 1 teaspoon red pepper flakes
- 1 teaspoon peppermint
- 1 teaspoon chicken seasoning
- A couple of shredded cheddar cheese
- A couple of chives, finely chopped
- A few shakes garlic and onion powder
- Two spins of pepper and salt

Directions:

1. Preheat oven to 350 F.
2. Utilize a little EVOO to grease a miniature muffin pan.
3. Combine all ingredients and blend thoroughly.
4. Fill each pit on top of the pan and then cook for approximately 15-20 minutes. Each toaster differs therefore when muffin temperature is 165 then remove.

Nutrition: Calories: 453 kcal Protein: 72.96 g Fat: 14.16 g Carbohydrates: 5.84 g

69. Sweet Potato Hash

Preparation time: 5 minutes
Cooking time: 10 minutes
Servings: 2

Ingredients:

- 1 sweet-potato
- 1/2 red pepper, diced
- 3 green onions, peppermint
- Leftover turkey, then sliced into bits (optional)
- 1 tbsp of butter - perhaps a bit less (I never quantify)
- Carrot powder - a few shakes
- Pepper - only a small dab to get a bit of heat
- Salt to flavor
- Shredded of cheddar cheese (optional)

Directions:

1. Poke a sweet potato and microwave for 5 minutes.
2. Remove from microwave, peel skin off and chop.
3. In a skillet, on medium-high heat, place peppers and butter and sauté to get a few minutes.
4. Insert potato bits and keep sautéing.
5. Whilst you sauté, add sweeteners, leafy vegetables, and green onions.
6. Insert a dab of cheddar and revel in the taste!

Nutrition: Calories: 104 kcal Protein: 3.65 g Fat: 8.88 g Carbohydrates: 2.89 g

70. Chocolate Curd With Banana

Preparation time: 10 minutes
Cooking time: 0 minutes
Servings: 1

Ingredients:

- 50 g dark chocolate
- 1 banana
- 250 g lactose-free low-fat curd
- 2 tbsp lactose-free milk (3.5% fat)

Directions:

1. Grate dark chocolate. Set aside about 1 tbsp of the rasp.
2. Peel the banana and finely dice the flesh. Set aside 1–
3. 2 tbsp for the garnish.
4. Stir the curd with milk until smooth. Fold in the grated chocolate and the banana cubes.
5. Spread the chocolate quark in two small bowls and garnish with the remaining grated chocolate and banana cubes.

Nutrition: Calories: 870 kcal Protein: 12.45 g Fat: 54.12 g Carbohydrates: 83.45 g

71. Pea Protein Sandwiches

Preparation time: 10 minutes
Cooking time: 50 minutes + 30 minutes cooling time
Servings: 4

Ingredients:

- 370 g frozen peas
- 225 g oatmeal
- 75 g peeled hemp seeds
- 1½ tsp fennel seeds
- 1 tsp coriander seeds
- 1 tsp caraway seeds
- 2 tsp baking powder
- 2 tsp seasoned salt
- 3 eggs (large)
- 2 carrots
- 250 g quark (20% fat in dry matter) salt pepper
- ½ bundle chives (10 g)

Directions:

1. Let the peas thaw. Grind oatmeal and hemp seeds to flour in a blender. Finely grate the fennel, coriander seeds, and caraway seeds in a mortar and add to the flour. Add baking powder and salt and mix.
2. Put the peas and eggs in the blender and chop until you get a smooth dough. Put a baking sheet with parchment paper and add the mixture.
3. Peel the carrots, quarter them lengthways and place them on the dough.
4. Cook it in the oven at 180°C for around 50 min.
5. Before eating, let it cool down for 30 minutes.
6. In the meantime, mix the curd with salt, pepper, and 2 tbsp of water. Wash chives, shake dry and cut into rings. Cut bread into slices, brush with the curd cheese, and garnish with chives.

Nutrition: Calories: 289 kcal Protein: 12.49 g Fat: 15.77 g Carbohydrates: 27.98 g

72. Bircher Muesli In The Caribbean Style

Preparation time: 15 minutes + 1 hour chilling time
Cooking time: 0 minutes
Servings: 4

Ingredients:

- 90 g pithy oatmeal
- 1 tbsp crushed linseed
- 270 g pineapple (1/4 pineapple)
- 25 g hazelnuts (2 tbsp)
- 60 g coconut drink
- 1 tbsp grated coconut

Directions:

1. Mix oatmeal and flaxseed with 250 ml of water and cover and let swell in the fridge overnight.
2. Peel the pineapple and cut or grate the pulp into small strips. Chop hazelnuts and add about half of the oatmeal together with the pineapple pieces and coconut drink.
3. Spread the Bircher muesli in two bowls and serve garnished with remaining nuts and coconut flakes.

Nutrition: Calories: 123 kcal Protein: 3.51 g Fat: 5.64 g Carbohydrates: 16.27 g

73. Buckwheat Groats With Banana And Chocolate Topping

Preparation time: 5 minutes
Cooking time: 20 minutes
Servings: 2

Ingredients:

- 400 ml oat drink (oat milk)
- ½ vanilla bean
- 1 map. ground cardamom
- 1 map. cinnamon powder
- 3 tsp cocoa powder
- 1 tbsp raw cane sugar
- 125 g buckwheat groats
- 1 banana
- 1 tbsp cocoa nibs
- 1 tsp chia seeds

Directions:

1. Heat the oat drink in a saucepan. Halve the length of the vanilla pod lengthways and scrape out the pulp with a knife. Add the vanilla pulp, the scraped-out vanilla pod, cardamom, cinnamon, cocoa, and raw cane sugar to the oat drink, stir and bring to the boil.
2. Stir in the buckwheat, bring to the boil briefly and let it swell for 10 minutes over medium heat, stirring occasionally.
3. Meanwhile, peel the banana and slice the pulp. Heat the butter in a pan and lightly brown the slices of banana over medium heat.
4. Fill buckwheat groats in small bowls and serve garnished with bananas, cocoa nibs, and chia seeds.

Nutrition: Calories: 129 kcal Protein: 6.42 g Fat: 4.2 g Carbohydrates: 20.35 g

74. Sweet Millet Casserole With Clementines

Preparation time: 10 minutes
Cooking time: 60 minutes
Servings: 4

Ingredients:

- 150 g golden millet
- 1 vanilla bean
- ½ organic lemon
- ½ tsp cinnamon powder
- 2 tbsp raw cane sugar
- 380 ml oat drink (oat milk)
- 2nd tangerines
- 3rd eggs
- 1 pinch salt
- 300 g lactose-free curd cheese (20% fat)
- 1 tbsp. butter
- 2 tbsp. sliced almonds

Directions:

1. Wash millet hot. Extract the vanilla seeds with a knife opening the vanilla pod lengthways. Rinse half of the lemon hot, pat dry and rub the zest finely. Squeeze out the juice.
2. Put millet, vanilla pulp, cinnamon, sugar, and oat drink in a saucepan. Boil and simmer over medium-high heat for about 7-10 minutes, stirring occasionally.
3. After that, take off from the heat and let soak for 10 minutes without a lid.
4. Meanwhile, peel the tangerines and cut them into thick slices. Beat egg whites with some salt until egg whites are stiff. Mix the egg yolks with lemon zest, lemon juice, and quark and add to the millet mass.
5. Carefully fold in the egg whites.
6. Butter the baking dish. Pour in the millet curd mixture, smooth out and top with the mandarins—

7. Bake the cake in the static oven (preheated) at 180 °
8. C for 40–50 minutes. Sprinkle millet casserole with grated almonds to serve.

Nutrition: Calories: 420 kcal Protein: 22.04 g Fat: 19.61 g Carbohydrates: 38.12 g

75. Vegan Overnight Soaked Oats With Blueberries And Coconut

Preparation time: 15 minutes + chilling time
Cooking time: 0 minutes
Servings: 1

Ingredients:

- 5 tbsp. oatmeal (75 g)
- 3 tbsp. coconut flakes (30 g)
- 150 g yogurt alternative from soy
- 150 ml of coconut drink
- 1 tbsp. syrup (e.g., coconut blossom syrup; 15 g)
- 100 g blueberries (fresh or frozen)
- 2 tbsp. pumpkin seeds (30 g)

Directions:

1. Mix the oatmeal with 2 tablespoons of coconut flakes, yogurt alternative, coconut drink, and coconut blossom syrup. Add half of the blueberries and refrigerate for at least 2 hours, better overnight.
2. The next morning, add vegan overnight oats with blueberries and coconut to two bowls or closable glasses. Sprinkle with pumpkin seeds and remaining blueberries and coconut flakes.

Nutrition: Calories: 475 kcal Protein: 25.54 g Fat: 18.6 g Carbohydrates: 57.76 g

76. Overnight Soaked Oats With Apple And Walnuts

Preparation time: 15 minutes + free
Cooking time: 0 minutes
Servings: 1

Ingredients:

- 75 g buckwheat flake
- 1 tsp cinnamon
- Salt
- 250 ml milk (3.5% fat)
- 1 tbsp. applesauce (15 g; no added sugar)
- 2 tbsp. chia seeds (10 g)
- 1 apple
- 1 tbsp. maple syrup (15 g)
- 2 tbsp. walnut kernels (30 g)

Directions:

1. Mix the buckwheat flakes with a little cinnamon and a pinch of salt. Add milk, applesauce, and 1 tablespoon of chia seeds, stir well and put in the fridge for at least 2 hours, better overnight.
2. The next morning, wash, quarter, and core the apple—
3. Half-cut into small slits, the other half into cubes. Put the apple cubes with maple syrup and the remaining cinnamon in a saucepan, heat, and let them caramelize.
4. Roughly chop walnut kernels. Put overnight oats in two bowls or closable glasses.
5. Spread apple slices, caramelized apple cubes, and walnut kernels over them and serve the overnight oats with apple and walnuts with the remaining chia seeds.

Nutrition: Calories: 407 kcal Protein: 13.3 g Fat: 16.15 g Carbohydrates: 58.81 g

77. Spread With Tomatoes

Preparation time: 20 minutes
Cooking time: 0minutes
Servings: 2

Ingredients:

- 100 g dried tomato in oil
- 100 g sunflower seeds
- 3 tbsp rapeseed oil salt pepper
- 3 stems basil
- 4 slices oat bread

Directions:

1. Let the tomatoes drain slightly and cut roughly. Then put in a tall container and puree together with 90 g sunflower seeds, rapeseed oil, and 3-4 tablespoons of water. Then season with salt and pepper.
2. Wash the basil and finely chop the leaves. Add 3/4 of the basil to the tomato spread and stir in.
3. Spread the spread with tomatoes on four slices of oat bread. Sprinkle with remaining sunflower seeds and basil and serve.

Nutrition: Calories: 668 kcal Protein: 20.41 g Fat: 52.5 g Carbohydrates: 35.47 g

78. Overnight Soaked Oats With Banana And Peanut Butter

Preparation time: 15 minutes + chilling time
Cooking time: 0 minutes
Servings: 1

Ingredients:

- 5 tbsp oatmeal (75 g)
- 2 tbsp crushed linseed (15 g)
- 200 ml almond drink (almond milk)
- 2 tbsp peanut butter (30 g)
- 1 tsp agave syrup (5 g)
- 1 banana
- 1 tbsp salted peanut kernel (15 g)

Directions:

1. Mix oatmeal and 1 tablespoon of flax seeds. Add almond milk, 1 tablespoon of peanut butter and agave syrup and stir thoroughly and put in the fridge for 2 hours or overnight.
2. The next morning, peel the banana and cut it into bite-size pieces. Roughly chop peanut kernels as desired.
3. Place overnight oats in two small bowls or closable glasses and spread the remaining peanut butter and bananas on top. Sprinkle overnight oats with peanut butter and banana with remaining flaxseed and peanut kernels.

Nutrition: Calories: 299 kcal Protein: 13.02 g Fat: 19.g Carbohydrates: 19.04 g

79. Overnight Soaked Oats With Chocolate And Figs

Preparation time: 15 minutes + chilling time
Cooking time: 0 minutes
Servings: 1

Ingredients:

- 1 pc dark chocolate (30 g; at least 70% cocoa)
- 5 tbsp spelled flakes (75 g)
- 1 tbsp cocoa powder (10 g; heavily oiled)
- 200 ml oat drink (oat milk)
- 2 tbsp pistachio kernels (30 g)
- 2nd figs
- 2 stems mint
- 1 tbsp cocoa nibs (10 g)

Directions:

1. Chop the chocolate and mix with spelled flakes, cocoa powder, and oat milk and put in the fridge for 2 hours, or better overnight.
2. The next morning, roughly chop the pistachio nuts.
3. Wash the figs, pat dry, and quarter them. Wash mint and pluck the leaves.
4. Put the overnight oats in two bowls or closable glasses, then spread figs and mint leaves on top. Sprinkle overnight oats with chocolate and figs with chopped pistachio nuts and cocoa nibs.

Nutrition: Calories: 597 kcal Protein: 13.43 g Fat: 24.62 g Carbohydrates: 88.07 g

80. Overnight Soaked Oats With Coffee And Blackberries

Preparation time: 15 minutes + chilling time
Cooking time: 0 minutes
Servings: 1

Ingredients:

- 5 tbsp multigrain flakes (75 g; e.g., barley, oats, rye, rice)
- 1 map. vanilla powder
- 1 tsp whole cane sugar (5 g)
- 100 ml coffee (cooled)
- 100 ml milk (3.5% fat)
- 100 g blackberry (fresh or frozen)
- 1 PC dark chocolate (15 g; at least 70% cocoa)
- 2 tbsp pecan half (30 g)

Directions:

1. Mix the multigrain flakes with vanilla powder and whole cane sugar. Add coffee and milk and stir
2. Thoroughly. Add blackberries and refrigerate for at least 2 hours, better overnight.
3. The next morning, roughly chop chocolate and pecans. Put overnight oats with coffee and blackberries in two bowls or closable glasses and sprinkle with chocolate and nuts.

Nutrition: Calories: 389 kcal Protein: 13.91 g Fat: 24.28 g Carbohydrates: 43.23 g

81. Sweet Pumpkin Buns

Preparation time: 10 minutes
Cooking time: 50 minutes
Servings: 2

Ingredients:

- 300 g Hokkaido pumpkin
- 50 ml of orange juice
- 450 g spelled flour type 1050
- 1 cube yeast
- 70 g whole cane sugar
- 150 ml lukewarm milk (3.5 % fat)
- 1 vanilla bean
- 1 egg (medium)
- 80 g room-temperature butter
- ½ tsp cinnamon
- 1 tsp. cardamom powder
- 1 pinch salt
- 1 egg yolk

Directions:

1. Wash, core, and dice the pumpkin. Place in a saucepan with orange juice and cook gently on a low heat for approx. 15 minutes. Puree and let cool.
2. Add the flour in a bowl and press a hollow in the middle. Crumble the yeast and add 1 tsp whole cane sugar and milk to the well. Cover and let rise for 10 minutes.
3. Add the vanilla seeds, remaining sugar, egg, butter, cinnamon, cardamom, 1 pinch of salt, and cooled pumpkin puree to the batter. Knead everything into a smooth dough and cover and let rise for 1 hour.
4. Divide the dough into eight equal pieces, shape them into rolls, and put them on a baking sheet covered with baking paper. Brush the rolls with the egg yolk mixed with water.
5. Bake the rolls in the oven at 180 ° C (forced air 160 °
6. C, gas: level 2–3) for 20–30 minutes until golden brown.

Nutrition: Calories: 2098 kcal Protein: 75.82 g Fat: 115.69 g Carbohydrates: 202.65 g

82. Chocolate, Strawberry & Coconut Crush

Preparation time: 5 minutes
Cooking time: 0 minutes
Servings: 1

Ingredients

- 100mls (3½fl oz) coconut milk
- 100g (3½oz) strawberries
- 1 banana
- 1 tablespoon 100% cocoa powder or cacao nibs
- 1 teaspoon matcha powder

Directions:

1. Toss all of the ingredients into a blender and process them to a creamy consistency. Add a little extra water if you need to thin it a little.

Nutrition: Calories: 132 Fat: 418.38 g Carbohydrates: 99.07 g

83. Cranberry & Kale Crush

Preparation time: 5 minutes
Cooking time: 0 minutes
Servings: 1

Ingredients:

- 75g (3oz) strawberries
- 50g (2oz) kale
- 120mls (4fl oz) unsweetened cranberry juice
- 1 teaspoon chia seeds
- ½ teaspoon matcha powder

Directions:

1. Place all of the ingredients into a blender and process until smooth. Add some crushed ice and a mint leaf or two for a refreshing drink.

Nutrition: Calories: 377 Protein: 2.64 g Fat: 15.86 g Carbohydrates: 2060.85 g

84. Poached Eggs & Rocket (Arugula)

Preparation time: 2 minutes
Cooking time: 5 minutes
Servings: 1

Ingredients:

- 2 eggs
- 25g (1oz) fresh rocket (arugula)
- 1 teaspoon olive oil
- Sea salt

Directions:

1. Scatter the rocket (arugula) leaves onto a plate and drizzle the olive oil over them. Bring a shallow pan of water to the boil, add in the eggs and cook until the whites become firm. Serve the eggs on top of the rocket and season with salt and pepper.

Nutrition: Calories: 387 kcal Protein: 24.98 g Fat: 30.01 g Carbohydrates: 2.94 g

85. Honey Cake With Orange Cream

Preparation time: 10 minutes
Cooking time:
25 minutes
Servings: 1

Ingredients:

- 200 g apples (1 apple)
- 3 eggs
- 200 g honey
- 100 ml rapeseed oil
- 1 pinch salt
- 1 tsp. cinnamon (preferably Ceylon cinnamon)
- 300 g wholemeal flour
- ½ packet baking powder
- 100 ml apple juice
- 70 g margarine
- 200 g organic orange (1 organic orange)
- 50 g unsulphured raisins
- 100 g carrots (1 carrot)
- 25 g unshelled almond kernels

Directions:

1. Wash, quarter, core, and grate the apple finely on a grater.
2. Separate eggs. Put the egg yolks with honey in a bowl and stir in a hand mixer until creamy.
3. Gradually fold in the rapeseed oil. Finally, add a pinch of salt, grated apple, and cinnamon.
4. Sieve wholemeal flour with baking powder to the egg yolk cream and stir in alternately with the apple juice.
5. Put the egg whites in another bowl. Whisk until stiff with a hand mixer and fold under the dough.
6. Grease a tin (29x10.5 cm) with 1 tbsp. Margarine.
7. Pour in the dough, smooth it with a rubber spatula and bake in the preheated oven at 180 ° C (fan oven: 160 ° C, gas: level 2-3) on the middle shelf for 50-60 minutes.
8. In the meantime, wash the orange in hot water, rub it dry and rub the peel finely.
9. Cut into 2 the orange and squeeze out the juice. Mix the juice in a small bowl with the raisins and let it soak a little.
10. Wash, clean, peel, and cut the carrot into large pieces. Finely chop with the almonds in the Blitzhacker.
11. Remove the raisins from the juice. Mix in the remaining carrot and almond mixture with the remaining margarine.
12. Stir in the grated orange peel and 2-3 tablespoons of orange juice. Pour into a small screw-top jar with a lid and chill.
13. Take the honey cake out of the oven and let it cool completely on a wire rack. Cut off 1 slice per serving and spread with 1 tablespoon of orange cream.

Nutrition: Calories 248 Protein 4 g, Fat 13 g, Carbs 27 g, Added Sugar 10 g, Fiber 3 g

86. Banana Bread With Walnuts

Preparation time: 5 minutes
Cooking time:
30 minutes
Servings: 2

Ingredients

- 300 g wheat flour type 1050
- 1 packet baking powder
- ½ tsp. salt
- Nutmeg
- 150 g walnut kernels
- 500 g ripe bananas (3 ripe bananas)
- 1 vanilla bean
- 1 apple
- 80 g butter
- 50 g coconut sugar
- 1 egg

Directions:

1. Strain the flour with baking powder and salt into a mixing bowl. Add a little nutmeg directly.
2. Finely chop walnuts in a blitz chopper or with a large knife and add to the flour mixture.
3. Peel the bananas, cut them into small pieces, put them in a bowl, and puree them with a hand blender or finely mash them with a fork.
4. Cut the vanilla pod into a lengthways, scrape out the pulp, and stir in the banana puree.
5. Wash the apple, grate, and stir in a bowl with butter and coconut blossom sugar in a bowl with the whisk of a hand mixer, stir in the egg. Then, alternately, gradually pull the banana puree and flour mixture under the butter mixture.
6. Grease a small baking tin (approx. 8x22 cm) if necessary. Pour in the dough and smooth it out with a rubber spatula.
7. Bake in the preheated oven at 175 ° C (fan oven: 150 ° C, gas: speed 2) on the middle shelf for 50–60 minutes. Put a wooden skewer in the middle of the cake: if it stays clean when pulled out, the cake is done; otherwise, continue baking for a few more minutes.
8. Remove the finished bread from the oven, let it cool in the baking pan for 5 minutes, then turn it over.

Nutrition: Calories 176 Protein 4 g, Fat 9 g, Carbs 19 g, Added Sugar 2.4 g, Fiber 1.8 g

87. Currant And Banana Croissants With Ground Almonds

Preparation time: 10 minutes
Cooking time: 40 minutes
Servings: 2

Ingredients:

- 135 ml milk (1.5% fat)
- ¼ cube yeast
- 125 g wheat flour type 1050
- 125 g wheat flour type 550
- 20 g liquid honey (1 heaped tablespoon)
- 30 g yogurt butter (2 tablespoons; room warm)
- 1 pinch salt
- 250 g red currants
- 50 g dried bananas
- 20 g ground almond kernels (2 tbsp.)

Directions:

1. Put the milk in a small saucepan, remove 1 tbsp, and set it aside in a small bowl. Warm the remaining milk slightly (35 to 40 degrees Celsius). Remove from the heat, crumble the yeast, stir thoroughly and cover, and let rise for about 10 minutes.
2. In the meantime, put both flours in a mixing bowl, mix, press a well in the middle with a tablespoon and add honey. Divide the butter into small portions with a teaspoon and put on the floured rim. Add a pinch of salt.
3. Pour the yeast and milk mixture into the recess and knead everything with the kneading hooks of the hand mixer to a smooth, shiny dough. Cover with a kitchen towel and leave in a warm place for about 40 minutes.

4. In the meantime, wash the currants for the stuffing, drain and rub off the panicles with a fork.
5. Chop dried bananas very finely, mix in a bowl with the ground almonds and currants.
6. Place baking paper on a baking sheet. Put the yeast dough on the lightly floured work surface and knead with your hands for about 2 minutes.
7. Roll out the dough into a circle of approx—32 cm. Cut into 12 equal triangles with a pizza wheel like a cake.
8. Put some water in a small bowl and thinly brush the edges of the triangles.
9. Put some of the fillings on the bottom wide third of each triangle. Roll up the triangles from the occupied side to the tip and form a croissant.
10. Place the croissant on the baking sheet with the rolled-up tip down and cover and leave to rise in a warm place for about 20 minutes.
11. Brush the croissants with the remaining milk and bake at 200 ° C (fan oven: 180 ° C, gas: level 3) in the preheated oven for about 25 minutes.
12. Take out the baking tray, pull the currant and banana croissants with the baking paper onto the upside-down oven rack and let cool.

Nutrition: Calories 126 Protein 3 g, Fat 3 g, Carbs 20 g, Added Sugar 2 g, Roughage 3 g

88. Avocado Smoothie With Yogurt And Wasabi

Preparation time: 5 minutes
Cooking time: 15 minutes
Servings: 2

Ingredients:

- 1 bunch coriander
- 1 spring onion
- 2 avocados
- 1 lime
- 1 tsp. wasabi paste
- 500 ml kefir
- 450g yogurt (0.3% fat)
- 2 handfuls ice cubes
- Salt
- Pepper

Directions:

1. Rinse the coriander, shake it dry, and pluck the leaves. Clean, rinse, drain the spring onions and cut them into rings.
2. Halve and stone avocados. Remove the pulp from the bowls with a tablespoon and place it in a blender or a tall container with coriander and spring onion rings.
3. Squeeze the lime. Add three tablespoons of juice, wasabi paste, kefir, and yogurt to the avocado.
4. Puree everything in the blender or with a hand blender, gradually adding the ice cubes. Season the avocado smoothie with salt and pepper and pour it into glasses.

Nutrition: Calories 172 Protein 7 g, Fat 11 g, Carbs 7 g, Fiber 1.5 g

89. Goat Cheese Omelet With Arugula And Tomatoes

Preparation time: 5 minutes
Cooking time:
15 minutes
Servings: 1

Ingredients:

- 4 Eggs
- 2 Eggs
- 1 small handful arugula
- 2 tomatoes
- 1 tsp. olive oil
- Salt
- Pepper
- 50 g young goat cheese

Directions:

1. In a bowl, separate four eggs and put the egg whites (use egg yolks elsewhere). Add the remaining two eggs and whisk everything with a whisk.
2. Wash the rocket, spin dry, and chop it roughly with a large knife.
3. Wash the tomatoes, cut out the stem ends in a wedge shape, and cut the tomatoes into slices.
4. Heat a coated pan (24 cm) and spread with the oil.
5. Add the whisked egg mixture. Season with salt and pepper.
6. Bake slightly over medium heat (the egg should still be a little runny) and turn using a plate.
7. Crumble goat cheese over the omelet with your fingers. Put the omelet on a plate, top with tomato slices and sprinkle the rocket. Whole grain toast goes well with this.

Nutrition: Calories 430 Protein 43 g, Fat 23 g, Carbs 10 g, Fiber 2.5 g

90. Summer Watermelon Juice

Preparation time: 2 minutes
Cooking time: 0minutes
Servings: 1

Ingredients:

- 4 mint leaves
- ½ cucumber, peeled if preferred, halved, seedless and roughly chopped
- 20g young kale leaves, stalks removed
- 250g watermelon chunks

Directions:

1. 1 Just whizz into your juicer or blender, and enjoy it right away.

Nutrition: Calories: 157 kcal Protein: 7.93 g Fat: 6.44 g Carbohydrates: 18.89 g

91. Grape And Melon Juice

Preparation time: 2 minutes
Cooking time: 0 minutes
Servings: 1

Ingredients:

- 100g red seedless grapes
- ½ cucumber, peeled if preferred, halved, seedless and roughly chopped
- 30g young spinach leaves, stalks removed
- 100g cantaloupe melon, peeled, deseeded and cut into chunks

Directions:

1. 1 Blend in a juicer or mixer, mix until smooth.

Nutrition: Calories: 185 kcal Protein: 7.96 g Fat: 6.41 g Carbohydrates: 26.27 g

92. Green Tea Smoothie

Preparation time: 3 minutes
Cooking time: 0 minutes
Servings: 2

Ingredients:

- 2 tsp matcha green tea powder
- Ripe bananas 250ml milk
- 2 tsp honey
- ½ tsp vanilla bean paste (not extract)

Directions:

1. 1 Easily mix all the ingredients into a blender and drink in two glasses.

Nutrition: Calories: 66 kcal Protein: 3.34 g Fat: 3.04 g Carbohydrates: 6.66 g

93. Blackcurrant And Oat Yogurt Swirl

Preparation time: 10 minutes
Cooking time: 0 minutes
Servings: 3

Ingredients:

- 100ml water 200g natural yogurt
- 100g blackcurrants washed and stalks removed
- 2 tbsp caster sugar
- 40g jumbo oats

Directions:

1. In a small pan, place the blackcurrants, water, and sugar and bring to the boil. Reduce heat marginally, maintain a robust simmer, and keep cooking for 5 minutes. Turn the heat down and encourage you to cool down. The compote blackcurrant can now be kept in the fridge until necessary.
2. Put the tofu and oats in a large pot and whisk. Distribute the compote of blackcurrant into two serving cups, then cover with yogurt then oats. Using a cocktail stick to pour the yogurt over the compote. Serve straight away.

Nutrition: Calories: 569 kcal Protein: 13.32 g Fat: 8.87 g Carbohydrates: 126.26 g

94. Thai Nut Mix

Preparation time: 5 minutes
Cooking time: 20 minutes
Servings: 1

Ingredients:

- ½ cup walnuts
- ½ cup coconut flakes
- ½ tsp soy sauce
- 1 tsp honey
- 1 pinch of cayenne pepper
- 1 dash of lime juice

Directions:

1. Add the above ingredients to a bowl, toss the nuts to coat, and place on a baking sheet, lined with parchment paper.
2. Cook at 250F for 15-20 minutes, checking as not to burn, but lightly toasted.
3. Remove from the oven. Cool first before eating.

Nutrition: Calories: 578 kcal Protein: 14.22 g Fat: 44.55 g Carbohydrates: 37.74 g

95. Eggs With Kale

Preparation time: 5 minutes
Cooking time: 15 minutes
Servings: 4

Ingredients:

- 2 tablespoons olive oil
- 1 red onion, chopped
- 2 garlic cloves, minced
- 1 cup tomatoes, chopped
- ½ pound fresh kale, tough ribs removed and chopped
- 1 teaspoon cumin, ground
- ¼ teaspoon red pepper flakes, crushed
- Salt and black pepper, ground
- 4 eggs
- 2 tablespoons fresh parsley, chopped

Directions:

1. Heat the oil in a big saucepan over heat and sauté the onion for about 4-5 minutes. Add garlic and sauté for about 1 minute.
2. Add the tomatoes, spices, salt, and black pepper and cook for about 2-3 minutes, stirring frequently.
3. Stir in the kale and cook for around 4-5 minutes. Carefully crack eggs on top of the kale mixture.
4. With the lid, cover the wok and cook for about 10 minutes or until the desired doneness of eggs.
5. Serve hot with the garnishing of parsley.

Nutrition: Calories: 266 kcal Protein: 14.09 g Fat: 18.72 g Carbohydrates: 12.22 g

96. Brussels Sprouts Egg Skillet

Preparation time: 5 minutes
Cooking time: 10 minutes
Servings: 4

Ingredients:

- ½ lb brussels sprouts, halved
- 1 small onion, chopped
- 10 cherry tomatoes, halved
- 4 eggs, beaten
- 1 tbsp. extra virgin olive oil

Directions:

1. Over medium heat, heat olive oil in a saucepan.
2. Add in onion and sauté for 1-2 minutes. Add in brussels sprouts and tomatoes and season with pepper and salt to taste.
3. Cook for 3-4 minutes and add the eggs.
4. Cook while covered until egg whites are ready, and egg yolk is to your wanted consistency.

Nutrition: Calories: 195 kcal Protein: 12.69 g Fat: 12.84 g Carbohydrates: 7.72 g

97. Berry Quinoa And Chia Seed Breakfast

Preparation time: 5 minutes
Cooking time: 20 minutes
Servings: 2

Ingredients:

- ½ cup quinoa
- 1½ cups milk
- 2 tbsp chia seeds
- ¼ cup fresh blueberries or raspberries
- 2 tbsp pistachios, silvered

Directions:

1. Combine quinoa and chia seeds with milk and bring to a boil.
2. Cover, lower heat, and simmer for 15 minutes.
3. When ready, serve into bowls and top with fresh berries and pistachios.

Nutrition: Calories: 380 kcal Protein: 16.73 g Fat: 15.2 g Carbohydrates: 45.19 g

98. South African Walnut Combo

Preparation time: 10 minutes
Cooking time: 0 minutes
Servings: 2

Ingredients:

- 1/8 cup (15g) walnuts sliced and chopped
- ½ cup (50g) celery
- 1/8 cup (10g) ginger
- 2 big Medjool dates
- 4 tsp. virgin oil

Directions:

1. Blend the walnuts and dates together until it becomes a mixture.
2. Add the celery and ginger to the mixture.
3. Add oil and serve.

Nutrition: Calories: 230 kcal Protein: 4.71 g Fat: 15.55 g Carbohydrates: 20.57 g

99. Kale And Blackcurrant Smoothie

Preparation time: 5 minutes
Cooking time: 0 minutes
Servings: 2

Ingredients:

- 2 tsp honey
- 1 cup freshly made matcha green tea
- Baby kale leaves, stalks removed
- 1 ripe banana
- 40 g blackcurrants, washed and stalks removed
- Ice cubes

Directions:

1. Stir the honey into the warm green tea until dissolved.
2. Whiz all the ingredients together in a blender until smooth. Serve immediately.

Nutrition: Calories: 69 kcal Protein: 4.04 g Fat: 3.1 g Carbohydrates: 6.86 g

100. Buckwheat Pancakes

Preparation time: 15 minutes
Cooking time: 15 minutes
Servings: 5

Ingredients:

- 1 cup of coconut milk
- 2 teaspoons apple cider vinegar
- 1 cup buckwheat flour
- 2 tablespoons ground flax seed
- 1 tablespoon baking powder
- ¼ teaspoon of sea salt
- ¼ cup maple syrup
- 1 teaspoon vanilla extract
- 1 tablespoon coconut oil

Directions:

1. In a medium bowl, blend the coconut milk and vinegar. Set aside.
2. In a large bowl, mix the flour, flaxseed, baking powder, and salt.
3. Add the coconut milk mixture, maple syrup, and vanilla extract and beat until well combined.
4. In a nonstick skillet, melt coconut oil over medium heat.
5. Place 1/3 cup of the mixture and spread in an even circle.
6. Cook for about 1-2 minutes.
7. Flip and cook for an additional 1 minute then remove from pan.
8. Repeat with the remaining mixture.
9. Serve warm.

Nutrition: Calories: 207 kcal Protein: 6.51 g Fat: 7.2 g Carbohydrates: 30.67 g

101. Kale & Broccoli Smoothie

Preparation time: 10 minutes
Cooking time: 0 Minutes
Servings: 2

Ingredients:

- 1 cup cucumber, peeled and chopped roughly
- 2 cups fresh baby kale
- 1 cup frozen broccoli
- 1 tablespoon fresh lime juice
- 1½ cup unsweetened almond milk
- ½ cup ice, crushed

Directions:

1. Add all ingredients in a high-power blender and pulse until smooth.
2. Pour the smoothie into two glasses and serve immediately.

Nutrition: Calories: 239 kcal Protein: 8.64 g Fat: 9.95 g Carbohydrates: 31.27 g

102. Scramble Eggs With Mushrooms

Preparation time: 10 Minutes
Cooking time: 20 Minutes
Servings: 2

Ingredients:

- 2 eggs
- 1 tsp ground turmeric
- 1 tsp mild curry powder
- 1 tsp extra virgin olive oil
- 100g mushrooms, thinly sliced
- 5g parsley, finely chopped

Directions:

1. Heat the oil the skillet over medium heat and fry the chili and mushrooms for 2– 3 minutes until they have started to brown. Mix the spices and add them to the eggs. Top with the parsley.

Nutrition: Calories: 199 kcal Protein: 14.08 g Fat: 14.01 g Carbohydrates: 4.37 g

103. Pink Omelets

Preparation time: 10 minutes
Cooking time: 30 minutes
Servings: 3

Ingredients:

- 2 eggs
- 100 g smoked salmon, sliced
- 20g capers
- 20 g rocket, chopped
- 10g parsley, chopped
- 1 tsp olive oil

Directions:

1. In a bowl, break the egg and mix well with salmon, capers, rocket, and parsley.
2. Heat the olive oil in a pan, add the egg mixture, and use a spatula or fish slice to move the mixture around the pan. Reduce the heat and let the omelets cook through.

Nutrition: Calories: 195 kcal Protein: 16.95 g Fat: 13.16 g Carbohydrates: 1.21 g

104. Chia Breakfast Bowl

Preparation time: 5 minutes
Cooking time: 15 minutes
Servings: 2

Ingredients:

- 1-3 tsp chia seeds
- 2/3 cup nut milk (almond or coconut)
- A pinch of salt
- Maple syrup, honey or nectar to taste
- Coconut flakes or seasonal fruit like blueberries as a topper

Directions:

1. Start with mixing the chia seeds in almond milk and continue to stir them efficiently,
2. After let the seeds sit for approximately 12 minutes until they become completely swollen.

3. In the end, put the honey, fruit you want, and a very little salt. Now enjoy and serve.

Nutrition: Calories: 91 kcal Protein: 5.78 g Fat: 5.7 g Carbohydrates: 3.91 g

105. Tofu Berry Smoothie

Preparation time: 16 minutes
Cooking time: 0 minutes
Servings: 1
Ingredients:

- 6 oz silken tofu
- 2/3 cup soy milk
- 1 tbs honey
- 1 medium-sized banana
- 1 cup fresh blueberries
- Ice cubes optional

Directions:

1. Start with removing water from tofu, now gather the ingredients.
2. In a blender, put banana, tofu, and soy milk to blend for 40 sec.
3. Now, put blueberries and start blending again until it turns smooth.
4. In the end, put the ice cubes, rest of berries and honey and blend a little again.
5. Serve and enjoy.

Nutrition: Calories: 1037 kcal Protein: 43.8 g Fat: 46.97 g Carbohydrates: 126.39 g

106. Rye Toast With Sunflower Seed Butter

Preparation time: 5 minutes
Cooking time: 0 minutes
Servings: 2
Ingredients:

- 4 slices Rye Bread
- ¼ cup sunflower seed butter
- 2 bananas

Directions:

1. Start the recipe with toasting your bread until it turns brown. Spread the sunflower seed butter all over it and slice it.
2. For the toppings, uses sliced bananas and enjoy your breakfast.

Nutrition: Calories: 368 kcal Protein: 12.98 g Fat: 22.35 g Carbohydrates: 31.61 g

107. Gooseberry Currant Yogurt Bowl

Preparation time: 5 minutes
Cooking time: 0minutes
Servings: 1
Ingredients:

- 1 cup or 150g vegan Yogurt
- ¼ cup or 30g black currants
- ½ cup or 60g granola
- 1/3 cup or 50g gooseberries

Directions:

1. Start with mixing the granola with yogurt in a bowl.
2. For the toppings, use currants and berries.
3. Serve and enjoy

Nutrition: Calories: 86 kcal Protein: 6.49 g Fat: 6.25 g Carbohydrates: 0.39 g

108. Muesli With Soy Yogurt

Preparation time 10 minutes
Cooking time: 0 minutes
Servings: 1
Ingredients:

- 1 cup of Soy yogurt
- ½ cup Granola
- 1tbs honey or nectar as a sweetener
- 1tbs chia seeds optional
- Seasonal fruit

Directions:

1. Start with mixing chia seeds in yogurt until seeds become swollen.
2. Put the sweetener like nectar or honey.
3. Garnish with seasonal fruit and granola.
4. Enjoy breakfast.

Nutrition: Calories: 209 kcal Protein: 23.14 g Fat: 0.77 g Carbohydrates: 31.56 g

109. Boiled Eggs With Rye Toasts

Preparation time: 10 minutes
Cooking time: 0 minutes
Servings: 2
Ingredients:

- 4 Boiled eggs
- 4 rye bread slices
- 4 tsp fat spread

Directions:

1. Start with toasting the rye bread until it becomes brown, then slice it and spread the fat you desired.
2. Take the boiled eggs, slice them, and put them on the slices; it's ready to serve.

Nutrition: Calories: 426 kcal Protein: 19.97 g Fat: 26.87 g Carbohydrates: 24.91 g

110. Berry Breakfast Bowl With Nuts And Seeds

Preparation time: 20 minutes
Cooking time: 0 minutes
Servings: 6
Ingredients:

- 400g bag frozen blueberries
- 400g bag frozen mixed berries
- Sugar optional
- For serving
- 1 tbsp flaked almonds, coconut, chia seeds and pistachios
- 2 tbsp natural yogurt

Directions:

1. Start with defrosting the berries by putting it berries in warm water in a pan on low heat.
2. After defrosting, enhance the heat and let the berries properly simmer for 1 min almost.
3. Further, mix the sugar according to your choice.
4. Use the almonds and fried seeds as toppers and serve it with yogurt.

Nutrition: Calories: 307 kcal Protein: 10.34 g Fat: 8.72 g Carbohydrates: 47.62 g

111. Tahini Porridge With Banana

Preparation time: 5 minutes
Cooking time: 10 minutes
Servings: 2
Ingredients:

- 150 ml milk
- 1 tbsp tahini
- 100g porridge oats
- 1 tbsp toasted sesame seeds
- Crushed seeds from 2 cardamom pods
- 2 sliced bananas

Directions:

1. Start with mixing the 1 tbsp milk, 1 tbsp water with tahini. Further add the salt, oats, 100ml milk, banana, 300 ml water and cardamom.
2. Star cooking all these at lower heat for almost 5-6 mins. Keep stirring it until it becomes hot and creamy.
3. Distribute this in two bowls, add more milk and garnish it with sliced bananas, spread the tahini over the mixture or sprinkle some sesame seeds.

Nutrition: Calories: 231 kcal Protein: 13.8 g Fat: 12.5 g Carbohydrates: 35.74 g

112. Miso Spinach Toast

Preparation time: 10 minutes
Cooking time: 5 minutes
Servings: 2

Ingredients:

- 200g spinach
- 1 tbsp. miso paste
- 2 tsp soy sauce
- 1 tbsp. melted butter
- 2 toast slices
- 2 tbsp. black sesame seeds
- 2 spring onions finely sliced

Directions:

1. Start with taking a pan and in the pan mix the miso paste with melted butter.
2. Further, place the spinach and cook until wilted and mix some soy sauce.
3. Distribute or spread it on two toasts. Top with sliced onions or sesame seeds and enjoy.

Nutrition: Calories: 229 kcal Protein: 11.89 g Fat: 17.13 g Carbohydrates: 9.87 g

113. Rye Toast With Peanut Butter

Preparation time: 5 minutes
Cooking time: 5 minutes
Servings: 1

Ingredients:

- 1 tbsp peanut butter
- ½ banana
- 1 pinch cinnamon
- 1 rye bread slice

Directions:

1. Start with toasting the bread and finely spread the butter on it.
2. Use the sliced bananas as toppings and use some cinnamon.

Nutrition: Calories: 193 kcal Protein: 9.66 g Fat: 9.77 g Carbohydrates: 16.04 g

114. Pumpkin Granola Yogurt Parfait

Preparation time: 1 hour 15minutes
Cooking time: 0 minutes
Servings: 4

Ingredients:

- Pumpkin Pie Cashew Cream:
- ½ cup of water
- ½ cup raw cashews
- 2 teaspoons pumpkin pie spice
- 2 cups pure pumpkin puree
- 2 tablespoons pure maple syrup
- pinch of salt
- ½ very ripe pear (cored)
- Parfaits
- the Pumpkin Pie Cashew Cream
- 2 cups coconut yogurt or Greek yogurt
- 1 cup + ¼ cup your favorite gluten-free granola

Directions:

1. Start with making the pumpkin cashew cream.
2. Soak the cashews in a half cup water for almost 1 hour, drain them and blend them finely.
3. Mix the maple syrup, pumpkin pie spice, pumpkin puree, pear, and salt in the blender with blended cashews and blend again until become smoothest.
4. Now, bring the four jars and place yogurt in every jar.
5. Then cover the yogurt with granola layer.
6. After that, put the pumpkin cashew cream over the granola layer.
7. Place the rest of the yogurt on every jar and use granola again for topping.

Nutrition: Calories: 634 kcal Protein: 24.59 g Fat: 47.95 g Carbohydrates: 36.3 g

115. Banana Peanut Butter Chia Pudding

Preparation time: 15 minutes + 3-4 hours chilling time
Cooking time: 0 minutes
Servings: 4

Ingredients:

- 2 medium bananas
- 1 ½ low-fat milk
- 1 ½ cup peanut butter
- 3 tbsp chia seeds

Directions:

1. Start with putting the banana, peanut butter, and milk in a blender to blend it.
2. Now take out the mixture from the blender and soak chia seeds in the mixture.
3. After that, cover the mixture and put it in the refrigerator for approximately 3-4 hours.
4. In the end, garnish and enjoy.

Nutrition: Calories: 278 kcal Protein: 6.81 g Fat: 17.3 g Carbohydrates: 23.78 g

116. Warm Fruit Bowl

Preparation time: 10 minutes
Cooking time: 20 minutes
Servings: 6

Ingredients:

- 2 cups blueberries
- 1 cup raspberries
- 1/2 cup strawberries
- 1-ounce dark chocolate shaved
- 1/2 cup large fresh figs
- 1 cup homemade almond or cashew
- 1 cup blackberries
- 1/4 cup dried mulberries, optional

Directions:

1. Start setting the oven at 350°F, and put all the fruits on a baking sheet, sprinkle cinnamon and salt on fruits.
2. Bring the baking tray in the oven and leave it in the oven for 20 mins.
3. Take the tray out, put in a bowl, garnish, and enjoy.

Nutrition: Calories: 208 kcal Protein: 3.19 g Fat: 3.7 g Carbohydrates: 43.42 g

117. Apple Avocado Smoothie

Preparation time: 5 minutes
Cooking time: 0 minutes
Servings: 2

Ingredients:

- 4 cups spinach
- 1 cup almond milk
- 2 medium apples
- 1 medium avocado peeled and pitted
- 1/2 teaspoon ground ginger
- 1 medium banana
- 2 teaspoons honey
- A small handful of ice cubes
- Chia seeds optional

Directions:

1. Start gathering all the ingredients in a blender to blend, blend it until it turns smooth.
2. Now, serve in two glasses and garnish with mint leaves or any additional fruit.

Nutrition: Calories: 815 kcal Protein: 22.61 g Fat: 44.63 g Carbohydrates: 95.7 g

118. Asparagus, Mushroom Artichoke Strata

Preparation time: 10 minutes
Cooking time: 1 hour and 10 minutes
Servings: 4

Ingredients:

- Inch little loaf of sourdough bread
- Four challah rolls
- Eight eggs
- 2 cups of milk
- 1 teaspoon salt
- 1/4 teaspoon black pepper
- 1 cup fontina cheese, cut into small
- 1/2 cup shredded parmesan cheese
- 1 tbsp butter (i used jojoba)
- 1 teaspoon dried mustard
- 1/2 can of artichoke hearts, sliced
- 1 bunch of green onions, grated
- 1 bunch asparagus, cut into 1-inch bits
- 10oz package of baby Bella (cremini) mushrooms, chopped

Directions:

1. Clean mushrooms and slice and trim asparagus and cut in 1-inch pieces. Reserve in a bowl and scatter 1/2 teaspoon salt mixture.
2. Drain and dice 1/2 may or humble artichoke hearts.
3. Melt butter in a pan over moderate heat, also sauté the asparagus and mushrooms before the mushrooms start to brown, about 10 minutes.
4. Blend the artichoke core pieces into a bowl with all a mushroom/asparagus mix. Setaside.
5. Cut or split a tiny sourdough loaf into 1-inch bits. (my bread was a little too small, therefore that I used four challah rolls also)
6. Grease a 9x13 inch baking dish and generate a base coating of bread at the plate. Spread 1/2 cup of fontina cheese bread, at a surface, and disperse half an apple mixture on the cheese.
7. Lay-down a different layer of these vegetables and bread and high using a 1/2 cup of fontina cheese.
8. Whisk together eggs, salt, milk, dry mustard, and pepper into a bowl and then pour the egg mixture on the vegetables and bread.
9. Cover the dish, and then simmer for three weeks.
10. Preheat oven to 375 degrees.
11. Eliminate the casserole from the fridge and let stand for half an hour.
12. Spread all the parmesan cheese at a coating within the strata.
13. Bake in the preheated oven until a toothpick inserted near the border comes out clean, 40 to 45 minutes. Let stand for around 5 to 10 minutes before cutting into squares.

Nutrition: Calories: 610 kcal Protein: 28.93 g Fat: 25.79 g Carbohydrates: 75.58 g

119. Egg White Veggie Wontons W/Fontina Topped W/ Crispy Prosciutto

Preparation time: 10 minutes
Cooking time: 30 minutes
Servings: 4

Ingredients:

- 1 cup egg whites
- Butter
- Fontina cheese
- Mixed shredded cheddar cheese
- Broccoli I utilized wheat, chopped bits
- Tomatoes - diced
- Salt and pepper
- Prosciutto - two pieces

Directions:

1. Remove won ton wrappers out of the freezer.
2. Preheat oven to 350.
3. Spray miniature cupcake tin with cooking spray.
4. After wrappers begin to defrost, peel off them carefully - apart, one at a time and press cupcake tin lightly.
5. I sliced the wrappers having a little bit of peanut butter. (optional)
6. Set a chunk of cheese in every bottom.
7. Satisfy desired lettuce - I used pre-cooked broccoli bits and diced tomatoes.
8. Pour egg whites all toppings.
9. Sprinkle each with some of those shredded cheddar cheese.
10. Cook for approximately 15 minutes, but get started watching them afterward 10 - whenever they poof up - assess them poking the middle with a fork.
11. While eggs are cooking, then spray a sheet of foil with cooking spray and then put two pieces of prosciutto onto it and then bake at precisely the same period as the egg whites. After 8 minutes, then take and let sit once it cools it becomes crispy and chop and high eggs!

Nutrition: Calories: 65 kcal Protein: 8.98 g Fat: 1.77 g Carbohydrates: 3.04 g

120. Berry Soy Yogurt Parfait

Preparation time: 2-4minutes
Cooking time: 0 minutes
Servings: 1

Ingredients:

- One 6-oz carton vanilla cultured soy yoghurt
- 1/4 cup granola (gluten-free)
- 1 cup berries (you can take strawberries, blueberries, raspberries, blackberries)

Directions:

1. Put half of the yogurt in a glass jar or serving dish.
2. On the top put half of the berries.
3. Then sprinkle with half of granola
4. Repeat layers.

Nutrition: Calories: 225 kcal Protein: 22.76 g Fat: 7 g Carbohydrates: 20.57 g

121. Matcha Green Tea Smoothie

Preparation time: 3 minutes
Cooking time: 0 minutes
Servings: 2
Ingredients:

- 2 ripe bananas
- 2 tsp. matcha green tea powder
- 2 tsp.honey
- 1/2 tsp. vanilla bean paste, not extract or seeds from a vanilla pod
- 250 ml of milk
- Six ice cubes

Directions:

1. Blend all the ingredients in a blender and serve in two glasses.

Nutrition: Calories: 66 kcal Protein: 3.34 g Fat: 3.g Carbohydrates: 6.66 g

122. Berry Chia Breakfast Bow

Preparation time: 10 minutes + chilling time
Cooking time: 0 minutes
Servings: 2
Ingredients:

- Eight pitted dates
- 1/2 cup canned coconut milk
- 2 tablespoons blanched almonds or raw cashews
- 2 teaspoons frozen orange juice concentrate
- 1 pinch salt
- 1/3 cup almond milk
- 1/2 teaspoon vanilla
- 2 cups diced, strawberries – divided
- 3/4 cup fresh blueberries
- 1/4 cup chia seed
- One small banana, sliced – optional

Direction:

1. In a blender, place dates, coconut milk, almond milk, almonds, orange juice concentrate, cinnamon, salt, and 1 cup strawberries and mix until smooth.
2. Shift mixture to medium bowl and stir in seed chia.
3. Place in the fridge for a minimum of 2 hours, or overnight.
4. Until serving, stir in the blueberries, remaining strawberries (sliced), and sliced bananas. Fresh berries work better than frozen.

Nutrition: Calories: 319 kcal Protein: 9.61 g Fat: 9.66 g Carbohydrates: 52.56 g

123. Flax Waffles

Preparation Time: 5 minutes
Cooking Time: 5 minutes
Servings: 2
Ingredients:

- ½ cup whole-wheat flour
- 1/3 tablespoon flaxseed meal
- ½ teaspoon baking powder
- 1 tablespoon olive oil
- ½ cup almond milk, unsweetened
- Extra:
- ¼ teaspoon vanilla extract, unsweetened
- 2 tablespoons coconut sugar

Directions:

1. Switch on a minute's waffle maker and let it preheat for 5 minutes.
2. Meanwhile, take a medium bowl, place all the ingredients in it, and then mix by using an immersion blender until smooth.
3. Ladle the batter evenly into the waffle maker, shut with lid, and let it cook for 3 to 4 minutes until firm and golden brown.
4. Serve straight away.

Nutrition: Calories 180 Fats 8.6 g Protein 4.1 g Carb 21.7 g Fiber 3.7 g

124. Peanut Butter Cup Protein Shake

Preparation time: 5 minutes
Cooking time: 0 minutes;
Servings: 2
Ingredients:

- 1 banana, peeled
- 1 scoop of chocolate protein powder
- 1 tablespoon nutritional yeast
- 2 tablespoons peanut butter
- ½ cup almond milk, unsweetened
- Extra:
- ½ teaspoon turmeric powder
- Bring all the ingredients in the order into a food processor or blender, and then pulse for 1 to 2 minutes until smooth.
- Distribute smoothie between two glasses and then serve.

Directions:

1. Divide smoothie between two jars or bottles, cover with a lid, and store the containers in the refrigerator for up to 3 days.

Nutrition: Calories 233 Fats 11.1 g Protein 14.6 g Carb 18.6 g Fiber 6.4 g

125. Apple And Cinnamon Smoothie

Preparation Time: 5 minutes
Cooking Time: 0 minutes
Servings: 2
Ingredients:

- 2 apples, peeled, cored, sliced
- 4 tablespoons pecans
- 4 Medjool dates pitted
- ½ teaspoon vanilla extract, unsweetened
- 2 cups almond milk, unsweetened
- Extra:
- 1 ½ tablespoon ground cinnamon

Directions:

1. Bring all the ingredients in the order into a food processor or blender, and then pulse for 1 to 2 minutes until smooth.
2. Distribute smoothie between two glasses and then serve.
3. Divide smoothie between two jars or bottles, cover with a lid and then store the containers in the refrigerator for up to 3 days.

Nutrition: Calories 363 Fats 12 g Protein 3.6 g Carb 60 g Fiber 8.9 g

126. Berries, Yogurt And Coconut Smoothie

Preparation Time: 5 minutes
Cooking Time: 0 minutes
Servings: 2
Ingredients:

- 3 ounces mixed berries

- ½ cup coconut flakes
- 2 ounces yogurt
- 1 ½ cup almond milk, unsweetened

Directions:

1. Bring all the ingredients in the order into a food processor or blender, and then pulse for 1 to 2 minutes until smooth.
2. Distribute smoothie between two glasses and then serve.
3. Divide smoothie between two jars or bottles, cover with a lid and then store the containers in the refrigerator for up to 3 days.

Nutrition: Calories 198 Fats 14.7 g Protein 3.5 g Carb 13 g Fiber 4.8 g

127. Carrot And Banana Smoothie

Preparation time: 5 minutes
Cooking time: 0 minutes
Servings: 2

Ingredients:

- 2 bananas, peeled
- 1 carrot, peeled, sliced
- 2 cups almond milk, unsweetened

Directions:

1. Bring all the ingredients in the order into a food processor or blender, and then pulse for 1 to 2 minutes until smooth.
2. Distribute smoothie between two glasses and then serve.
3. Divide smoothie between two jars or bottles, cover with a lid and then store the containers in the refrigerator for up to 3 days.

Nutrition: Calories156 Fats 2.8 g Protein 2.3 g Carb 30.4 g Fiber 4.1 g

128. Raspberry Vanilla Protein Smoothie

Preparation Time: 5 minutes
Cooking Time: 0 minutes
Servings: 2

Ingredients:

- 2 ounces raspberries
- 2 scoops of vanilla protein powder
- 1 ½ cup almond milk, unsweetened

Directions:

1. Bring all the ingredients in the order into a food processor or blender, and then pulse for 1 to 2 minutes until smooth.
2. Distribute smoothie between two glasses and then serve.
3. Divide smoothie between two jars or bottles, cover with a lid and then store the containers in the refrigerator for up to 3 days.

Nutrition: Calories148 Fats 2.1 g Protein 26.5 g Carb 5.5 g Fiber 1.9 g

129. Sweetcorn Fritters

Preparation time: 10 minutes
Cooking time: 10 minutes
Servings: 2

Ingredients:

- 8 ounces sweet corn
- 2/3 teaspoon ground flaxseed
- 4 tablespoons flour
- ½ teaspoon garlic powder
- 2 tablespoons olive oil
- Extra:
- ½ teaspoon salt
- ½ teaspoon ground cumin
- ½ teaspoon paprika
- 1/3 cup water

Directions:

1. Take a medium bowl, bring all the ingredients in it except oil, and then stir until well combined.
2. Take a frying pan, place it over medium heat, add oil, and when hot, scoop it corn batter in portions.
3. Shape the corn mixture into a patty by flattening it from the top and then cook for 3 to 4 minutes per side until golden brown.
4. Serve straight away.
5. Cool the fritters divide evenly between two meal prep containers, cover with a lid, and then store the containers in the refrigerator for up to 7 days. When ready to eat, reheat soup in the microwave oven for 1 to 2 minutes until hot and then serve.

Nutrition: Calories 244 Fats 15.2 g Protein 3 g Carb 23.7 g Fiber 2.8 g

130. Seared Tofu In Soy Sauce And Black Pepper

Preparation time: 35 minutes
Cooking time: 8 minutes
Servings: 2

Ingredients:

- 5 ounces tofu, ¼-inch thick sliced
- 1 green onion, chopped
- 2 tablespoons soy sauce
- ¼ teaspoon ground black pepper
- 1 teaspoon sesame seeds
- Extra:
- 1 tablespoon olive oil

Directions:

1. Cut tofu into ¼-inch pieces, place them into a medium bowl and then add soy sauce and black pepper.
2. Stir until coated and then let the tofu marinate for a minimum of 30 minutes.
3. Then take a medium skillet pan, place it over medium-high heat, add oil and when hot, add tofu pieces and cook for 2 to 3 minutes per side until golden brown and crisp.
4. When done, garnish tofu pieces with sesame seeds and onion and then serve.

Nutrition: Calories 154 Fats 11 g Protein 10 g Carb 3 g Fiber 1 g

131. Miso Sesame Chicken

Preparation time: 10 minutes
Cooking time: 15 minutes
Servings: 5

Ingredients:

- 1 skinless cod fillet
- ½ cup buckwheat
- ½ red onion, sliced
- 2 Celery stalks, sliced
- 10 green beans
- 2 Cups of chopped kale
- 3 Parsley sprigs
- 1 clove of garlic, finely chopped
- 1pinch of cayenne pepper or ½ chili pepper one teaspoon. Fresh ginger, finely chopped
- 1 A teaspoon of sesame seeds
- 2 Teaspoon of miso
- 1 tablespoon Mirin/rice wine vinegar
- 1 tablespoon extra-virgin olive oil
- 1tablespoon Soy sauce one teaspoon ground turmeric

Directions:

1. Cover the cod with a mixture of miso, mirin, and one teaspoon of oil and keep in the refrigerator for 30 minutes to an hour.
2. Heat the oven to 400 F and cook the cod for 10 minutes.
3. Sauté the onion and sauté in the remaining oil with the green beans, kale, celery, chili, garlic, and ginger. Sauté until kale is wilted, but beans and celery are tender. Add drops of water to the pan if necessary.
4. Cook the turmeric buckwheat for 3 minutes, depending on the package. Put the sesame, parsley, and tamari in the sauce and serve with vegetables and fish.

Nutrition: Calories 314 Fat 9.1g Protein 41.5g Carbohydrate 15.7g Fiber 1.3g Cholesterol 99mg Iron 1.9mg Sodium 608mg Calcium 29mg

132. Matcha Overnight Oats

Preparation time: 10 minutes
Cooking time: 0 minutes
Servings: 2
Ingredients:

- For the Oats
- 2 teaspoon Chia seeds
- 3 oz. Rolled oats
- 1 teaspoon Matcha powder
- 1 teaspoon Honey
- 1 ½ cups Almond milk
- 2 pinches ground cinnamon
- For the Topping
- 1 Apple (peeled, cored and chopped)
- A handful of mixed nuts
- 1 teaspoon Pumpkin seeds

Directions:

1. Get your oats ready a night before. Place the chia seeds and the oats in a container or bowl.
2. In a different jug or bowl, add the matcha powder and one tablespoon of almond milk and whisk with a hand-held mixer until you get a smooth paste, then add the rest of the milk and mix thoroughly.
3. Pour the milk mixture over the oats, add the honey and cinnamon, and then stir well. Cover the bowl with a lid and place in the fridge overnight.
4. When you want to eat, transfer the oats to two serving bowls, then top with the nuts, pumpkin seeds, and chopped apple.

Nutrition: Calories 324 Carbs37 g Dietary Fiber10 g Sugar8 g Fat14 g Saturated4 g

133. Cherry Tomatoes Red Pesto Porridge

Preparation time: 10 minutes
Cooking time: 5 minutes
Servings: 2
Ingredients:

- Salt, pepper
- 1 teaspoon hemp seed
- 1 teaspoon pumpkin seed
- 2 teaspoons nutritional yeast
- 1 teaspoon sun-dried tomato-walnut pesto
- 1 teaspoon tahini
- 1 tablespoon scallion
- 1 cup sliced cherry tomatoes
- 1 cup chopped kale
- 1 teaspoon dried basil
- 1.5 teaspoon dried oregano
- 2 cups veggie stock
- ½ cup couscous
- ½ cup oats

Directions:

1. In a small cooking pot, add oats, oregano, vegetable stock, basil, couscous, pepper, and salt and cook for about 5 minutes on medium heat stirring frequently until porridge is creamy and soft.
2. Add chopped kale but reserve a bit for garnish, tomatoes, and sliced scallion. Cook for an additional 1 minute, stir in pesto, tahini, and nutritional yeast.
3. Top with the reserved kale, pumpkin, and hemp seeds plus cherry tomatoes.

Nutrition: Calories: 259 Net carbs: 36g Fat: 7.68g Fiber: 7.4g Protein: 14.26g

134. Sautéed Veggies Bowl

Preparation time: 5 minutes
Cooking time: 5 minutes
Servings: 1
Ingredients:

- For tofu scramble:
- 1 cup of water
- Dash of soy sauce
- Pepper and salt
- 1 teaspoon turmeric
- 1 serving medium crumbled firm tofu
- For the Sautéed Veggies:
- 1/2 cup red onions, diced
- 1 cup mushrooms, sliced
- 1 big handful kale, de-stemmed and chopped
- For the Bowls
- 1/2 cup cooked brown rice
- 1/2 avocado, pitted

Directions:

1. Mix together the tofu scramble ingredients in a small dish, set aside.
2. Add a splash of water in a skillet over medium-high heat; add the onions, mushrooms, and kale. Cook, stirring periodically, for about 5-8 minutes or until it is evenly brown and soft. Set aside in a bowl.
3. Using the same skillet, pour in the tofu mixture and cook until it starts to brown and heated through for 5 minutes.
4. Transfer tofu scramble into a bowl, add the mushrooms/kale mixture, top with avocado, brown rice, and salsa. Serve with flatbreads, buckwheat, basmati rice, or couscous.

Nutrition: Calories: 122g Fats: 6.9g Sodium 867g Net carbs: 8.7g Fiber: 1.7g Sugar: 4.9g Protein: 7.3g

135. Green Chia Spinach Pudding

Preparation time: 30 minutes
Cooking time: 0 minutes
Servings: 1
Ingredients:

- 3 spoons of chia seeds
- 1 Medjool date, slice in half and remove the pit
- 1 handful fresh spinach
- 1 cup non-dairy milk
- Toppings
- Banana berries, etc.

Directions:

1. Blend the spinach, date, and milk in a high-speed blender until very smooth.

2. Pour the mixture in a bowl over the chia seeds. Stir the mixture well, and stirring every now and then for about 15 minutes.
3. Place it on the fridge and let it chill at least one hour or overnight.
4. Stir once more, just before serving; top with kiwi, banana berries, etc.

Nutrition: Calories: 232g Fats: 9.6g Sodium 86mg Net Carbs: 2.6g Fiber: 9.9g Protein 10.1g

136. Diced Seitan And Lentils

Preparation time: 5 minutes
Cooking time: 5 minutes
Servings: 2

Ingredients:

- 4 slices seitan
- 1 box lentils
- Half onion
- 1spoon soy cream
- Salt and pepper
- 1 tablespoon extra-virgin olive oil
- A handful of fresh parsley
- Turmeric (optional)

Directions:

1. Cut the seitan into cubes.
2. Chop the onion and put it in oil. When it is well colored - but not burnt - add the seitan cubes and, after a few minutes, the lentils drained and well washed. Add salt and pepper and sauté with a little hot water. Finish with the cream, turmeric, and chopped parsley, cook a few more minutes and then serve with a nice fresh salad and toasted whole meal bread.

Nutrition: Calories: 323 Net carbs: 36.7g Fat: 13.2g Fiber: 14.5g Protein: 16.4g

137. Beans On The Bird

Preparation time: 10 minutes
Cooking time: 25 minutes
Servings: 1

Ingredients:

- 2 cloves of garlic, minced
- 2 sage leaves
- 2 teaspoons extra virgin olive oil
- Boiled cannellini beans
- Fresh well ripe tomatoes
- Salt and pepper

Directions:

1. Brown for 2-3 minutes in a pan with oil, garlic, and sage. Then add the tomatoes, cut into segments, and let them brown for a couple of minutes. Add the beans, salt, and pepper to taste, stir. Cook in a covered pot for 20 minutes, checking and turning occasionally. Serve hot.

Nutrition: Calories: 153 Net carbs: 6.6g Fiber: 2.8g Protein: 3.4g

138. White Beans With Lemon

Preparation time: 5 minutes
Cooking time: 10 minutes
Servings: 1

Ingredients:

- A jar of white beans from Spain
- Breadcrumbs
- 4 Lemons
- A teaspoon of extra virgin olive oil
- A big onion

Directions:

1. Cut the onion into fillets, put them in a pan with a little water and oil and cook. After a few minutes, add the beans (rinse well under the tap). Stir and let it cook for a few minutes. Add salt, oil, and breadcrumbs and mix. After a while, pour the lemon juice. Wait a little longer, and the dish is ready. Add more lemon at the end of cooking and eat!

Nutrition: Calories: 314 Net carbs: 51.6g Fat: 2.5g Fiber: 9.9g Protein: 14.1g

139. Sponge Beans With Onion

Preparation time: 10 minutes
Cooking time: 3 hours
Servings: 2

Ingredients:

- 250 g boiled Spanish beans
- 1 red onion
- 1 parsley
- Salt
- 2 teaspoons oil
- 1 teaspoon apple vinegar
- 1 teaspoon dried oregano or 5 fresh oregano leaves

Directions:

1. Cut the onion into thin slices and cook it for a minute with water in the microwave at full power. Combine all the ingredients in a bowl and leave to rest a couple of hours before serving, stirring a couple of times so that the beans take on the seasoning flavor.

Nutrition: Calories: 832 Net carbs: 23.1g Fat: 11.1g Fiber: 13.9g Protein: 38.1g

140. Chickling Falafel

Preparation time: 24 hours
Cooking time: 30 minutes
Servings: 2

Ingredients:

- Half onion
- 200 grams chickling peas already soaked
- 80g of chickpea flour
- A teaspoon of cumin seed
- A clove of garlic
- Paprika

Directions:

1. Blend the chickling peas (previously soaked for 24 hours) together with the chopped onion, cumin, paprika, and garlic and chickpea flour. Blend until a fairly homogeneous mixture is obtained. Compact in a bowl and leave to rest in the fridge for about an hour. Take the dough and form some meatballs that will be baked in the oven at 180 degrees until golden brown. Notes Cumin can be reduced or eliminated completely.

Nutrition: Calories: 57 Net carbs: 5.4g Fat: 3g Protein: 2.2g

141. Arugula Linguine

Preparation time: 10 minutes
Cooking time: 25 minutes
Servings: 2

Ingredients:

- 12 ounces linguine or other dried pasta
- 3 s extra virgin olive oil
- 3 - 4 cloves garlic, sliced thinly
- 2 large handfuls baby arugula
- 2 scapers, drained
- ½ cup Parmesan, shredded or shaved
- 1/3 cup pine nuts, toasted

Directions:

1. In a large pan, put the pasta in a boiling salted water for about 8 minutes.
2. While pasta is cooking, heat oil in a large pan and sauté the garlic over medium heat for 2 – 3 minutes until just turning golden.
3. When your pasta is ready, drain and immediately add the remaining ingredients, including the garlic and toss to combine well.

Nutrition: Calories: 223 Net carbs: 0.3g Fiber: 0.2g Protein: 0.2g

142. Shepherd's Pie

Preparation time: 25 minutes
Cooking time: 1 hour 10 – 20 minutes
Servings: 4

Ingredients:

- For the mashed potatoes:
- 6 large potatoes, peeled and cubed
- ½ cup of soy milk
- ¼ cup extra virgin olive oil
- 2 teaspoons salt
- For the bottom layer:
- 1 teaspoon extra virgin olive oil
- 1 yellow onion, chopped
- 3 carrots, chopped
- 3 stalks celery, chopped
- ½ cup frozen peas
- 1 tomato, chopped
- 1 teaspoon dried parsley
- 1 teaspoon dried Lovage
- 1 teaspoon dried oregano
- 3 cloves garlic, minced
- 1/2 cup kasha (toasted buckwheat groats)
- 2/3 cup bulgur
- 2 cups fresh mushrooms, diced

Directions:

1. Set oven to 350°F then sprays a 2-quart baking dish with cooking spray.
2. Bring the potatoes into a large pot with enough cold water to cover them completely. Bring the water to a boil and then reduce heat to a low boil until the potatoes until tender, about 20 minutes. Drain and transfer to a large bowl.
3. Using a hand blender, mix the soy milk, olive oil, and salt into the potatoes, and blend until smooth. Cover and set aside until your bottom layer is ready.
4. At the same time, in a saucepan, bring 1 ½ cups water with ½ teaspoon salt to a boil. Stir in kasha. Lower the heat and simmer uncovered for 15 minutes.
5. Add 1 ½ cups more water and bring back to a boil. Add bulgur, cover, and remove from heat. Let stand for 10 minutes.
6. Warm the oil in a big pan, then sauté the onion, carrots, celery, frozen peas, and tomato on medium heat until they start to soften about 5 minutes. Add mushrooms and cook for another 3 – 4 minutes.
7. Sprinkle flour over vegetables; constantly stir for 2 minutes or until flour starts to brown. Pour the remaining 1 ½ cups milk over the vegetables and increase heat to high. Stir until sauce is smooth. Reduce heat and simmer for 5 minutes. Stir in parsley, Lovage, oregano, garlic, and salt and pepper to taste.
8. Combine vegetable mixture and kasha mixture in a large bowl and mix well.
9. Spoon into a greased 10" pie pan and smooth with a spatula. Spread mashed potatoes over the top, leaving an uneven surface.
10. Bake until the potatoes turn golden, and the Shepherd's Pie is hot throughout about 30 minutes.

Nutrition: Calories: 436 Net carbs: 59.6g Fat: 11.4g Protein: 20.2g

143. Plum Chutney

Preparation time: 5 minutes
Cooking time: 50 minutes
Servings: 4

Ingredients:

- 500 g pitted prunes
- 50 g ginger
- 350 g onions
- 2 s vegetable oil
- 250g brown sugar
- 300ml balsamic vinegar
- Salt, pepper

Directions:

1. Quarter the washed and pitted plums. Finely dice the ginger and onions and braise in 2 s of oil. Add the plums and steam briefly.
2. Add the brown sugar and let it melt while stirring. Then pour balsamic vinegar over it and let it boil for about 40 minutes on a low flame.
3. Season with salt and pepper and pour into boiled glasses.

Nutrition: Calories: 125 Net carbs: 19.6g Fat: 4.9g Fiber: 0.8g Protein: 1.7g

144. Chocolate Chip Gelato

Preparation time: 30 minutes
Cooking time: 0 minutes
Servings: 4

Ingredients:

- 2 cups dairy-free milk
- ¾ cup pure maple syrup
- 1 pure vanilla extract
- ⅓ Semi-sweet vegan chocolate chips, finely chopped

Directions:

1. Beat dairy-free milk, maple syrup, and vanilla together in a large bowl until well combined.
2. Pour the mixture carefully into the container of an automatic ice cream maker and process it according to the manufacturer's instructions.
3. During the last 10 or 15 minutes, add the chopped chocolate and continue processing until the desired texture is achieved. Enjoy the gelato immediately, or let it harden further in the freezer for an hour or more.

Nutrition: Calories: 94 Net carbs: 14.9g Fat: 3.4g Fiber: 0.5g Protein: 0.8g

145. Tasty Panini

Preparation time: 5 minutes
Cooking time: 0 minutes
Servings: 1

Ingredients:

- ¼ cup, hot water
- 1 tablespoon, cinnamon
- ¼ cup, raisins
- 2 teaspoons, cacao powder
- 1 ripe banana
- 2 slices, whole-grain bread
- ¼ cup, natural peanut butter

Directions:

1. In a bowl, mix the cinnamon, hot water, raisins, and cacao powder.
2. Spread the peanut butter on the bread.
3. Cut the bananas and put them on the toast.
4. Mix the raisin mixture in a blender and spread it on the sandwich.

Nutrition: Calories: 850,Fats 34 g, Carbohydrates 112 g,Proteins 27 g

146. Apple And Blueberry Buckwheat Cake

Preparation time: 10 minutes
Cooking time: 4o minutes
Servings: 8
Ingredients:

- For the topping:
- Three apples, peeled and cut into slices
- 75g blueberries
- 25g salted butter
- 2 tablespoons maple syrup
- For the cake:
- 75g butter, cut into cubes
- 75g organic virgin coconut oil
- 100g cane sugar
- 2 large free-range eggs, beaten
- 75g buckwheat flour
- 75g ground almonds
- ½ teaspoon bicarbonate of soda
- 1 teaspoon baking powder
- 1 teaspoon cinnamon

Directions:

1. Preheat the oven to 180°C. Caramelize the apples in a little water, adding the butter and maple syrup once softened.
2. Add the blueberries last. Set aside. Place the sugar, butter and coconut oil into a mixing bowl and cream until pale and fluffy.
3. Gradually add the beaten eggs, adding a bit of flour if the mixture begins to curdle. Continue to beat the mixture until fluffy. And then fold in the remaining flour, ground almonds, baking powder, and cinnamon.
4. Transfer the apple and blueberry mixture into the bottom of a greased Bundt cake mold (We use a silicon one), leveling well with the back of a spoon. Then pour the cake mixture over the top.
5. Bake for around 40 minutes, until a baking skewer comes out clean. Leave to cool. Delicious served with Greek yogurt.

Nutrition: Calories: 104 Cal Fat: 3 g Carbohydrates: 18 g Protein: 3 g Fiber: 0g

147. Peanut Butter, Banana Buckwheat Porridge

Preparation Time: 5 minutes
Cooking Time: 2 minutes
Servings: 1
Ingredients:

- 1/2 cup Buckwheat
- 1/2 cup milk, 2%,
- 1/2 cup water
- 1 medium Banana, fresh
- 1 tbsp. Peanut Butter, with salt
- 1 tbsp. Coconut Flakes

Directions:

1. Soak buckwheat for overnight
2. In the morning drain and rinse buckwheat
3. Combine all ingredients then microwave for 15 minutes.

Nutrition: Calories: 559.5 Cal Fat: 13.8 g Carbohydrates: 97.7 g Protein: 21. 4 g Fiber: 12.5 g

148. Raw Brownie Bites

Preparation Time: 10 minutes
Cooking Time: 30 minutes
Servings: 6
Ingredients:

- 2½ cups whole walnuts
- ¼ cup almonds
- 2½ cups medjool dates
- 1 cup cacao powder
- 1 teaspoon vanilla extract
- ⅛-¼ teaspoon sea salt

Directions:

1. Bring all the ingredients in a food processor until it is well combined.
2. Roll into balls and place on a baking sheet and freeze for 30 minutes or refrigerate for 2 hours.

Nutrition: Calories: 114 Cal Fat: 6 g Carbohydrates: 13 g Protein: 3 g Fiber: 2 g

149. Kale And Blackcurrant Smoothie

Preparation time: 2 minutes
Cooking time: 3 minutes
Servings: 2
Ingredients:

- 2 tsp honey
- 1 cup freshly made matcha green tea
- 10 baby kale leaves, stalks removed
- 1 ripe banana
- 40 g blackcurrants, washed and stalks removed
- 6 ice cubes

Directions:

1. 2 tsp honey
2. 1 cup freshly made matcha green tea
3. 10 baby kale leaves, stalks removed
4. 1 ripe banana
5. 40 g blackcurrants, washed and stalks removed
6. 6 ice cubes

Nutrition: Calories: 131 Cal Fat: 0 g Carbohydrates: 29 g Protein: 0 g Fiber: 3 g

150. Spiced Scrambled Eggs

Preparation time: 2 minutes
Cooking time: 10 minute
Servings: 1
Ingredients:

- 1 teaspoon extra virgin olive oil
- 1/8 cup (20g) red onion, finely chopped
- 1/2 Thai chili, finely chopped
- 3 medium eggs
- 1/4 cup (50ml) milk
- 1 teaspoon ground turmeric
- 2 tablespoons (5g) parsley, finely chopped

Directions:

1. Heat the oil in a frying pan and fry the red onion and chili until soft but not browned.
2. Whisk together the eggs, milk, turmeric, and parsley.
3. Add to the hot pan and continue cooking over low to medium heat, continually moving the egg mixture around the pan to scramble it and stop it from sticking/burning.
4. When you have achieved your desired consistency, serve.

Nutrition: Calories: 182 Cal Fat: 13 g Carbohydrates: 1 g Protein: 12 g Fiber: 6 g

151. Chocolate Strawberry Milk

Preparation time: 1 minute
Cooking time: 2-3 minutes
Servings: 2

Ingredients:

- 150g strawberries, hulled and halved
- 1 tbsp cocoa powder (100 % cocoa)
- 10g pitted Medjool dates
- 10g walnuts
- 200ml milk or dairy-free alternative

Directions:

1. In a blender, place and blend all the ingredients and blitz until smooth.

Nutrition: Calories: 230 Cal Fat: 13 g Carbohydrates: 28 g Protein: 2 g Fiber: 1 g

152. Poached Eggs With Arugula

Preparation time: 5 minute
Cooking time: 10 minutes
Servings: 2

Ingredients:

- 2 Egg
- 1 oz fresh arugula
- 1 tsp Olive oil
- Salt and pepper according to personal preference

Directions:

1. In a small container or bowl, toss arugula with your olive oil to get it coated. Leave it there if you intend to eat out of this receptacle, or plate it.
2. On your stovetop, place a small pot full of water and heat to boiling. Add the eggs and cook until the whites are firm. A tip for this would be cracking an egg onto a ladle, so you gently dip the egg into the boiling water. If you are too rough with the eggs when you plop it in, the yolks will break, and you will have the very bland beginnings of an egg drop soup.
3. Add the eggs over the greens. Salt and pepper your egg and arugula as needed and enjoy.

Nutrition: Calories: 203 kcal Protein: 12.98 g Fat: 15.06 g Carbohydrates: 3.66 g

153. Arugula And Bacon Omelet

Preparation time: 10 minute
Cooking time: 25 minutes
Servings: 3

Ingredients:

- 1 cup Arugula, chopped
- 2 slices Bacon
- 6 Eggs
- 1 cup Kale, chopped
- 1 tsp. Olive Oil
- 4 tbsp. Parsley
- 2 tsp. Turmeric powder

Directions:

1. Heat a frying pan and toss in your bacon slices. Crisp them up based on personal preference. When they get cooked to your liking, take the slices and pat them with a paper towel to remove excess fat. If you prefer a stronger bacon taste, leave some of the fat in the pan. If not, pour it out and wipe down the pan carefully, so it is ready to be used again.
2. In a large enough container, whip your eggs with the chopped arugula, kale, turmeric, and parsley.
3. Chop or crumble your bacon and toss it into the eggs.
4. Oil your pan as necessary and heat until it is nice and ready.
5. Using a swirling motion, pour the eggs into the oil, keeping things as flat and even as you can.
6. Set your burner's heat to medium-low and cook your omelet through.
7. Now you need to roll the egg up and serve.

Nutrition: Calories: 382 kcal Protein: 22.98 g Fat: 29.8 g Carbohydrates: 4.55 g

154. Caper And Salmon Omelet

Preparation time: 10 minute
Cooking time:
25 minutes
Servings: 2

Ingredients:

- 1.25 cups Arugula, chopped roughly
- 1 tsp capers
- 4 Eggs
- 1 tsp Olive oil
- 2 tsp Parsley, chopped roughly
- 1.33 cups Smoked salmon, sliced

Directions:

1. Whip your eggs in a bowl thoroughly.
2. Now toss in the capers, smoked salmon, arugula, and parsley into your eggs. Again, whip thoroughly.
3. Take a skillet and place it on a burner set to medium-high. Pour in the olive oil and wait for it to heat up. It is ready when shimmering; however, do not heat it to boiling.
4. Pour in the egg and spread it out nice and level on the skillet; you want this to cook evenly, after all.
5. Drop the heat on the burner to medium and cook until the egg has gotten firm.
6. Roll your omelet and plate it. Consider garnishing with a bit more freshly chopped parsley. It is a simple addition, but it does add to the presentation.

Nutrition: Calories: 323 kcal Protein: 21.49 g Fat: 24.65 g Carbohydrates: 2.57 g

155. Double Baked Potato

Preparation time: 10 minute
Cooking time:
50 minutes
Servings: 2

Ingredients:

- 2 Tbsp. Butter
- 0.5 cup Cheddar cheese, shredded
- Chives
- 4 slices cooked bacon
- 3 tbsp. Cream
- 4 Eggs
- Pepper
- 2 Russet potatoes
- Salt

Directions:

1. As the name implies, you will be baking your taters twice. For the first round, prepare your oven at 400°. Place the potatoes directly on the center rack of your oven and bake until tender. This may take approximately 40 minutes. After 45 minutes, take the potatoes from the grill. Once cooked through, place your potatoes on a cutting board and slice them in half, longways.
2. Using a spoon, scoop out the potato flesh and throw it into a bowl. Save the skins.

3. Take your butter and cream and stir into the potato until it is nice and smooth. Take the potato cream and spoon back into the potato skins. Sprinkle cheddar on top.
4. Grab the bacon and place one slice on each potato half. Crack an egg on top of each potato now as well. While being cautious, move your potatoes onto a baking sheet. Considering placing a parchment paper blanket on the sheet to make removal easier later.
5. Now to bake the potatoes a second time! For this final bake, prepare your oven at 375°. Place your tray in the center and bake until the eggs have set. If you like your bacon crispier, consider frying them a bit before placing them in the potatoes next time.
6. Extract the potatoes from the oven, and place more cheese shreds on top. Garnish with chives, and you are ready to serve. Baking the skins a second time will make them nice and crispy, and make for a great contrast to the soft mashed potato.

Nutrition: Calories: 927 kcal Protein: 37.07 g Fat: 55.13 g Carbohydrates: 72.09 g

156. Banana Blueberry Pancake

Preparation time: 15 minute
Cooking time: 45 minutes
Servings: 4

Ingredients:

- 1 tsp Baking powder
- 3Bananas
- 0.75 cup blueberries
- 1 Tbsp. Butter
- 3Eggs
- 5 Tbsp. Rolled oats, alternatively, use oat flour
- Salt (a pinch)

Directions:

1. If you do not have any oat flour on hand, then make your own. You will start by taking five tablespoons of rolled oats and tossing them into a blender or food processor. Blend them until you get a fine powder. Now you have the oat flour you need for these delicious pancakes.
2. Add in eggs, bananas, salt, and baking powder to a food processor. Make use of pulsing to combine the ingredients. Alternatively, utilize a hand mixer and a bowl or whip with a fork. You have just made your batter.
3. It does not matter if you are using frozen or fresh blueberries. Grab whichever you have on hand or prefer, and toss them into a bowl with the batter. Mix them around gently with a fork.
4. Allow your batter to stand at room temperature for about ten minutes.
5. Take a frying pan and rest it on a stovetop burner set to medium-high. Warm-up a frying pan on medium-high. Slap the butter in there and let it melt. There is no need to wait for it to brown. Once you have an even layer of butter covering the pan, scoop in the batter to your preferred thickness and shape. Pan Fry until golden brown, and the top side is bubbling. The sides should be firm, and the batter should not be leaking down to the pan. Flip and cook the bottom side.
6. Plate and serve with more fruit or a couple of slices of bacon.

Nutrition: Calories: 196 kcal Protein: 10.02 g Fat: 11.35 g Carbohydrates: 16.22 g

157. Chicken & Kale Muffins

Preparation time: 20 minute
Cooking time:
15 minutes
Servings: 4

Ingredients:

- 18 eggs
- Freshly ground black pepper, as required
- 2 tablespoons of filtered water
- 7 ounces cooked chicken, chopped finely
- 1½ cups fresh kale, tough ribs removed and chopped
- 1 cup onion, chopped
- 2 tablespoons fresh parsley, chopped

Directions:

1. Preheat the oven to 350 degrees F. Grease 8 cups of a muffin tin.
2. In a bowl, add eggs, black pepper, and water and beat until well combined.
3. Add chicken, kale, onion, and parsley and stir to combine.
4. Transfer the mixture in prepared muffin cups evenly.
5. Bake for around 18-20 minutes or until golden brown.
6. Remove the muffin tin from the oven and place onto a wire rack to cool for about 10 minutes.
7. Carefully invert the muffins onto a platter and serve warm.

Nutrition: Calories: 225 Fat: 10.3g Sat Fat: 3.2g Cholesterol: 366mg Sodium: 168mg Carbohydrates: 6.1g Fiber: 1.1g Sugar: 1.9g Protein: 26.6g

158. Mung Sprouts Salsa

Preparation time: 10 minutes
Cooking time: 0 minutes
Servings: 2

Ingredients:

- 1 red onion, chopped
- 2 cups mung beans, sprouted
- A pinch of red chili powder
- 1 green chili pepper, chopped
- 1 tomato, chopped
- 1 teaspoon chaat masala
- 1 teaspoon lemon juice
- 1 tablespoon coriander, chopped
- Black pepper to the taste

Directions:

1. In a salad bowl, mix onion with mung sprouts, chili pepper, tomato, chili powder, chaat masala, lemon juice, coriander, and pepper, toss well, and divide into small cups and serve.
2. Enjoy!

Nutrition: Calories: 100 Fat: 2g Fiber: 1 g Carbohydrates: 3g Protein: 6g

159. Salsa Bean Dip

Preparation time: 10 minutes
Cooking time: 20 minutes
Servings: 6

Ingredients:

- ½ cup of salsa
- 2 cups canned white beans, no-salt-added, drained and rinsed
- 1 cup low-fat cheddar, shredded
- 2 tablespoons green onions, chopped

Directions:

1. In a small pot, combine the beans with the green onions and salsa, stir, bring to a simmer over medium heat, cook for 20 minutes, add cheese, stir until it melts, take off heat, leave aside to cool down, divide into bowls and serve.
2. Enjoy!

Nutrition: Calories: 212 Fat: 5g Fiber: 6 g Carbohydrates: 10g Protein: 7g

160. Strawberry Iced Green Tea

Preparation time: 10 minutes
Cooking time: 0 minute
Servings: 4

Ingredients:

- 4 cups of water
- 4 tablespoons of Matcha green tea powder
- 2 cups of crushed ice
- 2 tablespoons of sugar (optional)
- 1 teaspoon of lemon zest
- 4 cups of strawberries, halved

Directions:

1. Boil water and let cool for five minutes.
2. Place the Matcha green tea powder in a large bowl, add the cooled hot water and whisk until smooth.
3. Add the lemon powder, strawberries, sugar and crushed ice to a large jug and mix well.
4. Pour the tea into the jug, and chill for at least one hour in your fridge.
5. Stir before serving.

Nutrition: Calories: 70 Carbohydrates: 21g Protein: 1g

161. Instant Choco Nut Iced Coffee

Preparation time: 5 minutes
Cooking time: 0 minute
Servings: 2

Ingredients:

- 2 cups of milk, chilled
- ¼ cup walnuts, crushed
- 2 teaspoons instant coffee
- 2 teaspoons sugar
- 1 teaspoon unsweetened cocoa
- 1 teaspoon vanilla (optional)

Directions:

1. Combine all ingredients to a blender and blend until frothy.
2. Serve in a chilled glass.

Nutrition: Calories: 100 Carbohydrates: 26g Protein: 1g

162. Sesame Dip

Preparation time: 10 minutes
Cooking time: 0 minutes
Servings: 6

Ingredients:

- 1 cup sesame seed paste, pure
- Black pepper to the taste
- 1 cup veggie stock
- ½ cup lemon juice
- ½ teaspoon cumin, ground
- 3 garlic cloves, chopped

Directions:

1. In your food processor, mix the sesame paste with black pepper, stock, lemon juice, cumin and garlic, pulse very well, divide into bowls and serve as a party dip.
2. Enjoy!

Nutrition: Calories: 120 Fat: 12g Fiber: 2 g Carbohydrates: 7g Protein: 4g

163. Breakfast Crepes

Preparation time: 8 Minutes
Cooking time: 12 Minutes
Servings: 4

Ingredients:

- 2 eggs
- 3 tablespoons full fat cream cheese
- 1 tablespoon grass-fed butter
- 1 teaspoon parmesan cheese, grated
- ¼ teaspoon baking powder

Directions:

1. Soften cream cheese on the countertop until malleable, or heat for 30 seconds in the microwave. Crack and beat eggs in a bowl. Combine with cream cheese, parmesan cheese, and baking powder. Mix thoroughly until no lumps are remaining. If necessary, heat the mixture in the microwave for no more than 20 seconds to further warm the cream cheese; microwaving for too long once the eggs are added can begin to cook them.
2. In a frying pan, heat the butter in medium-low heat. Pour in about a quarter of the crepe batter and tilt the frying pan so that its entire surface is coated in batter. Work quickly, as allowing the batter to sit too long, will cause it to begin to stiffen.
3. You must be left with a fairly thin layer of batter in the pan. Allow batter to cook undisturbed until it thickens enough to easily get your spatula underneath it, which should take around four minutes.
4. Then flip the crepe and allow it to cook for another three minutes. Both sides should be a warm golden-brown color. Remove the crepe from the pan by separating it carefully with the spatula, then sliding it off onto a plate. Repeat the cooking directions until all batter has been used.

Nutrition: Calories: 105 Total fat: 10 g Sodium: 151 mg Total carbohydrates: 1 g Fiber: 0 g Sugar: 1 g Protein: 4 g

164. Breakfast Burritos

Preparation time: 5 Minutes
Cooking time: 10 Minutes
Servings: 1

Ingredients:

- 1 breakfast crepe
- 1 egg
- ¼ pound skirt steak
- ¼ cup extra sharp cheddar cheese, grated
- 2 tablespoons grass-fed butter
- 2 tablespoons water

Directions:

1. Prepare breakfast crepes as outlined in the previous recipe.
2. Transfer skirt steak to a cutting board and cut into very thin, bite-sized slices. This will help the steak to cook quickly.
3. Melt one tablespoon of butter in a skillet over medium-high heat. Add steak and cook, frequently stirring until browned, about four minutes depending on the thickness of your pieces. Shut off the heat, but keep the steak warm.
4. Crack an egg into a small bowl and add water. Beat the egg until the yolk, white, and water have combined.
5. In a separate skillet, melt the remaining tablespoon of butter over medium heat and pour in the egg mixture. Cook scrambled eggs for five minutes, stirring frequently and using a spatula to break the cooked egg into forkful-sized bites.
6. Once steak and eggs have finished cooking, add both to the crepe and top with cheddar cheese. Roll the crepe into a burrito and enjoy it.

Nutrition: Calories: 543 Total fat: 52 g Sodium: 473 mg Carbohydrates: 1 g Fiber: 0 g Sugar: 1 g Protein: 38 g

165. Chicken And Bacon Sausage Patties

Preparation time: 5 Minutes
Cooking time: 25 Minutes
Servings: 12

Ingredients:

- ½ teaspoon salt
- 1-pound ground chicken 4 slices bacon
- 1 egg 1 tablespoon garlic powder
- ½ tablespoon onion powder
- 1 teaspoon ground black pepper

Directions:

1. Preheat oven to 425 degrees Fahrenheit.
2. Add bacon slices to a skillet over medium-low heat. Ensure that the bacon is not overlapping at that it touches the surface of the pan as evenly as possible. Cook bacon until fairly crispy, about eight to ten minutes, occasionally flipping to prevent sticking and burning. Alternatively, you can microwave the bacon for five minutes on a microwave-safe plate lined with paper towels.
3. Transfer cooked bacon to paper towels to soak up excess grease and allow it to cool. Once fully cooled, crumble and add to a food processor. Add in ground chicken, egg, garlic powder, onion powder, salt, and pepper. Process until well combined, about one minute. Line a baking sheet with parchment paper or aluminum foil. Scoop the meat mixture into tablespoon-sized balls, then flatten to make 12 thin patties of similar size. Keeping the patties similar to each other helps ensure that they all cook through completely. Put the baking sheet in the oven and bake for 18-20 minutes. Test to ensure there is no pink remaining in the sausage patties before serving or storing in the fridge or freezer for reheating.

Nutrition: Calories: 99 Total fat: 6 g Sodium: 147 mg Total carbohydrates: 1 g Fiber: 1g Sugar: 1 g Protein: 11 g

166. Hard Boiled Eggs With Smoked Salmon

Preparation time: 5 Minutes
Cooking time: 25 Minutes
Servings: 1

Ingredients:

- 2 eggs 4 ounces smoked salmon
- ½ teaspoon paprika
- ½ teaspoon ground black pepper

Directions:

1. Add eggs to an empty pot or saucepan. Pour in enough cold water that it covers the eggs, plus about one inch of water above them. Bring to a boil over high heat.
2. Cover the pot firmly with a lid and remove from heat. Allow to sit for the desired length of time. Four to six minutes will give you soft boiled eggs with runny yolks, while 10-12 minutes gives you a more standard hardboiled egg.
3. While the eggs are cooking, slice the smoked salmon into very thin strips. Cut the thin strips to about three inches in length.
4. Once the eggs have finished boiling, transfer them to a bowl filled with ice water. Allow to rest for around ten minutes before peeling the cooled eggs. Cut the eggs in half lengthwise.
5. Top the halved eggs with sliced smoked salmon, laying the pieces on top using a zig-zag motion or rolling them and laying them on top of the eggs. Sprinkle with paprika and pepper and serve.

Nutrition: Calories: 249 Total fat: 13 g Sodium: 1842 mg Total carbohydrates: 1 g Fiber: 1 g Sugar: 1 g Protein: 29 g

167. Chicken Breakfast Skillet

Preparation time: 5 Minutes
Cooking time: 30 Minutes
Servings: 2

Ingredients:

- 1 chicken breast
- 3 ounces ground sausage
- 2 eggs
- 3 slices bacon
- ½ teaspoon garlic powder
- ½ teaspoon ground black pepper

Directions:

1. Chop bacon and chicken breast into pieces roughly one inch in size. Add bacon to a skillet over medium heat and cook for two minutes, stirring frequently. Once bacon grease has begun to accumulate in the pan, stir in diced chicken and ground or crumbled sausage.
2. Add garlic powder and pepper to the meat in the skillet—Brown the meat over medium-high heat for about six to eight minutes.
3. Reduce heat to medium, on opposite sides of the pan, clear two pockets of space for the eggs. Break the eggs into the skillet and break the yolks apart. Cover the skillet and allow to cook so that the egg whites are firm about 10 minutes. Uncover and scoop onto a plate to serve.

Nutrition: Calories: 341 Total fat: 19 g Sodium: 631 mg Total carbohydrates: 1 g Fiber: 0 g Sugar: 1 g Protein: 36 g

168. Breakfast Turkey Skillet

Preparation time: 10 Minutes
Cooking time: 23 Minutes
Servings: 2

Ingredients:

- 2 tablespoons olive oil
- 1 enormous potato, stripped and cut into 3/4-inch pieces
- ½ cup cleaved onion
- ½ container refrigerated cooked disintegrated turkey wiener
- 1 ½ cups chilled or solidified egg item, defrosted
- ½ teaspoon dried Italian flavoring, squashed
- ¼ teaspoon garlic powder
- ¼ teaspoon dark pepper
- ⅛ Teaspoon salt

Directions:

1. Light kindling or charcoal and let open-air fire torch to medium-hot ashes or coals. Top with a flame broil rack.
2. Warmth a 10-inch cast-iron skillet over outdoor fire 5 minutes or until hot. Add oil to skillet. Include potato; cook 15 minutes, mixing every so often. Include onion and frankfurter. Cook 5 minutes extra or until vegetables are delicate, blending as often as possible.
3. Include the egg item, Italian flavoring, garlic powder, pepper, and salt. Cook, without blending, until blend starts to set on a base and around edges. Utilizing a spatula or huge spoon, lift, and overlay halfway cooked egg blend so uncooked segment streams underneath. Keep cooking for about 2 to 3 minutes or until the egg blend is cooked.

Nutrition: Calories: 341 Total fat: 19 g Sodium: 631 mg Carbohydrates: 3 g Fiber: 2 g Protein: 40 g

169. Blueberries Yoghurt Cereal

Preparation time: 3 Minutes
Cooking time: 0 Minute
Servings: 2

Ingredients:

- 1 cup nonfat plain yoghurt
- ½ cup little destroyed wheat grain
- ¼ cup new blueberries 1 teaspoon pumpkin seeds
- 2 teaspoons little chocolate chips
- ¼ teaspoon ground cinnamon

Directions:

1. Spot yoghurt in a bowl and top with destroyed wheat, blueberries, chocolate chips, pumpkin seeds, and cinnamon.

Nutrition: Calories: 290 Total fat: 19 g Sodium: 631 mg Carbohydrates: 3 g Fiber: 6 g Protein: 18.4 g

170. Fruit and Nut Porridge

Preparation time: 5 Minutes
Cooking time: 15 Minutes
Servings: 2

Ingredients:

- ½ teaspoon ground cinnamon
- 1 cup quinoa, flushed and well-depleted
- 1 cup sans fat milk
- 1 cup of water
- ½ cup slashed walnuts, toasted
- 1 cup crisp blackberries
- 1 cup crisp raspberries
- 2 teaspoons nectar

Directions:

1. In a medium pan, mix the quinoa, milk, water, cinnamon, and salt. Bring to bubbling over medium-high warmth; decrease heat. Stew, secured, around 15 minutes or until the vast majority of the fluid is assimilated. Expel from heat; let stand, secured, for 5 minutes. Mix in walnuts. Top each serving equitably with new berries. Sprinkle each presenting with one teaspoon nectar.

Nutrition: Calories: 325 Total fat: 12.8 g Sodium: 631 mg Carbohydrates: 3 g Fiber: 13 g Protein: 10.2 g

171. Lemon Yogurt Savory Turmeric Pancakes

Preparation time: 10 Minutes
Cooking time: 15 Minutes
Servings: 4

Ingredients:

- For the sauce with Yogurt:
- 1 cup of Greek straight yogurt
- 1 hairy garlic clove
- 1-2 tbsp. of Lemon juice to taste
- 1/4 tea cubicle ground turmeric
- 10 fresh, thinned mint leaves
- 2 citrus zest teaspoons (1 lemon)
- For Pancakes:
- 2 teaspoons of turmeric (grounded)
- 11/2 ground cumin teaspoons
- 1 tsp of salt
- 1 tablespoon coriander (grounded)
- 1/2 tea cubicle garlic powder.
- Fresh ground black pepper 1/2 teaspoon
- 1 head of broccoli, cut into blooms
- 3 big eggs, slightly beaten
- 2 tablespoons unflavored almond milk
- 1 cup of amber meal.
- 4 tea cubes of cocoa butter

Directions:

1. Make the sauce for yogurt. In a cup, mix milk, ginger, citrus oil, turmeric, mint, and zest. Flavor and season, if needed, with more lemon juice. Place aside or cool until ready to serve.
2. Make your pancakes. 2. Combine turmeric, cumin, cinnamon, coriander, garlic, and pepper in a tiny pot.
3. Place broccoli in the food processor and pulse it into small pieces until the blooms are broken up. Transfer broccoli to a big bowl, add eggs, almond milk, and meal of almond. Remove the spice mixture and mix well.
4. Heat 1-teaspoon of coconut oil in a medium-low heat non-stick pan. Put 1/4 cup of batter into the pot. Cook the bacon before tiny bubbles emerge on the top and golden brown on the bottom for 2 to 3 minutes. Make/cook the pancake for another 2 to 3 minutes. To stay warm, through the cooked pancakes in a 200°F oven with an oven-safe.
5. The remaining three pancakes continue to be made with the remaining oil and syrup.

Nutrition: Calories 250 Fat 2 g Cholesterol 0 mg Sodium 5 mg Carbohydrate 14 g

172. Sweet Potato Salad With Bacon

Preparation time: 55 Minutes
Cooking time: 30 Minutes
Servings: 1

Ingredients:

- 5 slices Bacon
- 2 pieces Sweet potato (peeled and diced)
- 3 cloves Garlic (pressed)
- 4 tablespoon Lime juice
- 3 tablespoon Olive oil
- 1 tablespoon Balsamic vinegar

Directions:

1. Set the oven to 220°C and cover a baking sheet with parchment paper.
2. Place the bacon on the baking sheet and bake until crispy in the oven (approx. 20 minutes).
3. Take the bacon off the baking sheet; let it cool and chop it.
4. Mix the sweet potato cubes with garlic on the same baking sheet, drizzle with a little mild olive oil and fry them in the oven for about 30 minutes.
5. Prepare a dressing made from olive oil, vinegar, and lime juice by mixing them in a bowl.
6. Take the potato cubes out of the oven, mix them with the bacon pieces, and drizzle them with the dressing.
7. If you like, add rocket and pine nuts at the end.

Nutrition: Calories: 205 Total Fat: 5g Saturated Fat: 2g Monounsaturated Fat: 2g Cholesterol: 0mg Sodium: 324mg Carbohydrate: 39g Dietary Fiber: 7g Sugar: 9g Protein: 4g

173. Salad With Melon And Ham

Preparation time: 15 Minutes
Cooking time: 5 Minutes
Servings: 1

Ingredients:

- 1-piece Cantaloupe melon
- 8 slices Serrano ham chopped
- 200 g Rocket
- 1-piece Cucumber (sliced)

- 1-piece Red onion (rings)
- 3 tablespoon Olive oil

Directions:

1. Quarter the melon. Take off the seeds using a spoon, cut the peel, and cut the melon into equal parts.
2. Wrap melon parts in ham.
3. Mix the arugula with the cucumber and onion in a bowl.
4. Drizzle the salad with olive oil.
5. Spread this on the plates and place the wrapped melon parts on it.

Nutrition: Calories: 90 Carbohydrates: 11 grams Fat: 2 grams Protein: 6 grams

174. Paleo Chicken Wraps

Preparation time: 10 Minutes
Cooking time: 15 Minutes
Servings: 5

Ingredients:

- 2 pieces Egg
- 240 ml of Almond milk
- 1 teaspoon Olive oil (mild)
- 1 / 4 TL Celtic sea salt
- 75 g Tapioca flour
- 3 tablespoon Coconut flour
- 10 slices Chicken breast
- Mixed salad

Directions:

1. Whip the eggs in a bowl, then add almond milk, olive oil, and salt.
2. Add tapioca and coconut flour and stir with a whisk until you get even better.
3. Grease a pan and pour 1/6 of the batter into the pan.
4. The wraps should have a diameter of approx—15 cm.
5. Fry the wraps on both sides until golden brown.
6. Repeat this step with the rest of the dough.
7. Fill the wraps with chicken and possibly additional salad or raw vegetables as you like.

Nutrition: Calories: 448 Carbohydrates: 14 grams Fat: 36 grams Protein: 21 grams

175. Chocolate Breakfast Muffins

Preparation time: 10 Minutes
Cooking time: 15 Minutes
Servings: 2

Ingredients:

- 250 g Almond paste
- 3 pieces Banana (ripe)
- 2 pieces Egg
- 1 teaspoon Vanilla extract
- 1/2 teaspoon Tartar baking powder
- 100 g Chocolate chips

Directions:

1. Set the oven to 200°C and bring a baking sheet with paper or silicone muffin tins.
2. Place all ingredients (except the optional chocolate chips) in a food processor and mix them into a smooth, sticky dough.
3. Optional: add pieces of chocolate and stir
4. Optional: add pieces of chocolate and stir
5. Bring the dough in the muffin tins and bake until golden brown and cooked in about 12-15 minutes.

Nutrition: Calories 377 Fat 16 g Cholesterol 30 mg Sodium 339 mg Potassium 115 mg Carbohydrate 54 g Protein 4.5 g

176. Fruit And Nut Porridge

Preparation time: 5 Minutes
Cooking time: 15 Minutes
Servings: 2

Ingredients:

- ½ teaspoon ground cinnamon
- 1 cup quinoa, flushed and well-depleted
- 1 cup sans fat milk
- 1 cup of water
- ½ cup slashed walnuts, toasted
- 1 cup crisp blackberries
- 1 cup crisp raspberries
- 2 teaspoons nectar

Directions:

1. In a medium pan, mix the quinoa, milk, water, cinnamon, and salt. Bring to bubbling over medium-high warmth; decrease heat. Stew, secured, around 15 minutes or until the vast majority of the fluid is assimilated. Expel from heat; let stand, secured, for 5 minutes. Mix in walnuts. Top each serving equitably with new berries. Sprinkle each presenting with one teaspoon nectar.

Nutrition: Calories: 325 Total fat: 12.8 g Sodium: 631 mg Carbohydrates: 3 g Fiber: 13 g Protein: 10.2 g

177. Walnut Medjool Porridge

Preparation time: 10 minute
Cooking time: 10 minutes
Servings: 1

Ingredients:

- 50 grams of strawberries, hulled
- 1 tsp of walnut butter or 4 chopped walnut halves
- 35 grams of Buckwheat flakes
- 1 chopped Medjool date
- 200 ml of almond or coconut milk, unsweetened

Directions:

1. Add the date and milk into a frying pan over medium low heat, then add in the flakes and cook to your desired consistency.
2. Add in the walnut butter, stir well—top porridge with strawberries.

Nutrition: Calories: 550 Net carbs: 25 g Fat: 45g Fiber: 9 g Protein: 6.57g

178. Avocado Tofu Breakfast Salad

Preparation time: 5 minute
Cooking time: 0 minutes
Servings: 1

Ingredients:

- Half a lemon juice
- Half a red onion, chopped
- 2 tomatoes, chopped
- One spoon of chili sauce
- 4 handfuls of baby spinach
- A handful of chopped almonds
- 1 pink chopped grapefruit
- 1 Avocado, chopped
- Half a pack of firm tofu, chopped
- 2 Tortillas

Directions:

1. Heat the tortillas in the oven for 8 to 10 minutes.
2. Combine tomatoes, tofu, and onions with some chilli sauce in a bowl place inside the refrigerator to cool.
3. Add the avocado, grapefruit, and almonds. Mix everything and place it into the bowl.
4. Top with a squeeze of fresh lemon juice!

Nutrition: Calories: 823 kcal Protein: 22.07 g Fat: 42.51 g Carbohydrates: 99.08 g

179. Omelette Fold

Preparation time: 3 minute
Cooking time: 5 minutes
Servings: 1

Ingredients:

- 1 tsp of extra virgin olive oil
- 5 grams of thinly sliced parsley
- 35 grams of thinly sliced red chicory
- 3 medium eggs
- 50 grams of streaky bacon, cut into thin strips

Directions:

1. Cook the bacon strips in a hot non-stick frying pan over high heat until crispy. Remove and drain any excess fat on a kitchen paper. Prepare the pan for another use.
2. Beat the eggs in a small bowl and mix with the parsley and chicory. Mix the drained bacon through the egg mixture.
3. Warm the olive oil in a non-stick pan; add the bacon/egg mixture. Cook until the omelet is set. Lose the omelet around the edges with a spatula and fold into a half-moon and serve.

Nutrition: Calories: 471 Net carbs: 3.3 g Fat: 38.72g Fiber: 1.5 g Protein: 27g

180. Cherry Tomatoes Red Pesto Porridge

Preparation time: 10 minute
Cooking time: 5 minutes
Servings: 2

Ingredients:

- Salt, pepper
- 1 tablespoon of hemp seed
- 1 tablespoon of pumpkin seed
- 2 tablespoon of nutritional yeast
- 1 tablespoon of sun-dried tomato-walnut pesto
- 1 teaspoon of tahini
- 1 scallion
- 1 cup of sliced cherry tomatoes
- 1 cup of chopped kale
- 1 teaspoon of dried basil
- 1, 5 teaspoons of dried oregano
- 1, 5-2 cups of veggie stock
- ½ cup of couscous
- ½ cup of oats

Directions:

1. In a small cooking pot, add oats, oregano, vegetable stock, basil, couscous, pepper, and salt and cook for about 5 minutes on medium heat stirring frequently until porridge is creamy and soft.
2. Add chopped kale but reserve a bit for garnish, tomatoes, and sliced scallion. Cook for an additional 1 minute, stir in pesto, tahini, and nutritional yeast.
3. Top with the reserved kale, pumpkin and hemp seeds plus cherry tomatoes, Enjoy!

Nutrition: Calories: 259 Net carbs: 36 g Fat: 7.68g Fiber: 7.4 g Protein: 14.26g

181. Parsley Smoothie

Preparation time: 2 minutes
Cooking time: 2 minutes
Servings: 2

Ingredients:

- 1 cup Flat-leaf parsley
- Juice of two lemons
- 1 (core removed) Apple
- 1 Avocado
- 1 cup Chopped kale
- 1 knob Peeled fresh ginger
- 1 tablespoon Honey
- 2 cups cold water

Directions:

1. Add all the ingredients except the avocado into your blender.
2. Blend on high until smooth, add the avocado, and then set your blender to slow speed and blend until creamy.
3. Add a little more iced water if the smoothie is too thick.

Nutrition: Calories: 75 Total Fat: 1 g Total Carbohydrates: 20 g Protein: 1 g Fiber: 2 g Sodium: 26 mg

182. Coffee And Cashew Smoothie

Preparation time: 2 minutes
Cooking time: 5 minutes
Serving: 1

Ingredients:

- 1 teaspoon Cashew butter
- ½ glass Chilled cashew
- 1 teaspoon Tahini
- 1 (pitted and chopped) Medjool date
- 1 shot Espresso coffee
- ½ teaspoon Ground cinnamon
- Tiny pinch of salt

Directions:

1. Bring all the ingredients into a high-speed blender. Blend until creamy and smooth.

Nutrition: Calories: 125 Total Fat: 4 g Sodium: 32 mg Fiber: 3 g Total Carbohydrates: 22 g Protein: 3 g

183. Buckwheat Pita Bread Sirtfood

Preparation time: 5 minutes
Cooking time: 20 minutes
Servings: 6

Ingredients:

- 1 x 8-gram Packet dried yeast
- 375ml lukewarm water
- 3 tablespoon extra-virgin olive oil
- 500 grams Buckwheat flour
- 1 teaspoon Sea salt
- Polenta for dusting

Directions:

1. Add the yeast in the lukewarm water, mix and set aside for about 10 to 15 minutes to activate.
2. Mix the buckwheat flour, olive oil, salt, and yeast mixture. Work slowly to make dough. Cover and place in a warm spot for approx. One hour – this is to get the dough to rise.
3. Divide the dough into six parts. Shape 1 of the pieces into a flat disc and place between two sheets of a baking paper. Gently roll out the dough into a round pita shape that is approximately ¼-inch thick.
4. Use a fork to pierce the dough a few times, and then dust lightly with polenta.
5. Heat your cast iron pan and brush the pan with olive oil. Cook the pita for about 5 minutes on one side until puffy, and then turn to the other side and repeat.
6. Fill the pita with your preferred veggies and meat, and then serve immediately.

Nutrition: Calories: 205 Total Fat: 7 g Total Carbohydrates: 30 g Protein: 6 g

184. Kale Caesar Salad

Preparation time: 10 minute
Cooking time:
20 minutes
Servings: 4

Ingredients:

- Garlic Peel Garlic Peel
- 19 oz. Cooked chickpeas (dry and rotten; about 2 cups)
- 1 tablespoon arrowroot starch (or all-purpose flour)
- 2 tablespoons garlic powder
- 1/2 teaspoon salt tsp
- 3Spoon Vegetable Oil
- Greek Yogurt Caesar Dressing:
- 1/4 cup Greek Yogurt
- 1/4 cup Avocado Mayonnaise (or your favorite mayo)
- 1 teaspoon Flavoring
- 4 teaspoons Rasch Mac
- 2 Cloves Garlic (minced)
- Pepper
- Chickpea Black Salad: Banana
- 1 (washed, Chopped, and dried)
- 1/4 cup Parmesan. Paneer (sliced)

Directions:

1. Roast the garlic peel and then spread them on a clean towel and blot with a second towel dry thoroughly.
2. Once the chickpeas dry, shake them until evenly coated with arrowroot starch, garlic powder, and salt.
3. Warm the vegetable oil in a pan on medium heat. Add the chickpeas the pan and cook for 15-20 minutes until they golden brown. Remove slightly from heat and funky.
4. Keel Caesar salad kale
5. While garlic chickpeas for cooking, slicing, washing, and drying.
6. Stir the dressing ingredients together, then toss until the bud evenly coated.
7. Serve
8. Keel Caesar Salad with Garlic Chole and a tablespoon of Parmesan Cheese
9. Eat the recipe
10. The salad best served fresh, although you have several ingredients ready after 4-5 days
11. Will- Shred, wash in a while in a container lined with dry towel within the fridge -
12. Stir store fridge kale handshake and store.

Nutrition: Calories: 315 kcal Protein: 17.38 g Fat: 7.19 g Carbohydrates: 47.49 g

185. Pineapple Buckle Pancake

Preparation time: 5 minute
Cooking time: 5 minutes
Servings: 4

Ingredients:

- 1 cup cereal flour
- 1/4 cup almond flour
- 2 tbsp asafetida seeds, plus toppings For
- 1 teaspoon. Yeast
- 1/2 teaspoon allspice
- 1/4 teaspoon salt
- Pineapple Mauna Pot Cheese 5.3 oz
- 1 egg
- 2 tablespoons syrup, services for more
- 1 teaspoon vanilla
- 1 cup sweet almond milk (or other milk)
- Plus, 1 small pineapple, outer Flake in chopped rings and cored, (you can also use canned pineapple rings)
- 1 tbsp. butter, split

Directions:

1. Heat a pancake grill or pan over medium heat.
2. Combine flour, hemp seeds, yeast, allspice, and salt during a large bowl and whisk until combined.
3. Add pot cheese, egg, syrup, vanilla the bowl. Slowly add everything until you add the milk gradually.
4. Add a little butter the pan. Once melted, place a pineapple ring on top and cook until golden brown and begin caramelizing. Flip the pineapple slices over, pour the spoon batter over it, cover the ring completely, and touch the edges. Cook until set (about 3 minutes), flip carefully and cook for 2 minutes on the other side.
5. Repeat with remaining pineapple rings and batter.
6. Serve with syrup and extra hemp seeds for topping.

Nutrition: Calories: 209 kcal Protein: 6.76 g Fat: 10.14 g Carbohydrates: 24.13 g

186. Ski Chalet Buckwheat Galette

Preparation time: 10 minute
Cooking time:
20 minutes
Servings: 4

Ingredients:

- For buckwheat galette: buckwheat 100 g
- Pinch salt
- 1 egg
- 300 ml of milk
- 50 g melt butter
- Oil fill:
- 1 onion, peeled and finely chopped
- 2 Clove Garlic, peeled and crushed 50 ml.
- 6 small new potatoes
- 4 large slices rebellion cheese (bracelet or gruyere will also work well here) Make a
- a handful of fresh parsley, finely chopped

Directions:

1. Batter - During a large bowl or jug, measure the flour and salt. During a separate pitcher, mix milk, egg, and melted butter, slowly pour it into the powder, and carefully ensure that there are no lumps. Set the batter aside rest.
2. Boil the potatoes in their skins for a quarter of an hour, then leave relaxed.
3. Meanwhile, heat 2 tablespoons oil during a fry, then add onion and garlic. Once it submerged in water, reduce the heat and cook for five minutes until it becomes soft. Then add the wine, bring back boil, boil once more, and cook for 5 minutes. Put in a small bowl and keep aside and clean the frypan.
4. Preheat oven 200C / 400F / gas mark.
5. Heat a touch more oil within the frypan, pour it in some batter, and roll around and fill the pan as thin as possible. Cook for a minute or 2 until golden brown, then flip over and cook for an additional minute on the opposite side. Remove a plate and the canopy with a squid paper or a clean dish towel. (NB - The first pancake usually bad do not panic; there enough batter makes at least five, so you will not be left short!).
6. Likewise, make the remaining pancakes.
7. Take each pancake, top with 1/4 of onion, potato, cheese, and parsley, then fold within four edges surround the filling and place on a baking tray. Repeat with the remaining pancakes. Enter the oven for 3-4 minutes until the cheese melts, and so the pancakes just start crisp.

Serve immediately with a fresh salad and cold glass of wine!

Nutrition: Calories: 701 kcal Protein: 21.91 g Fat: 21.97 g Carbohydrates: 107.62 g

187. Chorizo And Mozzarella Omelet

Preparation time: 5 minute
Cooking time:
10 minutes
Servings: 1

Ingredients:

- 2 eggs
- 6 basil leaves
- 2 ounces mozzarella cheese
- 1 tbsp butter
- 1 tbsp water
- 4 thin slices chorizo
- 1 tomato, sliced
- Salt and black pepper, to taste

Directions:

1. Whisk the eggs along with the water and some salt and pepper. Melt the butter in a skillet and cook the eggs for 30 seconds. Spread the chorizo slices over. Arrange the tomato and mozzarella over the chorizo. Cook for about 3 minutes. Cover the skillet and cook for 3 minutes until the omelet is set.
2. When ready, remove the pan from heat; run a spatula around the edges of the omelet and flip it onto a warm plate, folded side down. Serve garnished with basil leaves and green salad.

Nutrition: Calories: 451, Fat: 36.5g, Net Carbs: 3g, Protein: 30g

188. Fontina Cheese And Chorizo Waffles

Preparation time: 5 minute
Cooking time:
25 minutes
Servings: 6

Ingredients:

- 6 eggs
- 6 tbsp almond milk
- 1 tsp Spanish spice mix or allspice
- Sea salt and black pepper, to taste
- 3 chorizo sausages, cooked, chopped
- 1 cup fontina cheese, shredded

Directions:

1. Using a mixing bowl, beat the eggs, Spanish spice mix, black pepper, salt, and almond milk. Add in shredded cheese and chopped sausage. Use a non-stick cooking spray to spray a waffle iron.
2. Cook the egg mixture for 5 minutes. Serve alongside homemade sugar-free tomato ketchup.

Nutrition: Calories: 316; Fat: 25g, Net Carbs: 1.5g, Protein: 20.2g

189. Cauliflower & Cheese Burgers

Preparation time: 5 minute
Cooking time:
30 minutes
Servings: 6

Ingredients:

- 1 ½ tbsp olive oil
- 1 onion, chopped
- 1 garlic clove, minced
- 1 pound cauliflower, grated
- 6 tbsp coconut flour
- ½ cup gruyere cheese, shredded
- 1 cup Parmesan cheese
- 2 eggs, beaten
- ½ tsp dried rosemary
- Sea salt, to taste
- Ground black pepper, to taste

Directions:

1. Bring a cast-iron skillet over medium heat and warm oil. Add in garlic and onion and cook until soft, about 3 minutes. Stir in grated cauliflower and cook for a minute; allow cooling and set aside.
2. To the cooled cauliflower, add the rest of the ingredients, form balls from the mixture, then press each ball to form burger patty.
3. Set oven to 400°F and bake the burgers for 20 minutes. Flip and bake for another 10 minutes or until the top becomes golden brown.

Nutrition: Calories: 416; Fat: 33.8g, Net Carbs: 7.8g, Protein: 13g

190. Kielbasa And Roquefort Waffles

Preparation time: 5 minute
Cooking time:
15 minutes
Servings: 2

Ingredients:

- 2 tbsp butter, melted
- Salt and black pepper, to taste
- ½ tsp parsley flakes
- ½ tsp chili pepper flakes
- 4 eggs
- ½ cup Roquefort cheese, crumbled
- 4 slices kielbasa, chopped
- 2 tbsp fresh chives, chopped

Directions:

1. In a mixing bowl, bring all ingredients except fresh chives. Preheat waffle iron and spray with a cooking spray. Pour in the batter and close the lid.
2. Cook for 5 minutes or until golden brown, do the same with the rest of the batter. Decorate with fresh chives and serve while warm.

Nutrition: Calories: 470; Fat: 40.3g, Net Carbs: 2.9g, Protein: 24.4g

191. Cheese Ciabatta With Pepperoni

Preparation time: 5 minute
Cooking time:
25 minutes
Servings: 6

Ingredients:

- 10 ounces cream cheese, melted
- 2 ½ cups mozzarella cheese, shredded
- 4 large eggs, beaten
- 3 tbsp. Romano cheese, grated
- ½ cup pork rinds, crushed
- 2 ½ tsp baking powder
- ½ cup tomato puree
- 12 large slices pepperoni

Directions:

1. Combine eggs, mozzarella cheese, and cream cheese. Place in baking powder, pork rinds, and Romano cheese. Form into 6 ciabatta shapes. Set a non-stick pan over medium heat. Cook each ciabatta for 2 minutes per side.

Sprinkle tomato puree over each one and top with pepperoni slices to serve.

Nutrition: Calories: 464, Fat: 33.6g, Net Carbs: 9.1g, Protein: 31.1g

192. Bacon And Salsa Muffins

Preparation time: 10 minute
Cooking time:
30 minutes
Servings: 8

Ingredients:

- 4 slices bacon, cooked and chopped
- 4 eggs, beaten
- ½ cup almond flour
- ½ cup of salsa
- Special Equipment:
- 8 muffin cups, greased with olive oil

Directions:

1. Preheat the oven to 350°F.
2. Combine the chopped bacon, beaten eggs, almond flour, and salsa in a bowl. Stir to combine well.
3. Divide and pour the mixture into the muffin cups, then arrange them in the preheated oven.
4. Bake for 30 minutes or until the center is springy and a toothpick inserted into the muffin comes out dry.
5. Take them off from the oven and allow to cool for a few minutes before serving.
6. Keep in a tight container for 1 to 2 days or keep in the fridge for up to one week.
7. Microwave is covered until the desired temperature is reached or reheat in a frying pan or air fryer/instant pot, covered, on medium.
8. To make this a perfect meal, serve it with coconut milk or plain Greek yogurt.

Nutrition: Calories: 110 Total fat: 8.6g Carbs: 2.5g Protein: 5.7g Cholesterol: 99mg Sodium: 237mg

193. Bacon Wrapped-Egg

Preparation time: 10 minute
Cooking time:
20 minutes
Servings: 1

Ingredients:

- 1 slice bacon
- 1 teaspoon butter, melted
- 1 egg
- ¼ slice Cheddar cheese
- Special Equipment:
- A muffin cup

Directions:

1. Preheat the oven to 350°F.
2. Using a non-stick skillet, cook the bacon over medium-high heat for 3 to 4 minutes. When it starts to buckle and curl, loosen and flip the bacon slice so that it browns evenly and cook for another 3 to 4 minutes.
3. Arrange the bacon slice around the inside of a muffin cup. Grease the bottom of the muffin cup with the melted butter. Break the egg into the muffin cup.
4. Arrange the muffin cup into the preheated oven and bake for 10 minutes, then scatter the cheese on top of the egg and bake for 2 minutes more until the cheese melts.
5. Remove the muffin cup from the oven. Let it sit before serving. You can try to use more ingredients and muffin cups to make more bacon-embraced eggs at a time.
6. Store in an airtight container in the fridge for up to 3 days.
7. Microwave, covered, until the desired temperature is reached or reheat in an air fryer/instant pot, covered, on medium.

Nutrition: Calories: 174 Total fat: 14.3g Carbs: 0.6g Protein: 10.7g Cholesterol: 212mg Sodium: 305mg

194. Sausage Breakfast Casserole

Preparation time: 15 minute
Cooking time:
21 minutes
Servings: 4

Ingredients:

- 1.5 pounds (680 g) pork sausage, crumbled
- 1 (8 ounces / 227 g) package gluten-free crescent roll
- 4 eggs, beaten
- 2 cups mozzarella cheese, shredded
- ¾ cup of coconut milk
- Salt and ground black pepper, to taste

Directions:

1. Preheat the oven to 425°F.
2. Fry the sausage in a non-stick pan over medium heat temperature for 6 minutes until browned. Transfer the cooked sausage into a large bowl.
3. Add the beaten eggs, mozzarella cheese, coconut milk, salt, and ground black pepper to the bowl. Stir to combine well. Set aside.
4. Flatten the crescent rolls on a clean working surface with a rolling pin. Lay the flattened crescent rolls on a greased casserole dish.
5. Pour the sausage mixture over the crescent rolls. Arrange the casserole dish into the preheated oven and bake for 15 minutes. You can check the doneness by cutting a small slit in the center, if raw eggs run into the cut, then baking for another few minutes.
6. Take off the casserole dish from the oven and allow it to cool before serving.
7. Cover the casserole dish in plastic wrap and keep under room temperature for up to 3 days.
8. Bring the casserole dish back to the preheated oven and reheat at 300°F (150°C) for 10 minutes or until warmed through.

Nutrition: Calories: 389 Total fat: 31.8g Carbs: 9.3g Protein: 15.1g Cholesterol: 114mg Sodium: 671mg

195. Sweet And Sour Pancakes

Preparation time: 10 minute
Cooking time:
20 minutes
Servings: 4

Ingredients:

- ¾ cup of coconut milk
- 2 tablespoons white vinegar
- 1 egg, beaten
- 2 tablespoons butter, melted
- ¼ cup coconut flour or almond flour
- ½ teaspoon baking soda
- 1 teaspoon baking powder
- ¼ teaspoon liquid stevia
- ½ teaspoon salt

Directions:

1. Mix the milk with white vinegar in a bowl. Let it sit for 5 minutes for turning 'sour,' then pour the beaten egg and melted butter into the bowl. Stir to mix well.
2. In a separate bowl, mix the coconut flour, baking soda, baking powder, stevia, and salt, then pour the flour

mixture into the milk mixture. Thoroughly stir until smooth, but avoid over-mixing.

3. Warm a lightly greased baking pan over medium heat for 10 minutes. To make a pancake, pour ¼ cup of the mixture in the pan and cook for 3 minutes or until bubbles form on top. Flip the pancake over and cook for another 3 minutes until lightly browned.
4. Transfer the pancake onto a platter and allow to cool until ready to serve. Repeat with the remaining mixture.
5. Store in an airtight container in the fridge for up to 3 days.
6. Microwave, covered, until the desired temperature is reached.
7. You can top the pancake with different berries to add it to all kinds of flavor.

Nutrition: Calories: 216 Total fat: 19.0g Carbs: 8.7g Protein: 4.2g Cholesterol: 170mg Sodium: 526mg

196. Scrambled Egg And Sausage Muffins

Preparation time: 10 minute
Cooking time:
20 minutes
Servings: 12

Ingredients:

- 12 eggs
- 8 ounces (227 g) bulk pork sausage, crumbled
- 2 tablespoons olive oil
- ½ cup onion, chopped
- ½ cup chopped green bell pepper
- ½ cup Cheddar cheese, shredded
- ¼ teaspoon garlic powder
- ½ teaspoon salt
- ¼ teaspoon ground black pepper
- 12 muffin cups, greased with olive oil

Directions:

1. Preheat the oven to 350°F.
2. Warm a non-stick skillet over medium heat. Put in the sausage and sauté for 10 minutes or until well browned. Remove from the skillet and set aside.
3. Clean the skillet and drizzle with olive oil. Add the chopped onion into the skillet and sauté for 3 minutes or until the onion is half translucent, then break the eggs into the skillet and sauté for 3 minutes or until the eggs are scrambled, and then add the green bell pepper, shredded cheese, garlic powder, salt, and black pepper (ground) and cook for 2 minutes more until the cheese melts.
4. Fold in the cooked sausage and sauté to combine—Spoon ⅓ cup of the mixture in a muffin cup. Repeat with the remaining mixture and muffin cups. Arrange the muffin cups in the preheated oven.
5. Bake for about 20 minutes or until the tops of the muffins spring back when gently pressed with your fingers.
6. Remove from the oven. Allow cooling for 1-2 minutes before serving.
7. Keep in a closed container on the counter for up to 3 days or the fridge for up to one week.
8. Set on a plate and microwave until the desired temperature is reached.
9. You can arrange the muffins over a green bed to serve and sprinkle with Italian seasoning (without salt and black pepper).

Nutrition: Calories: 196 Total fat: 14.9g Carbs: 2.1g Protein: 12.7g Cholesterol: 202mg Sodium: 365mg

197. Citrus Green Smoothie

Preparation time: 5 minute
Cooking time:
0 minutes
Servings: 1

Ingredients:

- 8 oz. milk or non-dairy milk, of choice
- 1 scoop Micronutrients Greens Powder in Orange, a brand of your choice
- 1 Tbsp. MCT oil
- 1 Tbsp. lemon juice
- 1 Tbsp. lime juice
- 1 handful of ice
- 1 tsp. orange zest
- Optional:
- 1/8 tsp. xanthum gum, if desired to make the smoothie thicker
- 1 handful of spinach, if desired

Directions:

1. Add the milk, micronutrient green powder in orange, MCT oil, lemon juice, lime juice, ice, optional xanthum, optional spinach, and orange zest.
2. Pulse on high until smooth, for less than a minute.
3. Enjoy!

Nutrition: Calories: 207 Total Fat: 20g Protein: 3g Net Carbs: 3g

198. Cauliflower Hash Browns

Preparation time: 15 minute
Cooking time:
20 minutes
Servings: 4

Ingredients:

- Cauliflower:
- 1 lb. raw cauliflower, grated
- 1 tsp. salt
- Fritters:
- 3 large eggs
- 3 oz. onion chopped
- ½ cup almond flour
- ½ cup grated Parmesan cheese
- ½ tsp. baking powder
- 1 ½ tsp. lemon pepper

Directions:

1. Grate the cauliflower and place it into a colander, sprinkle with salt and mix thoroughly by hand, allow it to sit for 10 minutes.
2. Meanwhile, chop the onions and add them to a medium bowl.
3. Squeeze the water out of the cauliflower with clean hands.
4. Place the cauliflower into the medium bowl with the onions.
5. Add in the almond flour, cheese, baking powder, and seasoning, mix thoroughly.
6. Then add the eggs and mix well to combine.
7. Place a frying pan over medium heat; once hot, add 1 Tbsp. of oil.
8. Using a 1/4 cup measuring cup, scoop out the cauliflower fritter batter and place into the hot skillet, cook for 3 minutes on both sides - only flipping the fritter when the bottom is well cooked.
9. Once done, drain the fritters on paper towels and repeat with any leftover batter.
10. Serve!

Nutrition: Calories: 69 Total Fat: 4g Protein: 5g

199. Coconut Macadamia Bars

Preparation time: 5 minute
Cooking time:
5 minutes
Servings: 5

Ingredients:

- .03 oz. macadamia nuts
- ½ cup almond butter
- ¼ cup of coconut oil
- 6 Tbsp. unsweetened shredded coconut
- 20 drops stevia drops

Directions:

1. Using a food processor or use your hand, crush the macadamia nuts.
2. In a bowl, combine the almond butter, coconut oil, and shredded coconut.
3. Add the macadamia nuts and the stevia drops, mix thoroughly.
4. Pour the batter into a 9x9 parchment paper-lined baking dish.
5. Refrigerate the bars overnight.
6. The following day slice and enjoy.
7. Recipe Notes:
8. To make crunchier bars, store the bars in the freezer.

Nutrition: Calories: 425 Total Fat: 42g Protein: 6g Net Carbs: 4g

200. Coconut Flour Porridge Breakfast Cereal

Preparation time: 5 minutes
Cooking time:
5 minutes
Servings: 5

Ingredients:

- 2 Tbsp. coconut flour
- 2 Tbsp. golden flax meal
- ¾ cup of water
- Pinch of salt
- 1 large egg, beaten
- 2 tsp. butter or ghee
- 1 Tbsp. heavy cream or coconut milk
- 1 Tbsp. your favorite sweetener
- Optional:
- Fruits
- Nuts

Directions:

1. In a small pot over medium heat temperature, add the coconut flour, golden flax meal, water, and a pinch of salt, stir to combine.
2. Once the ingredients begin to simmer, turn it down to medium-low and whisk until it begins to thicken.
3. Remove the coconut flour porridge from heat.
4. Add the beaten egg, half at a time, while whisking continuously.
5. Place back on the heat and then continue to whisk until the porridge thickens.
6. Remove from the heat and continue to whisk for about 30 seconds.
7. Then add the butter, cream, and sweetener of your choice.
8. Garnish with your favorite toppings.

Nutrition: Calories: 453 Total Fat: 39g Protein: 13g Net Carbs: 5.6g

LUNCH

201. Colorful Vegetable Noodles

Preparation time: 5 minutes
Cooking time: 10 minutes
Servings: 2
Ingredients:

- 200 g little carrots (3 little carrots)
- 200 g little zucchini (1 little zucchini)
- 125 g leek (1 stick)
- 150 g linguine wholegrain pasta
- 2 tbsp. vegetable oil
- Salt
- Pepper
- 125 ml exemplary vegetable stock
- 150 ml soy cream
- 1 squeeze saffron strings
- Chervil freely

Directions:

1. Peel and clean carrots, wash zucchini, rub dry, and clean. Cut both lengthways into slim strips utilizing a peeler or a vegetable slicer.
2. Clean the leek, split lengthways, wash, and separate the individual leaves.
3. Within the interim, heat oil during a dish. Braise the carrots and zucchini in it over medium warmth for 1 moment, blending.
4. Add on the leek and braise for a further 1 moment. Season everything with salt and pepper.
5. Add the vegetable stock, soy cream, and, therefore, the saffron strings and convey them to the bubble. Cook until gloss over medium warmth for 2-3 minutes.
6. Drain the pasta during a strainer, channel well, and increase the dish.
7. Mix the pasta with the vegetables. Season another time. Placed on plates and serve sprinkled with chervil as you wish.

Nutrition: Calories: 359 kcal Protein: 10.03 g Fat: 17.99 g Carbohydrates: 43.23 g

202. Plaice Rolls On Pointed Cabbage

Preparation time: 10 minutes
Cooking time: 30 minutes
Servings: 4
Ingredients:

- 3 stems dill
- 2 stems parsley
- ½ pack chives
- 320 g plaice filet (without skin;
- 8 place filets)
- 100 g brilliant, seedless grapes
- 325 g cabbage
- 1 onion
- 1 tbsp. rape oil
- Salt
- Pepper
- Nutmeg
- 150 ml wine or light fruit juice
- 5 tbsp soy cream
- ½ lemon

Directions:

1. Wash and shake all herbs. Pluck and hack the leaves of dill and parsley, cut chives into little rolls.
2. Rinse the spot filets, pat them dry and spot them on the surface with the dim side looking up. Sprinkle with the hacked herbs.
3. Roll up the plaice filets immovably towards the sharp end and pin them with toothpicks.
4. Wash the grapes, channel well, and hamper the center. Clean, wash, and cut pointed cabbage into thin strips.
5. Peel the onion and dig fine strips.
6. Heat oil during a container. Braise the onions during a polished warmth for 2-3 minutes. Include pointed cabbage and braise for an extra 2 minutes while blending. Season with salt, pepper, and a few new ground nutmeg.
7. Put the grapes within the container and pour them within the wine or squeeze.
8. Lightly salt the plaice rolls and spread them over the cabbage. Spread and cook over medium warmth for 7-8 minutes.
9. Remove the highest, including the soy cream, and let it cook open for an additional 1-2 minutes. Crush lemon. Season the cabbage with salt, pepper, and lemon squeeze and serve directly.

Nutrition: Calories: 158 kcal Protein: 5.31 g Fat: 5.31 g Carbohydrates: 25.76 g

203. May Beet Salad With Cucumber

Preparation time: 20 minutes
Cooking time: 0 minutes
Servings: 2
Ingredients:

- 3 May turnips
- 1 cucumber
- 1 onion
- 2 stems parsley
- 150 g Greek yogurt
- 1 tbsp. fruit juice vinegar
- 1 tsp nectar
- 1 tsp mustard
- Sea-salt
- Cayenne pepper
- Pepper

Directions:

1. Clean, strip, and cut the turnips. Clean and wash the cucumber and slice. Clean, wash, and trim the spring onions into rings. Put everything during a serving of mixed greens bowl and blend.
2. Wash parsley, shake dry and slash finely. Combine dressing with yogurt, fruit juice vinegar, nectar, mustard, and 2–3 tbsp water. Season with salt and cayenne pepper.
3. Mix the plate of mixed greens dressing with the mayonnaise and cucumber and let it steep for around 10 minutes, at that time crush it with pepper and serve.

Nutrition: Calories: 135 kcal Protein: 12.6 g Fat: 3.67 g Carbohydrates: 13.67 g

204. Sweet Potatoes With Asparagus, Eggplant, And Halloumi

Preparation time: 10 minutes
Cooking time: 30 minutes

Servings: 2

Ingredients:

- 1 aubergine
- 9 tbsp. vegetable oil
- Chili drops
- Salt
- Pepper
- 2 yams
- 1 red bean stew pepper
- 2 tbsp. sunflower seeds
- 1 bundle green asparagus
- 4 tbsp. juice
- 200 g chickpeas (can; dribble weight)
- ½ pack basil
- ½ pack lemon demulcent
- 1 tsp mustard
- ½ tsp turmeric powder
- 1 tsp nectar
- 300 g halloumi

Directions:

1. Clean, wash and cut the eggplant. Warmth 2 tablespoons of oil during a dish and sauté the aubergine cuts in medium warmth on the 2 sides for 5–7 minutes until brilliant earthy colored and season with bean stew chips, salt, and pepper. Expel from the dish and put it during a safe spot.
2. Within the interim, strip the yam and cut it into 3D shapes. Split the bean stew lengthways, expel the stones, wash and dig cuts. Warmth 1 tablespoon of oil within the dish, fry the yam solid shapes in it for 10 minutes. Include 1 tbsp sunflower seeds and bean stew cuts and season with salt and pepper.
3. Wash asparagus as an afterthought, remove the woody finishes, and strip the lower third of the stalks if vital. Warmth 1 tablespoon of oil within the dish, fry the asparagus in it for five minutes over medium warmth. Deglaze with 1 tablespoon of juice, pour in 2 tablespoons of water, and spread it for a further 3 minutes.
4. Rinse the chickpeas and allow them to channel. Wash the basil and lemon medicine, shake dry and slash. Blend chickpeas in with half the herbs and 1 tablespoon of oil and season with salt and pepper.
5. Blend the rest of the oil with the remainder of juice, mustard, turmeric and nectar, season with salt and pepper, and blend within the remainder of the herbs.
6. Cut the halloumi and cut during a hot skillet on the 2 sides for five minutes over medium warmth until brilliant yellow.
7. Arrange yams, aubergine cuts on plates, present with chickpeas, asparagus, and halloumi and sprinkle with the dressing. Sprinkle with the remainder of the sunflower seeds.

Nutrition: Calories: 805 kcal Protein: 12.78 g Fat: 71.72 g Carbohydrates: 32.19 g

205. Lentil Salad With Spinach, Rhubarb, And Asparagus

Preparation time: 10 minutes

Cooking time: 30 minutes

Servings: 2

Ingredients:

- 100 g beluga lentils
- 2 tbsp. vegetable oil
- Salt
- 250 g white asparagus
- 100 g rhubarb
- 1 tsp nectar
- 50 g child spinach (2 bunches)
- 20 g pumpkin seeds

Directions:

1. Bring the beluga lentils to the overflow with multiple times the measure of water. Cook over medium warmth for around 25 minutes. Channel, flush, and channel. Blend in with 1 tablespoon of vegetable oil and a spot of salt. Meanwhile, wash, clean, strip, and cut asparagus into pieces. Wash, clean, and cut the rhubarb into pieces.
2. Heat 1 tablespoon of vegetable oil during a container and fry the asparagus in it for around 8 minutes over medium warmth, turning every so often. At that time, include rhubarb and nectar and fry and salt for a further 5 minutes. Wash spinach and switch dry. Generally, slash the pumpkin seeds.
3. Arrange spinach with lentils, asparagus, and rhubarb on two plates and serve sprinkled with pumpkin seeds.

Nutrition: Calories: 362 kcal Protein: 14.33 g Fat: 22.08 g Carbohydrates: 34.31 g

206. Strawberry And Avocado Salad With Chicken Nuggets

Preparation time: 10 minutes

Cooking time: 20 minutes

Servings: 2

Ingredients:

- 350 g chicken bosom
- 1 tbsp. soy
- Pepper
- 1 tsp sweet paprika powder
- 2 tsp tomato glue
- 4 bunches blended serving of mixed greens (arugula, lollo rosso, lettuce)
- 150 g strawberries
- 1 lemon
- 1 avocado
- 1 egg
- 2 tbsp. whole meal flour
- 70 g cornflakes (without sugar)
- 3 tbsp. rape oil
- 1 tbsp. nectar
- Salt
- ½ purple onion
- 5 g ginger
- 2 tsp sunflower seeds
- 2 tsp pine nuts

Directions:

1. Rinse the chicken bosom, pat dry, and dig 6 pieces. Blend during a bowl with soy, pepper, paprika powder, and tomato glue and let marinate for around 10 minutes.
2. Within the interim, clean, wash, and switch dry lettuce. Clean, wash pat dry strawberries and dig little pieces. Crush lemon. Divide the avocado, evacuate the stone, expel the mash from the skin, shakers and blend in with half the juice.
3. Place the egg during a plate and race with a fork. Put the flour on a subsequent plate. Disintegrate the cornflakes and put them on another plate. Bread chicken pieces first in flour, at that time in the egg, and afterward within the chips. Warmth the oil during a dish and fry the chicken on all sides over medium warmth.

4. Mix a dressing out of nectar, remaining lemon squeeze, salt, and pepper. Strip the onion and ginger, dice the onion and mesh the ginger, add both to the dressing. Blend sunflower and pine nuts and dish during a hot skillet without fat on low warmth for around 4 minutes.
5. Spread the serving of mixed greens on two plates, pour the strawberries and avocado over it and sprinkle with the dressing. Present with chicken tenders and sprinkle the serving of mixed greens with the seeds.

Nutrition: Calories: 853 kcal Protein: 53.09 g Fat: 52.41 g Carbohydrates: 48.23 g

207. Carrot Risotto With Eggplant And Pesto Sauce

Preparation time: 10 minutes
Cooking time: 30 minutes
Servings: 2
Ingredients:

- 2 carrots
- 1 clove of garlic
- 1 branch rosemary
- 4 tbsp. vegetable oil
- 100 g risotto rice
- 500 ml vegetable stock
- 3 tbsp. soy cream
- 1 tsp juice
- Salt
- Pepper
- 1 aubergine
- 1 tbsp. rosemary
- 1 squeeze cayenne pepper
- 1 tsp wholemeal spelled flour
- 100 ml oat drink (oat milk)
- 1 tbsp. pesto

Directions:

1. Clean, strip, and cut the carrots into little blocks. Strip and cleave garlic. Wash the rosemary, shake it dry, pluck the needles, and cut them into little pieces.
2. Heat 1 tablespoon of oil during a pan, braise the carrots and garlic for five minutes over medium warmth, at that time include the rice and braise for a further 2 minutes. At that time, pour during a little stock with the goal that everything is delicately secured, continually mixing. Step by step pours within the stock while blending until the stock is spent. At that time, let swell on low warmth for 10 minutes. At that time, mix in 1 tablespoon of soy cream and season with salt, pepper, half the rosemary, and juice.
3. Alongside, clean, wash, and cut the eggplant into little 3D shapes. Warmth 2 tablespoons of oil during a container, braise eggplant 3D shapes, and raisins in them for 8 minutes. Season with salt, pepper, remaining rosemary, and cayenne pepper.
4. Heat 1 tablespoon of oil during a pan, dust with flour, pour within the oat drink with a whisk while mixing and stew for 3 minutes until a light-weight bond is formed. Blend within the pesto and remaining soy cream and season with salt and pepper.

Nutrition: Calories: 403 kcal Protein: 7.33 g Fat: 35.44 g Carbohydrates: 16.06 g

208. Tofu And Vegetable Curry With Rice And Nuts

Preparation time: 10 minutes
Cooking time: 25 minutes
Servings: 2
Ingredients:

- 1 aubergine
- 2 carrots
- 1 parsnip
- 1 clove of garlic
- 3 tbsps. copra oil
- 1 tbsp. tomato glue
- 2 tbsp. yellow curry glue (somewhat fiery)
- 400 ml of coconut milk
- 250 g parboiled rice
- Salt
- ½ tsp turmeric powder
- 200 g cherry tomatoes
- 1 red stew pepper
- Pepper
- 300 g smoked tofu
- 70 g nut blend (salted)
- 1 bunch basil leaves

Directions:

1. Clean the eggplant, carrots, parsnips, strip, wash, and dig 3D squares if necessary. Strip and cleave garlic.
2. Heat 2 tablespoons of copra oil during a wok or huge dish, include vegetables and sauté for five minutes over high warmth. Include tomato glue and curry glue and fry for a further 3 minutes. At that time, pour in coconut milk and stew for five minutes over low warmth. Within the interim, stew the rice in bubbling salted water with turmeric for around 10-15 minutes and let it douse for five minutes until secured.
3. Wash and split tomatoes as an afterthought. Wash the bean stew pepper, dig dainty cuts, and add both to the curry. Season the curry with salt and pepper.
4. Meanwhile, cut the tofu into 3D shapes. Warmth the remainder of the oil during a skillet, sauté the tofu and nuts in it over medium warmth for five minutes and season with pepper. Wash the basil and shake dry.
5. Arrange rice with curry, tofu in bowls and serve sprinkled with basil.

Nutrition: Calories: 1058 kcal Protein: 37.94 g Fat: 80.3 g Carbohydrates: 63.21 g

209. Jackfruit Fricassee With Pea Rice

Preparation time: 10 minutes
Cooking time: 40 minutes
Servings: 2
Ingredients:

- 250 g earthy colored rice
- Salt
- 250 g solidified peas
- 400 g jackfruit (can; depleted weight)
- 1 little onion (40 g)
- 200 g mushrooms
- 3 carrots
- 2 tbsp. rape oil
- 25 g whole meal spelled flour (2 tbsp.)
- 400 ml vegetable stock
- 250 ml of soy cream
- Pepper
- ½ natural lemon (pizzazz and juice)
- Nutmeg
- ½ group chervil

Directions:

1. Put earthy colored rice in 500 ml of bubbling salted water, mix once, and cook during a shut pan over low warmth for 25–30 minutes until the rice has consumed the water. Include the peas over the first recent 5 minutes and obtain through with cooking. At that time, quickly relax up the rice within the pot and let it swell for a few moments within the stopped pan on the exchanged the hob.
2. While the rice is cooking, flush bits of jackfruit, channel well, and pluck into little pieces. Strip the onion and dig fine strips. Clean the mushrooms and cut them in cuts. Strip the carrots, divide lengthways and dig cuts.
3. Heat oil during a pot. Include the onion and braise for two minutes over medium warmth. Include bits of jackfruit and sauté for five minutes. At that time, add mushrooms and carrots and braise for 3 minutes. Residue everything with flour and pour within the vegetable stock while blending and stew on low warmth for 10 minutes, including touch water, if vital.
4. Then mix within the soy cream, season with salt, pepper, lemon pizzazz and juice, and newly ground nutmeg. Warmth rice over low warmth. Wash chervil, shake dry, and cleave. Serve fricassee sprinkled with rice and chervil.

Nutrition: Calories: 630 kcal Protein: 17.56 g Fat: 20.34 g Carbohydrates: 104.19 g

210. Vegan Raw Meatballs

Preparation time: 5 minutes
Cooking time: 20 minutes
Servings: 2

Ingredients:

- 250 g fine bulgur (köftelik bulgur)
- 1 clove of garlic
- 2 meat tomatoes
- 1 tsp salt
- ½ tsp cayenne pepper
- 1 tsp cumin
- 1 tsp paprika powder
- 1 squeeze bean stew chips
- 40 g paprika showcase (3 tbsp)
- 25 g tomato glue (2 level tablespoons)
- 2 spring onions
- ½ group parsley (10 g)
- ½ group mint (10 g)
- 2 lettuce hearts
- 1 natural lemon
- 5 radish

Directions:

1. Pour 250 ml of high temp water over the bulgur, mix and permit expanding for 10 minutes.
2. Peel and finely cleave the garlic. Singe the tomatoes with bubbling water, extinguish, and skin. Evacuate the seeds and cut the mash into fine 3D shapes.
3. Add garlic, tomatoes, salt, and flavors even as paprika and tomato glue to the bulgur and ply energetically for around 5 minutes (ideally with gloves). Let it rest for 20 minutes.
4. Within the interim, clean, wash, and cut the spring onions into exceptionally fine rings. Wash parsley and mint, shake dry, and cleave finely. Separate lettuce leaves from the lettuce head, wash and shake dry. Wash the lemon hot, grind dry, hamper the center, and cut. Clean, wash, and cut radishes into little solid shapes.
5. Knead parsley, half the mint and spring onions under the mixture. Stop around 30 pecans estimated pieces and pound them in your grasp with the goal that lengthened rolls (köfte) are made.
6. Place the kofte during a leaf of lettuce, sprinkle with the staying mint and radishes, and present with lemon.

Nutrition: Calories: 475 kcal Protein: 18.86 g 35% Fat: 9.19 g Carbohydrates: 93.5 g

211. Pide With Eggplant And Bell Pepper Filling

Preparation time: 10 minutes
Cooking time: 25 minutes
Servings: 4

Ingredients:

- ½ shape yeast
- ½ tsp fluid nectar
- 200 g yogurt (3.5% fat)
- 2½ tbsp. vegetable oil
- 200 g spelled flour type 630
- 230 g spelled flour type 1050
- 1 tsp salt
- 1 shallot
- 1 clove of garlic
- 1 enormous eggplant (400 g)
- 2 red peppers
- 1 tsp ground cumin
- 1 tsp rose hot paprika powder
- ½ tsp cinnamon
- ½ tsp sumac (oriental zest)
- 2 tbsp. tomato glue (30 g)
- ½ group mint (10 g)
- 20 g pistachios (1 stored tablespoon)
- ½ pomegranate

Directions:

1. Dissolve yeast in 150 ml of heated water. Include the nectar, 2 tablespoons of yogurt, a couple of tablespoons of vegetable oil, and mix and put it during a safe spot. Blend the 2 kinds of flour in with the salt during a subsequent bowl. Add the yeast blend to the flour and manipulate well for 5-10 minutes. Shape the mixture into a ball and spread and leave to ascend during a warm spot for an hour.
2. Within the interim, strip the shallot and clove of garlic and cleave finely. Clean, wash, and cut the eggplant and peppers into little pieces. Warmth the staying vegetable oil during a huge skillet. Braise shallot and garlic in it over low warmth for two minutes. Include flavors and stew for 1 moment.
3. Put the vegetables and tomato glue within the container and sauté for 10 minutes over medium warmth, salt.
4. Pull it from the oven then allow it to chill.
5. Meanwhile, wash the mint, shake it dry, pluck the leaves, dig fine strips, and put half under the container vegetables.
6. Knead the yeast batter again on a floured surface and partition it into 6 equivalent segments. Reveal the bits lengthened and shape them into vessels. Top every batter with vegetable filling, forgetting about the mixture's sides and afterward collapsing them inside. Heat during a preheated stove at 240 ° C (fan broiler 220 ° C; gas: level 4) for 10 minutes.
7. Meanwhile, generally slash the pistachios and expel the pomegranate seeds from the organic product. Remove the pide from the broiler and let it chill off a bit. Orchestrate pide with pistachios, staying mint, outstanding yogurt, and pomegranate seeds.

Nutrition: Calories: 649 kcal Protein: 21.75 g Fat: 15.17 g Carbohydrates: 108.22 g

212. Vegetarian Asparagus Baked With Grilled Eggplant

Preparation time: 10 minutes
Cooking time: 30 minutes
Servings: 4

Ingredients:

- 24 sticks white asparagus
- 2 eggplants
- Salt
- 2 tbsp. spread (30 g)
- 2 tbsp. whole meal spelled flour
- 500 ml milk (3.5% fat)
- Pepper
- Nutmeg
- 1 tbsp. juice
- 1 pack chervil
- 1 tbsp. vegetable oil
- 100 g veggie lover mountain cheddar (45% fat in dry issue)

Directions:

1. Peel the asparagus, remove the woody finishes, and cook the asparagus in bubbling salted water for 10 minutes. At that time, pour and put during a safe spot. Clean, wash, and cut the eggplants lengthways into 1/2 cm cuts. Sprinkle with salt and put it during a safe spot.
2. Heat the margarine during a pan. Residue with flour, mix with a whisk, pour within the milk, and convey to the bubble while blending. Expel from the heat, season with salt, pepper, nutmeg, and juice. Wash chervil, shake dry, cleave and blend half into the sauce.
3. Pat the eggplant cuts dry and brush with vegetable oil. Warmth a flame broil container and burn the 2 sides' cuts for 1 moment over high warmth. Mesh mountain cheddar.
4. Bundle 3 stalks of asparagus, wrap with 1 eggplant cut, and a spot during a preparing dish. Pour sauce over, pour cheddar over it. Prepare during a preheated broiler at 200 ° C (fan stove: 180 ° C; gas: speed 3) for 15–20 minutes. Take it out from the broiler and sprinkle with the remainder of the chervil.

Nutrition: Calories: 206 kcal Protein: 10.1 g Fat: 8.67 g Carbohydrates: 24.87 g

213. Vegan Mushroom Ragout With Broccoli

Preparation time: 15 minutes
Cooking time: 25 minutes
Servings: 4

Ingredients:

- 500 g blended mushrooms (white mushrooms, clam, and shitake mushrooms)
- 1 carrot
- 1 clove of garlic
- 2 branches marjoram
- 2 tbsp. vegetable oil
- 200 ml oat cream (or soy cream)
- Pepper
- 1 squeeze ground cumin
- ¼ natural lemon
- 300 g broccoli

Directions:

1. Clean mushrooms, wash, and split if necessary. Clean, strip, and cut the carrot into little solid shapes. Strip garlic and slash finely. Wash marjoram, shake dry and pluck leaves.
2. Heat the oil during a dish, sauté the garlic and carrot shapes over medium warmth for five minutes. At that time, include mushrooms and braise for 7 minutes. Season with marjoram, salt, pepper, and caraway. Include oat cream and blend in. Flush the lemon quarter, grind the strip, and stub out the juice. Season ragout with lemon get-up-and-go and squeeze.
3. Bring tons of salted water to the bubble. Clean, wash, and separation broccoli into florets and cook in water for five minutes. Orchestrate the mushroom ragout with broccoli on plates and serve everything sprinkled with pepper.

Nutrition: Calories: 579 kcal Protein: 28.46 g Fat: 37.36 g Carbohydrates: 46.92 g

214. Spinach & Feta Quiche

Preparation time: 10 minutes
Cooking time: 45 minutes
Servings: 4

Crust Ingredients:

- 2 cup quinoa, (cooked)
- 1 large egg
- Pinch of black pepper

Filling Ingredients:

- ½ onion, finely sliced
- 5 oz. baby leaf spinach, chopped
- ½ cup milk
- 4 large eggs
- 2 large egg whites
- 1½ oz. feta cheese, crumbled
- ¼ tsp crushed red pepper
- ¼ tsp ground black pepper
- ½ tsp salt
- 1 tsp olive oil

Crust Directions:

1. Preheat oven to 375°c
2. Whisk egg and stir together cooked quinoa, egg, and pepper
3. Grease a 9" quiche dish and press quinoa mixture into base and sides
4. Bake for at least 20 minutes then let it to cool

Filling Directions:

5. Put oil in a frying pan over medium heat.
6. Add onions and cook for 3 minutes
7. Add spinach and cook for a further 3 minutes
8. Remove from heat and allow to cool
9. Whisk together eggs and egg whites
10. Whisk in milk, red pepper, black pepper and salt
11. Spread spinach and onion mix over the baked quinoa base
12. Pour egg mixture into the quiche base and sprinkle with feta cheese
13. Return to oven and bake for 35 minutes

Nutrition: Calories: 282 Fat: 11.6g Protein: 17g Carbohydrate: 28g Fiber: 5g

215. Fennel, Spinach & Shrimp Salad

Preparation time: 5 minutes
Cooking time: 10 minutes
Servings: 4

Ingredients:

- ½ cup red onion, finely sliced

- 2 tbsp finely chopped white onion
- 1 cup cherry tomatoes, halved
- 3 rashers bacon
- 9oz baby leaf spinach
- 1lb jumbo shrimp, deveined and peeled
- 1 medium fennel bulb, finely sliced
- 1 tsp Dijon mustard
- 1 tbsp. balsamic vinegar
- 3 tbsp. extra virgin olive oil
- ¼ tsp salt
- ¼ tsp black pepper

Directions:

1. Put oil in a frying pan then heat over a medium temperature.
2. Roughly chop bacon and add to the frying pan. Cook until crispy and remove from pan. Retain the oil in a frying pan
3. Add shrimp to pan and fry for 2 minutes, tossing shrimp occasionally
4. Remove from heat and set aside
5. In a large bowl put and combine the cooked bacon, red onion, fennel, tomatoes, and baby leaf spinach
6. In a separate bowl, mix together the remaining unused ingredients then stir in the shrimp
7. Mix salad and oil mixtures and toss lightly before serving

Nutrition: Calories: 274 Fat: 13.5g Protein: 27.5g Carbohydrate: 11.2g Fiber: 3.5g

216. Quinoa Salad

Preparation time: 15 minutes
Cooking time: 30 minutes
Servings: 8

Salad Ingredients:

- 2 tbsp. finely diced red onion
- ½ cup finely diced onion
- 5 dates, pitted and chopped
- ½ lb. cooked asparagus, roughly chopped
- 1 cup quinoa, uncooked
- 2 cups water
- 1 large orange, peeled and segmented
- ¼ cup chopped, roasted pecans
- ½ jalapeno pepper, deseeded and finely chopped
- ½ tsp salt
- 1 tsp olive oil

Dressing Ingredients:

- 1 clove garlic, finely chopped
- 2 tbsp. fresh mint, finely chopped
- 2 tbsp. freshly squeezed lemon juice
- ¼ tsp salt
- ¼ tsp pepper
- 1 tbsp. extra virgin olive oil

Salad Directions:

1. Put oil to a frying pan and heat over a medium to high heat
2. Add white onions and fry for 2 minutes
3. Add quinoa and fry, stirring regularly, for a further 5 minutes
4. Add water and salt to frying pan and bring to a boil
5. Reduce heat and simmer for 15 minutes
6. Pull it out from the heat and let it cool until water is absorbed, usually around 10 to 15 minutes
7. Transfer to a large bowl and add the remaining salad ingredients
8. Toss gently to combine ingredients

Dressing Directions:

9. Mix all ingredients, except mint
10. Drizzle over salad
11. Garnish with mint and serve

Nutrition: Calories: 164 Fat: 6.3g Protein: 4.3g Carbohydrate: 24.7g Fiber: 3.4g

217. Spicy Sweet Potato Soup

Preparation time: 10 minutes
Cooking time: 30 minutes
Servings: 4

Crust Ingredients:

- 1 onion, diced
- 2 cloves garlic, finely chopped
- 1 large sweet potato, peeled and diced
- ¼ cup shredded coconut
- 15 oz. coconut milk
- ¼ cup chopped, fresh coriander
- 2 tbsp. coconut oil
- Juice of 1 lime, freshly squeezed
- 2 tbsp. curry powder
- ¼ tsp cayenne pepper
- ½ tsp cumin
- ½ tsp salt

Directions:

1. Put oil in a skillet then heat over a medium temperature.
2. Add onions and fry until soft
3. Add garlic and cook for a further 1 minute
4. Add sweet potatoes and cook for an additional 5 minutes, stirring occasionally
5. Stir in curry powder, cayenne pepper, cumin, and salt and continue cooking for another minute
6. Stir in coconut milk and bring up to a fast simmer
7. Reduce to low heat and simmer for 20 to 25 minutes
8. Remove from heat and pour into a blend
9. Blend until smooth
10. Pour into a serving dish and stir in lime juice
11. Sprinkle with coconut and coriander to serve

Nutrition: Calories: 246 Fat: 18g Protein: 2g Carbohydrate: 19g Fiber: 5g

218. Vegetable Rice

Preparation time: 5 minutes
Cooking time: 5minutes
Servings: 4

Ingredients:

- 1 1/3 cups cooked and cooled brown rice
- 1 cup cherry tomatoes, halved
- 1 cup green soybeans, shelled
- ¼ cup toasted pine nuts
- 2 cups chopped courgette
- 3 tbsp. freshly squeezed lemon juice
- 2 tsp lemon zest
- ½ cup fresh basil, roughly chopped
- ½ oz. fresh parmesan cheese, finely grated
- 3 tbsp. olive oil
- 1 tsp salt
- ¼ tsp ground black pepper

Directions:

1. In a big mixing bowl, blend all the ingredients except olive oil, courgette, and parmesan
2. Heat 1 tbsp olive oil in a frying pan over a medium to high heat
3. Add the courgette and cook for 4 – 5 minutes, stirring occasionally

4. Remove from pan and allow to cool
5. Stir courgette into the remaining 2 tbsp.'s oil
6. Combine courgette mixture with other ingredients and toss well
7. Sprinkle with parmesan shavings to serve

Nutrition: Calories: 305 Fat: 19.1g Protein: 9.6g Carbohydrate: 25.4g Fiber: 4.9 g

219. Vegetable Pasta & Prawns With Avocado Dressing

Preparation time: 5 minutes
Cooking time: 10 minutes
Servings: 1

Ingredients:

- 3 small courgettes
- 5 oz. cooked prawns, deveined and peeled
- ½ cup cherry tomatoes halved
- 2 cups water

Dressing Ingredients:

- ¼ avocado
- 1 garlic clove, finely chopped
- ½ cup fresh chopped basil
- Juice of ¼ lemon
- Pinch salt & pepper

Dressing Directions:

1. Place garlic, lemon juice, salt, pepper, basil, and avocado into a blender
2. Blend until almost smooth

Directions:

3. Peel courgettes and slice into long, thin strips, (like thick spaghetti)
4. Bring water to boil and blanch courgette strips for 30 seconds
5. Remove from boiling water and rinse in cold water then set to one side
6. In a large mixing bowl, place courgettes, prawns, cherry tomatoes and dressing and stir together well
7. Press quinoa mixture into base and sides of the quiche dish

Nutrition: Calories: 224 Fat: 5.9g Protein: 26.3g Carbohydrate: 20.6g Fiber: 8.5g

220. Baked Sweet Potato

Preparation time: 10 minutes
Cooking time: 60 minutes
Servings: 4

Ingredients:

- 4 medium sweet potatoes
- 425g canned chickpeas, rinsed and drained
- ½ tbsp. olive oil
- ½ tsp cumin
- ½ tsp coriander
- ½ tsp paprika
- ½ tsp cinnamon
- ½ tsp fresh lemon juice
- Sauce Ingredients
- ¼ cup hummus
- 3 garlic cloves, finely chopped
- 1 tsp dill
- 1 tbsp. fresh lemon juice
- Unsweetened almond milk, (to the thin sauce)
- Sauce Directions:
- Mix all sauce ingredients, (except almond milk)
- When fully mixed, slowly add 1 tbsp. almond milk at a time and stir well. Continue until sauce is pourable

Directions:

1. Set oven to 400°c and line a baking sheet with foil
2. Clean sweet potatoes and halve, lengthways
3. Rub potatoes with a little olive oil and place face down on baking sheet
4. Mix olive oil, cumin, coriander, paprika, cinnamon, and lemon juice and stir in the chickpeas
5. Spread chickpea mixture over the baking sheet and place in over for 45 – 60 minutes
6. Remove from oven and plate up sweet potatoes, 2 halves per serving
7. Sprinkle with chickpea mixture and drizzle over sauce to serve

Nutrition: Calories: 313 Fat: 5g Protein: 8.6g Carbohydrate: 60g Fiber: 11.7g

221. Chicken Kell And Miso Drinking-Strut Buckle Nulls Keli With Recipes

Preparation time: 5 minutes
Cooking time: 20 minutes
Servings: 2

Ingredients:

- 2-3 fist Britain (roughly removing the stems as chopped)
- 150 g / 5 oz. buckwheat noodles (100% buckwheat, no wheat)
- -4 shiitake mushrooms, sliced
- 1 teaspoon copra oil or ghee
- 1 brown onion, finely diced
- 1 medium free-range pigeon breast, sliced or diced
- 1 long red chili, finely chopped (in seeds or how much Warm you out on the count) Wish)
- 2 large garlic cloves, finely diced
- 2-3 tbsp. Tamari chutney (gluten-free soy sauce) for
- Miso dressing
- 1 organic tbsp. fresh organic miso
- 1 tbsp. Tamari sauce
- 1 tbsp. virgin vegetable oil
- 1 1 tbsp. lemon or juice
- 1 tsp vegetable oil (optional)

Directions:

1. Bring a medium saucepan of water boil. Add bananas and cook for 1 minute, until slightly boiled. Remove and keep aside but preserve the water and boil it back. Add soba noodles and prepays per package instructions (usually about 5 minutes). Rinse under cold water and keep aside.
2. Meanwhile, fry the shiitake mushrooms with a little ghee or copra oil (about a teaspoon) for 2-3 minutes, fry lightly on all sides. Sprinkle with sea salt and keep aside.
3. Within the same frypan, heat more copra oil or ghee over medium-high heat. Add onions and peppers for 2-3 minutes, then add chicken pieces. Cook for 5 minutes on medium heat, shake a few times, add garlic, tamarind chutney, and a touch of water. Cook for an additional 2-3 minutes, frequently stirring until the chicken cooked through.
4. Finally, add the kale and soba noodles through the chicken heat and toss.
5. Wrongly dressing and drizzling over noodles on top of cooking the wrong way; you will keep all those beneficial probiotics alive and active within the miso.

Nutrition: Calories: 321 kcal Protein: 13.09 g Fat: 15.66 g Carbohydrates: 35.91 g

222. Lamb, Butternut Squash And Date Tangine

Preparation time: 20 minutes
Cooking time: 1 hour and 15 minutes
Servings: 4

Ingredients:

- 2 tablespoons vegetable oil
- 1 purple onion, chopped
- 2cm ginger, grated
- 3 garlic cloves, grated or
- 1 tablespoon pepper flakes (taste) or
- 2 tablespoons cumin
- 1 cinnamon, Cinnamon.
- Teaspoon 1 teaspoon turmeric
- 800 g lamb fillet, dig 2cm chunk
- Spoon salt
- 100 g Medrol dates, chopped and sliced
- 400 g tin can chop tomatoes, plus half of water
- 500 g butternut squash, 1 cm sliced in cubes
- 400 g tin chickpeas, drained
- 2 tablespoons fresh coriander (plus) garnish)
- Buckwheat, Flatbread or Rochefort

Directions:

1. Oven at 140C.
2. Describe 2 tablespoons of vegetable oil in an outsourced ovenproof saucepan or forged iron casserole dish. Add the chopped onion and cook on a light heat, with the lid for about 5 minutes, until the onion becomes soft but brown.
3. Add grated garlic and ginger, chili, cumin, cinnamon, and turmeric. Mix well and cook for 1 more minute with the lid closed. Add a splash of water if it dries too much.
4. Next, add within the lamb pieces. Stir thoroughly coat the meat within the onions and spices, add salt, chopped dates, and tomatoes, plus add about half a can of water (100-200 ml).
5. Boil again, put the lid on the Rogaine, and keep it in your preheated oven for 1 hour and quarter-hour.
6. On top of the cooking time, thirty minutes before, add chopped butternut squash and dry chickpeas within. Mix everything, put the lid back on and return the oven for the final half-hour of cooking.
7. When the tagine prepared, remove from the oven and shake through the chopped coriander.
8. Serve with buckwheat, couscous, flatbreads, or basmati rice.

Nutrition: Calories: 1140 kcal Protein: 75.17 g Fat: 49.16 g Carbohydrates: 104.14 g

223. Prawn Arrabiata

Preparation time: 10 minutes
Cooking time: 35 minutes
Servings: 4

Ingredients:

- Raw or cooked prawns (ideally king prawns)
- 65g buckle pasta
- 1 tbsp. vegetable oil
- Arrabbiata 40g
- Purple onion, finely chopped
- 1 clove, finely chopped
- 30g celery, finely chopped.
- 1 bird's eye chili, finely chopped
- 1 teaspoon dried mixed herbs
- 1 teaspoon extra virgin vegetable oil
- 2 tablespoons wine (optional)
- 400 grams chopped tomatoes
- 1 tbsp. chopped parsley

Directions:

1. Onion, garlic, celery, and chili and dried Fry the herbs. Oil over medium-low heat for 2–2 minutes. Turn the heat medium, add the wine, and cook for 1 minute. Add the tomatoes and leave the sauce boil over medium-low heat for 20-30 minutes, until it has a pleasant creamy consistency. If you feel that the sauce is getting too thick, just add a touch of water.
2. While the sauce cooking, bring a pan of water boil and cook the pasta according to the directions of the pasta. When cooked, your liking, drain, toss, and pan the pan with vegetable oil until needed.
3. If you are using raw prawns, put them the sauce and cook for 3 4 minutes, until they become pink and opaque, add parsley, and serve. If you are using cooked prawns, combine them with parsley, simmer the sauce and serve.
4. Add cooked pasta sauce, mix well but serve gently.

Nutrition: Calories: 192 kcal Protein: 13.66 g Fat: 10.74 g Carbohydrates: 10.65 g

224. Turmeric Baked Salmon

Preparation time: 5 minutes
Cooking time: 25 minutes
Servings: 2

Ingredients:

- 125-150 grams of salmon
- 1 teaspoon extra virgin vegetable oil
- 1 teaspoon ground turmeric
- 1/4 lime juice for
- Spicy celery
- 1 teaspoon extra virgin vegetable oil
- 40 grams purple onion, finely chopped
- 60 grams tinned. Green lentils
- 1 clove, finely chopped
- 1 cm fresh ginger, finely chopped
- 1 bird's eye chili, finely chopped
- 150 grams celery, 2cm length
- 1 teaspoon light flavor
- 130 grams tomatoes, 8 wedges
- 100 ml chicken or vegetable stock
- 1 Tbsp. chopped parsley

Directions:

1. Heat the oven the 200C / gas mark 6.
2. Start with pickled celery. Heat the frying over medium-low heat, add vegetable oil, then onion, garlic, ginger, chili, and celery. Fry for at least 2-3 minutes or until softened but not colored, then add flavor and cook for an additional minute.
3. Then add tomatoes and stock and boil gently for 10 minutes. You want to increase or decrease the cooking time, depending on how crunchy you of your celery desire.
4. Meanwhile, mix turmeric, oil, and juice and rub on top of salmon. Set on a baking tray then cook for 8-10 minutes.
5. Finally, stir parsley through celery and serve with salmon.

Nutrition: Calories: 418 kcal Protein: 41.65 g Fat: 21.65 g Carbohydrates: 14.5 g

225. Spike Chickpea With Surgut Types

Preparation time: 20 minutes

Cooking time: 1 hour and 45 minutes
Servings: 4
Ingredients:

- 4-6 baking potatoes, everywhere
- 2 tablespoons vegetable oil
- 2 red onions, finely chopped
- 4 cloves garlic, grated or crushed
- 2cm ginger, grated
- ½ -2 teaspoons of chili flakes (how hot things you want)
- 2 tablespoons cumin seeds Spoon
- 2 Turmeric
- Water splash
- 2 x 400 g tins chopped tomatoes
- 2 tbsp. chocolate (or cocoa)
- 2 x 400 g tins Chole (or kidney beans if you wish) Do not eat, including chickpeas!!
- 2 yellow peppers (or whatever color you prefer!), Chopped in bite-size pieces
- 2 tablespoons parsley extra
- And salt taste (optional)
- Side salad (optional)

Directions:

1. Turn off the oven Wash 200C. Meanwhile, you did. Prep all your materials.
2. When the oven hot, put your baking potatoes inside the oven and cook for 1 hour or until they work how you wish for them.
3. Place the vegetable oil and chopped purple onions in a large wide saucepan and cook gently, with the lid on for five minutes, until the onions soft, but not brown until the potatoes within the oven. Would have been.
4. Remove the lid and add garlic, ginger, cumin, and chili. Cook for an additional minute over the coffee's heat, then add turmeric and a small splash of water and cook for an extra minute, taking not let the pan dry too much.
5. Next, add tomatoes, chocolate (or cocoa), chickpeas (including chickpea water), and yellow pepper within. Bring back the boil, then simmer over the coffee's heat for 45 minutes until the sauce becomes thick and thick (but do not let it burn!). The stew should be served at approximately an equal time because of the potatoes.
6. Usually stir within 2 tablespoons of parsley, and some salt and pepper if you wish, and serve the stew on top of the baked potato, perhaps with a smooth side salad.

Nutrition: Calories: 534 kcal Protein: 13.05 g Fat: 10.18 g Carbohydrates: 99.82 g

226. Horseradish Flaked Salmon Fillet & Kale

Preparation time: 10 minutes
Cooking time: 15 minutes
Servings: 2
Ingredients:

- 200g skinless, boneless salmon fillet
- 50g green beans
- 75g kale
- 1 tbsp. extra virgin olive oil
- ½ garlic clove, crushed
- 50g red onion, chopped
- 1 tbsp. fresh chives, chopped
- 1 tbsp. freshly chopped flat-leaf parsley
- 1 tbsp. low-fat crème Fraiche
- 1tbsp horseradish sauce
- Juice of ¼ lemon
- A pinch of salt and pepper

Direction:

1. Preheat the grill.
2. Sprinkle a salmon fillet with salt and pepper. Place under the grill for 10-15 minutes. Flake and set aside.
3. Using a steamer, cook the kale and green beans for 10 minutes.
4. In a skillet, warm the oil over high heat. Add garlic and red onion and fry for 2-3 minutes. Toss in the kale and beans, and then cook for 1-2 minutes more.
5. Mix the chives, parsley, crème Fraiche, horseradish, lemon juice, and flaked salmon.
6. Serve the kale and beans topped with the dressed flaked salmon.

Nutrition: Calories: 247 kcal Protein: 29.9 g Fat: 9.53 g Carbohydrates: 11.12 g

227. Indulgent Yoghurt

Preparation time: 10 minutes
Cooking time: 15 minutes
Servings: 3
Ingredients:

- 125 mixed berries
- 150g Greek yoghurt
- 25 walnuts, chopped
- 10g dark chocolate at least 85% cocoa solids, grated

Directions:

1. Toss the mixed berries into a serving bowl. Cover with yoghurt and top with chocolate and walnuts. Voila!

Nutrition: Calories: 6452 kcal Protein: 155.89 g Fat: 639.09 g Carbohydrates: 137.47 g

228. Tuna Salad

Preparation time: 5 minutes
Cooking time: 5 minutes
Servings: 1
Ingredients:

- 100g red chicory
- 150g tuna flakes in brine, drained
- 100g cucumber
- 25g rocket
- 6 Kalamata olives, pitted
- 2 hard-boiled eggs, peeled and quartered
- 2 tomatoes, chopped
- 2 tbsp. fresh parsley, chopped
- 1 red onion, chopped
- 1 celery stalk
- 1 tbsp. capers
- 2 tbsp. garlic vinaigrette

Directions:

1. Put the ingredients in a bowl and serve.

Nutrition: Calories: 699 kcal Protein: 60.65 g Fat: 30.47 g Carbohydrates: 49.19 g

229. Chicken & Bean Casserole

Preparation time: 10 minutes
Cooking time: 15 minutes
Servings: 2
Ingredients:

- 400g 14oz chopped tomatoes
- 400g 14oz tinned cannellini beans or haricot beans
- 8 chicken thighs, skin removed
- 2 carrots, peeled and finely chopped
- 2 red onions, chopped
- 4 sticks of celery
- 4 large mushrooms

- 2 red peppers bell peppers, de-seeded and chopped
- 1 clove of garlic
- 2 tablespoons soy sauce
- 1 tablespoon olive oil
- 1.75 liters 3 pints chicken stock broth

Directions:

1. Put and heat olive oil, add the garlic and onions and cook for 5 minutes.
2. Add in the chicken and cook for 5 minutes, then add the carrots, cannellini beans, celery, red peppers bell peppers, and mushrooms.
3. Pour in the stock broth soy sauce and tomatoes.
4. Bring it to the boil, reduce the heat and simmer for 45 minutes.
5. Serve with rice or new potatoes.

Nutrition: Calories: 2946 kcal Protein: 310.11 g Fat: 165.18 g Carbohydrates: 41.2 g

230. Mussels In Red Wine Sauce

Preparation time: 20 minutes
Cooking time: 10 minutes
Servings: 2

Ingredients:

- 800g 2lb mussels
- 2 x 400g 14oz tins of chopped tomatoes
- 25g 1oz butter
- 1 tablespoon fresh chives, chopped
- 1 tablespoon fresh parsley, chopped
- 1 bird's-eye chili, finely chopped
- 4 cloves of garlic, crushed
- 400mls 14fl oz. red wine
- Juice of 1 lemon

Directions:

1. Wash the mussels, remove their beards, and set them aside.
2. Put butter in a saucepan. Add in the red wine.
3. Reduce the heat and add the parsley, chives, chili, and garlic while stirring.
4. Add in the tomatoes, lemon juice, and mussels.
5. Cover the saucepan and cook for 2-3.
6. Remove the saucepan from the heat and take out any mussels which haven't opened and discard them.
7. Serve and eat immediately.

Nutrition: Calories: 1626 kcal Protein: 53.88 g Fat: 22.25 g Carbohydrates: 34.76 g

231. Sirtfood Cauliflower Couscous & Turkey Steak

Preparation time: 10 minutes
Cooking time: 15 minutes
Servings: 2

Ingredients:

- 150g cauliflower, roughly chopped
- 1 garlic clove, finely chopped
- 40g red onion, finely chopped
- 1 bird's eye chili, finely chopped
- 1 tsp. finely chopped fresh ginger
- 2 tbsp. extra virgin olive oil
- 2 tsp. ground turmeric
- 30g sun-dried tomatoes, finely chopped
- 10g parsley
- 150g turkey steak
- 1 tsp. dried sage
- Juice of ½ lemon
- 1 tbsp. capers

Directions:

1. Disintegrate the cauliflower using a food processor. Blend in 1-2 pulses until the cauliflower has a breadcrumb-like consistency.
2. In a skillet, fry garlic, chili, ginger, and red onion in 1 tsp. Olive oil for 2-3 minutes. Throw in the turmeric and cauliflower then cook for another 1-2 minutes. Remove from heat and add the tomatoes and roughly half the parsley.
3. Garnish the turkey steak with sage and dress with oil. In a skillet, over medium heat, fry the turkey steak for 5 minutes, occasionally turning once the steak is cooked add lemon juice, capers, and a dash of water. Stir and serve with the couscous.

Nutrition: Calories: 503 kcal Protein: 20.01 g Fat: 42.9 g Carbohydrates: 9.94 g

232. Mushroom & Tofu Scramble

Preparation time: 10 minutes
Cooking time: 10 minutes
Servings: 1

Ingredients:

- 100g tofu, extra firm
- 1 tsp. ground turmeric
- 1 tsp. mild curry powder
- 20g kale, roughly chopped
- 1 tsp. extra virgin olive oil
- 20g red onion, thinly sliced
- 50g mushrooms, thinly sliced
- 5g parsley, finely chopped

Directions:

1. Place 2 sheets of kitchen towel under and on top of the tofu, then rest a considerable weight such as saucepan onto the tofu, to ensure it drains off the liquid.
2. Combine the curry powder, turmeric, and 1-2 tsp. of water to form a paste. Using a steamer cook kale for 3-4 minutes.
3. In a skillet, warm oil at medium heat. Add the chili, mushrooms, and onion, cooking for several minutes or until brown and tender.
4. Break the tofu into small pieces and toss in the skillet. Coat with the spice paste and stir, ensuring everything becomes evenly coated. Cook for up to 5 minutes, or until the tofu has browned, then add the kale and fry for 2 more minutes. Garnish with parsley before serving.

Nutrition: Calories: 415 kcal Protein: 26.89 g Fat: 28.95 g Carbohydrates: 18.83 g

233. King Prawn Stir-Fry & Soba

Preparation time: 15 minutes
Cooking time: 20 mutes
Servings: 3-4 servings

Ingredients:

- 150g shelled raw king prawns, deveined
- 2 tsp. tamari
- 2 tsp. extra virgin olive oil
- 75 soba
- 1 garlic clove, finely chopped
- 1 bird's eye chili, finely chopped
- 1 tsp. finely chopped fresh ginger
- 20g red onions, sliced
- 40g celery, trimmed and sliced
- 75g green beans, chopped
- 50g kale, roughly chopped

- 100ml chicken stock

Directions:

1. Warm a skillet over high heat, and then fry for the pawns in 1 tsp. of the tamari and 1 tsp. of olive oil. Transfer the skillet contents to a plate and then wipe the skillet with a kitchen towel to remove the lingering sauce.
2. Boil water and cook the soba for 8 minutes, or according to packet instructions. Drain and set aside for later. Using the remaining 1 tsp. Olive oil, fry the remaining ingredients for 3-4 minutes. Make the stock boil, simmering until the vegetables are tender but still have a bite.
3. Add the lavage, noodles, and prawn into the skillet, stir, bring back to the boil and then serve.

Nutrition: Calories: 156 kcal Protein: 9.66 g Fat: 8.44 g Carbohydrates: 10.77 g

234. Miso Caramelized Tofu

Preparation time: 10 minutes
Cooking time: 25
Servings: 3

Ingredients:

- 1 tbsp. mirin
- 20g miso paste
- 1 * 150g firm tofu
- 40g celery, trimmed
- 35g red onion
- 120g courgette
- 1 bird's eye chili
- 1 garlic clove, finely chopped
- 1 tsp. finely chopped fresh ginger
- 50g kale, chopped
- 2 tsp. sesame seeds
- 35g buckwheat
- 1 tsp. ground turmeric
- 2 tsp. extra virgin olive oil
- 1 tsp. tamari or soy sauce

Directions:

1. Pre-heat your over to 200C or gas mark 6. Cover a tray with baking parchment.
2. Combine the mirin and miso. Dice the tofu and coat it in the mirin-miso mixture in a resealable plastic bag. Set aside to marinate.
3. Chop the vegetables except for the kale at a diagonal angle to produce long slices. Using a steamer, cook for the kale for 5 minutes and set aside.
4. Disperse the tofu across the lined tray and garnish with sesame seeds. Roast for 20 minutes, or until caramelized.
5. Rinse the buckwheat using running water and a sieve. Add to a pan of boiling water alongside turmeric and cook the buckwheat according to the packet instructions.
6. Heat the oil in a skillet over high heat. Toss in the vegetables, herbs, and spices, then fry for 2-3 minutes. Reduce to medium heat and fry for a further 5 minutes or until cooked but still crunchy.

Nutrition: Calories: 99 kcal Protein: 4.94 g Fat: 5.47 g Carbohydrates: 8.61 g

235. Sirt Super Salad

Preparation time: 10 minutes
Cooking time: 0 minutes
Servings: 2

Ingredients:

- 1 3⁄4 ounces (50 g) of arugula
- 1 3⁄4 ounces (50 g) of endive leaves
- 3 1⁄2 ounces (100 g) of smoked salmon slices
- 1⁄2 cup (80 g) of avocado, peeled, stoned and sliced
- 1⁄2 cup (50 g) of celery including leaves, sliced
- 1⁄8 cup (20 g) of red onion, sliced
- 1⁄8 cup (15 g) of walnuts, sliced
- 1 1⁄2 cup (15 g) of capers
- 1 large Medjool date, pitted and chopped
- 1 tablespoon of extra celery.

Directions:

1. Mix all the remaining ingredients and serve over the leaves.

Nutrition: Calories: 571 kcal Protein: 22.42 g Fat: 43.69 g Carbohydrates: 30.84 g

236. Char-Grilled Steak

Preparation time: 10 minutes
Cooking time: 45 minutes
Servings: 2

Ingredients:

- 5g parsley, finely chopped
- 100g potatoes, cut into 2cm dice and peeled
- 50g Lettuce, chopped
- 1 tbsp. extra virgin coconut oil
- 50g Red onion, chopped into circles
- 1 garlic clove, finely chopped
- 120--150g 3.5cm-thick beef noodle beef or 2cm-thick sirloin beef
- 40ml Red wine
- 150ml Beef inventory
- 1 Tsp tomato purée
- 1 Tsp corn flour, dissolved in 1 tablespoon water

Direction:

1. Heating the oven to 220°C/gas.
2. Put the sausage in a saucepan of boiling water, then return to the boil and then cook 4minutes, then empty. Put in a skillet with 1 tbsp. of the oil and then roast in the oven for 3-5 --4-5 minutes. Twist the berries every 10 minutes to ensure even cooking. After cooking, remove from the oven, sprinkle with the chopped parsley, and mix well.
3. Fry the onion 1 tsp of the oil over a moderate heat for 5 minutes --1 minute, until tender and well caramelized. Maintain heat. Steam the kale for two-three minutes. Stir the garlic lightly in 1/2 tsp of oil for 1 minute, until tender but not colored. Insert the spinach and simmer for a further 1--two minutes, until tender. Maintain heat.
4. Heating an ovenproof skillet on high heat until smoking. Lay the beef from 1/2 a tsp of the oil and then fry from the skillet over a moderate-high temperature in accordance with just how you would like your beef done. If you prefer your beef moderate, it'd be wise to sear the beef and also transfer the pan into a toaster place in 220°C/petrol 7 and then finish the cooking which manner to your prescribed occasions.
5. Remove the meat from the pan and put aside to break. Add your wine into the skillet to bring any meat up residue. Bubble to decrease the wine by half an hour until syrupy, along with a concentrated flavor.
6. Insert the inventory and tomato purée into the beef pan and bring it to the boil, add the corn flour paste to thicken your sauce, then add it only a little at a time until you've got your preferred consistency. Stir in just about any juices out of the dinner that is rested and serve with the roasted lettuce, celery, onion rings, and red berry sauce.

Nutrition: Calories: 22739 kcal Protein: 2485.7 g Fat: 1339.27 g Carbohydrates: 2.43 g

237. Coronation Steak Salad

Preparation time: 5 minutes
Cooking time: 0 minutes
Servings: 1

Ingredients:

- 75 G Natural yogurt
- Juice Of 1/4 of a lemon
- 1 Tsp'Coriander, sliced
- 1 Tsp Ground turmeric
- 1/2 Tsp darkened curry powder
- 100 G Cooked chicken, cut to bite-sized pieces
- Walnut halves, finely chopped
- 1 Medjool date, finely chopped
- 20 G Crimson pumpkin, diced
- 1 Bird's eye illuminates
- 40 Gram Rocket, to function

Directions:

1. Mix the lemon, carrot juice, spices, and coriander in a bowl. Add all of the other ingredients and serve on a bed of this rocket.

Nutrition: Calories: 8630 kcal Protein: 384.24 g Fat: 773.14 g Carbohydrates: 6.24 g

238. Sauteed Potatoes In Chicken Broth In

Preparation time: 5 minutes
Cooking time: 10 minutes
Servings: 2

Ingredients:

- Six medium-sized potatoes
- 1 onion
- Chicken broth
- 100ml of water
- 1 tbsp. extra virgin olive oil
- Salt to taste

Directions:

1. First, peel the potatoes then slice it across into pieces.
2. Proceed by peeling the onions and chop into small pieces.
3. Fry minced onion pieces in oil for five minutes. Add in the potatoes and cook for another ten minutes while stirring gently.
4. Dilute the chicken broth with water and add to the cooker, and cook for five minutes.
5. Add salt to taste and serve.

Nutrition: Calories: 232 kcal Protein: 7.56 g Fat: 6.25 g Carbohydrates: 37.37 g

239. Chicken In Pepper Sauce

Preparation time: 15 minutes
Cooking time: 30 minutes
Servings: 2

Ingredients:

- 1 jar of 340 ml roasted peppers
- 1 cup (250 mL) canned coconut milk
- 15 ml red wine vinegar
- 2cloves of garlic
- 1 tsp. paprika
- 1 tsp. dried oregano
- 1 tsp. salt
- 1/4 cup of chopped fresh parsley, chopped
- 1 tbsp. extra virgin olive oil
- 4 boneless skinless chicken breasts or thighs
- Salt and pepper
- 1 minced onion
- 1 red bell pepper (minced)
- 1/4 of chopped fresh parsley, for garnish

Direction:

1. In a blender, mix all the ingredients for the sauce (everything above except chicken, olive oil, onions, salt, and pepper) until you get a mixture of smooth consistency.
2. Put a rack at the center of the oven and preheat to 400 ° F.
3. In your large non-stick skillet (you can use a cast iron), heat the olive oil over high heat and fry the chicken breasts. Generously season with salt and pepper. Give it time by allowing all the sides of the chicken to fry for at least three minutes and then set aside on a plate.
4. Lower the heat level back to medium, then add the onions, and allow to heat for six minutes over medium heat, stirring often.
5. Add the red pepper and cook for another minute only.
6. Return the chicken to the pan and sprinkle with the roasted pepper sauce.
7. Bake the dish for fifteen minutes. Before serving, remove from the oven and grace it by adding some parsley. Serve with pasta in olive oil and chives or white rice.

Nutrition: Calories: 206 kcal Protein: 9.73 g Fat: 10.6 g Carbohydrates: 20.22 g

240. Wardolf Salad

Preparation time: 15 minutes
Cooking time: 0 minutes
Servings: 1

Ingredients:

- 125g of mayonnaise
- 2 tablespoons white vinegar
- 1 apple, peeled and cut into pieces
- 1 celery stalk, diced
- 125g of grapes
- 125g of chopped walnuts
- Salt and pepper to taste

Directions:

1. In a huge bowl, blend the mayonnaise and vinegar.
2. Put the apple, celery, raisins, and walnuts.
3. Sprinkle in salt and pepper. Mix everything and serve fresh.

Nutrition: Calories: 755 kcal Protein: 17.63 g Fat: 63.97 g Carbohydrates: 36.88 g

241. Whole Wheat Pita

Preparation time: 10 minutes
Cooking time: 20 minutes
Servings: 2

Ingredients:

- 250g of whole wheat flour
- 2 tbsp. extra virgin olive oil
- 5g salt
- 10g dry baker's yeast
- One hundred and fifty-ml hot water

Directions:

1. Add the whole flour and the salt in a bowl and stir. Then add the rest of the ingredients: oil, yeast, and water. Stir thoroughly to mix.
2. Mix all the ingredients well until the pita bread dough is formed. Knead the dough for a few minutes on the table. If the dough looks too dry, you may add a little more water.

3. When kneaded, make the dough into a ball and put it in a bowl. Have it covered, and let it be there for two hours.
4. Take out the whole pita bread dough and knead again. Work the dough into balls of about 80g each. Use a roller to make the dough well-rounded. Make the pieces of bread ten-to-twelve cm wide and One cm thick.
5. Put the pitas on a tray. Preheat the oven to 200 ° C, slot in the tray, and let the pieces of bread bake for ten minutes, depending on the oven.
6. Finally, take out the pieces of bread, let them cool a little and serve!

Nutrition: Calories: 485 kcal Protein: 14.09 g Fat: 8.82 g Carbohydrates: 95.16 g

242. Scrambled Tofu With Mushroom (Vegan)

Preparation time: 5 minutes
Cooking time: 10 minutes
Servings: 2-4

Ingredients:

- 125 g of plain firm tofu
- 100g silky tofu
- 1 tbsp. fresh cream
- 1tbsp. sesame puree
- 1tsp. Mustard
- ½ tsp. ground turmeric
- 4 sprigs of fresh chives
- 1/2 onion (optional)
- 1garlic clove (optional)
- 50g mushrooms
- 2 tbsp. Extra Virgin Olive Oil
- 1 tbsp. Tamari soy sauce (gluten-free, organic soy sauce)
- Salt and pepper to taste

Directions:

1. In a bowl, crush the firm tofu, add in the silky tofu, cream, tahini, mustard, turmeric, and chopped chives.
2. Mix thoroughly, and add salt and pepper to taste.
3. Peel and chop the onion and the garlic.
4. Rinse the mushrooms under a stream of water. Cut off the ends of the stalks and cut the mushrooms into strips. Gently fry the mushrooms, onions, and garlic over medium-high heat in a pan with a little olive oil.
5. Once the mushrooms, onions, and garlic are very tender and slightly brown, add the mixture to the tofu and cook over medium heat for about 5 minutes. Stir the mixture continuously with a spatula.
6. Serve hot, and enjoy.

Nutrition: Calories: 199 kcal Protein: 12.73 g Fat: 14.37 g Carbohydrates: 7.91 g

243. Chicken Thighs With Creamy Tomato Spinach Sauce

Preparation time: 45 minutes
Cooking time: 10 minutes
Servings: 2

Ingredients:

- One tablespoon olive oil
- 1.5 lb. chicken thighs, boneless skinless
- ½ teaspoon salt
- ¼ teaspoon pepper
- 1 oz. tomato sauce
- 2 garlic cloves, minced
- ½ cup overwhelming cream
- 4 oz. new spinach
- Four leaves fresh basil (or utilize ¼ teaspoon dried basil)

Directions:

1. The most effective method to cook boneless skinless chicken thighs in a skillet: In a much skillet heat olive oil on medium warmth. Boneless chicken with salt and pepper. Add top side down to the hot skillet. Cook for 5 minutes on medium heat, until the high side, is pleasantly burned. Flip over to the opposite side and heat for five additional minutes on medium heat. Expel the chicken from the skillet to a plate. Step by step instructions to make creamy tomato basil sauce: To the equivalent, presently void skillet, include tomato sauce, minced garlic, and substantial cream. Bring to bubble and mix. Lessen warmth to low stew. Include new spinach and new basil. Mix until spinach withers and diminishes in volume. Taste the sauce and include progressively salt and pepper, if necessary. Include back cooked boneless skinless chicken thighs, increment warmth to medium.

Nutrition: Calories: 1061 kcal Protein: 66.42 g Fat: 77.08 g Carbohydrates: 29.51 g

244. Prawn & Chili Pak Choi

Preparation time: 30 minutes
Cooking time: 15 minutes
Servings: 1

Ingredients:

- 75g (2 ¼ oz.) brown rice
- 1 pak choi
- 60ml (2 fl. oz.) chicken stock
- 1 tbsp. extra virgin olive oil
- 1 garlic clove, finely chopped
- 50g (1 ⅝ oz.) red onion, finely chopped
- ½ bird's eye chili, finely chopped
- 1 tsp. freshly grated ginger
- 125g (4 ¼ oz.) shelled raw king prawns
- 1 tbsp. soy sauce
- 1 tsp. five-spice
- 1 tbsp. freshly chopped flat-leaf parsley
- A pinch of salt and pepper

Directions:

1. Place a medium-sized saucepan of water to the boil, cook the brown rice for 25-30 minutes, or soften it.
2. Tear the pak choi into pieces. Warm the chicken stock in a skillet over medium heat and toss in the pak choi, cooking until the pak choi has slightly wilted.
3. In another skillet, warm olive oil over high heat. Toss in the ginger, chili, red onions and garlic frying for 2-3 minutes.
4. Throw in the pawns, five-spice and soy sauce and cook for 6-8 minutes, or until the cooked throughout. Drain the brown rice and add to the skillet, stirring and cooking for 2-3 minutes. Add the pak choi, garnish with parsley and serve.

Nutrition: Calories: 403 kcal Protein: 16.15 g Fat: 15.28 g Carbohydrates: 50.87 g

245. Yummy Peanut Chicken

Preparation time: 10 minutes.
Cooking time: 20 minutes
Servings: 4

Ingredients:

- 16 ounces chicken breast
- 2 red bell peppers, diced
- 2 green onions, diced
- 1 tablespoon ginger, grated
- ½ teaspoon cayenne pepper

- ½ cup crunchy organic peanut butter
- ¼ cup coconut aminos
- Coconut oil

Directions:

1. Cut chicken breast into 1" cubes and sprinkle with salt.
2. Warm 2 tablespoons coconut oil in a skillet at medium temperature.
3. Brown chicken breast, remove to plate.
4. In the same skillet, add bell peppers, green onions, and ginger and sauté for 4 minutes.
5. Return chicken to pan, mix, add peanut butter, coconut aminos, and cayenne pepper.
6. Stir-fry ingredients for 3 minutes and cover, reduce heat to low, and cook for 10 minutes.

Nutrition: Calories 439 Fat 24 Sodium 152 (mg) Carbs 11 Sugar 4 Protein 43

246. Shelled Turkey

Preparation time: 10 minutes
Cooking time: 25 minutes
Servings: 6

Ingredients:

- 3/4-pound ground turkey (lean)
- 1 medium seeded and chopped green bell pepper
- 1 large peeled and chopped onion
- 1 can dice tomatoes (without salt)
- 1/2 cup barbecue sauce (prepared)
- 1 cup canned, rinsed, and drained black beans (low-sodium)
- 1 teaspoon liquid smoke
- 1 teaspoon garlic powder
- 3 bell peppers

Directions:

1. In a skillet, brown ground turkey and drain excess fat.
2. Add onion and cook for 5 minutes.
3. Add all other ingredients except for bell peppers.
4. Simmer over medium heat for 10 minutes.
5. Cut bell peppers lengthwise. Take out the seeds. In a microwave-safe dish, put a little water and add in the bell peppers.
6. Cover and put in microwave for 5 minutes on high setting.
7. Fill bell pepper shells with turkey mixture and serve.

Nutrition: Protein: 49g Carbs: 1g Fats: 13g Calories: 327

247. Broccoli Rabe

Preparation time: 15 minutes
Cooking time: 15 minutes
Servings: 8

Ingredients:

- 2 oranges, sliced in half
- 1 lb. broccoli rabe
- 2 tablespoons sesame oil, toasted
- Salt and pepper to taste
- 1 tablespoon sesame seeds, toasted

Directions:

1. Put the oil into a pan over medium heat.
2. Add the oranges and cook until caramelized.
3. Transfer to a plate.
4. Put the broccoli in the pan and cook for 8 minutes.
5. Squeeze the oranges to release juice in a bowl.
6. Stir in the oil, salt, and pepper.
7. Coat the broccoli rabe with the mixture.
8. Sprinkle seeds on top.

Nutrition: Calories: 59 Fat: 4.4g Potassium: 160mg Carbohydrates: 4.1g Fiber: 1.6g Sugar: 2g Protein: 2.2g

248. Whipped Potatoes

Preparation time: 20 minutes
Cooking time: 35 minutes
Servings: 10

Ingredients:

- 4 cups water
- 3 lb. potatoes, sliced into cubes
- 3 cloves garlic, crushed
- 6 tablespoons vegan butter
- 2 bay leaves
- 10 sage leaves
- ½ cup Vegan yogurt
- ¼ cup low-fat milk
- Salt to taste

Directions:

1. Boil the potatoes in water for at least 30 minutes or until tender.
2. Drain.
3. In a pan over medium heat, cook the garlic in butter for 1 minute.
4. Add the sage and cook for 5 more minutes.
5. Discard the garlic.
6. Use a fork to mash the potatoes.
7. Whip using an electric mixer while gradually adding the butter, yogurt, and milk.
8. Season it with salt.

Nutrition: Calories: 169 Fat: 7.6g Cholesterol: 21mg Sodium: 251mg Potassium: 519mg Carbohydrates: 22.1g Fiber: 1.5g Sugar: 2g Protein: 4.2g

249. Chicken Skewers With Satay Sauce

Preparation time: 10-15 minutes
Cooking time: 1 hour
Servings: 1

Ingredients:

- 150 g Chicken breast, cut into chunks
- 1 tsp. ground turmeric
- 1/2 tsp. extra virgin olive oil
- 50 g Buckwheat
- 30 g Kale, stalks removed and sliced
- 30 g Celery, sliced
- 4 Walnut halves, chopped, to garnish
- For the sauce
- 20 g Red onion, diced
- 1 Garlic clove, chopped
- 1 tsp. extra virgin olive oil
- 1 tsp. Curry powder
- 1 tsp. ground turmeric
- 50 ml Chicken stock
- 150 ml Coconut milk
- 1 tbsp. Walnut butter or peanut butter
- 1 tbsp. Coriander, chopped

Directions:

1. Combine the chicken with the turmeric and olive oil then set aside to marinate – 30 minutes to 1 hour.
2. Cook the buckwheat base to the packet instructions, adding the kale and celery for the last 5–7 minutes of the cooking time. Drain.
3. Heat the grill on a high setting.
4. For the sauce, fry the red onion and garlic in the olive oil for 2–3 minutes until soft. Add the spices and cook for a more minute. Put the stock and coconut milk and bring

to the boil, then add the walnut butter and stir through. Lower the heat and simmer the sauce for 8–10 minutes, or until creamy and rich.

5. Once the sauce is simmering, thread the chicken on to the skewers and put under the hot grill for 10 minutes, turning them after 5 minutes.
6. To serve, mix the coriander through the sauce, pour it over the skewers, and then scatter over the chopped walnuts.

Nutrition: Calories: 114 Total Fat: 10 g Cholesterol: 18 mg Sodium: 236 mg Potassium: 195 mg Total Carbohydrates: 7.6 g Protein: 7.7 g

250. Chicken Curry

Preparation time: 15 minutes
Cooking time: 30 minutes
Servings: 3

Ingredients:

- 1 red onion, roughly chopped
- 3 garlic cloves, roughly chopped
- 2cm fresh ginger, peeled and roughly chopped
- 2 teaspoons garam masala
- 2 teaspoons ground cumin
- 2 teaspoons ground turmeric
- 1 cinnamon stick (optional)
- 6 cardamom pods (optional)
- 1 tablespoon olive oil
- Chicken thighs or 4 chicken breasts, boneless and skinless, cut into bite-size
- 1 x 400ml tin coconut milk
- 2 tablespoons fresh coriander, (plus extra for garnish)
- 200g buckwheat, brown rice or basmati rice to serve

Directions:

1. Put the onion, garlic, and ginger in a food processor and blitz until it is a paste. Alternatively, you can also do this with a hand blender, or if you don't have one, just chop the 3 ingredients finely then continue the direction.
2. Put the garam masala, cumin, and turmeric to the paste and mix then set aside.
3. Put 1 tablespoon of oil in a wide and deep non-stick pan. Heat the pan on high heat for one minute and then add the chopped-up chicken thighs. Stir-fry the chicken on high heat for 2 minutes, then turn the heat down and add the curry paste.
4. Let the chicken cook in the paste for 3 minutes and then add half the coconut milk (200ml), plus the cinnamon and cardamom (if using). Place to the boil and then turn down and allow simmering for 30 minutes until the curry sauce is thick and delicious!
5. If the curry begins to get dry, put a splash more coconut milk. It is not necessary, but if you like a slightly saucier curry, add a lot.
6. While the curry is cooking, make accompaniment (buckwheat/rice) and any side dishes.
7. Once the curry is ready, put the chopped coriander and serve immediately with buckwheat or rice and a nice glass of chilled white wine or water.

Nutrition: Calories: 110 Total Fat: 3 g Cholesterol: 8 mg Sodium: 154 mg Potassium: 179 mg Total Carbohydrates: 16 g Protein: 6 g

251. Chilli Con Carne

Preparation: 10 minutes
Cooking time: 10 minutes
Servings: 4

Ingredients:

- 1 red onion, finely chopped
- 3 garlic cloves, finely chopped
- 2 bird's eye chilies, finely chopped
- 1 tbsp. extra virgin olive oil
- 1 tbsp. ground cumin
- 1 tbsp. ground turmeric
- 400g lean minced beef (5 percent fat)
- 150ml red wine
- 1 red pepper, cored, seedless and cut into bite-size
- 2 x 400g tins chopped tomatoes
- 1 tbsp. tomato purée
- 1 tbsp. cocoa powder
- 150g tinned kidney beans
- 300ml beef stock
- 5g coriander, chopped
- 5g parsley, chopped
- 160g buckwheat

Directions:

1. In a casserole, put oil, fry the onion, garlic, and chili at medium heat for 2-3 minutes, then add the spices and cook for a minute.
2. Add the minced beef and brown over high heat. Add the red wine and allow it to bubble to reduce it by half.
3. Put the red pepper, tomatoes, tomato purée, cocoa, kidney beans, and stock and leave to cook for at least 1 hour.
4. You can put a little water to achieve a thick, sticky consistency.
5. Before serving, mix in the chopped herbs.
6. Meanwhile, cook the buckwheat base to the packet instructions and serve with the chili.

Nutrition: Calories: 276.5 Total Fat: 3.7 g Cholesterol: 32.5 mg Protein: 24.4 g

252. Miso & Sesame Glazed Tofu Stir-Fry

Preparation time: 15 minutes
Cooking time: 25 minutes
Serving: 4

Ingredients:

- 2 tbsp. mirin
- 2 tbsp. Brown miso paste
- 250g firm tofu
- 1 stick of celery, cut, stringy pieces peeled away and chopped
- 1 red onion,
- 1 courgette,
- 2 bird's eye chili, seeds removed and finely chopped (optional as quite spicy)
- 2 garlic cloves, finely chopped
- 2 teaspoons fresh ginger, chopped
- 100g kale washed and chopped
- 4 teaspoon sesame seeds
- 70g buckwheat or buckwheat noodles
- 235 ml (1 cup) water
- 2 teaspoon ground turmeric
- 4 teaspoons extra virgin olive oil
- 2 teaspoon tamari or soy sauce

Directions:

1. Set the oven to 200°C.
2. Line a small roasting tin using greaseproof or parchment paper.
3. Mix the mirin and miso in a bowl. Cut the tofu lengthways, and then cut each piece in half, make

triangles. Cover the tofu with the miso mixture, leave to marinate while preparing the other ingredients.

4. Cook the kale in a steamer for around 5 minutes, take and leave to one side. If you don't have a steamer, put a pan of water on the hob and bring it to a rolling boil, place a collider over the top with the kale in, and act as a steamer.
5. While the kale is cooking, slice the trimmed celery, red onion, and courgette on the angle. Then finely chop the chili (make sure all seeds are removed), garlic and ginger and leave to one side.
6. Put the marinated tofu in the roasting tin, dust the sesame seeds over the tofu and roast for 15-20 minutes, until nicely caramelized.
7. Wash the buckwheat in a sieve, place a cup of water on to boil, add the turmeric, and a pinch of salt to taste. When the water started to boil, add the buckwheat and leave on high heat.
8. Once the buckwheat has expanded and started to absorb the water, lower the temperature, place the lid on, and cook for a remaining 10-15 minutes. When all the water is absorbed, the buckwheat is cooked.
9. When the tofu has 5 minutes remaining, heat the olive oil in a frying pan, when hot add the celery, onion, courgette, chili, garlic, and ginger and fry on high heat for 1-2 minutes, then reduce to medium heat for 3-4 minutes until the vegetables are cooked through but still crunchy. You may need to put a tablespoon of water if the vegetables start to stick to the pan. Add the kale and tamari and cook for a further minute.
10. When the tofu is ready, serve with the greens and buckwheat.

Nutrition: Calories: 550 Total Fat: 22 g Cholesterol: 0 mg Sodium: 1110 mg Total Carbohydrates: 70 g Protein: 23 g

253. Slow Cooked Chilli Beef

Preparation time: 15 minutes
Cooking time: 3 hours
Servings: 4

Ingredients:

- 2 tablespoons olive oil
- 1 large onion sliced
- 800 g stewing beef, diced into 1cm cubes
- 2 cloves garlic, finely chopped
- 1 teaspoon dried chili flakes
- 2 teaspoons paprika
- 2 teaspoons cumin
- 2 teaspoons oregano
- 1 tin chopped tomato
- Salt and pepper
- 1 large red pepper chopped into small
- 1 tin kidney bean
- Rice or tortillas to serve
- Optional:
- Guacamole sour cream & fresh coriander to serve

Directions:

1. Set the oven to 140C.
2. Place the onion and olive oil in an ovenproof saucepan or hob proof casserole dish and fry gently, with the lid on for 5 minutes, until the onions are softened.
3. Turn the heat up then add the beef. Fry for about 5 minutes, then add the garlic, chili flakes, herbs, and spices. Lower the temperature, then fry for 2 minutes.
4. Put the tinned tomatoes, salt, and pepper and bring to the boil. Put the lid on and take it to the oven. (If you haven't used a pan you can put in the oven, transfer to an oven dish, before putting in the oven). Cook for at least 2 hours 30 minutes.
5. After 2 hours 30 minutes, add the kidney beans and the red pepper and stir—Cook for a further 30 minutes.

Nutrition: Calories: 448.0 Total Fat: 21.4 g Cholesterol: 52.5 mg Sodium: 1294.3 mg Potassium: 654.1 mg Total Carbohydrates: 39.1 g Protein: 28.7 g

254. Soba In A Miso Broth With Tofu, Celery, And Kale

Preparation time: 20 minutes
Cooking time: 25 minutes
Servings: 1

Ingredients

- 3 ounces (75g) soba (buckwheat noodles)
- 1 tablespoon extra-virgin olive oil
- 1/8 cup (20g) red onion, sliced
- 2 garlic cloves, finely chopped
- 1 teaspoon finely chopped fresh ginger
- 1 1/4 cups (300ml) vegetable stock, plus a little extra, if necessary
- 1 3/4 tablespoons (30g) miso paste
- 3/4 cup (50g) kale, roughly chopped
- 1/2 cup (50g) celery, roughly chopped
- 1 teaspoon sesame seeds
- 3 1/2 ounces (100g) form tofu, cut into
- 1/4- to 1/2-inch (0.5 to 1cm) cubes (about 3/8 cup)
- 1 teaspoon tamari (optional; or soy sauce, if you are not avoiding gluten)

Directions:

1. Bring the noodles in a pan of boiling water and cook for 5 to 8minutes or according to the package instructions.
2. Heat the oil in a saucepan; add the onions, garlic, and ginger and fry over medium heat in the oil until soft but not browned.
3. Add the stock and miso and bring to a boil.
4. Add the kale and celery to the miso broth and simmer gently for 5 minutes (try not to boil the miso, as you will destroy the flavor and cause it to go grainy in texture). You can add a little more stock as required.
5. Add the cooked noodles and sesame seeds and allow warming through. Then add the tofu.
6. Serve in a bowl drizzled with a little tamari, if desired.

Nutrition: Calories: 370 Total Fat: 4.17 g Cholesterol: 0 mg Sodium: 856 mg Total Carbohydrates: 68.1 g Protein: 14.69 g

255. Tofu And Shiitake Mushroom Soup

Preparation time: 10 minutes
Cooking time: 10 minutes
Servings: 4

Ingredients

- 1/3 ounce (10g) dried wakame (seaweed)
- 1-quart (1 liter) vegetable stock
- 7 ounces (200g) shiitake mushrooms, sliced
- 1/3 cup (120g) miso paste
- 1 x 14-ounce (400g) block form tofu, cut into small cubes
- 2 scallions, cut and sliced on the diagonal
- Optional:
- 1 Thai chili, finely chopped

Directions:

1. Soak the wakame in warm water for 10 minutes, then drain.
2. Bring the stock to a boil, then add the mushrooms and simmer gently for 1 to 2 minutes.

3. Dissolve the miso paste in a bowl with some of the warm stock to ensure it dissolves thoroughly.
4. Add the miso and tofu to the remaining stock, not let the soup boil as this would spoil the delicate miso flavor. Add the drained wakame, scallions, and chili, if using, and serve.

Nutrition: Calories: 116 Total Fat: 7 g Total Carbohydrates: 2 g Protein: 8 g

256. Portuguese Kale Stew With Shrimp

Preparation time: 15 minutes
Cooking time: 16 minutes
Servings: 5

Ingredients:

- 4 Portions
- 3 onions
- 2 garlic cloves
- 100g soft chorizo
- 300g potatoes (5 potatoes)
- 4 tbsp. olive oil
- 1 tsp. cumin
- 800ml classic vegetable broth
- 450g kale
- ½ organic lemon
- 3 inlaid Piri-Piri
- 350g shrimp (ready to cook; without head and shell)
- Salt
- Pepper

Directions:

1. Peel onions and garlic and dice finely. Cut the sausage into fine cubes. Peel, wash, and diced potatoes.
2. In a steel saucepan, put 2 tablespoons of olive oil. Braise the onions until glazed in 7–8 minutes. Put the garlic and chorizo then fry for another 2 minutes. Add cumin, potatoes, and broth, bring to the boil once, and cook over medium heat for about 20 minutes.
3. In the meantime, clean the kale, wash it thoroughly, and let it drain well. Cut kale into very fine strips or finely chop it. Rinse the lemon hot, rub dry, and finely grate a little peel. Drain the Piri-Piri pods and collect the oil. Finely chop the pods and mix with the remaining oil and lemon zest.
4. Puree the potatoes, onions, garlic, and sausage in the broth with the hand blender. Put the cabbage in the stock and cook for a further 10 minutes over medium heat. Rinse the shrimp, pat dry, and put in the stew. Bring everything to a boil again and let it cook for another 2 minutes. Season with salt and pepper. Drizzle the stew with the Piri-Piri oil and serve.

Nutrition: Calories: 39 Fat: 20g Carbohydrates: 50g Protein: 12g

257. Chilli Salmon Fillet

Preparation time: 50 minutes
Cooking time: 10 minutes
Servings: 4

Ingredients:

- 4 Portions
- 2 jalapeños (glass)
- 3 organic limes
- 1 tbsp. chili powder
- 1 tsp. brown sugar
- 5½ tbsp. oil
- 720g salmon fillet (4 salmon fillets)
- 300g red bell pepper (2 red bell peppers)
- 200g fully ripe, small mango (1 fully ripe, small mango)
- 1 red onion
- ½ bundle coriander
- Salt
- Pepper
- Sugar
- 150g sour cream

Directions:

1. Drain the jalapeños, cut them in half, remove the stones, and crush them with the knife's back to a fine paste. Squeeze the limes. Rub the peel from 1 squeezed lime half. Mix the jalapeños in a bowl with the chili powder, brown sugar, 2 tablespoons of oil and 2 tablespoons of lime juice. Rinse the salmon fillets, pat them dry, and put them in the seasoning liquid (marinate). Chill until further use. Clean, quarter, core, wash and place the peppers on a baking sheet with the skin facing up. Roast under the hot grill until the skin turns black and blisters.
2. Put the roasted peppers in a bowl, cover with a plate and let them steam for 10 minutes. Then peel off the skin and cut the peppers into fine rhombuses. Peel the mango with the peeler. Cut the pulp into slices from the stone and also divide it into diamonds. Peel the onion and chop very finely. Wash and shake coriander dry. Pluck and chop leaves. Mix the bell pepper, mango, onions, and coriander in a bowl with the remaining lime juice and oil (keep 1/2 tbsp.). Season a pinch of sugar, salt, and pepper.
3. Mix the sour cream with the grated lime zest, salt, and pepper until smooth. Heat a grill pan and spread with the oil that has been retained. Lift the salmon fillets out of the marinade and let them drain. Grill for 3-4 minutes on each side of the grill pan. Put sour cream in a disposable piping bag and spray decoratively on 4 plates, arrange 1 serving of paprika-mango sauce, and salmon fillet on each and serve.

Nutrition: Calories: 234 Fat: 20.9g Protein: 20.3g Carbohydrate: 3.4g Fiber: 0.9g

258. Tuna And Chilli Linguine

Preparation time: 15 minutes
Cooking time: 45 minutes
Servings: 4

Ingredients:

- 320 grams of linguine;
- 250 gr of fresh tuna in its natural state;
- 15/20 cherry quality tomatoes;
- Fresh red peppers two;
- Extra virgin olive oil just enough; A pinch of salt and pepper to taste; Parsley.

Direction:

1. Carefully clean and dice the fresh tuna naturally, taking care to remove any bones;
2. In a non-stick pan heat a tablespoon of extra virgin olive oil over high heat, and once hot add the chopped tuna;
3. Cook it until it turns golden, taking care to stir it from time to time;
4. Wash and cut the cherry tomatoes in half and add them to the tuna that is cooking;
5. Wash and cut the chili peppers in two and add to the sauce;
6. Add salt and pepper with care;
7. Keep cooking the sauce for five more minutes, then turn off the stove and let it rest;
8. In the meantime, cook the linguine, taking care to add salt and keep the tooth cooking;

9. Once cooked, drain the linguine, then turn on the sauce and pour the linguine into the pan;
10. Mix well and add the chopped parsley;
11. Put out the fire and pour it on the plate.

Nutrition: Calories: 80 kcal Protein: 13.98 g Fat: 2.17 g Carbohydrates: 1.24 g

259. Spaghetti With Garlic Oil And Chilli Pepper

Preparation time: 10 minutes
Cooking time: 30 minutes
Servings: 4

Ingredients:

- 320 gr of spaghetti restaurant-style;
- Garlic cloves (at least two);
- Extra virgin olive oil;
- 1 fresh chili pepper;
- Salt;
- At will, chopped parsley.

Directions:

1. Bring a pot of water and coarse salt to medium heat, pour the restaurant-style spaghetti and let it cook turning from time to time, so that it doesn't stick. Drain al dente;
2. In the meantime, pour the extra-virgin olive oil, garlic cloves with the skin removed and chilli pepper, chopped into a fairly large saucepan;
3. Let the garlic brown for a few minutes. When the garlic has perfumed the oil, remove it and pour the spaghetti into the pot, mix well adding, if necessary, a ladle of water from the pasta cooking;
4. Add a sprinkling of chopped parsley, as desired;
5. Mix well the spaghetti with the sauce and serve immediately.

Nutrition: Calories: 168 kcal Protein: 8.59 g Fat: 8.48 g Carbohydrates: 14.67 g

260. Buckwheat Noodles With Yoghurt And Mushrooms

Preparation time: 20 minutes
Cooking time: 30 minutes
Servings: 4

Ingredients for kneading noodles:

- 200 grams of flour type 00;
- 200 grams of buckwheat flour;
- 4 whole eggs.
- Ingredients for the seasoning:
- 400 gr of mixed mushrooms, even frozen;
- 1 white onion;
- 1 clove of garlic;
- 1 jar of 125 gr of natural whole yoghurt;
- Fresh parsley;
- Extra virgin olive oil;
- Salt and pepper to taste

Directions:

1. Prepare the dough: In a big bowl pour the two flours, with your hands form a hole in the middle and add the eggs (I advise you to break the eggs in a separate bowl to see if they are good first);
2. Knead with your hands: you have to make a smooth and elastic dough. When it has the right consistency, leave it at room temperature wrapped in a food-grade film for at least 30 minutes;
3. After 30 minutes, roll out the dough with the special machine or don't have it with the help of a rolling pin. The result must be not very thick sheets of dough: cut them with the appropriate tool and finish them.
4. For the noodles. They must dry on a floured table, or a tray, while you prepare the dressing;
5. In a non-stick pan, wither the finely chopped onion in oil with the clove of garlic;
6. As soon as it becomes transparent, add i clean mushrooms e cut into cubes e let it cook for 15 minutes;
7. Add salt and pepper and put out the fire;
8. Cook the tagliatelle in boiling salted water (it will take about five minutes), drain them and set aside a ladle of the cooking water;
9. Pour the tagliatelle into the pan with the mushrooms, the yoghurt and the spoon of water left over, and mix everything to absorb the seasoning;
10. Remove from the fire and make the portions of buckwheat noodles, decorating the plates with parsley.

Nutrition: Calories: 792 kcal Protein: 30.61 g Fat: 12.73 g Carbohydrates: 153.73 g

261. Rice, Blueberries, And Bacon

Preparation time: 5 minutes
Cooking time: 15 minutes
Servings: 2

Ingredients:

- Carnaroli rice 360 gr;
- Fresh blueberries or other soft fruits
- 200 gr;
- A pound of bacon;
- Vegetable broth a liter;
- Butter 30 gr;
- Parmesan 40 gr;
- A little white onion;
- Some rosemary stalks;
- Red wine type Lambrusco 100 cc;
- Extra virgin olive oil;
- Salt and pepper to taste

Direction:

1. Put the blueberries in a pan with a bit of butter and cook them, turning them from time to time, until they soften. To speed things up, keep the pan covered. As soon as they're ready, blend them in a blender. Set aside the mash obtained;
2. Heat another pan with a drizzle of oil, add the onion and let it wither. When it becomes clearer, add the chopped speck and cook it by turning it occasionally so that it doesn't burn;
3. Put the rice and let it toast for 2-3 minutes;
4. Turn up the flame, pour the red wine and let it evaporate;
5. Decrease the flame and cook the risotto by adding the broth a little at a time;
6. Halfway through cooking, add the blueberry puree and finish cooking the rice with the broth;
7. When cooked, remove from the heat, add the Parmesan cheese and rosemary, and complete it by mixing everything with the knob of butter;
8. Give the risotto time to rest for a few minutes, then transfer it to the serving dishes.

Nutrition: Calories: 521 kcal Protein: 19.1 g Fat: 40.59 g Carbohydrates: 26.73 g

262. Basmati Rice With Chicken, Peppers, Chilli, And Turmeric

Preparation time: 5 minutes
Cooking time: 20 minutes
Servings: 2

Ingredients:

- 350 grams of basmati rice;
- 200 grams of chicken meat;
- 1 small onion;
- 1 red pepper;
- 1 liter of vegetable stock;
- 4 cardamom seeds;
- Half a teaspoon of turmeric;
- 1 chili;
- Extra virgin olive oil;
- Salt and chives.

Directions:

1. In a pan with 3 tablespoons of olive oil, sauté the finely chopped onion, chopped pepper, cardamom, and turmeric dissolved in half a glass of hot water. Cook over high heat for five minutes;
2. Chopped the chicken into pieces and put it in the pan with i peppers. Cook for a few minutes, add salt and chilli pepper and mix well;
3. Cook the basmati rice in vegetable stock for about 9 minutes. Drain it well, put it on the plate and pour the chicken with the peppers in the middle.

Nutrition: Calories: 308 kcal Protein: 24.34 g Fat: 13.03 g Carbohydrates: 22.31 g

263. Fusilli With Walnut Pesto

Preparation time: 10 minutes
Cooking time: 30 minutes
Servings: 4

Ingredients:

- 80 grams of shelled nuts;
- 20 grams of pine nuts;
- 60 grams of grated grits;
- 1 tablespoon of extra virgin olive oil;
- 2 tablespoons of milk;
- 1 shaved spoon of breadcrumbs;
- Half a clove of garlic;
- Salt and pepper to taste
- 300 gr of pasta type fusilli.

Directions:

1. Clean the nuts;
2. Bring the frying pan on the stove with water to cook the fusilli;
3. Put the dried fruit in the centrifuge, blend for a few minutes, and maintain an average speed to avoid spilling the oil;
4. Add the milk, salt, and pepper and mix well;
5. Drain the pasta al dente and add it to the sauce;
6. Serve and eat now.

Nutrition: Calories: 321 kcal Protein: 7.72 g Fat: 21.63 g Carbohydrates: 27.72 g

264. Penne Ziti, Arugula, Salmon And Ginger

Preparation time: 5 minutes
Cooking time: 25 minutes
Servings: 4

Ingredients:

- 400 grams of fusilli;
- 150 grams of salmon;
- 30 grams of fresh ginger;
- 80 grams of arugula; • 1 clove of garlic;
- Extra virgin olive oil;
- Salt and pink pepper grains.

Directions:

1. Put the water on the stove for the pasta. When it boils, pour in the penne ziti and a handful of salt. Leave the penne to cook for ten minutes, stirring occasionally;
2. Cut the arugula finely and leave it aside;
3. Cut the salmon into small pieces and brown it in a pan with crushed garlic and oil until it flakes;
4. Add the grated ginger, chopped rocket, crushed pink peppercorns, and salt. Stir from time to time letting the salmon season;
5. Drain the penne ziti al dente, pass them immediately in the pan with the salmon, and add some cooking water;
6. After a couple of minutes, take it out of the fire and pour it on the plate.

Nutrition: Calories: 118 kcal Protein: 10.97 g Fat: 4.38 g Carbohydrates: 9.01 g

265. Soy Spaghetti With Vegetables

Preparation time: 15 minutes
Cooking time: 45 minutes
Servings: 4

Ingredients:

- 150 grams of soy spaghetti;
- 1 small piece of 5 cm leek;
- 1 big orange carrot;
- 1 Genoese zucchini;
- 1 strip of red radicchio;
- 1 teaspoon of fresh ginger;
- Juice of 1 lime;
- Soy sauce;
- Extra virgin olive oil;
- 1 clove garlic;
- 1 small piece of fresh chilli pepper;
- Salt, coriander or parsley to taste;

Directions:

1. Clean a leek price, cut it into thin sticks, peel the carrot, and cut it into strands. You can use the tool to make vegetable noodles. Do the same thing with the zucchini;
2. Thinly cut the red radicchio with the help of a mandolin;
3. Take a wok-like pot, or a wide-bottom pan, and put it on a high flame;
4. Pour a round of olive oil, add a clove of garlic, and a price of chili pepper. When the garlic begins to fry, put the leek stirring often with a wooden spoon;
5. When the leek has withered, proceed adding the carrots and zucchini.
6. Skip the vegetables for 1 minute and then add the red radicchio;
7. Add a pinch of salt and keep stirring until the red radicchio starts to wither;
8. Grate the fresh ginger, dissolve it in the juice of half a lime and pour it into the pan. The lime juice, in addition to giving a pleasantly citrusy note, gives the red radicchio a nice bright color;
9. It fumes with a little soy sauce;
10. Cook the soy spaghetti in salted water, drain them, rinse them with water and pour them into the pan where you cooked the vegetables;
11. Mix the soy spaghetti with the sautéed vegetables to make them flavor.
12. If it becomes too dry, put a little cooking water;
13. It fumes again with a drizzle of soy sauce;
14. Finish the dish by decorating it before serving with fresh coriander or chopped parsley.

Nutrition: Calories: 275 kcal Protein: 23.27 g Fat: 7.06 g Carbohydrates: 34.41 g

266. Red Wine Butterflies

Preparation time: 10 minutes
Cooking time: 30 minutes
Servings: 4

Ingredients:

- 250 gr butterflies;
- 300 ml red wine;
- Extra virgin olive oil;
- 1 chili;
- 1 clove of garlic;
- Salt and parsley.
- Grated Pecorino 5-6 spoon.

Directions:

1. Place a pan with a wide bottom and pour in a couple of tablespoons of extra virgin olive oil. Add a clove of garlic, whole or chopped, and a bit of chilli pepper, better if fresh. According to your taste, if you want you can also add some anchovy fillets in oil;
2. When the garlic begins to fry, pour the red wine into the pan;
3. Slightly salt and add finely chopped parsley;
4. Let the red wine simmer, meanwhile, cook the butterflies in plenty of salted water. Halfway through cooking, pass them in the pan with the red wine and continue cooking inside;
5. In case the butterflies should cook by absorbing too much wine, complete the cooking by adding a spoon of pasta cooking water;
6. Before serving, dust the butterflies with a handful of grated pecorino cheese.

Nutrition: Calories: 312 kcal Protein: 4.99 g Fat: 13.74 g Carbohydrates: 42.34 g

267. Linguine Pistachios, Chia Seeds, And Eggplant Pesto

Preparation time: 10 minutes
Cooking time: 40 minutes
Servings: 4

Ingredients:

- Whole linguine (about 30 g per person), 4 nests;
- One small eggplant;
- A handful of pistachios;
- Garlic;
- Chia seeds, a spoon;
- Extra virgin olive oil and salt.

Directions:

1. Slice the eggplant, put it in a colander with a weight on top (this way you will remove excess water), rest for 30 minutes and then grill the eggplant slices;
2. Put the water on the stove for the pasta. When it boils, toss the linguine and cook for 5 minutes. Set aside some cooking water;
3. Once cooked, cool the pasta under running water and leave it on a plate;
4. Prepare the eggplant pesto: pour the grilled eggplant, pistachios, chia seeds, garlic and oil into a centrifuge, blend and add a little cooking water from the pasta;
5. In a pan, pour the eggplant pesto and linguine and heat over high heat stirring for two minutes, serve the linguine sprinkling each plate with chia seeds

Nutrition: Calories: 219 kcal Protein: 11.77 g Fat: 7.05 g Carbohydrates: 32.22 g

268. Tuna And Kale

Preparation time: 5 minutes
Cooking time: 20 minutes
Servings: 4

Ingredients:

- 1 pound tuna fillets, boneless, skinless and cubed
- 2 tablespoons olive oil
- 1 cup kale, torn
- ½ cup cherry tomatoes, cubed
- 1 yellow onion, chopped

Directions:

1. Heat a pan with the oil at medium heat; add the onion and sauté for 5 minutes.
2. Add the tuna and the other ingredients, toss, cook everything for 15 minutes more, divide between plates and serve.

Nutrition: Calories 251 Fat 4 Fiber 7 Carbs 14 Protein 7

269. Lemongrass And Ginger Mackerel

Preparation time: 10 minutes
Cooking time: 25 minutes
Servings: 4

Ingredients:

- 4 mackerel fillets, skinless and boneless
- 2 tablespoons olive oil
- 1 tablespoon ginger, grated
- 2 lemongrass sticks, chopped
- 2 red chilies, chopped
- Juice of 1 lime
- Handful parsley, chopped

Directions:

1. In a roasting pan, combine the mackerel with the oil, ginger, and the other ingredients, toss and bake at 390 degrees F for 25 minutes.
2. Divide everything between plates and serve.

Nutrition: Calories 251 Fat 3 Fiber 4 Carbs 14 Protein 8

270. Scallops With Almonds And Mushrooms

Preparation time: 5 minutes
Cooking time: 10 minutes
Servings: 4

Ingredients:

- 1 pound scallops
- 2 tablespoons olive oil
- 4 scallions, chopped
- ½ cup mushrooms, sliced
- 2 tablespoon almonds, chopped
- 1 cup coconut cream

Directions:

1. Warm a pan with the oil over medium heat, add the scallions and the mushrooms and sauté for 2 minutes.
2. Add the scallops cook over medium heat for 8 minutes more, divide into bowls and serve.

Nutrition: Calories 322 Fat 23.7 Fiber 2.2 Carbs 8.1 Protein 21.6

271. Rosemary Endives

Preparation time: 10 minutes
Cooking time: 45 minutes
Servings: 2

Ingredients:

- 2 tbsps. Olive oil
- 1 tsp. dried rosemary
- 2 halved endives
- ¼ tsp. Black pepper
- ½ tsp. turmeric powder

Directions:

1. In a baking pan, combine the endives with the oil and the other ingredients, toss gently, introduce in the oven and bake at 400 0F for 20 minutes.
2. Divide between plates and serve.

Nutrition: Calories: 66 Fat: 7.1 g Carbs: 1.2 g Protein: 0.3 g Sugars: 1.3 g Sodium: 113 mg

272. Kale Sauté

Preparation time: 10 minutes
Cooking time: 35 minutes
Servings: 2

Ingredients:

- 1 chopped red onion
- 3 tbsps. Coconut aminos
- 2 tbsps. Olive oil
- 1 lb. torn kale
- 1 tbsp. chopped cilantro
- 1 tbsp. lime juice
- 2 minced garlic cloves

Directions:

1. Warm a pan with the olive oil over medium heat. Add the onion and the garlic and sauté for 5 minutes.
2. Add the kale and the other ingredients, toss, cook over medium heat for 10 minutes, divide between plates and serve.

Nutrition: Calories: 200 Fat: 7.1 g Carbs: 6.4 g Protein: 6 g Sugars: 1.6 g, Sodium: 183 mg

273. Roasted Beets

Preparation time: 10 minutes
Cooking time: 40 minutes
Servings: 2

Ingredients:

- 2 minced garlic cloves
- ¼ tsp. black pepper
- 4 peeled and sliced beets
- ¼ c. chopped walnuts
- 2 tbsps. Olive oil
- ¼ c. chopped parsley

Directions:

1. In a baking dish, mix the beets with the oil and the other ingredients, toss it to coat, introduce it in the oven at 420 0F, and bake for 30 minutes.
2. Divide between plates and serve.

Nutrition: Calories: 156 Fat: 11.8 g Carbs: 11.5 g Protein: 3.8 g Sugars: 8 g, Sodium: 670 mg

274. Minty Tomatoes And Corn

Preparation time: 10 minutes
Cooking time: 65 minutes
Servings: 2

Ingredients:

- 2 c. corn
- 1 tbsp. rosemary vinegar
- 2 tbsps. Chopped mint
- 1 lb. Sliced tomatoes
- ¼ tsp. black pepper
- 2 tbsps. Olive oil

Directions:

1. In a salad bowl, combine the tomatoes with the corn and the other ingredients, toss and serve.
2. Enjoy!

Nutrition: Calories: 230 Fat: 7.2 g Carbs: 11.6 g Protein: 4 g Sugars: 1 g Sodium: 53 mg

275. Pesto Green Beans

Preparation time: 10 minutes
Cooking time: 55 minutes
Servings: 2

Ingredients:

- 2 tbsps. Olive oil
- 2 tsp. Sweet paprika
- Juice of 1 lemon
- 2 tbsps. Basil pesto
- 1 lb. Trimmed and halved green beans
- ¼ tsp. black pepper
- 1 sliced red onion

Directions:

1. Warmth a pan with the oil over medium-high temperature, add the onion, mix and sauté for 5 minutes.
2. Put the beans and the rest of the ingredients, toss then cook at medium heat for 10 minutes, divide between plates and serve.

Nutrition: Calories: 280 Fat: 10 g Carbs: 13.9 g Protein: 4.7 g, Sugars: 0.8 g, Sodium: 138 mg

276. Scallops And Sweet Potatoes

Preparation time: 5 minutes
Cooking time: 22 minutes
Servings: 4

Ingredients:

- 1 pound scallops
- ½ teaspoon rosemary, dried
- ½ teaspoon oregano, dried
- 2 tablespoons avocado oil
- 1 yellow onion, chopped
- 2 sweet potatoes, peeled and cubed
- ½ cup chicken stock
- 1 tablespoon cilantro, chopped

Directions:

1. Warmth a pan with the oil over medium heat; add the onion and sauté for 2 minutes.
2. Add the sweet potatoes and the stock, toss and cook for 10 minutes more.
3. Add the scallops and the remaining ingredients, toss, cook for another 10 minutes, divide everything into bowls and serve.

Nutrition: Calories 211 Fat 2 Fiber 4.1 Carbs 26.9 Protein 20.7

277. Citrus Salmon

Preparation time: 10 minutes
Cooking time: 45 minutes
Servings: 2

Ingredients

- 1 ½ lb. salmon fillet with skin on
- Salt and pepper to taste
- 1 medium red onion, chopped
- 2 tablespoons parsley, chopped
- 2 teaspoons lemon rind, grated
- 2 teaspoons orange rind, grated
- 2 tablespoons extra virgin olive oil
- 1 lemon, sliced thinly
- 1 orange, sliced thinly
- 1 cup vegetable broth

Directions

1. Line your crockpot with parchment paper and top with the lemon slices.
2. Season salmon with salt and pepper and place it on top of the lemon.
3. Cover the fish with the onion, parsley, and grated citrus rinds and oil over fish. Top with orange slices, reserving a few for garnish.

4. Pour broth around, but not directly overtop, your salmon.
5. Cook and cover on low temperature for 2 hours.
6. Preheat oven to 400 degrees F.
7. When salmon is opaque and flaky, remove from the crockpot carefully using the parchment paper and transfer to a baking sheet. Place in the oven for 5 – 8 minutes to allow the salmon to brown on top.
8. Serve garnished with orange and lemon slices.

Nutrition: Calories 294 Fat 3 Fiber 8 Carbs 49 Protein 21

278. Turkey Mole Tacos

Preparation time: 10 minutes
Cooking time: 15 minutes
Servings: 3

Ingredients:

- 75 pound Lean ground turkey
- 4 stalks Green onion, chopped
- 2 Garlic cloves, minced
- 1 rib Celery, chopped
- 3 Ounces Roasted sweet peppers, chopped and drained
- 7 ounces diced tomatoes, canned
- 6 Corn tortillas, 6 inches, warmed
- 1 Red onion, thinly sliced
- 2 tablespoons Walnuts, roasted, chopped
- 2 ounces Dark chocolate, chopped
- .25 teaspoon Sea salt
- 4 teaspoons Chili powder
- .5 teaspoon Cumin
- .125 teaspoon Cinnamon, ground

Directions:

1. In a big non-stick skillet, cook the ground turkey with the green onions, celery, and garlic over medium heat. Cook till there is no pink remaining, the turkey has reached a temperature of one-hundred and sixty-five degrees, and the vegetables are tender.
2. Into the skillet with the cooked turkey, add the canned tomatoes, roasted red peppers, cinnamon, chocolate, chili powder, cumin, and sea salt. Allow the liquid from the tomatoes to come to a boil before reducing the heat to medium-low, covering the skillet with a lid, and simmering for ten minutes. Stir occasionally to prevent sticking and burning.
3. Remove the cooked ground turkey from the heat and stir in the walnuts.
4. Divide the taco meat between the corn tortillas, topping it off with the sliced red onion. Serve while warm.

Nutrition: Calories: 8619 kcal Protein: 1065.69 g Fat: 479.97 g Carbohydrates: 10.31 g

279. Sweet And Sour Tofu

Preparation time: 5 minutes
Cooking time: 20 minutes
Servings: 4

Ingredients:

- 14 ounces Tofu, firm
- 8 tablespoons Cornstarch, divided
- 1 Egg white
- 1 cup Pineapple, chopped
- 2 Bell pepper, chopped
- 6 tablespoons Rice vinegar
- 6 tablespoons Date sugar
- 2 tablespoons Tamari sauce
- 1 teaspoon Sea salt
- 2 tablespoons Tomato paste
- 2 teaspoons Water
- 2 tablespoons Cornstarch
- 1 teaspoon sesame seeds, toasted

Directions:

1. Line an aluminum baking sheet with kitchen parchment or a silicone sheet and set the oven to Fahrenheit three-hundred and fifty degrees.
2. Begin by pressing your tofu and then slicing it into bite-sized cubes. Sprinkle two of the eight divided tablespoons of cornstarch over the tofu, tossing it until the tofu is evenly coated.
3. Place the remaining six tablespoons of divided cornstarch in one bowl and the egg white (or aquafaba) in another.
4. Dip a few tofu cubes at a time first in the egg white and then in the cornstarch. Transfer the breaded cubes to the prepared baking sheet and continue it until all the cubes are ready. Arrange the tofu cubes on the pan evenly so that they don't touch, and then bake until crispy, about fifteen to twenty minutes.
5. While the tofu cooks, whisk together the rice vinegar, date sugar, tamari sauce, sea salt, tomato paste, water, two tablespoons of corn starch, and the sesame seeds.
6. Add the peppers and pineapple to a large skillet and saute them until slightly tender. Add in the mixed sauce and deglaze the skillet. Add the cooked tofu to the skillet and continue to cook it in the sauce until it is coated and sticky, and the sauce has thickened.
7. Serve while warm over brown rice or buckwheat.

Nutrition: Calories: 481 kcal Protein: 20.94 g Fat: 22.12 g Carbohydrates: 55 g

280. Asian Slaw

Preparation time: 15 minutes
Cooking time: 0 minutes
Servings: 4

Ingredients:

- 2 cups Red cabbage, shredded
- 2 cups Broccoli florets, chopped
- 1 cup Carrots, shredded
- 1 Red onion, finely sliced
- .5 Red bell pepper, finely sliced
- .5 cup Cilantro, chopped
- 1 tablespoon sesame seeds
- .5 cup Peanuts, chopped
- 2 teaspoons Sriracha
- .25 cup Rice wine vinegar
- .5 teaspoon Sesame seed oil
- 1 teaspoon Sea salt
- 1 clove Garlic, minced
- 2 tablespoons Peanut butter, natural
- 2 tablespoons extra virgin olive oil
- 2 tablespoons Tamari sauce
- 2 teaspoons ginger, peeled and grated
- 2 teaspoons Honey
- .25 teaspoon Black pepper, ground

Directions:

1. In a big salad bowl, throw together the vegetables, cilantro, and peanuts.
2. In a smaller bowl, whisk together the remaining ingredients until emulsified. Pour this dressing over the vegetables and toss together until fully coated.
3. Chill the slaw for at least ten minutes so that the flavors meld. Refrigerate the Asian slaw for up to a day in advance for deeper flavors.

Nutrition: Calories: 324 kcal Protein: 13.94 g Fat: 19.94 g Carbohydrates: 26.44 g

281. Red Cabbage And Apple Salad

Preparation time: 5 minutes
Cooking time: 0 minutes
Servings: 6

Ingredients:

- 6 cups Red cabbage, shredded
- .5 cup Green onions, chopped
- 1 Green apple, finely diced
- 1 cup English cucumber, sliced
- .5 cup Sauerkraut, liquid well drained
- 1 tablespoon White vinegar
- .5 teaspoon Sea salt
- 1 tablespoon Dill, fresh, chopped
- .25 cup extra virgin olive oil

Directions:

1. Set all the ingredients into a bowl, toss well to combine. Taste and adjust the seasoning to your preference.
2. Enjoy the salad immediately, or store it in the fridge for up to three days before serving. The longer you chill the salad, the more the flavors will deepen and meld.

Nutrition: Calories: 96 kcal Protein: 2.63 g Fat: 5.12 g Carbohydrates: 11.64 g

282. Chickpea And Blueberry Salad

Preparation time: 5 minutes
Cooking time: 0 minutes
Servings: 4

Ingredients:

- 1 cup Red cabbage, finely sliced
- .5 cup Chickpeas, cooked
- .25 cup dried cranberries
- 1 cup Arugula
- .5 cup Blueberries
- 3 tablespoons Walnuts, roasted, chopped
- 3 tablespoons Lemon juice
- 3 tablespoons Water
- .25 cup Tahini paste
- 1 teaspoon Garlic powder
- 2 tablespoons Honey
- 1 teaspoon Sea salt

Directions:

1. In a small kitchen, bowl whisks together the lemon juice, water, tahini paste, garlic powder, honey, and sea salt until it forms a cohesive and emulsified dressing.
2. In a salad bowl, put the remaining ingredients and then drizzle the prepared dressing over it. Toss it together until the vegetables and fruits are fully coated. Serve immediately.

Nutrition: Calories: 298 kcal Protein: 10.26 g Fat: 10.66 g Carbohydrates: 44.11 g

283. Fruity Curry Chicken Salad

Preparation time: 15 minutes
Cooking time: 0 minutes
Servings: 8

Ingredients:

- 4 skinless, boneless chicken pliers - cooked and diced
- 1 tsp celery, diced
- 4 green onions, sliced
- 1 delicious golden apple peeled, cored and diced
- 1/3 cup golden raisins
- 1/3 cup seedless green grapes, halved
- 1/2 cup sliced toasted pecans
- ⅛ Teaspoon ground black pepper
- 1/2 tsp curry powder
- 3/4 cup light mayonnaise

Directions:

1. In a big bowl, combine the chicken, onion, celery, apple, celery, celery, pecans, pepper, curry powder, and carrot. Mix altogether. Enjoy!

Nutrition: 229 carbohydrates; 14 grams Total fat; 44 cholesterol188 Sodium. 12.3 g Carbs; 15.1

284. Zuppa Toscana

Preparation time: 25 minutes
Cooking time: 60 minutes
Servings:

Ingredients:

- 1 lb ground Italian sausage
- 1 1/4 tsp red pepper flakes,
- 4 pieces bacon, cut into ½ inch bits
- 1 big onion, diced
- 1 tbsp. minced garlic
- 5 (13.75 oz.) can chicken broth
- 6 celery, thinly chopped
- 1 cup thick cream
- 1/4 bunch fresh spinach, tough stems removed

Directions:

1. Cook that the Italian sausage and red pepper flakes in a pot on medium-high heat until crumbly, browned, with no longer pink, 10 to 15minutes. Drain and put aside.
2. Cook the bacon at the exact Dutch oven over moderate heat until crispy, about 10 minutes. Drain, put a couple of tablespoons of drippings with all the bacon at the bottom of the toaster. Mix in the garlic and onions cook until onions are tender and translucent, about five minutes.
3. Pour the chicken broth to the pot with the onion and bacon mix; contribute to a boil on high temperature. Add the berries, and boil until fork-tender, about 20 minutes. Reduce heat to moderate and stir in the cream and also the cooked sausage – heat throughout. Mix the lettuce to the soup before serving.

Nutrition: 554 carbs; 32.6 grams fat; 45.8 grams carbs 19.8 grams protein; 99 milligrams cholesterol 2386 ounce sodium.

285. Choc Processor Granola

Preparation time: 30 minutes
Cooking time: 30 minutes
Servings: 8

Ingredients:

- 200g jumbo oats
- 50g pecans, chopped
- 3 tablespoon olive oil
- 20g butter
- 1 tbsp. dark brown sugar
- 2 tbsp. rice malt syrup
- 60g good quality (70 percent) dark chocolate chips

Directions:

1. Preheat the oven to 160°c (140°c fan/gas 3). Line a large baking dish having a silicone sheet or baking parchment.
2. Mix the oats and pecans in a huge bowl. In a small skillet, gently warm the coconut oil, butter, brown sugar, and rice malt butter before the butter has melted and the sugar and butter have simmered. Don't let it boil. Pour the syrup on the ginger and stir thoroughly before the oats are wholly covered.
3. Distribute the granola within the skillet, dispersing straight into the corners. Leave clumps of mix with spacing as opposed to an additional disperse. Bake in the oven for about 20 minutes before only tinged gold-brown

at the edges. Pull it out from the oven and leave it cool altogether.

4. If cool, divide some larger lumps onto the plate together with your palms and mix in the chocolate chips. Consume or put the granola in an airtight jar or tub.

Nutrition: Calories: 233 kcal Protein: 6.37 g Fat: 16.17 g Carbohydrates: 25.97 g

286. Fragrant Asian Hotpot

Preparation time: 15 minutes
Cooking time: 15 minutes
Servings: 6

Ingredients:

- 1 tsp tomato purée
- 1 Star of anise, crushed (or even 1/4 tsp ground anise)
- Small amount of (10g) parsley, stalks finely chopped
- Small amount (1og) coriander, stalks finely sliced
- Juice of all 1/2 lime
- 500ml chicken stock, fresh or left using inch block
- 1/2 carrot, peeled and cut into match sticks
- 50g broccoli, cut into small florets
- 50g beansprouts
- 1oog raw tiger prawns
- 1oog firm carrot, sliced
- 50g rice noodles, cooked as per packet directions
- 50g cooked water chestnuts, drained
- 20g sushi ginger, sliced
- 1 tbsp. high miso glue

Directions:

1. Put the tomato purée, star anise, parsley stalks, coriander stalks, carrot juice, and chicken stock in a large pan and bring to a simmer for about 10 minutes.
2. Insert the prawns, tofu, noodles, and water chestnuts and simmer gently until the prawns are cooked through. Remove from heat and stir at the skillet along with miso paste.
3. Drink sprinkled with the parsley and coriander leaves.

Nutrition: Calories: 60 kcal Protein: 2.67 g Fat: 1.57 g Carbohydrates: 9.38 g

287. Tender Spiced Lamb

Preparation time: 10 minutes
Cooking time: 4 hours and 10 minutes
Servings: 8

Ingredients:

- 1.35kg (3lb) lamb shoulder
- 3 red onions, sliced
- 3 cloves of garlic, crushed
- 1 bird's eye chili, finely chopped
- 1 teaspoon turmeric
- 1 teaspoon ground cumin
- ½ teaspoon ground coriander (cilantro)
- ¼ teaspoon ground cinnamon
- 2 tablespoons olive oil

Directions:

1. In a bowl, combine the chili, garlic, and spices with a tablespoon of olive oil. Coat the lamb with the spice mixture, marinate it for an hour, or overnight. Heat the remaining oil in a pan, add the lamb and brown it for 3-4 minutes on all sides to seal it. Place the lamb in an ovenproof dish. Add in the red onions and cover the dish with foil. Transfer to the oven and roast at 170C/325F for4 hours. The lamb should be incredibly tender and falling off the bone. Serve with rice or couscous, salad or vegetables.

Nutrition: Calories: 305 kcal Protein: 34.27 g Fat: 18.22 g Carbohydrates: 1.13 g

288. Steak & Mushroom Noodles

Preparation time: 10 minutes
Cooking time: 20 minutes
Servings: 4

Ingredients:

- 100g (3½oz) shitake mushrooms, halved, if large
- 100g (3½oz) chestnut mushrooms, sliced
- 150g (5oz) udon noodles
- 75g (3oz) kale, finely chopped
- 75g (3oz) baby leaf spinach, chopped
- 2 sirloin steaks
- 2 tablespoons miso paste
- 2.5cm (1in) piece fresh ginger, chopped
- 2 tablespoons olive oil
- 1 star anise
- 1 red chili, finely sliced
- 1 red onion, finely chopped
- 1 tablespoon fresh coriander (cilantro) chopped
- 1 liter (1½ pints) warm water

Directions:

1. Pour the water into a saucepan and add in the miso, star arise and ginger. Bring it to the boil, reduce the heat and simmer. In the meantime, cook the noodles base to their instructions then drain them. Heat the oil in a saucepan, put the steak, and cook for around 2-3 minutes on each side (or 1-2 minutes, rare meat). Remove the meat and set aside. Place the mushrooms, spinach, coriander (cilantro), and kale into the miso broth and cook for 5 minutes. In the meantime, heat the remaining oil in a separate pan and fry the chili and onion for 4 minutes, until softened. Serve the noodles into bowls and pour the soup on top. Thinly cut the steaks and put them to the top.
2. Serve immediately.

Nutrition: Calories: 320 kcal Protein: 10.67 g Fat: 9.65 g Carbohydrates: 55.27 g

289. Roast Lamb & Red Wine Sauce

Preparation time: 20 minutes
Cooking time: 1 hour and 30 minutes
Servings: 6

Ingredients:

- 1.5kg (3lb 6oz) leg of lamb
- 5 cloves of garlic
- 6 sprigs of rosemary
- 3 tablespoons parsley 1 tablespoon honey
- 1 tablespoon olive oil
- ½ teaspoon of sea salt
- 300mls (½ pint) red wine

Directions:

1. Place the rosemary, garlic, parsley, and salt into a pestle and mortar or small bowl and blend the ingredients. Make small slits in the lamb and press a little of the mixture into each incision. Put the oil over the meat and cover it with foil—roast in the oven for around 1 hour 20 minutes.
2. Pour the wine into a small saucepan and stir in the honey. Warm the liquid then reduce the heat and simmer until reduced. Once the lamb is ready, pour the sauce over it, then return it to the oven to cook for another 5 minutes.

Nutrition: Calories: 373 kcal Protein: 51.81 g Fat: 16.49 g Carbohydrates: 0.95 g

290. Cannellini & Spinach Curry

Preparation time: 10 minutes
Cooking time: 45 minutes
Servings: 4

Ingredients:

- 400g (14oz) cannellini beans
- 400g (14oz) tinned tomatoes
- 150g (5oz) cauliflower florets
- 75g (3oz) spinach
- 1 red onion, chopped
- 1 carrot, chopped
- 3 cloves of garlic, chopped
- 1 teaspoon ground cumin
- 1½ teaspoons turmeric
- 1 teaspoon curry powder
- 1 bird's-eye chili, finely chopped
- 600mls (1 pint) vegetable stock (broth)
- 2 tablespoons olive oil

Directions:

1. Heat the oil in a saucepan. Add the onion, cauliflower, carrots, and garlic and cook for 5 minutes until the vegetables soften. Add the cumin, turmeric, curry powder, and chili and stir for 2 minutes. Add the tomatoes, cannellini beans, and stock (broth). Bring to the boil, reduce the heat and simmer for 25-30 minutes. Stir in the spinach for the last two minutes of cooking, until it has wilted. Serve with brown rice.

Nutrition: Calories: 160 kcal Protein: 6 g Fat: 9.39 g Carbohydrates: 16.08 g

291. Honey, Garlic And Chilli Oven-Roasted Squash

Preparation time: 15 minutes
Cooking time: 50 minutes
Servings: 4

Ingredients:

- 1 kg assorted squash and pumpkin (at least five different types), cut in medium size pieces
- 3 tbsp. (15 ml) olive oil
- Three whole garlic cloves, lightly crushed
- Four red or green chilies, slit down the middle
- 2 sprigs thyme
- 3 Tbsp (15 ml) honey
- One sprig rosemary
- Salt and pepper to taste

Directions:

1. Preheat the oven to 300°F.
2. Take a large bowl and add al the ingredients and allow to stand for 30 minutes, mixing occasionally.
3. In a roasting tray, place the Squash and cover with foil.
4. Roast covered at 300°F for 10 minutes.
5. Increase the oven temperature to 350°F, remove the foil, and roast for another 10 minutes to allow the Squash to caramel lightly.

Nutrition: Calories: 1597 kcal Protein: 76.47 g Fat: 134.29 g Carbohydrates: 50.82 g

292. Baked Potatoes With Spicy Chickpea Stew

Preparation time: 20 minutes
Cooking time: 1 and 45minutes
Servings: 4

Ingredients:

- 4-6 baking potatoes, pricked all over
- 1 ounce olive oil
- Four cloves garlic, grated or crushed
- 2cm ginger, grated
- 2 red onions, finely chopped
- ½ -2 teaspoons chili flakes (depending on how hot you like things)
- 1 ounce cumin seeds
- 2 tablespoons turmeric
- Splash of water
- 2 x 14-ounce tins chopped tomatoes
- 1 ounce unsweetened cocoa powder (or cacao)
- 2 x 14-ounce tins chickpeas (or kidney beans if you prefer) including the chickpea water DON'T DRAIN!!
- Two yellow peppers (or whatever color you prefer!), chopped into bite-size pieces
- 1 ounce parsley plus extra for garnish
- Salt and pepper to taste (optional)
- Side salad (optional)

Directions:

1. Preheat the oven to 390°F while you can prepare all the supplies you need.
2. Put your baking potatoes in the oven when the oven is hot enough, and cook them for 1 hour or until as long as they are done as you like them.
3. Add the olive oil and chopped red onion in a large wide saucepan once the potatoes are in the oven and cook gently with the lid until the onions are soft but not brown for 5 minutes.
4. Remove the lid and add the garlic, cumin, ginger, and Chilli. Cook on low temperature for more minutes, then add the turmeric and a few drops of water, cook for another minute, and be careful not to let the saucepan get too hot.
5. Add cocoa (or cacao) powder, chickpeas (including chickpea water), and yellow pepper in the tomatoes. Put to boil and cook for 45 minutes at low heat until the sauce is heavy and unctuous (but don't let it burn!). The stew should be handled at the same time as the potatoes.
6. At last, stir in the 1 ounce of parsley and some salt and pepper, if desired, and serve the stew over the baked potatoes, perhaps with a simple side salad.

Nutrition: Calories: 463 kcal Protein: 14.55 g Fat: 5.9 g Carbohydrates: 90.84 g

293. Kale And Red Onion Dhal With Buckwheat

Preparation time: 5 minutes
Cooking time: 10 minutes
Servings: 1

Ingredients:

- 0.5 ounce olive oil
- 1 small red onion, sliced
- 3 garlic cloves, grated or crushed
- 2 cm ginger, grated
- 2 teaspoons turmeric
- 2 teaspoons garam masala
- 1 Ounce red lentils
- 400ml coconut milk
- 1 Ounce water
- 1 birds eye chili, deseeded and finely chopped
- 1 Ounce kale (spinach can also be used)
- 1 Ounce buckwheat (or brown rice)

Directions:

1. In a big, deep saucepan, place the olive oil and add the sliced onion. Cook at low pressure, with the cover on until softened for 5 minutes.
2. Add the garlic, Chilli, and ginger and cook for 1 minute.
3. Add the turmeric, garam masala, sprinkle with water and cook for 1 minute.
4. Add the red lentils, coconut milk, and 200 ml of water (simply fill the coconut milk with water and tap it into the casserole).

Nutrition: Calories: 268 kcal Protein: 14.92 g Fat: 9.2 g Carbohydrates: 33.42 g

294. Chargrilled Beef With Onion Rings, Garlic Kale, And Herb Roasted Potatoes.

Preparation time: 10 minutes
Cooking time: 50 minutes
Servings: 2

Ingredients:

- 3.5-ounce potatoes, peeled and cut into 2cm dice
- 0.5 ounce extra virgin olive oil
- 0.17 ounce parsley, finely chopped
- 1.76 ounce red onion, sliced into rings
- 1.76 ounce kale, sliced
- 1 garlic clove, finely chopped
- 5-ounce 3.5cm-thick beef fillet steak or 2cm-thick sirloin steak
- 40ml red wine
- 150ml beef stock
- 0.166 ounce tomato purée
- 0.166 ounce corn flour, dissolved in 0.5 ounce water

Directions:

1. The oven heats up to 430°F.
2. Place the potatoes in a boiling water saucepan, bring it back to the boil, cook for 4–5 minutes, and then drain it. Put 0.166 ounce of oil in a roasting tin and fry half an hour in a hot oven. Turn the potatoes after every 10 minutes to ensure that they cook evenly. Remove from oven when cooked, sprinkle with the chopped parsley and mix well.
3. Fry the onion 5–7 minutes over medium heat in 1 teaspoon of oil until soft and beautifully caramelized. Keep dry. Steam the kale, then steam for 2–3 minutes. In 1⁄2 teaspoon of oil, fry the garlic gently for 1 minute, until soft but not colored. Add the kale and fry, until tender, for another 1–2 minutes. Keep dry.
4. Heat a frying pan, which is ovenproof over high heat until it smokes. Cover the meat in 1⁄2 teaspoon of the oil and fry over medium-high heat in the hot pan, depending on how you like your meat cooked. If you want your meat medium, it would be easier to sear the meat and then move the pan to a 430°F oven and finish the cooking according to the prescribed times.
5. Take off the meat in the saucepan and set aside for rest. Add the wine to the hot saucepan to produce any meat residue—bubble to halve the liquor, syrupy, and a strong flavor.
6. Transfer the stock and tomato purée to the steak pan and bring to the boiling point, then add the corn flour paste to thicken your sauce, add it a little at a time until the texture you want has been achieved. Attach some of the remaining steak juices and eat with the roasted potatoes, spinach, onion rings, and red wine sauce.
7. Thoroughly mix everything and cook over a gentle heat for 20 minutes with the lid on. When the dhal starts sticking, mix regularly, and apply a little more water.
8. Add the kale After 20 minutes, stir thoroughly and replace the lid and cook for another 5 minutes (1-2 minutes if spinach is used instead!)

Nutrition: Calories: 303 kcal Protein: 19.74 g Fat: 18.88 g Carbohydrates: 13.45 g

295. Kale, Edamame And Tofu Curry

Preparation time: 10 minutes
Cooking time: 1 hour and 10 minutes
Servings: 4

Ingredients:

- 0.5 ounce rapeseed oil
- 1 large onion, chopped
- 4 cloves garlic, peeled and grated
- 1 large thumb (7cm) fresh ginger, peeled and grated
- 1 red chili, deseeded and thinly sliced
- 0.083 ounce ground turmeric
- 1/4 tsp cayenne pepper
- 0.166 ounce paprika
- 0.083 ounce ground cumin
- 0.166 ounce salt
- 8.8 ounce dried red lentils
- 1 liter boiling water
- 1.76 ounce frozen soya edamame beans
- 1ounce firm tofu, chopped into cubes
- 2 tomatoes, roughly chopped
- Juice of 1 lime
- 1 ounce kale leaves stalk removed and torn

Directions:

1. Put the oil over low-medium heat in a heavy-bottomed oven. Add the onion and cook for at least 5 minutes before inserting the garlic, ginger, and Chilli, then simmer for another 2 minutes. Add the turmeric, cayenne, cumin, paprika, and salt. Remove and mix again, before introducing the red lentils.
2. Pour in the boiling water and cook for 10 minutes until the curry has a thick 'porridge' consistency, then reduce the heat and cook for another 20-30 minutes.
3. Remove the soya beans, Tofu, and tomatoes and continue cooking for another 5 minutes. Add the juice of lime and kale leaves, then simmer until the kale is soft.
4. Place the buckwheat in a medium saucepan around 15 minutes until the curry is ready, and add a lot of boiling water. Bring the water back to the boiling point and cook for 10 minutes (or somewhat longer if you want a softer buckwheat. Empty the buckwheat in a sieve and serve with the dhal.

Nutrition: Calories: 324 kcal Protein: 19.2 g Fat: 7.6 g Carbohydrates: 48.07 g

296. Spaghetti With Pumpkin And Spinach And Goat's Cream Cheese Sauce

Preparation time: 15minutes
Cooking time: 30 minutes
Servings: 4

Ingredients:

- 400 g whole grain spaghetti
- Salt
- 1 red onion

- 300 g Hokkaido pumpkin pulp
- 300 g spinach leaves
- 2 tbsp. olive oil
- Pepper
- 150 g goat cream cheese (45% fat in dry matter)
- 45 g pumpkin seeds (3 tbsp.)

Directions:

1. Cook the pasta bite-proof in plenty of boiling salted water according to the package instructions. Then pour off in a sieve and drain.
2. In the meantime, peel, halve and cut the onion into strips. Cut the pumpkin pulp into strips. Clean spinach leaves, wash thoroughly and cut into strips.
3. Heat 1 tablespoon of oil in a pan. Add the spinach and braise for 5 minutes over medium heat until it collapses. Heat the remaining oil in another pan. Braise the onions and pumpkin for 5 minutes over medium heat; then season with salt and pepper.
4. Add cream cheese and about 4–5 tablespoons of water to the spinach and simmer with stirring for 2 minutes, then salt and pepper.
5. Place the pumpkin noodles on a plate, drizzle the spinach sauce over them and serve sprinkled with pumpkin seeds.

Nutrition: Calories: 843 kcal Protein: 38 g Fat: 62.18 g Carbohydrates: 46.9 g

297. Salad Boat With Chickpeas And Tzatziki

Preparation time: 10 minutes
Cooking time: 20 minutes
Servings: 4

Ingredients:

- 200 g chickpeas (canned; drained)
- 1 tbsp. sesame oil
- Salt
- Cayenne pepper
- ¼ tsp. turmeric powder
- 1 clove of garlic
- ¼ cucumber
- 200 g Greek yogurt
- 1 tsp. lemon juice
- 200 g red cabbage
- 8 sheets romaine lettuce
- 2 stems parsley
- 50 g feta (45% fat in dry matter)

Directions:

1. Rinse and drain the chickpeas. Heat oil in a pan. Roast the chickpeas in the medium heat for 5-7 minutes. Season with salt, cayenne pepper, and turmeric.
2. In the meantime, peel and chop the garlic for the Zaziki. Clean and wash the cucumber, grate half, and slice the rest. Mix the garlic and sliced cucumber with the yogurt and lemon juice and season with salt.
3. Clean, wash, and trimmed the red cabbage into fine strips. Wash lettuce leaves and parsley and shake dry. Roughly chop parsley. Crumble the cheese.
4. Put the chickpeas, red cabbage, and cucumber slices in the lettuce leaves. Sprinkle the salad boat with parsley and feta and serve with tzatziki.

Nutrition: Calories 200 Protein 9 g Fat 12 g Carbs 14 g Fiber 4.4 g

298. Stuffed Peppers With Quinoa, Ricotta, And Herbs

Preparation time: 5 minutes
Cooking time: 25 minutes
Servings: 4

Ingredients:

- 150 g quinoa
- 1 clove of garlic
- 1 shallot
- 2 tbsp. olive oil
- 2 eggs
- 250 g ricotta
- Salt
- Pepper
- 1 tbsp. lemon juice
- 1 bunch mixed herbs (20 g; e.g., thyme, rosemary, oregano, sage)
- 1 map. Cayenne pepper
- 4 small red peppers (600 g)
- ¼ bund petersilie (5 g)

Directions:

1. Rinse quinoa in a sieve with water. Put in a saucepan with twice the quantity of the water, bring it to the boil, and cook on a low heat for 10-15 minutes. Then pour off, quench, and drain.
2. Peel and finely chop the garlic and shallot—heat 1 tablespoon of olive oil in a pan. Braise the garlic and shallot in it for 2 minutes over medium heat.
3. Mix the eggs and ricotta, season with salt and pepper, and lemon juice. Wash herbs, shake dry, pluck leaves, chop finely, and add cayenne pepper to the egg-ricotta mixture. Fold in the quinoa, garlic, and shallot.
4. Wash the peppers, pat dry, cut in half and remove the seeds. Spread a baking dish with the remaining oil. Put the pepper halves in and fill evenly with the ricotta mixture.
5. Bake the filled pepper halves in a preheated oven at 200 ° C (fan oven 180 ° C; gas: setting 3) for about 25 minutes.

Nutrition: Calories 394 Protein 18 g Fat 20 g Carbs 35 g Fiber 8.6 g

299. Dill Patties With A Dandelion Dip

Preparation time: 5 minutes
Cooking time: 45 minutes
Servings: 4

Ingredients:

- 150 g tender oatmeal
- 20 g dill (1 bunch)
- 1 shallot
- 1 clove of garlic
- 2½ tbsp. olive oil
- 300 g small cucumber (1 small cucumber)
- 50 g Gouda (1 piece; 45% fat in dry matter)
- 1 egg
- 20 g crushed flax seeds (2 tbsp.)
- 90 g whole grain bread crumbs
- Salt
- Pepper
- ½ lemon
- 10 g dandelion (3 sheets)
- 250 g yogurt (3.5% fat)

Directions:

1. Put the oatmeal in a bowl, pour twice the boiling water over it, mix well, and let it swell for about 10 minutes.
2. In the meantime, wash the dill, shake dry and chop finely. Peel the shallot and garlic and chop finely. Heat 1 teaspoon of oil in a small pan. Braise shallot and garlic in

it for 3 minutes over medium heat. Clean, wash, and roughly grate the cucumber. Rub Gouda.

3. Mix oatmeal with egg, linseed, herbs, cucumber, cheese, shallot, garlic, and breadcrumbs and season with salt and pepper; add breadcrumbs depending on the consistency.
4. Form the mass into 12 patties and bake one after the other. To do this, heat 1 teaspoon of oil in a pan. Add four patties and fry until golden on each side in 3-4 minutes over medium heat. Fry the remaining patties as well. Let the patties cook for 15 minutes in a preheated oven at 100 ° C (fan oven 80 ° C; gas: setting 1).
5. In the meantime, squeeze half the lemon, wash the dandelions, shake dry and chop. Process together with one tablespoon of lemon juice, yogurt, salt, and pepper into a dip. Serve the patties with the dip.

Nutrition: Calories 407 Protein 16 g Fat 19 g Carbs 43 g Fiber 7.1 g

300. Konjac Pasta With Berries

Preparation time: 10 minutes
Cooking time: 20 minutes
Servings: 4-6

Ingredients:

- 1 organic lime
- 2 shallots
- 1 clove of garlic
- 1 red chili pepper
- 200 g celery (3 stalks)
- 2 tbsp. rapeseed oil
- 100 ml vegetable broth
- 200 ml almond cuisine or soy cream
- 30 g pine nuts (2 tbsp.)
- 75 g strawberries (5 strawberries)
- 10 g parsley (0.5 bunch)
- Salt
- Pepper
- 400 g konjac noodles (spaghetti)

Directions:

1. Rinse the lime hot, pat dry, and rub a little peel finely. Cut the lime into two and squeeze out the juice.
2. Peel the shallots and garlic, then dice finely. Halve, chop, wash, and chop lengthways. Clean the celery, if necessary untangle, wash and cut into 1 cm thick slices. Roughly chop celery green.
3. Heat oil in a pot. Add the shallots, garlic, chili, celery, and celery greens and sauté for 3-4 minutes over medium heat. Deglaze with broth. Pour in the almond cuisine, bring to the boil and let simmer for 5–6 minutes.
4. On the other hand, roast pine nuts in a hot pan without fat over medium heat for 3 minutes. Clean, wash pat dry strawberries, and cut into small cubes. Wash parsley, shake dry and chop.
5. Add parsley to the sauce. Season with salt, pepper, lime peel, and juice. Rinse konjac spaghetti thoroughly and cook in boiling salted water for 2 minutes. Drain, add to the herb-lime sauce and mix well. Put on a plate, garnish with pine nuts and strawberries.

Nutrition: Calories 409 Protein 8 g Fat 36 g Carbs 9 g Fiber 11.4 g

301. Tandoori Chicken And Peas

Preparation time: 10 minutes
Cooking time: 40 minutes
Servings: 2-4

Ingredients:

- 2 tsp tandoori masala powder
- Juice of 1 lemon
- × 150g skinless chicken breast fillets, cut into large pieces 300g new potatoes
- 1 tsp ground turmeric
- 2 shallots, peeled and finely diced
- 150g fresh or frozen soya/edamame beans 2 tsp olive oil
- Salt and freshly ground black pepper

Directions:

1. Red chili, deseeded and cut into rings 1 green pepper, deseeded and chopped 2 cloves garlic, peeled and thinly sliced 30g parsley, roughly chopped
2. Put the lemon juice in a large bowl and the spices. Remove the chicken then turn over the marinade once completely coated. Cover and chill for at least one hour.
3. Heat the new potatoes, until tender, for 18–20 minutes. If the soya beans were frozen or need cooking, cook as instructed by the packet.
4. In a big skillet with oil, add the chili, shallots, and pepper. Slowly fry for five min. turn on the heat to medium, and add the marinade chicken. Do not apply the bowl marinade, but book it for earlier. Cook chicken for about 10–14 minutes, frequently stirring until cooked.
5. Add the garlic and the leftover marinade and bubble the sauce for a minute, then reduce the heat to medium. Remove the soya beans and the potatoes and temperature until warm. Switch off the heat and substitute the parsley. Season happily and work afterward.

Nutrition: Calories: 206 kcal Protein: 10.29 g Fat: 17.55 g Carbohydrates: 1.33 g

302. Tofu Curry

Preparation time: 15 minutes
Cooking time: 60 minutes
Servings: 4

Ingredients:

- 1-liter water
- 1 tablespoon grapeseed oil
- 1 red onion – chopped
- 1 bird's eye chili
- 4 garlic cloves – chopped
- 1 teaspoon paprika
- ¼ teaspoon cayenne pepper
- ½ teaspoon turmeric – ground
- 7cm piece of ginger – grated
- 1 teaspoon salt
- 250 grams red lentils – dry
- 50 grams edamame beans – frozen
- 200 grams tofu – firm, cubed
- 1 lime - juiced
- 200 grams kale
- 2 tomatoes - chopped

Directions:

1. Set the stove to low, medium heat, and put the oil in a pan. Add onions and cook for 5 minutes with occasional stirring. After the onions are cooked, add ginger, garlic, and chili. Cook for 2 more minutes then add cumin, salt, cayenne, paprika, and turmeric. Stir the ingredients to combine with the onion mixture then add the lentils. As you are preparing this base for your dish, take a large cooking pot and pour 1 liter of water. Place the water to a boil then add the boiling water to the pan to bring the ingredients to simmer for 10 minutes. Reduce the heat to low and allow the curry to cook for 20 to 30 minutes on low heat until the dish's consistency is porridge-like. Add edamame beans, tofu, and tomatoes. Cook the curry for another 5 minutes after adding the three ingredients then

add lime juice and kale. Cook until kale is softened. Serve warm and enjoy. Refrigerate leftover curry for a day.

Nutrition: Calories: 342 Sugar: 12 grams Fat: 5 grams Carbs: 15 grams Fiber: 1 gram Protein: 28 grams

303. Veggie Jambalaya

Preparation time: 5 minutes
Cooking time: 30 minutes
Servings: 4

Ingredients:

- ¼ cup dark red beans – canned
- ¼ cup red onion – chop
- ¼ cup red bell pepper – chopped
- ¼ cup yellow pepper – chopped
- ¾ cups brown rice - cooked
- 1 garlic clove – minced
- 50 grams tomato paste – canned
- 25 grams silk five-grain tempeh
- ½ cup vegetable broth
- 1 bird's eye chili pepper
- 1 tablespoon extra-virgin olive oil
- Salt to taste

Directions:

1. Heat a skillet on medium-high temperature then put the oil. Add garlic and onion and sauté for a minute or two. Reduce the heat to medium. Add sliced tempeh and peppers and cook until the veggies are softened to your preference. Add the spices and salt, broth, and tomato paste. Stir in to combine then bring the mixture to a simmer. Once the jambalaya starts to simmer, add cooked brown rice and stir to combine. Serve while hot and enjoy your lunch.

Nutrition: Calories: 509 Sugar: 14 grams Fat: 16 grams Carbs: 75 grams Fiber: 13 grams Protein: 15 grams

304. Grilled Salmon

Preparation time: 5 minutes
Cooking time: 30 minutes
Servings: 4

Ingredients:

- 200 grams salmon – fillet, preferably wild Atlantic salmon
- Sea salt – pinch
- Black pepper – ground, pinch
- 50 grams rocket salad
- ½ lemon - juiced

Directions:

1. Trim and clean the salmon fillet then sprinkle with salt and pepper on each side. Heat the grill then place the salmon on the grill. Make sure the grill is hot. Grill on both sides for 6 minutes. Juice the lemon over rocket salad and serve with salmon.

Nutrition: Calories: 241 Sugar: 0 grams Fat: 11 grams Carbs: 0.9 grams Protein: 33 grams

305. Lemon And Garlic Chili Chicken

Preparation time: 5 minutes
Cooking time: 20 minutes
Servings: 4

Ingredients:

- 200 grams of chicken breasts – skinless
- ½ lemon – juiced
- 1 teaspoon lemon zest
- 2 garlic cloves
- 1 bird's eye chili – sliced
- Salt to taste
- 5 grams parsley – roughly chopped
- 2 tablespoons extra virgin olive oil

Directions:

1. Pour olive oil into a cooking pan and heat the pan on medium-high. Once the oil is hot, place the bird's eye chili and garlic in the pan. Stir and cook for a minute or two. Once slightly browned and fragrant, add chicken breasts seasoned with salt. Cook the chicken for 5 minutes each side until soft – don't fork it while cooking to save the juices. Add lemon zest once all sides are browned then juice the lemon over the chicken. Cook for 2 more minutes, then add parsley, stir in and serve.

Nutrition: Calories: 239 Sugar: 0 grams Fat: 14 grams Carbs: 0 grams Fiber: 0 grams Protein: 28 grams

306. Rocket Caesar Salad With Flax Seed

Preparation time: 10 minutes
Cooking time: 30 minutes
Servings: 4

Ingredients:

- 150 grams grilled chicken – strips
- 1 teaspoon ground flax seeds
- ½ cup cauliflower florets – cooked, diced
- 2 teaspoons parmesan cheese
- 2 cups rocket salad – chopped
- ¼ cup Caesar salad dressing – low-calorie version

Directions:

1. If you haven't prepared grilled chicken in advance, heat your grill and bake chicken breasts on both sides for around 6 minutes each side. Spice the chicken with salt and pepper before grilling. Cut the chicken to strips and set aside. Prepare the rest of the ingredients – chop the cauliflower and cook it for 10 minutes after boiling or longer until you reach the preferred tenderness. Set the rocket salad on the bottom of a salad bowl and add all the ingredients except flaxseeds and the dressing. Mix well to combine, then add the remaining ingredients and toss to combine.

Nutrition: Calories: 256 Sugar: 13 grams Fat: 9 grams Carbs: 20 grams Protein: 21 grams

307. Baked Chicken With Herbs

Preparation time: 10 minutes
Cooking time: 15 minutes
Servings: 4

Ingredients:

- 150 grams chicken breasts – skinless
- ¼ cup chicken broth
- ¼ teaspoon rosemary
- ¼ teaspoon thyme
- 2 tablespoons white wine
- 1 teaspoon lovage
- 1 teaspoon parsley

Directions:

1. Preheat the oven to 350°F. Take a mixing bowl and combine chicken broth, white wine, and herbs. Whisk well until combined. Place the chicken breasts in a baking dish then pour the mixture over it. Place in the preheated oven and bake for 15 minutes or until the chicken is well cooked and tender.

Nutrition: Calories: 129 Sugar: 0.5 grams Fat: 2.3 grams Carbs: 1.4 grams Fiber: 0.2 grams Protein: 19 grams

308. Vegetable Chili

Preparation time: 10 minutes
Cooking time: 35 minutes
Servings: 4

Ingredients:

- ½ cup zucchini – fresh, chopped
- 50 grams Cremini mushrooms
- 2 cups tomatoes – diced
- 1 cup kidney beans – canned
- ½ cup red onion – chopped
- 1 tablespoon olive oil
- ½ cup red bell pepper – chopped
- 2 teaspoons cumin seeds – ground
- 1 teaspoon chili powder
- ½ bird's eye chili – sliced
- 1 garlic clove – minced

Directions:

1. Heat up a 1 tbsp. of oil in a saucepan over medium-high temperature. Add the onions and garlic and sauté while occasionally stirring for a minute or two. Add zucchini, peppers, and mushrooms. Sauté and stir for another 2 minutes or so, then add cumin and chili powder. After combining all the ingredients, add the beans and tomatoes. Bring the mixture to a boil. Lower the temperature to medium and simmer for the next 20 to 30 minutes. Serve and enjoy.

Nutrition: Calories: 157 Sugar: 9 grams Fat: 2 grams Carbs: 27 grams Fiber: 7 grams Protein: 7 grams

309. Blueberry Salmon

Preparation time: 5 minutes
Cooking time: 10 minutes
Servings: 1

Ingredients:

- 1 ounce (30g) salmon
- 1/8 cup (15g) blueberries, sliced and chopped
- ½ cup (50g) sliced celery leaves
- 1 sprig rosemary

Directions:

1. Bake, the salmon for 10 min.
2. Blend the blueberry and the celery and pour it over the salmon.
3. Put the sprig rosemary on top.
4. Serve.

Nutrition: Calories: 163 kcal Protein: 12.82 g Fat: 8.29 g Carbohydrates: 8.85 g

310. Salmon Kebabs

Preparation time: 5 minutes
Cooking time: 40 minutes
Servings: 6

Ingredients:

- Shallots ends trimmed, halved
- Zucchinis, cut in 2-inch cubes
- 1 cup cherry tomatoes
- 6 skinless salmon fillets, cut into 1-inch pieces
- Limes, cut into thin wedges

Directions:

1. Preheat a barbecue or chargrill on medium-high.
2. Thread fish cubes onto skewers, then zucchinis, shallots, and tomatoes.
3. Repeat to make 12 kebabs. Bake the kebabs for about 3 minutes each side for medium cooked.
4. Move to a plate, cover using a foil, and set aside for 5 min to rest.

Nutrition: Calories: 41 kcal Protein: 2.2 g Fat: 1.27 g Carbohydrates: 6.28 g

311. Cheesy Mushrooms Caps

Preparation time: 10 minutes
Cooking time: 30 minutes
Servings: 20

Ingredients:

- 20 white mushroom caps
- 1 garlic clove, minced
- 3 tablespoons parsley, chopped
- 2 yellow onions, chopped
- Black pepper to the taste
- ½ cup low-fat parmesan, grated
- ¼ cup low-fat mozzarella, grated
- A drizzle of olive oil
- 2 tablespoons non-fat yogurt

Directions:

1. Warm the pan with oil in medium heat, add garlic and onion, stir, cook for 10 minutes, and transfer it to a bowl.
2. Add black pepper, garlic, parsley, mozzarella, parmesan, and yogurt, stir well, stuff the mushroom caps with this mix, arrange them on a lined baking sheet, bake in the oven at 400 degrees F for 20 minutes and serve them as an appetizer.
3. Enjoy!

Nutrition: Calories: 120 Fat: 1 Fiber: 3 Carbohydrates: 11 Protein: 7

312. Shrimp And Pineapple Salsa

Preparation time: 10 minutes
Cooking time: 40 minutes
Servings: 4

Ingredients:

- 1-pound large shrimp, peeled and deveined
- 20 ounces canned pineapple chunks
- 1 tablespoon garlic powder
- 1 cup red bell peppers, chopped
- Black pepper to the taste

Directions:

1. Place shrimp in a baking dish, add pineapple, garlic, bell peppers, and black pepper, toss a bit, introduce it in the oven, bake at 375 degrees F for 40 minutes, and divide into small bowls and serve cold.
2. Enjoy!

Nutrition: Calories: 170 Fat: 5 Fiber: 4 Carbohydrates: 14 Protein: 12

313. Corn Spread

Preparation time: 10 minutes
Cooking time: 10 minutes
Servings: 4

Ingredients:

- 30-ounce canned corn, drained
- 2 green onions, chopped
- ½ cup coconut cream
- 1 jalapeno, chopped
- ½ teaspoon chili powder

Directions:

1. Take a pan and add corn, green onions, jalapeno, and chili powder, stir well.
2. Bring to a simmer over medium heat and cook for 10 minutes.
3. Let it chill and add coconut cream.
4. Stir well.
5. Serve and enjoy!

Nutrition: Calories: 192 Fat: 5g Carbohydrates: 11g Protein: 8g

314. Butternut Pumpkin With Buckwheat

Preparation time: 10 Minutes
Cooking time: 30 Minutes
Servings: 4
Ingredients:

- 1 tablespoon of extra virgin olive oil
- 1 red onion, finely chopped
- 1 tablespoon fresh ginger, finely chopped
- 3 cloves of garlic, finely chopped
- 2 small chilies, finely chopped
- 1 tablespoon cumin
- 1 cinnamon stick
- 2 tablespoons turmeric
- 800g chopped canned tomatoes
- 300ml vegetable broth
- 100g dates, seeded and chopped
- 1 400g tin of chickpeas, drained
- 500g butter squash, peeled, seedless
- 200g buckwheat
- 5g coriander, chopped
- 10g parsley, chopped

Directions:

1. Set the oven to 400 °.
2. Heat a frying pan with oil and sauté the onion, ginger, garlic, and tai chili. After two minutes, add cumin, cinnamon, and turmeric and cook for another two minutes while stirring.
3. Put the tomatoes, dates, stock, and chickpeas, stir well and cook over low heat for 45 to 60 minutes. Add some water as required.
4. On the other hand, mix the pumpkin pieces with olive oil and bake in the oven for about 30 minutes until soft. Cook the buckwheat base on the direction then add the remaining turmeric.
5. When everything is cooked, put the pumpkin to the other ingredients in the roaster and serve with the buckwheat. Sprinkle with coriander and parsley.

Nutrition: Calories: 164 kcal Carbs: 44 g Protein: 4 g Fiber: 14 g

315. Cucumber & Onion Salad

Preparation time: 10 minutes
Cooking time: 0 Minutes
Servings: 4
Ingredients:

- 3 large cucumbers, sliced thinly
- ½ cup red onion, sliced
- 2 tablespoons olive oil
- 1 tablespoon fresh apple cider vinegar
- Sea salt, to taste
- ¼ cup fresh parsley, chopped

Directions:

1. In a salad bowl, set all the ingredients and toss to coat well. Serve immediately.

Nutrition: Calories 81 Total Fat 5.8 g Saturated Fat 0.9g Cholesterol 0 mg Sodium 49 mg Total Carbs 7.7 g Fiber 1.2 g Sugar 3.5 g Protein 1.3 g

316. Mixed Berries Salad

Preparations time: 15 minutes
Cooking time: 0 Minutes
Servings: 4
Ingredients:

- 1 cup fresh strawberries, hulled and sliced
- ½ cup fresh blackberries
- ½ cup fresh blueberries
- ½ cup fresh raspberries
- 2 cups fresh arugula
- 2 tablespoons extra-virgin olive oil
- Salt and ground black pepper, as required

Directions:

1. In a salad bowl, set all the ingredients and toss to coat well.
2. Serve immediately.

Nutrition: Calories 105 Total Fat 7.6 g Saturated Fat 1 g Cholesterol 0 mg Sodium 48 mg Total Carbs 10.1 g Fiber 3.6 g Sugar 5.7 g Protein 1.6 g

317. Orange & Beet Salad

Preparation time: 15 minutes
Cooking time: 0 minutes
Servings: 4
Ingredients:

- 3 large oranges, peeled, seeded and sectioned
- 2 beets, trimmed, peeled and sliced
- Cups fresh rocket
- ¼ cup walnuts, chopped
- 3 tablespoons olive oil
- Pinch of salt

Directions:

1. In a salad bowl, put all ingredients and gently, toss to coat.
2. Serve immediately.

Nutrition: Calories 233 Total Fat 15.6 g Saturated Fat 1.8 g Cholesterol 0 mg Sodium 86 mg Total Carbs 23.1 g Fiber 5.3 g Sugar 17.6 g Protein 4.8 g

318. Strawberry, Apple & Arugula Salad

Preparation time: 15 Minutes
Cooking time: 0 Minutes
Servings: 4
Ingredients:

- For Salad:
- 4 cups fresh baby arugula
- 2 apples, cored and sliced
- 1 cup fresh strawberries, hulled and sliced
- ¼ cup walnuts, chopped
- 4 tablespoons olive oil
- Salt and ground black pepper, as required

Directions:

1. For the salad, set all the ingredients in a large bowl and mix well.
2. For the dressing, set all the ingredients in a bowl and beat until well combined.
3. Pour the dressing over the salad and toss it all to coat well.
4. Serve immediately.

Nutrition: Calories 243 Total Fat 19.1 g Saturated Fat 2.3 g Cholesterol 0 mg Sodium 46 mg Total Carbs 19.7 g Fiber 4.3 g Sugar 13.9 g Protein 2.9 g

319. Beef And Red Cabbage Soup

Preparation time: 5 minutes
Cooking time: 55 minutes
Servings: 4
Ingredients:

- 4 cups Beef broth

- 28 ounces Fire-roasted crushed tomatoes
- 1 pound Ground beef
- 2 stalks Celery, chopped
- 1Onion, diced
- 1 Carrot, chopped
- 1Bell pepper, diced
- 3 cloves Garlic, minced
- 1 head Red cabbage, chopped
- 1.5 teaspoons Sea salt
- 1 tablespoon Italian herb seasoning
- 2 sprigs fresh thyme
- 1 tablespoon Spicy brown mustard
- 25 teaspoon Black pepper, ground

Directions:

1. Add the ground beef to a large steel soup pot and brown it over medium-high heat until fully cooked. Once done cooking, drain off most of the excess fat, leaving only about two tablespoons in the pot. Set the ground beef aside.
2. Into the now empty soup pot, add the reserved beef fat and the carrot, celery, onion, and bell pepper. Cook until the vegetables are tender for at least 6 minutes. Put in the garlic and cook until fragrant for al least 1 more minute.
3. Return the cooked ground beef to the soup pot along with the beef broth, crushed tomatoes, seasonings, and spicy brown mustard, stirring it all together to combine. Bring the pot of beef and tomatoes to a boil and then reduce to a simmer, cooking for fifteen to twenty minutes.
4. Stir the cabbage into the soup, allowing it to cook until tender, about ten to fifteen minutes. Serve alone or over either cooked rice or buckwheat.

Nutrition: Calories: 368 kcal Protein: 37.15 g Fat: 14.96 g Carbohydrates: 23.19 g

320. Cauliflower Couscous

Preparation time: 10 minutes
Cooking time: 30 minutes
Servings: 3
Ingredients:

- 150 g of turkey
- 150 g of cauliflower
- 40 g of red onion
- 1 teaspoon of fresh ginger
- 1 clove of garlic
- 3 tablespoons of extra virgin olive oil
- 2 teaspoons of turmeric
- 2 g of parsley
- 1 tablespoon of capers
- 1/4 of fresh lemon juice

Directions:

1. Blend the raw cauliflower tops and cook them in a teaspoon of extra virgin olive oil, garlic, red onion, chili pepper, ginger, and a teaspoon of turmeric. Leave to flavor for a minute, then add 5 g of parsley over low heat.
2. Season the turkey slice with a teaspoon of extra virgin olive oil and cook it in another teaspoon of extra virgin olive oil. Once ready, season with a tablespoon of capers, 1/4 of lemon juice, 5 g of parsley, a tablespoon of water and add the cauliflower.

Nutrition: Calories: 349 kcal Protein: 13.12 g Fat: 30.51 g Carbohydrates: 5.7 g

321. Sirloin Steak On A Bed Of Rocket

Preparation time: 10 minutes
Cooking time: 40 minutes
Servings: 3
Ingredients:

- 500 g sirloin
- 100 g rocket
- 100 g tomato
- 10g olive oil

Directions:

1. Wash and dry the rocket well.
2. And then wash and cut the tomatoes into two. Place the grill on the stove and heat it well, over high heat. When the grill is very hot lay the meat, then reduce the heat which must be medium-high and cook for about 3 minutes. Then you can turn the meat with tongs and cook for another 3-4 minutes. Remove from the grill and leave a minute on the cutting board to relax so that the juices are better kept (if you have to leave it longer, you can cover it with aluminum foil). Then cut transversely to obtain several slices with a well-sharpened smooth blade knife. Place a bed of rocket, the tagliata, and a few tomatoes on a serving plate.

Nutrition: Calories: 222 kcal Protein: 36.13 g Fat: 6.91 g Carbohydrates: 1.42 g

322. Fresh Salad With Walnuts And Rocket

Preparation time: 10 minutes
Cooking time: 50 minutes
Servings: 3
Ingredients:

- 100g rockets
- 100g grana cheese
- 2 pears
- 80g walnut
- 1 teaspoon turmeric
- 1 teaspoon olive oil
- 1 teaspoon vinegar

Directions:

1. To prepare the rocket salad, pears, parmesan, and walnuts, first, wash the rocket. Then dry it using a kitchen towel or using a salad spinner and pour it into a bowl. Wash the pears as well, then cut them into wedges and peel them, also removing the central part of the core. At this point, cut the pears into very thin slices, pour them into the rocket and mix gently so as not to break the pear slices.
2. Coarsely chop the walnuts (you can do it using a knife or breaking them by hand) and add them to the salad. With a grater, then make the parmesan flakes and add them too. Stir again, then season with salt, oil, and vinegar.

Nutrition: Calories: 315 kcal Protein: 11.76 g Fat: 28.02 g Carbohydrates: 7.25 g

323. Tuna With Lemon-Herb Dressing

Preparation time: 10 Minutes
Cooking time: 60 Minutes
Servings: 3
Ingredients:

- 4 tuna steaks
- 1 tablespoon olive oil
- For the dressing:

- 25g (1oz) pitted green olives, chopped
- 2 tablespoons fresh parsley, chopped
- 1 tablespoon fresh basil, chopped
- 2 tablespoons olive oil
- Freshly squeezed juice of 1 lemon

Directions:

1. Heat a griddle pan with oil. Add the tuna steaks and cook on high heat for 2-3 minutes on each side. Reduce the cooking time if you want them rare. Place the ingredients for the dressing into a bowl and combine them well. Serve the tuna steaks with a dollop of dressing over them. Serve alongside a leafy rocket salad.

Nutrition: Calories: 163 kcal Protein: 2.38 g Fat: 16.86 g Carbohydrates: 1.61 g

324. Honey Mustard Dressing

Preparation time: 10 minutes
Cooking time: 0 minutes
Servings: 2

Ingredients:

- 4 tablespoon Olive oil
- 11/2 teaspoon Honey
- 11/2 teaspoon Mustard
- 1 teaspoon Lemon juice
- 1 pinch Salt

Directions:

1. Mix olive oil, honey, mustard, and lemon juice into an even dressing with a whisk.
2. Season with salt.

Nutrition: Calories: 306 kcal Protein: 0.58 g Fat: 27.47 g Carbohydrates: 16.96 g

325. Paleo Chocolate Wraps With Fruits

Preparation time: 25 minutes
Cooking time: 0 minutes
Servings: 2

Ingredients:

- 4 pieces Egg
- 100 ml Almond milk
- 2 tablespoons Arrowroot powder
- 4 tablespoons Chestnut flour
- 1 tablespoon Olive oil (mild)
- 2 tablespoons Maple syrup
- 2 tablespoons Cocoa powder
- 1 tablespoon Coconut oil
- 1 piece Banana
- 2 pieces Kiwi (green)
- 2 pieces Mandarins

Directions:

1. Mix all ingredients (except fruit and coconut oil) into an even dough.
2. Melt some coconut oil in a small pan and pour a quarter of the batter into it.
3. Bake it like a pancake baked on both sides.
4. Place the fruit in a wrap and serve it lukewarm.
5. A wonderfully sweet start to the day!

Nutrition: Calories: 555 kcal Protein: 20.09 g Fat: 34.24 g Carbohydrates: 45.62 g

326. Vegetarian Curry From The Crock Pot

Preparation time: 10 minutes
Cooking time: 6 hours
Servings: 2

Ingredients:

- 4 pieces Carrot
- 2 pieces Sweet potato
- 1 piece Onion
- 3 cloves Garlic
- 2 tablespoon Curry powder
- 1 teaspoon Ground caraway (ground)
- 1/4 teaspoon Chili powder
- 1/4 TL Celtic sea salt
- 1 pinch Cinnamon
- 100 ml Vegetable broth
- 400 g Tomato cubes (can)
- 250 g Sweet peas
- 2 tablespoon tapioca flour

Directions:

1. Roughly chop vegetables and potatoes and press garlic. Halve the sugar snap peas.
2. Put the carrots, sweet potatoes, and onions in the slow cooker.
3. Mix tapioca flour with curry powder, cumin, chili powder, salt, and cinnamon and sprinkle this mixture on the vegetables.
4. Pour the vegetable broth over it.
5. Close the lid of the slow cooker and let it simmer for 6 hours on a low setting.
6. Stir in the tomatoes and sugar snap peas for the last hour.
7. Cauliflower rice is a great addition to this dish.

Nutrition: Calories: 397 kcal Protein: 9.35 g Fat: 6.07 g Carbohydrates: 81.55 g

327. Fried Cauliflower Rice

Preparation time: 55 minutes
Cooking time: 10 minutes
Servings: 2

Ingredients:

- 1 piece Cauliflower
- 2 tablespoon Coconut oil
- 1 piece Red onion
- 4 cloves Garlic
- 60 ml Vegetable broth
- 1.5 cm fresh ginger
- 1 teaspoon Chili flakes
- 1/2 pieces Carrot
- 1/2 pieces Red bell pepper
- 1/2 pieces Lemon (the juice)
- 2 tablespoon pumpkin seeds
- 2 tablespoon fresh coriander

Directions:

1. Cut the cauliflower into small rice grains in a food processor.
2. Finely chop the onion, garlic, and ginger, cut the carrot into thin strips, dice the bell pepper and finely chop the herbs.
3. Melt 1 tablespoon of coconut oil in a pan and add half of the onion and garlic to the pan and fry briefly until translucent.
4. Add cauliflower rice and season with salt.
5. Pour in the broth and stir everything until it evaporates, and the cauliflower rice is tender.
6. Take the rice out of the pan and set it aside.
7. Melt the rest of the coconut oil in the pan and add the remaining onions, garlic, ginger, carrots, and peppers.
8. Fry for a few minutes until the vegetables are tender. Season them with a little salt.

9. Add the cauliflower rice again, heat the whole dish, and add the lemon juice.
10. Garnish with pumpkin seeds and coriander before serving.

Nutrition: Calories: 230 kcal Protein: 5.13 g Fat: 17.81 g Carbohydrates: 17.25 g

328. Cowboy Caviar

Preparation time: 45 minutes
Cooking time: minutes
Servings: 5

Ingredients:

- 1/3 cup lime juice
- 1 cup fresh corn kernels, about 2 ears
- 1/2 cup fresh cilantro, chopped
- 1 15.5-oz can black-eyed peas, rinsed
- 2 scallions, finely chopped
- Salt and pepper
- 1 yellow pepper, finely chopped
- 1 large jalapeño, finely chopped
- 1/2 lb. Campari or plum tomatoes, cut into 1/4-inch pieces
- 1 tbsp. olive oil
- Chips, for serving

Directions:

1. Start with taking a bowl, combine the garlic, salt, oil, lime juice, and pepper.
2. Add in the jalapeno, peas, corn, tomatoes, yellow pepper, and scallions.
3. Keep them in the refrigerator for approximately 2 hours.
4. Garnish with cilantro and avocado and serve.

Nutrition: Calories: 316 kcal Protein: 22.28 g Fat: 12.12 g Carbohydrates: 32.13 g

329. Turmeric Chicken & Kale Salad With Honey-Lime Dressing

Preparation time: 20 minutes
Cooking time: 30 minutes
Servings: 2

Ingredients:

- For your poultry
- 1 tsp ghee or one tablespoon coconut oil
- 1/2 moderate brown onion, diced
- 250 300 grams / 9 oz. Chicken mince or pops upward chicken thighs
- 1 large garlic clove, finely-manicured
- 1 tsp turmeric powder
- Decision 1teaspoon lime zest
- Juice of 1/2 lime
- 1/2 tsp salt
- For your salad
- 6 broccoli two or two cups of broccoli florets
- 2 tbsp. pumpkin seeds (pepitas)
- 3 big kale leaves, stalks removed and sliced
- Decision 1/2 avocado, chopped
- Bunch of coriander leaves, chopped
- Couple of fresh parsley leaves, chopped
- For your dressing table
- 3 tbsp. lime juice
- 1 small garlic clove, finely diced or grated
- 3 tbsp. extra virgin coconut oil (i used 1. Tsp avocado oil and 2 tbsp Evo)
- *1 tsp raw honey
- 1/2 tsp wholegrain or Dijon mustard
- 1/2 tsp sea salt and salt

Directions:

1. Heat the ghee or coconut oil at a tiny skillet pan above medium-high heat. Bring the onion and then sauté on moderate heat for 45 minutes, until golden. Insert the chicken blossom and garlic and simmer for 2-3 minutes on medium-high heat, breaking it all out.
2. Add the garlic, lime zest, lime juice, and salt and soda and cook often stirring to get a further 3-4 minutes. Place the cooked mince aside.
3. As the chicken is cooking, make a little spoonful of water. Insert the broccoli and cook 2 minutes. Rinse under warm water and then cut into 3-4 pieces each.
4. Insert the pumpkin seeds into the skillet out of the toast and chicken over moderate heat for two minutes, often stirring to avoid burning. Season with a little salt. Set-aside. Raw pumpkin seeds will also be helpful to utilize.
5. Put chopped spinach at a salad bowl and then pour over the dressing table. With the hands, massage, and toss the carrot with the dressing table. This will dampen the lettuce, a lot similar to what citrus juice will not steak or fish Carpaccio– it 'hamburgers' it marginally.
6. Finally, throw throughout the cooked chicken, broccoli, fresh herbs, pumpkin seeds, and avocado pieces.

Nutrition: Calories: 20948 kcal Protein: 1168.13 g Fat: 1409.1 g Carbohydrates: 893.51 g

330. Buckwheat Noodles With Chicken Kale & Miso Dressing

Preparation time: 15 minutes
Cooking time: 15 minutes
Servings: 2

Ingredients:

- For the noodles
- 2 3 handfuls of kale leaves (eliminated out of the stem and approximately trimming)
- 150 g / 5 oz buckwheat noodles (100 percent buckwheat, no wheat)
- 34 shiitake mushrooms, chopped
- 1 tsp coconut oil or ghee
- 1 brown onion, finely diced
- 1 moderate free-range chicken, chopped or diced
- 1 red chili, thinly chopped (seeds out based on how hot you want it)
- 2 large garlic cloves, finely-manicured
- 23 tbsp. tamari sauce (fermented soy sauce)
- For your miso dressing
- 1/2 tbsp. fresh organic miso
- 1 tbsp. tamari sauce
- 1 tbsp. peppermint oil
- 1 tbsp. lime or lemon juice
- 1 tsp sesame oil (optional)

Directions:

1. Bring a medium saucepan of water. Insert the kale and cook 1 minute, until slightly wilted. Remove and put aside but book the water and make it straight back into the boil. Insert the soba noodles and cook according to the package directions (usually about five minutes). Rinse under warm water and place aside.
2. Meanwhile, pan presses the shiitake mushrooms at just a very little ghee or coconut oil (about a tsp) for 23 minutes, until lightly browned on each side. Sprinkle with sea salt and then place aside.

3. At the exact skillet, warm olive oil ghee over medium-high heating system. Sauté onion and simmer for 2 3 minutes and add the chicken bits. Cook five minutes over moderate heat, stirring a few days; you can put in the garlic, tamari sauce, and just a tiny dab of water. Cook for a further 2-3 minutes, often stirring until chicken is cooked through.
4. Last, add the carrot and soba noodles and chuck throughout the chicken to heat up.
5. Mix the miso dressing and scatter on the noodles at the end of ingestion, this manner, you can retain dozens of enzymes that are beneficial at the miso living and busy.

Nutrition: Calories: 950 kcal Protein: 112.16 g Fat: 22.25 g Carbohydrates: 81.51 g

331. Asian King Prawn Stir-Fry Together With Buckwheat Noodles

Preparation time: 5 minutes
Cooking time: 20 minutes
Servings: 4

Ingredients:

- 150g shelled raw king prawns, deveined
- 2 tsp tamari (it is possible to utilize soy sauce if you aren't quitting gluten)
- 2tsp extra virgin coconut oil
- 75g soba (buckwheat noodles)
- Inch garlic clove, finely chopped
- Inch bird's eye chili, finely chopped
- Inch tsp finely chopped ginger
- 20g red onions, chopped
- 40g celery, trimmed and chopped
- 75g green beans, sliced
- 50g kale, approximately sliced
- 100ml poultry inventory
- 5g lovage or celery leaves

Directions:

1. Heating a skillet on high heat, cook the prawns into 1 tsp of this tamari and one tsp of the oil 2--three minutes. Transfer the prawns into your plate. Wipe out the pan with kitchen paper, even because you are going to make use of it.
2. Cook the noodles in boiling water --8 minutes as directed on the package. Drain and put aside.
3. Meanwhile, squeeze the garlic, chili and ginger, red onion, celery, lettuce, and beans at the rest of the oil over a moderate-high temperature for two-three moments. Bring the stock and bring to the boil, then simmer for one moment or 2, before the veggies have been cooked but still crunchy.
4. Insert both the prawns, noodles, and lovage/celery leaves into the pan, then return to the boil and then remove from heat and function.

Nutrition: Calories: 229 kcal Protein: 12.24 g Fat: 9.86 g Carbohydrates: 24.75 g

332. Baked Salmon Salad With Creamy Mint Dressing

Preparation time: 20 minutes
Cooking time: 25 minutes
Servings: 1

Ingredients:

- One salmon shrimp (130g)
- 40g mixed salad leaves
- 40g young spinach leaves
- 2 radishes, trimmed and thinly chopped
- 5cm slice (50g) cucumber, cut into balls
- 2 spring onions, trimmed and chopped
- 1 small number (10g) parsley, roughly sliced
- To get the dressing table:
- 1 tsp low-fat mayonnaise
- 1 tablespoon organic yogurt
- 1 tbsp. rice vinegar
- 2 leaves mint, finely chopped
- Salt and freshly ground black pepper
- 1pre heat the oven to 200°c (180°c fan/gas 6).

Directions:

1. Set the salmon fillet onto a baking dish and bake for 16--18 minutes until cooked. Remove from the oven and place aside. The salmon is every bit as beautiful cold or hot in the salad. If your poultry contains skin, then brush down the surface and eliminate the salmon from the skin, employing a fish piece after ingestion. It will slide easily once cooked.
2. In a small bowl, put and combine the mayonnaise, yogurt, rice vinegar, coriander leaves, and salt, then leave to stand for at least 5 minutes to permit the tastes to grow.
3. Four arrange the salad lettuce and leaves onto the serving plate and top with the radishes, cucumber, spring onions, and parsley. Flake the carrot on the salad and drizzle the dressing.

Nutrition: Calories: 690 kcal Protein: 19.28 g Fat: 45.96 g Carbohydrates: 54.72 g

333. Miso Marinated Baked Cod

Preparation time: 15 minutes
Cooking time: 40 minutes
Servings: 2

Ingredients:

- 20g miso
- 1tbsp mirin
- 1tbsp extra virgin olive oil
- 200g skinless cod fillet
- 20g red onion, sliced
- One clove garlic, finely chopped
- 40g celery, sliced
- 1tsp fresh ginger, finely chopped
- One bird's eye chili, finely chopped
- 60g green beans
- 30g buckwheat
- 50g kale, roughly chopped
- 1tsp ground turmeric
- 5g parsley, roughly chopped
- 1tbsp tamari or soy sauce
- 1tsp sesame seeds

Directions:

1. Heat the oven to 220 ° C/200oC, a fan/gas limit of 7.
2. Blend the miso, mirin and 1tsp oil, whisk in the cod and marinate 30 minutes. Transfer to a baking tray, then cook 10 minutes.
3. Meanwhile, heat the remaining oil over a large frying pan. For a few minutes, add the onion and stir-fry, then add the celery, garlic, chili, ginger, green beans, and kale. Keep frying until the kale is tender and cooked through, adding a little water if necessary to soften the kale.
4. Cook the buckwheat with the turmeric as directed on the box. Attach the parsley, sesame seeds, and tamari or soy sauce.
5. Serve to the stir-fry with greens and fish.

Nutrition: Calories: 236 kcal Protein: 22.98 g Fat: 9.9 g Carbohydrates: 14.45 g

334. Greek Salad Skewers

Preparation time: 15 minutes
Cooking time: 0 minutes
Servings: 2

Ingredients:

- 2 wooden skewers, soaked in water for around 30 minutes before use
- 8 large black olives
- 8 cherry tomatoes
- 1yellow pepper, cut into eight squares
- ½ red onion, chopped in half and separated into eight pieces
- 100g (about 10cm) cucumber, cut into four slices and halved
- 100g feta, cut into eight cubes
- For the dressing:
- 1 tbsp. extra virgin olive oil
- 1 tsp balsamic vinegar
- Juice of ½ lemon
- Few leaves basil, finely chopped (or ½ tsp dried mixed herbs to replace basil and oregano)
- A right amount of salt and freshly ground black pepper
- Few leaves oregano, finely chopped
- ½ clove garlic, peeled and crushed

Directions:

1. Thread each skewer in the order with salad ingredients: olive, tomato, yellow pepper, red onion, cucumber, feta, basil, and olive, yellow pepper, red ointment, cucumber, feta.
2. Put all the ingredients of the dressing in a small bowl and blend well together. Pour over the spoils.

Nutrition: Calories: 319 kcal Protein: 22.25 g Fat: 20.44 g Carbohydrates: 12.71 g

335. Sesame Chicken Salad

Preparation time: 12 minutes
Cooking time: 5 minutes
Servings: 2

Ingredients:

- 1 tbsp. Mushroom
- Sesame seeds
- 100g baby kale, roughly chopped
- One cucumber, peeled, halved lengthways, deseeded with a teaspoon and sliced
- ½ red onion, very finely sliced
- 60g pak choi, very finely shredded
- 150g cooked chicken, shredded
- Large handful (20g) parsley, chopped
- For the dressing
- 1 tbsp. extra virgin olive oil
- 1 tsp clear honey
- Juice of 1 lime
- 2 tsp soy sauce
- 1 tsp sesame oil

Directions:

1. Roast the sesame seeds for 2 minutes in a dry frying pan until slightly brown and fragrant. Transfer to cool plate.
2. Mix the olive oil, sesame oil, lime juice, honey, and soy sauce in a small bowl to form a dressing.
3. Put the cucumber, kale, pak choi, red onion, and parsley in a large bowl and combine gently. Pour over the sauce, then again blend.
4. Spread the salad with the grilled chicken between two plates, and top. Just before eating, brush over the sesame seeds.

Nutrition: Calories: 501 kcal Protein: 22.57 g Fat: 40.55 g Carbohydrates: 13.42 g

336. Thyme Mushrooms

Preparation time: 10 minutes
Cooking time: 45 minutes
Servings: 2

Ingredients:

- 1 tbsp. chopped thyme
- 2tbsps. olive oil
- 2tbsps. chopped parsley
- 4 minced garlic cloves
- Black pepper
- 2 lbs. halved white mushrooms

Directions:

1. In a baking pan, combine the mushrooms with the garlic and the other ingredients, toss, introduce in the oven and cook at 400 0F for 30 minutes.
2. Divide between plates and serve.

Nutrition: Calories: 251 Fat: 9.3 g Carbs: 13.2 g Protein: 6 g Sugars: 0.8 g Sodium: 37 mg

337. Sage Carrots

Preparation time: 10 minutes
Cooking time: 25 minutes
Servings: 2

Ingredients:

- 2 tsp. Sweet paprika
- 1 tbsp. chopped sage
- 2tbsps. olive oil
- 1 lb. peeled and roughly cubed carrots
- ¼ tsp. black pepper
- 1 chopped red onion

Directions:

1. In a baking pan, combine the carrots with the oil and the other ingredients, toss and bake at 380 0F for 30 minutes.
2. Divide between plates and serve.

Nutrition: Calories: 200 Fat: 8.7 g Carbs: 7.9 g Protein: 4 g Sugars: 19 g Sodium: 268 mg

338. Turkey Meatball Skewers

Preparation time: 5 minutes
Cooking time: 75 minutes
Servings: 4

Ingredients:

- 4 sticks of lemongrass
- 400g minced turkey
- 2 cloves of garlic, finely chopped
- 1 egg
- 1 red chili, finely chopped
- 2 tablespoons lime juice
- 2 tablespoons chopped coriander
- 1 teaspoon turmeric
- Pepper

Directions:

1. Clean lemon grass cut in half lengthwise and wash.
2. Mix the meat with the egg, chili, garlic, coriander, olive oil, lime juice, turmeric, and a little pepper. Make little balls out of them.

3. Put the balls on the lemongrass skewer and grill them as you like. Cook them in the oven or fry them in the pan until the balls are ready. A small salad goes with it.

Nutrition: Calories 280.0 Fat 35 g Cholesterol 340 mg Fiber 3 g Protein 2.6g

339. Moong Dahl

Preparation time: 10 minutes
Cooking time: 10 minutes
Servings: 4-6

Ingredients:

- 300g/10oz split mung beans (moong dahl)
- Preferably soaked for a few hours
- 600ml/1pt of water
- 2 tbsp./30g olive oil, butter or ghee
- 1 red onion, finely chopped
- 1-2 tsp coriander seeds
- 1-2 tsp cumin seeds
- 2-4 tsp fresh ginger, chopped
- 1-2 tsp turmeric
- ¼ tsp of cayenne pepper – more if you want it spicy
- Salt & black pepper to taste

Directions:

1. First, drain and rinse the split mung beans. Place it in a pan and cover using a water. Bring to the boil and skim off any foam that arises. Turn down the heat, cover, and simmer.
2. Meanwhile, heat the oil in a pan and sauté the onion until onion gets soft.
3. Dry fry the coriander and cumin seeds in a heavy-bottomed pan. Fry until they start to pop. Grind them in a pestle and mortar.
4. Put the ground spices to the onions and also add ginger, turmeric, and cayenne pepper. Cook for a few minutes.
5. Once the mung beans are almost done, add the onion and spice mix to them. Season it with salt and pepper and cook for a further 10 minutes.

Nutrition: Calories 347 Protein 25.73 Fiber 18.06

340. Chickpea Burger

Preparation time: 5 minutes
Cooking time: 10 minutes
Servings: 3

Ingredients:

- 1 cup Garbanzo Bean Flour
- 1/2 cup diced Onions
- 1/2 cup diced Green Peppers
- 1/2 cup diced Kale
- 1 diced Plum Tomato
- 2 tsp. Basil
- 2 tsp. Oregano
- 2 tsp. Onion Powder
- 2 tsp. Sea Salt
- 1 tsp. Dill
- 1/2 tsp. Ginger Powder
- 1/2 tsp. Cayenne Powder
- 1/2 cup Clean Water
- Grape Seed Oil

Directions:

1. In a bowl, blend all the vegetables and seasonings then mix them in flour.
2. Slowly add drinking water and mix properly until the mixture could be formed right into a patty. Put more flour if it is too loose.
3. In a skillet, pour oil and cook the patties on moderate heat for 3 minutes on both sides as you continue flipping until the sides are brown.
4. Serve on alkaline flatbread.
5. Serve.

Nutrition: Calories: 272 kcal Carbs: 39g; Fat: 9g Proteins: 7g

341. Alkaline Flatbread

Preparation time: 5 minutes
Cooking time: 30 minutes
Servings: 5

Ingredients:

- 2 cups Spelt Flour
- 2tbsps. Grapeseed Oil
- 3/4 cup Clean Water
- 1 tbsp. Sea Salt
- 2 tsp. Oregano
- 2 tsp. Basil
- 2 tsp. Onion Powder
- 1/4 tsp. Cayenne

Directions:

1. In a bowl, mix the flour and the seasonings until properly blended.
2. Add in the oil and 1/2 cup of the clean water into the mix. Slowly mix in the water until it forms a ball.
3. Add in flour to the workspace, knead the dough for about five minutes, and divide it into 6 equal portions.
4. Roll out each ball into 4-inch circles.
5. Place an un-greased skillet on moderate heat.
6. Cook the rolled balls as you flip them after every 3 minutes until done.
7. Enjoy.

Nutrition: Calories: 107 kcal Fat: 3.9g Carbs: 1.5g Protein: 0.001g

342. Sweet Angel Eggs

Preparation time: 10 minutes
Cooking time: 15 Minutes
Servings: 2

Ingredients:

- 4 large free-range eggs, hardboiled and peeled
- 2 tablespoons mayonnaise
- 1 tablespoon Sugar-Free Vanilla Bean Sweetener (here; optional)
- ⅛ Teaspoon ground cinnamon

Directions:

1. Halve the eggs lengthwise, spoon the yolks into a small bowl, and put the egg white halves on a plate.
2. Put the mayonnaise, sweetener (if using), and cinnamon to the yolks and mash them together.
3. Take the yolk mixture to a zipper-top plastic bag and cut off a small corner of the bag at the bottom. Pipe some of the yolk mixture into each egg white half. Serve.

Nutrition: Calories: 184 Total fat: 15g Saturated fat: 4g Protein: 12g Cholesterol: 33mg Carbohydrates: 1g Fiber: 0g Net carbs: 1g

343. Garlic And Thyme Baked Egg

Preparation time: 10 minutes
Cooking time: 5 minutes
Servings: 2

Ingredients:

- 1 garlic clove, minced
- Leaves from 1 thyme sprig
- 1½ teaspoons grated organic Parmesan cheese
- Pinch sea salt
- Freshly ground black pepper
- 1 tablespoon organic heavy (whipping) cream

- 1½ teaspoons Golden Ghee (here) or grass-fed butter
- 1 large free-range egg

Directions:

1. Set the oven to broil.
2. In a small bowl, put and mix the garlic, thyme, Parmesan cheese, salt, and a couple of pepper cranks.
3. Combine the heavy cream and ghee in an 8-ounce ramekin. Put the ramekin on a rimmed baking sheet (for easier transport) and place it under the broiler until it begins to boil, about 1 minute (keep an eye on it as it could take less time).
4. Remove the baking sheet from the oven. Then gently and quickly beat the egg into the ramekin. Quickly spoon the herb mixture on the top of the egg. Bring the baking sheet back under the broiler until the egg white is opaque, about 3 minutes more.
5. Take off the baked egg from the oven and let it rest and carryover cook for another minute. Serve immediately.

Nutrition: Calories: 182 Total fat: 17g Saturated fat: 9g Protein: 6g Cholesterol: 203mg Carbohydrates: 1g Fiber: 0g Net carbs: 1g

344. Shredded Chicken Bowl

Preparation time: 10 minutes
Cooking time: 35 minutes
Serving 3-5

Ingredients:

- 1 jar of roasted tomato salsa or corn salsa/black bean
- 2-3 cups organic spinach (for your base)
- 1/2 cup cilantro
- Lime
- Coconut aminos
- 2 organic chicken breasts
- 1 jar of salsa Verde
- 2 ripe avocados
- 1/4-1/2 cup jalapeño sauerkraut

Directions:

1. Put/place the chicken breasts in a saucepan with one full salsa Verde jar and half a roasted tomato jar of black bean/corn salsa.
2. Cover and cook for 25 minutes on medium to low heat, or until chicken is cooked through.
3. When cooked through, remove the chicken, shred it with two forks, and then put it back in the pot and then heat for another 5 minutes-10 minutes.
4. Place your spinach base and drizzle with the coconut aminos in your serving bowls.
5. Add the shredded, cooked chicken into the bowl. (Vegetarian Sub Sweet Potatoes.) 6. For each bowl, add half a cut ripe avocado.
6. Add 2 spoonful of sauerkraut per bowl.
7. On each bowl, squeeze half a lime, and sprinkle with cilantro.

Nutrition: Calories 520 (2176 kJ) Cholesterol 85 mg Sodium 1200 mg Total Carbohydrate 54 g Dietary Fiber 9 g

345. Buckwheat And Nut Loaf

Preparation time: 5 minutes
Cooking time: 10 minutes
Servings: 4

Ingredients:

- 2 tbsp. olive oil
- 225g/8oz mushrooms
- 2-3 carrots, finely diced
- 225g/8oz buckwheat
- 2-3 tbsp. fresh herbs, finely chopped eg: marjoram, oregano, thyme, parsley
- 225g/8oz nuts eg: almonds, hazelnuts, walnuts
- 2 eggs, beaten
- Salt and pepper

Directions:

1. Place the buckwheat in a pan with 350ml/1.5 cup pan of water and a pinch of salt. Take to boil. Cover and cook with the lid until all the water is absorbed about 10-15 minutes.
2. Meanwhile, sauté the olive oil into the mushrooms and carrots until tender.
3. Blitz, the food processor's nuts, until well chopped.
4. Stir in the eggs and combine the vegetables, cooked buckwheat, herbs, and chopped nuts. Using tahini instead of eggs, mix this with some water before stirring it into the buckwheat to create a thick pouring consistency.
5. Mix with pepper and salt.
6. Transfer to an oiled or lined loaf tin and bake for 30 minutes in the oven at gas mark 5/190C until set and just brown on top.

Nutrition: Calories 204.0 Total Fat 7.2 g Saturated Fat 0.9 g Cholesterol 67.7 mg Dietary Fiber 0.9 g Sugars 2.6 g Protein

346. Sweet Potato And Salmon Patties

Preparation time: 10 minutes
Cooking time: 30 minutes
Servings: 4

Ingredients:

- Rice flour or buckwheat flour
- 225g/8oz wild salmon, cooked or tinned
- 225g/8oz sweet potato cooked and mashed
- Herb salt and pepper to taste

Directions:

1. Preheat the oven up to 160C / gas mark 3.
2. Mix the sweet potato, salmon, herbal salt, and pepper. Take a small size handful of the mixture and shape it into a ball. Flatten into a shape of burger then dip into the flour on each side. Place it on a lined baking tray. Repeat until the blend is used up.
3. Bake only turning once for 20 minutes. Serve with a sizeable green salad.

Nutrition: 116 Cal 13g Carbs 2g Fat 9g Protein

347. Trout With Roasted Vegetables

Preparation time: 25 minutes
Cooking time: 20 minutes
Servings: 2

Ingredients:

- 2 turnips, peeled and cut into segments
- Olive oil
- Dried dill
- Juice of 1 lemon
- 2 carrots cut into batons
- 2 parsnips, peeled and cut into wedges
- Tamari
- 1 trout fillet per person

Directions:

1. Put the sliced vegetables into a baking tray. Sprinkle with a dash of tamari and olive oil. Set on gas mark 7 in the oven. Take the vegetables out of the oven after 25 minutes, and stir well.
2. Put the fish over it. Sprinkle with the dill and lemon juice. Cover with foil, and go back to the oven.

3. Turn down the oven to gas mark 5/190C/375F and cook till the fish is cooked through for 20 minutes.

Nutrition: Calories 154.0 Total Fat 2.2 g Saturated Fat 0.7 g Cholesterol 67.7 mg Dietary Fiber 0.9 g Sugars 2.6 g

348. Baked Salmon With Stir-Fried Vegetables

Preparation time: 20 minutes
Cooking time: 30 minutes
Servings: 2

Ingredients:

- Grated zest and juice of 1 lemon
- 1 tsp. toasted sesame oil
- 2 tsp. olive oil
- 2 carrots cut into matchsticks
- Bunch of kale, chopped
- 2 tsp. of root ginger, grated
- 2 wild salmon fillets
- 1 tin of water chestnuts, drained, rinsed & chopped

Directions:

1. Mix the lemon juice and ginger and zest. Place the salmon in a shallow, ovenproof dish and pour over the lemon-ginger mixture. Cover with foil and leave for 30-60 minutes to marinate.
2. Bake the salmon on gas mark 5/190C in the oven for 15 minutes while cooking heat up a wok, or frying pan, then add the toasted sesame oil and olive oil. Put the vegetables then cook, constantly stirring for a few minutes.
3. When the salmon is cooked, scoop some of the salmon marinade onto the vegetables and cook for a few more minutes.
4. Serve the vegetables onto a plate and top with salmon.

Nutrition: Calories 160.0 Total Fat 3.2 g Saturated Fat 0.7 g Cholesterol 67.7 mg Dietary Fiber 0.9 g Sugars 2.6 g Protein

349. Raw Carrot And Almond Loaf

Preparation time: 10 minutes
Cooking time: 20 minutes
Servings: 4

Ingredients:

- ½ cup of almonds
- Fresh parsley, finely chopped
- 6-8 carrots, grated
- Juice of ½ a lemon
- 4 tbsp. of tahini

Directions:

1. With the S blade, place the grated carrots in a food processor.
2. Whizz over the carrots with the lemon juice until well homogenized. Put them in a saucepan.
3. Then whizz up in the food processor until the almonds are ground down.
4. Adding the carrot mixture to the almonds, and mix with the chopped parsley and tahini.
5. Pack this into a tin loaf and cut it into slices for serving.

Nutrition: Calories: 360 Net carbs: 49.2g Fat: 17.4g Protein: 3.9g

350. Vegan Bolognese Sauce

Preparation time: 35 minutes
Cooking time: 4 hours and 15 minutes
Servings: 8

Ingredients:

- ½ ounce dried porcini mushrooms¾ cup dried black or small French lentils
- 2 tbsp. extra virgin olive oil, divided
- 1 pound shiitake mushrooms
- 1 onion, chopped
- 2 carrots, chopped
- 3 tbsp. Earth Balance or Vegan Butter, divided
- Freshly ground black pepper
- 1 cup unsweetened oat milk
- 2 celery stalks, chopped
- ¼ teaspoon freshly ground nutmeg
- 1 cup dry white wine
- Salt to taste
- 1.28 ounces can of Italian tomatoes, (Don't drain)
- Vegan Parmesan Cheese, optional

Directions:

1. Start with preparing the dried mushrooms by placing them in ½ cup of warm water and letting them sit for 30 minutes. Once ready, remove the mushrooms and drain the water through a fine-mesh strainer and into a separate measuring cup. Set the mushroom water aside.
2. Put lentils and 4 cups of cold water in a small saucepan and place it to a boil. Simmer for at least 20-25 minutes until the lentils are tender. Drain and set lentils aside.
3. Preheat an oven over medium heat and add 1 Tbsp. of olive oil, vegan butter, and onion. Cook for at least 3-5 minutes until the onions are translucent. Add the carrot and celery, and stir. Cook for another 3-5 minutes, stirring occasionally.
4. Now, add in mushrooms (porcini and shiitake), 1 tbsp. Olive oil, ¼ tsp. of salt, and freshly ground pepper then cook for at least 7-10 minutes, allowing the mushrooms to soften.
5. Further, put oat milk, reserved mushroom water, and ¼ tsp. of nutmeg, and place to boil over high heat. When boiling, lower the temperature to medium and simmer rapidly, occasionally stirring, until most of the milk is evaporated. It may take for at last 10-15 minutes.
6. Next, put the wine and place to another boil, turning up the heat if necessary. Cook until all the wine has evaporated.
7. Put the tomatoes, bring the liquid to a boil, and turn the heat down to low, so the sauce is just barely bubbling. Cook for about 2-3 hours until the flavors concentrate. Put also a little water or extra tomato juice along the way if needed.
8. When flavors have concentrated to your satisfaction, add cooked lentils and allow the sauce to cook another 10 minutes. Scatter the Vegan Parmesan Cheese, optional
9. Finally, serve with rigatoni or Tagliatelle pasta. Stick to a 1 cup sized portion – including pasta and sauce.

Nutrition: Calories 208 Fat 1.5 g Carbohydrate 12.4 g Protein 35.5 g

351. Spicy Mushroom Noodle

Preparation time: 5 minutes
Cooking time: 10 minutes
Servings: 1

Ingredients:

- 1/4 block extra-firm tofu, cut into bite-sized cubes
- 1/4 of a small onion, chopped thinly
- 1 tsp. sesame oil
- 1 serving of noodles
- 1/2 cup chopped mushrooms
- 1 stalk green onion, chopped (optional garnish)
- 1 tsp. toasted sesame seeds (optional garnish)
- Sauce ingredients:
- 1 tbsp. gochujang

- 1/2 tbsp. mirin (optional)
- 1 tbsp. soy sauce or tamari

Directions:

1. Firstly, heat a non-stick pan on high heat. Cook noodles according to given instructions.
2. Take a pan, put a small amount of oil, and add the tofu pieces. Let the tofu cook on each side while you preparing the vegetables or mix the sauce.
3. Mix the sauce ingredients in a small bowl.
4. Flip over the tofu and allow cooking on the other side.
5. Once the tofu is done cooking, remove from pan and add in the mushrooms and onions. Sauté until mushrooms start to brown and onions soften.
6. Once noodles are cooked, drain and put into the pan. Add the tofu back in along with the sauce and stir well. Turn off the heat then mix in sesame oil.
7. Garnish with green onion and sesame seeds and enjoy.

Nutrition: Calories 502 Fat 22 g Carbohydrate 43.5 g Protein 20.4 g

352. Scalloped Eggplant

Preparation time: 0 minute
Cooking time: 40 minutes
Servings: 2

Ingredients:

- 1 large eggplant, diced
- 1 onion, thinly sliced
- 1 bell pepper, thinly sliced
- 2 cups mushrooms, thinly sliced
- 3 tbsp. oil
- 2 cups toasted breadcrumbs
- 1 cup soymilk
- 1 tsp. salt
- 1/2 tsp. paprika
- 1/4 tsp. cayenne
- 1 cup Yeast Cheese Sauce or soy mozzarella, shredded

Directions:

1. Firstly, preheat oven to 350F. In a large skillet, sauté the eggplant, mushrooms, onion, and bell pepper in the oil until the eggplant becomes tender, about 10-15 minutes.
2. Now, add the soymilk, 1 cup of breadcrumbs and the spices, and stir well. Set in a baking dish and top with the remaining breadcrumbs and the Yeast Cheese Sauce/soy mozzarella. Bake for almost 25 minutes.

Nutrition: Calories 230 Fat 15 g Carbohydrate 15.9 g Protein 9.3 g

353. Matcha Pancakes

Preparation time: 15 minutes
Cooking time: 24 minutes
Servings: 6

Ingredients:

- 2 tablespoons flax meal
- 5 tablespoons warm water
- 1 cup spelt flour
- 1 cup buckwheat flour
- 1 tablespoon matcha powder
- 1 tablespoon baking powder
- Pinch of salt
- ¾ cup unsweetened almond milk
- 1 tablespoon olive oil
- 1/3 cup raw honey

Directions:

1. In a bowl, put the flax meal and warm water and mix well. Set aside for about 5 minutes.
2. In another bowl, place the flours, matcha powder, baking powder, and salt, and mix well.
3. In the bowl of flax meal mixture, place the almond milk, oil, and vanilla extract, and beat until well combined.
4. Now, place the flour mixture and mix until a smooth textured mixture is formed.
5. Heat a lightly greased non-stick wok over medium-high heat.
6. Add desired amount of mixture and, with a spoon, spread into an even layer.
7. Cook for about 2–3 minutes.
8. Carefully, flip the side and cook for about 1 minute.
9. Repeat with the remaining mixture.
10. Serve warm with the drizzling of honey.

Nutrition: Calories 232 Total Fat 4.6 g Saturated Fat 0.6 g Cholesterol 0 mg Sodium 56 mg Total Carbs 46.3 g Fiber 5.3 g Sugar 16.2 g Protein 6 g

354. Roasted Artichoke Hearts

Preparation time: 5 minutes
Cooking time: 40 minutes
Servings: 3

Ingredients:

- 2 cans artichoke hearts
- 4 garlic cloves, quartered
- 2 tsp extra virgin olive oil
- 1 tsp dried oregano
- Salt and pepper, to taste
- 2-3 tbsp. lemon juice, to serve

Directions:

1. Preheat oven to 375F.
2. Drain the artichoke hearts and rinse them very thoroughly.
3. Toss them in garlic, oregano, and olive oil.
4. Arrange the artichoke hearts in a baking dish and bake for about 45 minutes tossing a few times if desired.
5. Season with salt and pepper and serve with lemon juice.

Nutrition: Calories: 35 Cal Fat: 20 g Carbohydrates: 3 g Protein: 1 g Fiber: 1 g

355. Turkey Escalope With Cauliflower Couscous

Preparation time: 5 minutes
Cooking time: 50 minutes
Servings: 2

Ingredients:

- 150g cauliflower, roughly chopped
- 1 clove of garlic, finely chopped
- 40g red onions, finely chopped
- 1 Thai chili, finely chopped
- 1 teaspoon chopped fresh ginger
- 2 tablespoons of extra virgin olive oil
- 2 teaspoons turmeric
- 30g dried tomatoes, finely chopped
- 10g parsley leaves
- 150g turkey escalope
- 1 teaspoon dried sage
- Juice of a 1/4 lemon
- 1 tablespoon capers

Directions:

1. Using a food processor, mix the cauliflower until the individual pieces are slightly smaller than a grain of rice.
2. Heat the garlic, onions, chili, and ginger in a frying pan with a tablespoon of olive oil until they are slightly glazed. Add turmeric and cauliflower, mix well, and heat for about 1 minute. Then remove from heat and add half of the parsley and all the tomatoes and mix well.

Nutrition: Calories: 188 Cal Fat: 9 g Carbohydrates: 15 g Protein: 10 g Fiber: 4 g

356. Parmesan Chicken And Kale Sauté

Preparation time: 5 minutes
Cooking time: 10 minutes
Servings: 6
Ingredients:

- 1.5 pounds Chicken breasts, skinless
- 2 tablespoons extra virgin olive oil
- 1 teaspoon Sea salt
- 1Onion, diced
- .25 teaspoon Red pepper flakes
- 1 tablespoon Lemon juice
- .25 teaspoon Black pepper, ground
- 3 cloves Garlic, minced
- .5 cup Chicken broth
- .5 cup Parmesan cheese, grated
- 12 ounces kale, chopped

Directions:

1. Slice the chicken breasts into long strips, each half an inch thick.
2. Add the extra virgin olive oil to a large skillet and set the stove to medium heat. Allow the olive oil to heat until it shimmers, but do not let it smoke. Add the chicken, sea salt, and black pepper, sautéing it until the chicken is fully cooked through, about five to seven minutes. The chicken breasts are ready when they reach an internal temperature of Fahrenheit one-hundred and sixty-five degrees.
3. Transfer the cooked chicken breast to a plate and cover it with aluminum or a lid to keep it warm.
4. Add the minced garlic, diced onion, and red pepper flakes to the now-empty skillet, sautéing for about two minutes until the onions soften.
5. Add the kale and broth to the skillet and then cover with a lid. Stir occasionally, allowing the kale to cook until tender, about five minutes.
6. Add the cooked chicken breast back into the skillet along with the lemon juice and Parmesan cheese. Stir everything to combine and then remove the skillet from the heat before serving.

Nutrition: Calories: 261 Cal Fat: 15 g Carbohydrates: 12 g Protein: 247 g Fiber: 3 g

357. Mexican Bell Pepper Filled With Egg:

Preparation time: 55 minutes
Cooking time: 20 minutes
Servings: 2
Ingredients:

- 1 tablespoon Coconut oil
- 4 pieces Egg
- 1 piece Tomato
- 1 pinch Chilli flakes
- 1/4 teaspoon ground cumin
- 1/4 teaspoon Paprika powder
- 1/2 pieces Avocado
- 1 piece green peppers
- 2 tablespoon fresh coriander

Directions:

1. Cut the tomatoes and avocado into cubes and finely chop the fresh coriander.
2. Melt the coconut oil in a pan over medium heat, beat the eggs in the pan, and add the tomato cubes.
3. Keep stirring until the eggs solidify and season with chilli, caraway, paprika, pepper, and salt.
4. Finally, add the avocado.
5. Place the egg mixture in the pepper halves and garnish with fresh coriander.

Nutrition: Calories: 497 kcal Protein: 20.91 g Fat: 41.27 g Carbohydrates: 14.41 g

358. Honey Mustard Dressing

Preparation time: 10 minutes
Cooking time: 0 minutes
Servings: 2
Ingredients:

- 4 tablespoon Olive oil
- 11/2 teaspoon Honey
- 11/2 teaspoon Mustard
- 1 teaspoon Lemon juice
- 1 pinch Salt

Directions:

1. Mix olive oil, honey, mustard, and lemon juice into an even dressing with a whisk.
2. Season with salt.

Nutrition: Calories: 306 kcal Protein: 0.58 g Fat: 27.47 g Carbohydrates: 16.96 g

359. Salmon And Spinach Quiche

Preparation time: 55 minutes
Cooking time: 45 minutes
Servings: 2
Ingredients:

- 600 g frozen leaf spinach
- 1 clove of garlic
- 1 onion
- 150 g frozen salmon fillets
- 200 g smoked salmon
- 1 small bunch of dill
- 1 untreated lemon
- 50 g butter
- 200 g sour cream
- 3 eggs
- Salt, pepper, nutmeg
- 1 pack of puff pastry

Directions:

1. Let the spinach thaw and squeeze well.
2. Peel the garlic and onion and cut into fine cubes.
3. Cut the salmon fillet into cubes 1-1.5 cm thick.
4. Cut the smoked salmon into strips.
5. Wash the dill, pat dry and chop.
6. Wash the lemon with hot water, dry, rub the zest finely with a kitchen grater, and squeeze the lemon.
7. Heat the butter in a pan. Sweat the garlic and onion cubes in it for approx. 2-3 minutes.
8. Add spinach and sweat briefly.
9. Add sour cream, lemon juice, and zest, eggs, and dill and mix well.
10. Season with salt, pepper, and nutmeg.
11. Preheat the oven to 200 degrees top/bottom heat (180 degrees convection).
12. Grease a spring form pan and roll out the puff pastry in it and pull up on edge. Prick the dough with a fork (so that it doesn't rise too much).
13. Pour in the spinach and egg mixture and smooth out.
14. Spread salmon cubes and smoked salmon strips on top.

15. The quiche in the oven (grid, middle inset) about 30-40 min. Yellow gold bake.

Nutrition: Calories: 903 kcal Protein: 65.28 g Fat: 59.79 g Carbohydrates: 30.79 g

360. Nut & Chocolate Bark

Preparation time: 30 minutes
Cooking time: 3 hours
Servings: 2

Ingredients:

- 1 thin peel orange
- ¾ cup pistachio nuts, roasted, chilled and chopped into large pieces
- ¼ cup hazelnuts, toasted, chilled, peeled and chopped into large pieces
- ¼ cup pumpkin seeds, toasted and chilled
- 1 tablespoon chia seeds
- 1 tablespoon sesame seeds, toasted and cooled
- 1 teaspoon grated orange peel
- 1 cardamom pod, finely crushed and sieved
- 12 ounces (340 g) tempered, dairy-free dark chocolate (65% cocoa content)
- 2 teaspoons flaky sea salt
- Candy or candy thermometer

Directions:

1. Preheat the oven to 100-150 ° F (66 ° C). Line a baking sheet with parchment paper.
2. Finely slice the orange crosswise and place it on the prepared baking sheet. Bake for 2 to 3 hours until dry but slightly sticky. Remove it from the oven and let it cool.
3. When they cool enough to handle them, cut the orange slices into fragments; set them aside.
4. In a large bowl, mix the nuts, seeds, and grated orange peel until completely combined. Place the mixture in a single layer on a baking sheet lined with kitchen parchment. Set it aside.
5. Melt the chocolate in boiled water until it reaches 88 to 90 ° F (32 to 33 ° C) and pours it over the nut mixture to cover it completely.
6. When the chocolate is semi-cold but still sticky, sprinkle the surface with sea salt and pieces of orange.
7. Place the mixture in a cold area of your kitchen or refrigerate until the crust cools completely, and cut it into bite-sized pieces.

Nutrition: Protein: 20.7 g Calories: 523 kcal Fat: 40.76 g Carbohydrates: 26.65 g

361. Coconut Shrimp Curry

Preparation time: 15 minutes
Cooking time:
20 minutes
Servings: 4

Ingredients:

- 2Bird's eye chilies
- 1 14 oz. can Coconut milk
- 0.5 tsp, ground Coriander
- 1 oz., chopped Cilantro
- 3, crushed Garlic cloves
- 1, juiced Lime
- 1 Tbsp. Olive oil
- 3, chopped Red onion
- 1 lb. Shrimp shelled
- 14 oz. Tomatoes, chopped
- 0.5 tsp Turmeric

Note: You can replace the shrimp with seared tofu instead, mixing it in just before serving.

Directions:

1. Using a food processor, pulse half the fresh cilantro, ground coriander, lime juice, turmeric, chilies, garlic, tomatoes, and onions. Continue pulsing until you get a smooth paste for your curry. Pulse until you get a smooth curry paste.
2. Grab a pan and place it on a burner set to medium. Toss in the oil and let it get up to temp. Add the curry paste, cooking only until it is warmed through entirely.
3. Pour in the coconut milk and mix it in. Now you can finally toss in the shrimp. Cook until the shrimp turn pink.
4. At this point, wrap up by stirring in the remaining cilantro. Serve with some rice or with a side of veggies.

Nutrition: Calories: 272 kcal Protein: 28.35 g Fat: 6.13 g13% Carbohydrates: 28.47 g

362. Kale And Chorizo Salad

Preparation time: 25 minutes
Cooking time:
10 minutes
Servings: 4

Ingredients:

- 8 Cherry tomatoes
- 3 oz. Chorizo sausage, sliced
- 2 Garlic cloves
- 8 oz. Kale leaves, chopped
- 2 Tbsp. Olive oil
- Pepper
- 1 Red onion, chopped
- 2 Tbsp. Red wine vinegar
- Salt

Note: You could substitute out chorizo for crushed walnuts to make a vegan or vegetarian option.

Directions:

1. Prepare a frying pan by setting it on a burner set to medium. Give it a coating of oil. When the oil glimmering, toss in the chorizo, onion, garlic, and tomatoes.
2. It should only take approximately five minutes for everything to cook through, so keep an eye on things, so they do not burn.
3. Throw in the kale and pour in the red wine vinegar. The goal at this point is to get the kale nice and soft, so keep an eye and cut the heat once the kale goes limp.
4. Adjust the season with salt and pepper and serve.

Nutrition: Calories: 182 kcal Protein: 8.6 g Fat: 12.71 g Carbohydrates: 11.2 g

363. Sticky Chicken Water Melon Noodle Salad

Preparation time: 15 minutes
Cooking time:
25 minutes
Servings: 4

Ingredients:

- 2 pieces of skinny rice noodles
- 1/2 tbsp. sesame oil
- 2 cups Water Melon
- Head of bib lettuce
- Half of a Lot of scallions
- Half of a Lot of fresh cilantro
- 2 skinless, boneless chicken breasts
- 1/2 Tbsp. Chinese five-spice

- 1 tbsp. extra virgin olive oil
- 2Tbsp sweet skillet (I utilized a mixture of maple syrup using a dash of Tabasco)
- 1 tbsp. sesame seeds
- Couple of cashews - smashed
- Dressing - can be made daily
- 1 tbsp. low-salt soy sauce
- 1 teaspoon sesame oil
- 1 tbsp. peanut butter
- Half of a refreshing red chili
- Half of a couple of chives
- Half of a couple of cilantro
- 1 lime - juiced
- 1 small spoonful of garlic

Directions:

1. At a bowl, cook the noodles in boiling drinking water for 2 minutes.
2. On a big sheet of parchment paper, toss the chicken with pepper, salt, and five-spice.
3. Twist over the newspaper, put the chicken using a rolling pin.
4. Place into the large skillet with 1 Tbsp. of olive oil, turning 3 or 4 minutes, until well charred and cooked
5. Drain the noodles and put 1 tbsp. of sesame oil into a bowl.
6. Put the half of noodles into the skillet, frequently stirring until crispy and nice.
7. Peel the watermelon, then slice the flesh to inconsistent balls, and then increase the platter.
8. Reduce the lettuces, cut them into small wedges, and half of a whole lot of leafy greens and scatter the dish.
9. Put another 1 / 2 the cilantro pack, the soy sauce, coriander, chives, peanut butter, a dab of water, 1 teaspoon of sesame oil, and the lime juice mix till smooth.
10. Place the chicken back to heat, garnish with all the sweet skillet (or my walnut syrup mixture), and sprinkle with sesame seeds.
11. Put the dressing on the salad, then mix until well coated, add crispy noodles, and then smash cashews.
12. Blend chicken pieces and add them to the salad.

Nutrition: Calories: 147 kcal Protein: 5.28 g Fat: 8.26 g Carbohydrates: 15.72 g

364. Flank Steak With Salad

Preparation time: 15 minutes
Cooking time:
8 minutes
Servings: 4

Ingredients:

For Steak:

- 2 tablespoons extra-virgin olive oil
- 4 (6-ounce) flank steaks
- Salt and ground black pepper, as required

For Salad:

- 6 cups fresh baby arugula
- 1 cup cherry tomatoes, halved
- 1 cup cucumber, chopped
- 3 tablespoons extra-virgin olive oil
- 2 tablespoons red wine vinegar
- Salt and ground black pepper, as required

Directions:

1. In a sauté pan, heat the oil over medium-high heat and cook the steaks with salt and black pepper for about 4-5 minutes per side or desired doneness.
2. Meanwhile, for the salad: in a salad bowl, place all ingredients and toss to coat well.
3. Divide the arugula salad onto serving plates and top each with 1 steak.
4. Serve immediately.

Nutrition: Calories: 501 Fat: 32g Sat Fat: 8.4g Cholesterol: 94mg Sodium: 145mg Carbohydrates: 3.9g Fiber: 1.2g Sugar: 2.3g Protein: 48.7g

365. Glazed Flank Steak

Preparation time: 15 minutes
Cooking time: 20 minutes
Servings: 4

Ingredients:

- 2 tablespoons arrowroot flour
- Salt and ground black pepper, as required
- 1½ pounds flank steak, cut into ¼-inch thick slices
- ½ cup extra-virgin olive oil, divided
- 1 onion, sliced
- 2 garlic cloves, minced
- 1 teaspoon fresh ginger, minced
- ¼ teaspoon red pepper flakes, crushed
- 1/3 cup raw honey
- ½ cup homemade beef broth
- ½ cup low-sodium soy sauce
- 5 tablespoons cashews
- 2 tablespoons fresh parsley, chopped

Directions:

1. In a bowl, mix together arrowroot flour, salt, and black pepper.
2. Coat the beef slices in arrowroot flour mixture evenly and then shake off excess mixture.
3. Set aside for about 10-15 minutes.
4. For the sauce: in a pan, heat 1 tablespoon of oil over medium heat and sauté the onion for about 3-4 minutes.
5. Put garlic, ginger, and red pepper flakes then sauté for about 1 minute.
6. Add the honey, broth, and soy sauce and stir to combine well.
7. Increase the heat to high and cook for about 3 minutes, stirring continuously.
8. Remove the sauce from heat and set aside.
9. In a large sauté pan, heat remaining oil over medium-high heat and fry the beef slices for about 3-4 minutes.
10. With a slotted spoon, transfer the beef slices onto a paper towel-lined plate to drain.
11. Remove the oil from the sauté pan, leaving about 1 tablespoon inside.
12. Return the beef slices into sauté pan over medium heat and sear the beef slices for about 2-3 minutes.
13. Stir in honey sauce and cook for about 3-5 minutes.
14. Serve hot with the garnishing of cashews and parsley.

Nutrition: Calories: 581 Fat: 35.7g Sat Fat: 8.4g Cholesterol: 75mg Sodium: 1597mg Carbohydrates: 26.4g Fiber: 1g Sugar: 21.6g Protein: 41.9g

366. Beans & Veggie Salad

Preparation time: 15 minutes
Cooking time: 0 minutes
Servings: 4

Ingredients:

- For Dressing:
- 4 tablespoons extra-virgin olive oil
- 3 tablespoons fresh lime juice
- 1 tablespoon apple cider vinegar
- 2 tablespoons agave nectar

- Salt and ground black pepper, as required
- For Salad:
- 4 cups cooked red kidney beans, drained
- 2 cups cherry tomatoes, halved
- 1 cup onion, sliced
- ¼ cup fresh parsley, minced
- 6 cups fresh baby kale

Directions:

1. For the dressing:
2. Set all ingredients in a small bowl and beat until well combined.
3. For the salad: in a large salad bowl, add all ingredients and mix.
4. Add dressing and toss to coat well.
5. Serve immediately.

Nutrition: Calories: 445 Fat: 15.2g Sat Fat: 2.3g Cholesterol: 0mg Sodium: 751mg Carbohydrates: 64.9g Fiber: 17.7g Sugar: 15.9g Protein: 17.7g

367. Cucumber & Grapefruit Juice

Preparation time: 10 minutes
Cooking time: 0 minutes
Servings: 2

Ingredients:

- 2 cucumbers, chopped
- 3 grapefruits
- 1 cup cold water

Directions:

1. Set all ingredients in a high-powered blender and pulse until well combined.
2. Through a fine mesh strainer, strain the juice and transfer it into two glasses.
3. Serve immediately.

Nutrition: Calories: 107 Fat: 0.5g Sat Fat: 0.1g Cholesterol: 0mg Sodium: 6mg Carbohydrates: 26.4g Fiber: 3.6g Sugar: 18.4g Protein: 3.2g

368. Spiced Fish Tacos With Fresh Corn Salsa

Preparation time: 10 minutes
Cooking time: 20 minutes
Servings: 4

Ingredients:

- 1 cup corn
- 1/2 cup red onion, diced
- 1 cup jicama, peeled and chopped
- 1/2 cup red bell pepper, diced
- 1 cup fresh cilantro leaves, finely chopped
- 1 lime, zested and juiced
- 2 tablespoons sour cream
- 2 tablespoons cayenne pepper
- Salt and pepper to taste
- 8 (4 ounce) fillets tilapia
- 2 tablespoons olive oil
- 8 corn tortillas, warmed
- If you don't have any, you can replace for water chestnuts, celery, or radishes.

Direction:

1. Preheat grill for high heat.
2. For the Corn Salsa:
3. In a medium bowl, mix corn, red onion, jicama, red bell pepper, and cilantro. Stir in lime juice and zest.
4. Brush each fillet with olive oil, and sprinkle with the cayenne and season to taste.
5. Arrange fillets on the grill and cook for 3 minutes per side. For each fish taco, top two corn tortillas with fish, sour cream, and corn salsa.

Nutrition: Calories: 297 Protein: 25 g Fat: 1 g Carbohydrates: 23g

369. Bacon-Wrapped Chicken

Preparation time: 5 minutes
Cooking time: 25 minutes
Servings: 4

Ingredients:

- 2 ½ pounds chicken breasts
- 8 slices bacon
- 1 teaspoon garlic powder
- ½ teaspoon ground black pepper

Directions:

1. Preheat oven to 350 degrees Fahrenheit.
2. Season chicken breasts with garlic powder and black pepper. Wrap chicken breasts in two slices of bacon each so that they are completely covered. Stick one or two toothpicks through each breast to hold the bacon in place.
3. Line a deep baking dish with aluminum foil. Arrange chicken on the baking sheet to avoid overlap and give each piece of chicken as much space as possible.
4. Move a baking dish to the oven and cook for about 25 minutes. The bacon around the exterior of the chicken should be crisp, and the interior should have no pink remaining when cut open. If pink remains, return chicken to the oven for an additional three to four minutes.

Nutrition: Calories: 309 Total fat: 12 g Sodium: 476 mg Total carbohydrates: 1 g Fiber: 1 g Sugar: 0 g Protein: 45 g

370. Shredded Chicken

Preparation time: 5 minutes
Cooking time: 40 minutes
Servings: 4

Ingredients:

- 1 ½ pounds chicken thighs
- 1 cup bone broth or chicken broth
- 2 teaspoons garlic powder
- ½ teaspoon pink Himalayan sea salt
- ½ teaspoon ground black pepper

Directions:

1. Preheat oven to 350 degrees Fahrenheit. Add chicken thighs, garlic powder, salt, and pepper to a large pot. Combine with warmed bone broth or chicken broth, and fill the pot with water until chicken thighs are covered. Place to a boil in medium-high heat, reduce heat to low, and let simmer for about 30 minutes. The chicken must be tender enough to be easily pierced by a fork and provide little resistance. Move chicken to a cutting board or other clean flat surface. Do not discard the leftover broth, as you will use it later. Using 2 forks or a pair of meat shredder claws, pull the chicken apart into thin shreds. If using a pair of forks, use one fork to stabilize the chicken thigh and the other to shred the chicken by inserting it near the first fork and pulling away towards the edge of the thigh. If using shredder claws, simply pull both claws away from each other until all meat has been shredded. Line a baking sheet using an aluminum foil or parchment paper. Spread the shredded chicken out across the surface and drizzle about half a cup of the broth from the pot over the top. Bring the baking sheet in the oven and cook for around 10 minutes so that the chicken is slightly crispy and ready to serve.

Nutrition: Protein: 34 g Calories: 294 Total fat: 18 g Sodium: 542 mg Total carbohydrates: 1 g Fiber: 1 g Sugar: 1 g

371. Tuna And Strawberry Tartare

Preparation time: 20 Minutes
Cooking time: 0 Minute
Servings: 10

Ingredients:

- 400 g fresh tuna fillets previously slaughtered
- 3 tablespoons extra virgin olive oil
- Chives
- 1 lemon juice and zest
- 250 g strawberries
- Salt
- Pepper

Directions:

1. Cut the tuna into small cubes of the same thickness with a well-sharpened knife.
2. Place the diced tuna in a bowl, sprinkle it with 2 and a half tablespoons of oil, finely chopped chives, lemon juice, grated lemon zest, salt, and pepper, mix thoroughly and leave to marinate.
3. In the meantime, wash the strawberries, cut them into very small cubes
4. Tuna and strawberry tartare
5. Season with the rest of the oil, salt, and a pinch of pepper.
6. Assemble the tartare: place a round pasta bowl in a plate, fill it with ¼ of the strawberries.
7. Then cover with 1/4 of the tuna cubes, compact again with a spoon, and take out the pasta bowl to form the tartare.
8. Repeat this to make three more tartars and serve immediately.

Nutrition: Calories: 128 Carbohydrate: 2 g Fat: 9 g Protein: 8 g

372. Curry Chicken - Light Nuggets

Preparation time: 10 Minutes
Cooking time: 15 Minutes
Servings: 1

Ingredients:

- 500 g of chicken breast
- 250 ml of low-fat yogurt
- 2 tablespoons of extra virgin olive oil
- 2 heaped spoons of curry
- Salt
- Pepper
- 100 ml of dry white wine
- Untreated lemon juice

Directions:

1. Cut the chicken breast into cubes. Pour everything into a bowl, adding a drizzle of oil, 1 heaped spoonful of curry, the juice of half a lemon, pepper, and salt.
2. Leave the chicken to the season for at least an hour to flavor.
3. After the necessary time, heat a pan and brown the chicken nuggets.
4. After browning the chicken, blend with the dry white wine and continue cooking over low heat for about 10-15 minutes.
5. Meanwhile, prepare the accompanying sauce: mix the natural white yogurt with a spoonful of curry.
6. Once ready, remove the lid from the pan and allow any excess liquid to dry. Remove the pan from the heat and spread the curry yogurt sauce directly over the chicken nuggets. Close with the lid to heat the sauce and flavor the morsels.
7. Serve immediately.

Nutrition: Calories: 227 Carbohydrate: 20 g Fat: 11 g Protein: 12 g

373. Chicken Nuggets With Vegetables

Preparation time: 10 Minutes
Cooking time: 15 Minutes
Servings: 1

Ingredients:

- 400 g of chicken breast
- 300 g of carrots
- 300 g of courgettes
- 50 g of white type 00 flour
- 2-3 tablespoons of extra virgin olive oil
- 1 pinch of salt Pepper
- 1 splash of balsamic vinegar glaze

Directions:

1. First, clean the vegetables: peel the carrots, remove the ends from the courgettes and wash them in cold water. Grate carrots and courgettes finely to obtain a julienne of vegetables.
2. Sauté the julienne vegetables in a pan with a drizzle of oil, salt, and pepper: cook for about 10 minutes.
3. Cut the chicken breast into cubes. Salt and pepper to taste. Quickly roll the chicken nuggets into the flour.
4. The right idea for those with celiac disease can replace white flour with corn starch or rice starch: the result will still be excellent.
5. Warm a pan with a small amount of oil and brown the chicken nuggets on all sides. In the meantime, the vegetables will have softened and browned: then add the mix of vegetables to the browned chicken and cook for another 5 minutes.
6. Serve the steaming chicken nuggets, finishing with a drop of balsamic vinegar glaze.

Nutrition: Calories: 202 Carbohydrate: 17 g Fat: 9 g Protein: 11 g

374. Baked Chicken Nuggets

Preparation time: 10 Minutes
Cooking time: 15 Minutes
Servings: 12

Ingredients:

- 350 g of chicken breast
- 50 g of breadcrumbs
- 20 g of white type 00 flour
- 60 ml of milk
- 60 g (1 medium) of eggs
- 1 teaspoon mustard
- 1 teaspoon of roasting flavors
- Pepper
- Salt
- 50 g of spreadable cheese
- 2 tablespoons of extra virgin olive oil

Directions:

1. Remove the chicken breast from the nervous and fatty parts. Cut the meat into cubes and combine the pieces in a blender container, together with the spreadable cheese, salt, pepper, mustard paste, and roast flavors. Blend everything until a creamy mixture is obtained. If the dough is too dry, mix with a spoonful of milk.
2. As an alternative to spreadable cheese, you can use an egg, or the same amount of fresh ricotta or bread softened in milk.
3. Prepare a bowl with an egg, milk, salt, and pepper solution: emulsify the mixture with a whisk or fork.
4. On a plate, collect the breadcrumbs and, in a bowl, combine the white flour.

5. Take a portion of the chicken mixture (about 35 g), rolling it between your hands until you get a small meatball. Flatten the meatball to get a medallion. Do this with all the dough.
6. Roll each chicken meatball in the flour, removing the excess. Then quickly pass the medallion over the egg and breadcrumbs. Repeat this last step twice for each croquette: in this way, you will get a double breading.
7. Preheat the oven to 180 ° C (ventilated).
8. Place the nuggets in a pan lined with parchment paper. Brush the surface with two tablespoons of extra virgin olive oil and cook at 180 ° C until golden brown.
9. Serve the hot nuggets, with yogurt sauce or simple mayonnaise

Nutrition: Protein: 26 g Calories: 220 Carbohydrate: 17 g Fat: 4 g

375. Chunks Of Chicken With Yogurt

Preparation time: 10 Minutes
Cooking time: 15 Minutes
Servings: 1

Ingredients:

- 500 g of chicken breast
- 100 g of cornstarch
- 2 tablespoons of extra virgin olive oil
- 1 teaspoon mustard
- 1 sprig of rosemary
- A few sage leaves
- 1 teaspoon of garlic powder
- 1 tablespoon of pink pepper berries
- Salt
- 250 g of yogurt
- 100 ml of milk

Directions:

1. First, prepare the marinade for the chicken. In a bowl, collect the whole, unsweetened white yogurt, add a pinch of salt, pink peppercorns, garlic powder, and chopped herbs to taste (sage, rosemary). Season with a teaspoon of mustard paste.
2. Chopped the chicken breast into chunks or strips and dip it in the marinade. Leave the chicken to marinate in the yogurt sauce for at least two hours, preferably overnight.
3. At this point, remove the pieces of chicken from the tanning, drain them to eliminate the excess, and roll them in the corn starch.
4. In a stone pan, put 2 tbsp. of oil: when the oil is hot, collect the floured chicken pieces and brown them for a couple of minutes, keeping a happy flame.
5. Did you know that the browning is used to trap the meat's juices and make the morsels softer and tastier? The marinade with yogurt makes the dish creamier.
6. After browning, lower the heat, pour the remaining marinade mixed with milk, and cover the pan with the lid: cook slowly (keeping a low flame) for another 5-8 minutes or until the meat is soft and juicy.
7. Turn off the heat then serve the chicken with the yogurt still hot.

Nutrition: Calories: 40 Carbohydrate: 0 g Fat: 1 g Protein: 8 g

376. Roasted Turkey With Vegetables

Preparation time: 10 Minutes
Cooking time: 15 Minutes
Servings: 1

Ingredients:

- 1 (800 g) turkey 300 g of carrots
- Something (150 g) of celery 200 g of potatoes
- 2 cubes of meat nut or vegetable nut
- 200 ml of dry white wine 1 clove of garlic
- 1 sprig of rosemary

Directions:

1. Wash all the vegetables, peel the carrots and the potato, and then remove the hard filaments from the celery. Cut the vegetables into very small pieces. To speed up the time, the vegetables can be finely chopped with a blender! Those who wish can also add an onion or a small shallot. Heat a pot and brown the meat without adding other seasonings.
2. In this recipe, it is unnecessary to add oil: in fact, the turkey spindle's skin will be more than enough to create a delicious sauce! Once the turkey is browned, blend with the dry white wine, add the aroma (garlic and rosemary), and the homemade meat nut (as an alternative to the nut).
3. Cover with the lid, wait for boiling, and cook on a very gentle flame for 60-90 minutes. If the liquid dries too much during cooking, add more water, avoiding losing the boil. Occasionally, turn the turkey in a pot.
4. When cooked, pull the turkey from the pan and blend the sauce until a sauce is obtained. If necessary, add more water and a little salt.
5. Cut the turkey into slices and serve with the sauce.

Nutrition: Calories: 250 Carbohydrate: 37 g Fat: 2 gProtein: 20 g

377. Baked Spicy Chicken Wings

Preparation time: 20 Minutes
Cooking time: 40 Minutes
Servings: 10

Ingredients:

- 10 pieces (1.6 kg) of chicken wings
- 20 g of breadcrumbs ½ cup soy sauce
- 1 teaspoon spicy paprika or sweet paprika
- 1 teaspoon of garlic powder
- 1 teaspoon of mustard seeds
- 1 teaspoon of ginger powder
- 1 teaspoon coriander seeds 1 chili pepper
- Untreated lemon juice and zest
- 3 tablespoons of tabasco 1 cinnamon stick

Directions:

1. Divide each chicken wing into two parts, taking care to cut them at the cartilage level. Prepare the spice mix. In a mortar, crush the coriander seeds, the mustard seeds, the chili pepper, and the cinnamon. Mix everything adding garlic, paprika, and ginger powder. Squeeze the half of lemon and blend it with soy sauce and tabasco. Arrange the chicken wings on a bowl and drizzle them with the emulsion and the spice mix, adding the grated lemon zest to taste. Leave the fins to marinate for a couple of hours in the refrigerator. Arrange the chicken wings on a baking dish lined with parchment paper, not overlapping them. Complete with a sprinkle of breadcrumbs and bake in a hot oven at 200-220 ° C for about 40 minutes. Finish cooking by turning on the grill. Grated bread is an essential device for promoting the formation of crunchy crust! In this recipe, we do not suggest using oil because the fat present in the fin skin is sufficient. You can add other spices to taste or eliminate some, according to your taste. Serve the chicken wings with a yogurt sauce and fresh salad.

Nutrition: Calories: 420 Carbohydrate: 0 g Fat: 3 g Protein: 7 g

378. Light Chicken Sausages

Preparation time: 20 Minutes

Cooking time: 10 Minutes
Servings: 10
Ingredients:

- 300 g of chicken breast
- 100 g of fresh bacon 1 clove of garlic Salt
- Pepper 1 teaspoon of roast flavor mix
- 1 pinch of cinnamon 1 grated nutmeg

Directions:

1. Grind the chicken breast and the bacon very finely, going over the mixture several times in the meat grinder.
2. Put the mince in a bowl. Add a pinch of salt, pepper, a teaspoon of mixed roast flavors, a pinch of cinnamon, and grated nutmeg.
3. Crush a clove of garlic with the garlic squeezer (or reduce it to a puree with the mortar). Add the garlic paste to the meat and mix everything with your hands until the ingredients are mixed. Divide the dough thus obtained into 6 equal parts and form each obtain a sausage, working it with your hands. Wrap the sausages on a sheet of plastic wrap suitable for cooking and keep in the fridge for 2-3 days or in the freezer for 2 months. Chicken sausages can be boiled or cooked in a pan. In the first case, the sausages are cooked with cling film for 10 minutes. In the second case, the film must instead be removed before cooking: the sausages must then be browned in a pan (which must already be hot). For cooking in a pan, it is unnecessary to use oil or butter: the bacon present in the dough will be more than enough to obtain optimal browning. Serve the sausages hot, together with crispy potatoes or a mixed salad.

Nutrition: Calories: 190 Carbohydrate: 1 g Fat: 11 g Protein: 9 g

379. Tofu Wraps

Preparation time: 10 minutes
Cooking time:
35 minutes
Servings: 4
Ingredients:

- 1 block, Tofu Extra firm, pressed and drained
- 6 Tbsp. Cornstarch
- 1 cup Buckwheat, processed until coarse and the texture of breadcrumbs
- 2 Tbsp. Olive oil
- 1 tsp Oregano, dried
- Salt and pepper to taste
- 6 Whole wheat tortillas
- Any desired toppings, such as lettuce, kale, or tomato.
- .33 cups Soy milk
- .5 tsp Paprika

Directions:

1. Set oven to 425 degrees Fahrenheit.
2. Prepare a sheet pan by lining with parchment paper or lightly greased aluminum foil to prevent sticking.
3. Take pressed tofu and cut into 24 bite-sized pieces. Set aside into another bowl.
4. In a shallow bowl, combine buckwheat crumbs, oil, and seasoning. Mix thoroughly and set aside.
5. Create an assembly line with tofu, cornstarch, soy milk, and buckwheat mixture with the baking sheet at the end.
6. Dip tofu in cornstarch, soy milk, and then buckwheat mixture, setting it onto the baking sheet when coated thoroughly. All tofu should have at least 2 inches of space around them to crisp properly.
7. Bake for 25 minutes, then pull out to turn all pieces over. Cook another 10 minutes until crispy.
8. Remove from the oven and put onto a tortilla wrap with desired toppings.

Nutrition: Calories: 477 kcal Protein: 21.23 g Fat: 21.9 g Carbohydrates: 52.19 g

380. Stir Fry Chicken Satay

Preparation time: 5 minutes
Cooking time: 15 minutes
Servings: 2
Ingredients:

- 1/4 cup coconut milk (light)
- 2 tbsps. Peanut butter (crunchy)
- 2 tsp. Olive oil
- 500 grams of chicken tenderloins
- 2cloves of garlic (chopped)
- 2 tsp. Ginger (chopped)
- 400 grams pumpkin (peeled, deseeded, chopped)
- 1 bunch of broccolini (halved)
- Red chili (optional)
- Coriander sprigs (for serving)
- Steamed rice (for serving)
- Halves of lime (for serving)

Directions:

1. Put and combine peanut butter and coconut milk in a bowl. Keep it aside for later usage.
2. Take a wok and heat it over a high flame. Add oil to the wok. Add the chicken tenderloins to the oil and cook for about three minutes.
3. Transfer the chicken to a bowl and let it cool. Chop the chicken into thirds.
4. Add ginger and garlic to the wok. Stir fry the mixture for one minute or until you can smell the aroma.
5. Add pumpkin to the wok and cook week for coating. Add one-third cup of water to the wok and cook for five minutes.
6. Add broccolini to the wok and cover—Cook for three more minutes or until soft.
7. Put coconut milk mixture and chicken to the wok.
8. Toss properly for coating.
9. Simmer the mixture for two minutes for making the sauce thick.
10. Serve with rice and lime halves. Garnish with coriander and chili from the top.

Nutrition: Calories: 360 Protein: 30g Fat: 12g Carbs: 36g Fiber: 7.9g

381. One Pan Chicken

Preparation time: 5 minutes
Cooking time: 10 minutes
Servings: 4
Ingredients:

- ½ shallot (chopped)
- 1 clove of garlic (chopped)
- 2 tbsps. Olive oil (extra virgin)
- 1/2 cup basil leaves (chopped)
- 2 breasts of chicken (halved)
- 250 grams baby tomatoes (halved)
- 4 bocconcini (sliced)
- 1 tbsp. red wine vinegar
- 1 tsp. caster sugar
- Crusty bread (for serving)

Directions:

1. Take a bowl and mix garlic, shallot, basil, and one tbsp. oil. Season the mixture.

2. Heat a pan and add oil to it. Season the pieces of chicken and add to the pan—Cook for five minutes. Make sure the chicken is golden in color.
3. Preheat your oven to high.
4. Add tomato to the chicken along with half of the basil mixture.
5. Sprinkle vinegar from the top.
6. Top the chicken with bocconcini.
7. Grill for about five minutes or until the cheese gets melted.
8. Serve with basil from the top along with bread.

Nutrition: Calories: 368 Protein: 50g Fat: 17g Carbs: 16g Fiber: 3.6g

382. Healthy Chicken Korma

Preparation time: 10 minutes
Cooking time: 35 minutes
Servings: 4
Ingredients:

- 2 tsp. macadamia oil
- 500 grams of chicken breast (sliced)
- 2 onions (sliced)
- 2 tbsps. korma paste
- 1 stick of cinnamon
- 8 pods of cardamom (crushed)
- 1/2 tsp. chicken stock powder
- 2 carrots (sliced)
- 200 grams of green beans (halved)
- 1 bunch broccolini
- 1/4 cup plain yogurt
- 1 tbsp. almond meal

Directions:

1. Take a skillet and add oil to it—heat oil over a medium flame.
2. Add chicken to the oil and cook for three minutes.
3. Heat the remaining oil in another pan over a high flame. Add the onions and cook them for four minutes. Add korma paste, pods of cardamom, and cinnamon stick.
4. Cook for two minutes and stir occasionally.
5. Put 1 cup of water to the pan along with the stock powder. Add the carrots.
6. Add chicken to the pan. Boil the mixture.
7. Cover the pan and reduce the flame. Simmer for about ten minutes or until the carrots are soft.
8. Add broccoli and beans to the pan. Simmer for five more minutes or until all the veggies are soft. Remove the stick of cinnamon.
9. Remove the pan from heat and add yogurt to the korma.
10. Serve with hot roti.

Nutrition: Calories: 320 Protein: 32g Fat: 11.2g Carbs: 23g Fiber: 10g

383. Caper And Lemon Grilled Chicken With Caprese Salad

Preparation time: 15 minutes
Cooking time: 40 minutes
Servings: 4
Ingredients:

- 2 tbsps. Lemon juice
- 1 tbsp. vinegar (balsamic)
- 1 tbsp. olive oil
- 1 tsp. lemon rind
- 1 tbsp. baby capers (rinsed, chopped)
- 4 fillets of chicken breast
- 2 bunches of asparagus (trimmed)
- 300 grams of tomato medley (halved)
- Half cup basil leaves
- 70 grams arugula
- 60 grams bocconcini
- 1 tbsp. sunflower seeds (toasted)

Directions:

1. Mix vinegar, lemon juice, olive oil, capers, and lemon rind in a small bowl.
2. Pull a shallow dish then marinate the chicken pieces with half of the dressing. Marinate for twenty minutes.
3. Preheat a chargrill or barbecue grill. Spray the asparagus and chicken with oil—Cook the chicken for five minutes and the asparagus for two minutes.
4. Slice the cooked chicken and keep it aside.
5. Cut grilled asparagus in half. Mix tomato, asparagus, basil, arugula, and bocconcini in a mixing bowl. Add the remaining dressing and toss.
6. Serve in plates and top with cooked chicken.
7. Sprinkle sunflower seeds from the top.

Nutrition: Calories: 250 Protein: 26g Fat: 12g Carbs: 3.1g Fiber: 6g

384. Stir-Fry Hoisin Chicken

Preparation time: 10 minutes
Cooking time: 35 minutes
Servings: 4
Ingredients:

- 400 grams chicken breast (sliced)
- Half cup hoisin sauce
- 80 ml of peanut oil
- 2 cloves of garlic (sliced)
- 3 cm ginger (julienne)
- 1 red onion (cut in wedges)
- 1 bunch pay choy (chopped)
- 1 red capsicum (sliced)
- 1yellow capsicum (sliced)
- 2 spring onions (sliced)

Directions:

1. Take a bowl and combine chicken with two tbsps. of hoisin sauce. Season the chicken with pepper and salt. Marinate for 20 minutes.
2. Heat two tbsps. of olive oil in a wok and add chicken to it. Stir-fry, the chicken for five minutes or until browned. Transfer chicken to a bowl.
3. Add two tbsps. oil to the wok. Add ginger, garlic, beans, red onion, pak choy, and capsicums to the wok. Fry for two minutes. Put the chicken to the wok along with the remaining hoisin sauce. Add two tbsps. of water.
4. Stir-fry the chicken mix for three minutes.
5. Serve with rice.

Nutrition: Calories: 308 Protein: 26g Fat: 20g Carbs: 12g Fiber: 9g

385. Beef Red Onion Potatoes Burgers

Preparation time: 15 minutes
Cooking time:
30 minutes
Servings: 1
Ingredients:

- (Optional) 1 gherkin
- 10 grams of rocket
- 30 grams of tomato, sliced
- 150 grams of red onion, sliced into rings
- 10 grams of sliced or grated Cheddar cheese
- 1 unpeeled garlic clove
- 1 tsp of dried rosemary

- 1 tsp of olive oil
- 150 grams of sweet potatoes, peel and cut into 1cm- thick chips
- 1 tsp of olive oil
- 1 tsp of finely chopped parsley
- 15 grams of finely chopped red onion
- 125 grams of lean minced beef (5% fat)

Directions:

1. Preheat the oven to 450 f.
2. Toss sweet potato chips with the oil, garlic clove, and rosemary. Add to the baking pan and roast in the oven until nice and crispy, about 30 minutes.
3. Mix the minced beef with parsley and onion. Mold using your hands into an even patty or use a pastry cutter and mold, if you have one.
4. In a hot frying pan, warm the oil at medium heat temperature; add onion rings towards one side of the frying pan and the burger over the other. Cook onion rings to your liking and burger for about 6 minutes per side until burger is cooked through.
5. Top the burger with the red onion and cheese and transfer it to the preheated oven until cheese is melted. Take it out in the oven and top with the tomato, gherkin, and rocket. Serve along with the fries.

Nutrition: Calories: 406 Net carbs: 35g Fat: 17g Fiber: 5.5 g Protein: 32.17 g

386. Braised Carrots Puy Lentils

Preparation time: 40 minutes
Cooking time: 60 minutes
Servings: 1

Ingredients:

- 20 grams of rocket
- 1 tbsps. of parsley, chopped
- 50 grams of kale, roughly chopped
- 220 ml of vegetable stock
- 75 grams of puy lentils
- 1 tsp of thyme (dry or fresh)
- 1 tsp of paprika
- 40 grams of carrots, peeled and thinly sliced
- 40 grams of thinly sliced Celery
- 1 finely chopped garlic clove
- 40 grams of thinly sliced red onion
- 2 tsp of extra virgin olive oil
- 8 cherry tomatoes, halved

Directions:

1. Heat the oven to 120 C
2. Roast the tomatoes in the oven in a small baking pan for 35–45 minutes.
3. Heat 1 teaspoon of the olive oil at low–medium heat temperature in a saucepan. Add the onion, celery, garlic, and carrot slices and cook for 1 to 2 minutes until tender. Add the thyme and paprika and cook for an extra 1 minute.
4. Add lentils and vegetable stock into the pan, and bring to the boil. Lower the heat temperature and simmer with the lid on for 20 minutes. Add more of water if necessary and make sure you stir 5-7 minutes intervals.
5. Add in kale and keep cooking for another 10 minutes. Stir in the roasted tomatoes and parsley. Serve along the rocket and drizzle top with the remaining olive oil.

Nutrition: Calories: 283 Net carbs: 45g Fat: 17g Fiber: 9.6g Protein: 5.71 g

387. Sweet Potato Hummus With Bean Falafel And Couscous

Preparation time: 30 minutes
Cooking time:
30 minutes
Servings: 4

Ingredients:

- For the hummus
- 1 tbsp. of olive oil
- 1 crushed garlic clove
- Juice of 1 lemon
- 3 tbsp. of tahini
- 350 grams of sweet potato
- For The falafel
- 3 tbsp. of olive oil, plus additional for greasing
- Small handful of coriander, roughly chopped
- Small handful of parsley, roughly chopped
- 125 grams of self-rising flour
- 1 medium egg
- 2 tsp of ground cumin
- 3 crushed garlic cloves
- 1 roughly chopped red onion
- 1/2 green chilli, remove seeds and chopped finely
- 400 grams of tin mixed beans, drained and rinsed
- For the herby couscous
- 150 ml hot of vegetable stock
- 150 grams of couscous

Directions:

1. Heat-up the oven to 395 f. Line your baking tray with parchment paper.
2. Scrub the potatoes under a running tap and cut into small pieces. Mix ½ tsp olive oil and sweet potato with a generous seasoning in a large roasting tin. Cook until softened about 20 minutes. Set aside until ready to use. (Do not turn off the oven).
3. To Make the Falafel :
4. Meanwhile, blend the entire falafel ingredients with a generous seasoning (except oil) in a blender until partially smooth. To make it firm, chill it into the fridge for at least 30 minutes.
5. Warm 3 tablespoons of the oil at medium-high heat temperature in a large skillet. Use two grease spoons to drop the falafel mixture, about the size of a walnut into the hot oil. You can do it in batches. Cook for at least 8 minutes, constantly stirring until golden brown.
6. Place falafel balls into the prepared baking tray and cook in the oven for 15 minutes.
7. While falafel balls are cooking, place the couscous and hot vegetable stock in a large heatproof dish. Cover with cling wrap and let sit about 5 minutes. Fluff up the couscous using a fork, put the cherries/sultanas, herbs, lemon juice with the seasoning and mix well.
8. Combine the cooked potatoes, remaining half tablespoon of oil, lemon juice, tahini, garlic, and water into the blender until smooth. Taste and adjust seasoning if needed. Serve in 4 bowls and add the falafel over the top along with the hummus.

388. Baked Mackerel Fillets With Potatoes

Preparation time: 5 minutes
Cooking time: 25 minutes
Servings: 4

Ingredients:

- 1/4 pint of vegetable stock
- 1 tbsp of olive oil
- 7-ounces of cherry tomatoes
- 2-ounces of pitted black olives
- 11-ounces of mackerel fillets
- 1 lemon
- 2 sweet potatoes, chopped
- 2 leeks, chopped

Directions:

1. Heat-up the oven to 375 F. Place the leeks and sweet potatoes in a roasting pan. Add the stock and drizzle with 1 tablespoon of olive oil.
2. Place pan in the oven and roast for 15-20 minutes until potatoes are soft. Add the cherry tomatoes, mackerel fillets, and black olives. Top with lemon juice and roast for an extra 10 minutes.

Nutrition: Calories 230; Net carbs: 21g; Fat: 7.4g; Fiber: 4g; Protein: 18.22 g

389. Levi Roots

Preparation time: 5 minutes
Cooking time:
20 minutes
Servings: 4

Ingredients:

- 250 g firm tofu, diced cm died in 2 cm (3/4)
- 1onion, roughly
- Chopped 1 clove, finely chopped
- ¼ hot red chili, deseeded and finely
- 2 lemon juice
- 2 tablespoons. Soy sauce
- 1 large spoon. Of sunflower seed oil
- 200 gems pack digging broccoli 2 cm diagonal slices
- 100 g cashew
- Salt and pepper taste
- Garnish for fresh green coriander

Directions:

1. Onion, garlic, ginger, chili, juice, and soy mix during a medium Size, non-reactive container. Add tofu and gently stir and hide with pickle; do not be too loud or break it.
2. Take the tofu out of the marinade. Turn off the liquid and reserve. Oil head during a pan over high heat. Add onion, garlic, chili, and ginger the pan and fry for a few minutes. Add the broccoli and cook for a few more minutes. Basketballs shoot the nuts and fry until they patched with sawdust. Now add tofu and shake it gently. Pour within the liquid from the marinade with 200 ml of water. Reduce heat, cover, and cook for 2 minutes or until everything hot.

Nutrition: Calories: 376 kcal Protein: 27.19 g Fat: 23.83 g Carbohydrates: 17.54 g

390. Banana, Walnuts And Lemon Barley

Preparation time: 5 minutes
Cooking time:
10 minutes
Servings: 4

Ingredients:

- 1 onion, finely chopped
- 2 cloves of garlic, chopped
- 2 tbsp vegetable oil
- 300 grams barley, rinsed
- 1.5 liters chicken broth
- 50 grams Carmi cheese
- 70 grams walnuts, Broken
- 50g butter
- 4 handfuls chopped fresh bananas, green or purple
- Half a lemon juice
- Salt
- Pepper

Directions:

1. Fry your onions and garlic in vegetable oil. Stir through your rinsed barley and cook for 2 minutes. Toast your walnuts until they turn brown.
2. Add chicken broth one-full at a time, expecting to include each before adding later. Once the barley thickened and cooked through adding the stock and takes the risk away from the heat.
3. Stir cheese, butter, and walnuts through your cooked risotto, pop the lid and keep aside take a seat for 3-4 minutes.
4. Finally, stir through the banana, drizzle with fresh juice before tasting, and serving.

Nutrition: Calories: 621 kcal Protein: 14.88 g Fat: 33.51 g Carbohydrates: 70.42 g

DINNER

391. Veal Cabbage Rolls – Smarter With Capers, Garlic And Caraway Seeds

Preparation time: 15 minutes
Cooking time: 50 minutes
Servings: 4
Ingredients:

- 1 kg white cabbage (1 white cabbage)
- Salt
- 2 onions
- 1 clove of garlic
- 3 tbsp. oil
- 700 g veal mince (request from the butcher)
- 40 g escapades (glass; depleted weight)
- 2 eggs
- Pepper
- 1 tsp favorer
- 1 tbsps. paprika powder (sweet)
- 400 ml veal stock
- 125 ml soy cream

Directions:

1. Wash the cabbage and evacuate the outer leaves. Cut out the tail during a wedge. Spot an enormous pot of salted water and warmth it to the purpose of boiling.
2. Within the interim, expel 16 leaves from the cabbage during a steady progression, increase the bubbling water and cook for 3-4 minutes
3. Lift out, flush under running virus water and channel. Spot on a kitchen towel, spread with a subsequent towel and pat dry
4. Cut out the hard, center leaf ribs.
5. Peel and finely cleave onions and garlic. Warmth 1 tablespoon of oil. Braise the onions and garlic until translucent.
6. Let cool during a bowl. Include minced meat, tricks, eggs, salt, and pepper and blend everything into a meat player.
7. Put 2 cabbage leaves together and put 1 serving of mince on each leaf. Move up firmly and fasten it with kitchen string.
8. Heat the remainder of the oil during a pan, and earthy colored the 8 cabbage abounds in it from all sides.
9. Add the caraway and paprika powder. Empty veal stock into the pot and warmth to the purpose of boiling. Cover and braise the cabbage turns over medium warmth for 35–40 minutes, turn within the middle. Mix the soy cream into the sauce and let it bubble for a further 5 minutes. Season with salt and pepper. Put the cabbage roulades on a plate and present with earthy colored rice or pureed potatoes.

Nutrition: Calories: 661 kcal Protein: 45.52 g Fat: 40.85 g Carbohydrates: 32.34 g

392. Prawns During A Sweet And Spicy Glaze With China-Cole-Slav

Preparation time: 10 minutes
Cooking time: 10 minutes
Servings: 4
Ingredients:

- 250 g Chinese cabbage (0.25 Chinese cabbage)
- Salt
- 50 g little carrots (1 little carrot)
- 1 little purple onion
- ½ lime
- 75 ml coconut milk (9% fat)
- 2 tsp granulated sugar
- 1 tsp wine vinegar
- Pepper
- 2 stems coriander
- 3 tbsps. pure sweetener
- 1 dried stew pepper
- 2 tbsp. Thai fish sauce
- 1 clove of garlic
- 3 spring onions
- 400 g shrimps (with shell, 8 shrimps)
- 2 tbsp. oil

Directions:

1. Clean the cabbage and evacuate the tail. Cut the cabbage into fine strips over the rib. Sprinkle with somewhat salt, blend vivaciously and let steep for a half-hour.
2. Within the interim, strip the carrot, dig fine strips. Strip the purple onion and dig strips. Crush the lime.
3. Mix coconut milk with granulated sugar, vinegar, 1 tbsp juice, and a touch pepper. Channel the cabbage and blend it in with the carrot and onion strips with the coconut milk.
4. Wash the coriander leaves, shake dry, pluck the leaves, cleave and blend within the plate of mixed greens. Let it steep for a further half-hour.
5. Boil the natural sweetener, stew pepper, fish sauce, and three tablespoons of water during a little pot and cook while mixing until the sugar has weakened. Allow chill to off.
6. Peel and smash garlic. Wash and clean the spring onions then chop it into pieces around 2 cm long.
7. Break the shrimp out of the shells, however, leave the rear ends on the shrimp.
8. Cut open the rear, evacuate the dark digestion tracts. Wash shrimp and pat dry.
9. Heat oil within the wok and to the purpose of smoke. Include the shrimp and garlic and fry quickly. Season with pepper.
10. Add 3-4 tablespoons of the bean stew fish sauce and cook while mixing until the sauce adheres to the shrimp; that takes around 2 minutes.
11. Add the onion pieces and fry for a further 45 seconds. Season the coleslaw another time. Put the shrimp on a plate and present it with the serving of mixed greens.

Nutrition: Calories: 298 kcal Protein: 19.67 g Fat: 10.13 g Carbohydrates: 33.18 g

393. Buckwheat Noodles With Chicken Kale And Miso Dressing

Preparation time: 5minutes
Cooking time: 30 minutes
Servings: 2
Ingredients:

- For the Noodles
- 150 g buckwheat noodles
- 2-3 handfuls of kale leaves
- 3-4 shiitake mushrooms, sliced

- 1 brown onion, finely diced
- 1 teaspoon coconut oil or ghee
- 1 medium chicken breast, sliced or diced
- 2 large garlic cloves, finely diced
- 1 long red chili, thinly sliced
- 2-3 tablespoons Tamari sauce (gluten-free soy sauce)
- For the Miso Dressing
- 1½ tablespoon fresh organic miso
- 1 tablespoon Tamari sauce
- 1 tablespoon extra-virgin olive oil
- 1 tablespoon lemon or lime juice
- 1 teaspoon sesame oil (optional)

Directions:

1. Bring a medium saucepan of boiling water. Put the kale and cook until it turns slightly wilted, for 1 minute. Remove and set aside, but bring the water back to the boil. Add the soba noodles and cook (usually about 5 minutes) according to packaging instructions. Set aside and rinse under cold water.
2. Meanwhile, in a little ghee or coconut oil (about a teaspoon), pan fry the shiitake mushrooms for 2-3 minutes, until lightly browned on either side. Sprinkle with salt from the sea, and set aside.
3. Heat more coconut oil or ghee in the same frying pan over medium to high heat. Stir in onion and chili for 2-3 minutes, then add pieces of chicken. Cook over medium heat for 5 minutes, stirring a few times, then add the garlic, tamari sauce, and splash of water. Cook for another 2-3 minutes, often stirring until chicken is cooked through.
4. Finally, add the kale and noodles and warm up by tossing through the chicken.
5. Right at the end of the cooking, mix the miso dressing and drizzle over the noodles, so you'll keep all those beneficial probiotics alive and active.

Nutrition: Calories: 506 kcal Protein: 39.29 g Fat: 25.37 g Carbohydrates: 31.74 g

394. Asian King Prawn Stir-Fry With Buckwheat Noodles

Preparation time: 10 minutes
Cooking time: 30 minutes
Servings: 1

Ingredients:

- 150g shelled raw king prawns, deveined
- 75g soba (buckwheat noodles)
- 2 tsp. extra virgin olive oil
- 2 tsp. tamari (you can also use soy sauce for alt)
- 1 garlic clove, finely chopped
- 1 bird's eye chili, finely chopped
- 1 tsp. finely chopped fresh ginger
- 20g red onions, sliced
- 40g celery, trimmed and sliced
- 75g green beans, chopped
- 50g kale, roughly chopped
- 100ml chicken stock
- 5g lavage or celery leaves

Directions:

1. Heat a pan over high heat, then cook the prawns for 2–3 minutes in 1 teaspoon tamari and one teaspoon oil. Put the prawns onto a plate. Wipe the pan out with paper from the kitchen, as you will be using it again.
2. Cook the noodles 5–8 minutes in boiling water, or as directed on the packet. Drain and put away.
3. Meanwhile, over medium-high heat, fry the garlic, chili, and ginger, red onion, celery, beans, and kale in the remaining leftover oil for 2 to 3 minutes. Add chicken stock and then bring to a boil, then cook for one or two minutes until the vegetables are cooked but crunchy.
4. Add the noodles, prawns, lovage/celery leaves to the saucepan, and bring back to boil and remove from heat.

Nutrition: Calories: 873 kcal Protein: 49.01 g Fat: 34.31 g Carbohydrates: 99.01 g

395. Fragrant Asian Hotspot

Preparation time: 10 minutes
Cooking time: 15 minutes
Servings: 2

Ingredients:

- 1 tsp. tomato purée
- 1-star anise, crushed (or 1/4 tsp. ground anise)
- Small handful (10g) parsley, stalks finely chopped
- Small handful (1Og) coriander, stalks finely chopped
- Juice of 1/2 lime
- 500ml chicken stock, fresh or made with one cube
- 50g beansprouts
- 50g broccoli, cut into small florets
- 1/2 carrot
- 1OOg raw tiger prawns
- 50g rice noodles
- 1OOg firm tofu, chopped
- 20g sushi ginger, chopped
- 50g cooked water chestnuts, drained
- 1 tbsp. good-quality miso paste

Directions:

1. In a large saucepan, place the tomato purée, star anise, parsley stalks, coriander stalks, lime juice, and chicken stock, and bring it to simmer for 10 minutes.
2. Add in the carrot, broccoli, prawns, tofu, noodles, and water chestnuts and cook gently until the prawns are cooked. Remove from heat, and add sushi and miso paste to the ginger.
3. Serve sprinkled with the leaves of the parsley and coriander.

Nutrition: Calories: 174 kcal Protein: 7.54 g Fat: 4.7 g Carbohydrates: 26.75 g

396. Prawn Arrabbiata

Preparation time: 10 minutes
Cooking time: 30minutes
Servings: 1

Ingredients:

- 125g Raw or cooked prawns (Ideally king prawns)
- 1 tbsp. extra virgin olive oil
- 65 g Buckwheat pasta
- For arrabbiata sauce
- 40 g Red onion, finely chopped
- 1 Garlic clove, finely chopped
- 30 g Celery, finely chopped
- 1 Bird's eye chili, finely chopped
- 1 tsp. Dried mixed herbs
- 1 tsp. extra virgin olive oil
- 2 tbsp. White wine (optional)
- 400 g Tinned chopped tomatoes
- 1 tbsp. Chopped parsley

Directions:

1. Fry the onion, garlic, celery, and chili over medium-low heat and dry herbs in the oil for 1–2 minutes. Put the heat to medium, then add the wine and cook for a minute.

Add the tomatoes and let the sauce cook over medium-low heat for 20-30 minutes until it has a nice, rich consistency. If you feel the sauce is getting way too thick, just add some water.

2. While the sauce is cooking, set a pan of water to a boil, and cook the pasta as directed by the packet. Drain, toss with the olive oil when cooked to your liking, and keep in the pan until needed.
3. Add the raw prawns to the sauce and cook for another 3–4 minutes until they have turned pink and opaque, then add the parsley and serve. If you are using cooked prawns, add the parsley, bring the sauce to the boil and serve.
4. Add the cooked buckwheat pasta to the prepared sauce and mix well but gently and serve.

Nutrition: Calories: 448 kcal Protein: 14.77 g Fat: 15.34 g Carbohydrates: 70.15 g

397. Buckwheat Pasta Salad

Preparation time: 40 minutes
Cooking time: 0 minutes
Servings: 1
Ingredients:

- 50g buckwheat pasta
- Large handful of rocket
- A small handful of basil leaves
- Eight cherry tomatoes halved
- 1/2 avocado, diced
- Ten olives
- 1 tbsp. extra virgin olive oil
- 20g pine nuts

Directions:

1. Gently combine all the above ingredients, arrange them on a plate or in a bowl, and then put some pine nuts over the top.

Nutrition: Calories: 492 kcal Protein: 13.06 g Fat: 41.68 g Carbohydrates: 22.86 g

398. Lemon Chicken Kebabs

Preparation time: 5 minutes + cooling time
Cooking time: 10 minutes
Servings: 2
Ingredients:

- 6oz boneless, skinless chicken breast, chopped into 1 ½" pieces
- 1 cup cherry tomatoes, chopped
- 3 tbsp. fresh lemon juice
- 1 tbsp. garlic, finely chopped
- 1½ tsp oregano
- ¾ tsp salt
- ¾ tsp ground black pepper
- 2 cups fresh parsley
- 3 tbsp. extra virgin olive oil

Directions:

1. In a small bowl, mix 2 tbsp. lemon juice, 2 tsp chopped garlic, 1 tsp oregano, ½ tsp salt, ½ tsp pepper and 1 tbsp. olive oil
2. Add chicken and stir well.
3. Put in the refrigerator to marinate then leave for 2 – 4 hours
4. Remove chicken from bowl and divide into 4 portions
5. Thread each portion onto 1 or 2 skewers
6. Cook under a grill or on a griddle, turning regularly until fully cooked, usually around 6 to 10 minutes
7. Mix remaining ingredients, excluding parsley, and whisk together well
8. Drizzle over cooked kebabs and garnish with parsley

Nutrition: Calories: 311 Fat: 14.9g Protein: 38g Carbohydrate: 6g Fiber: 2g

399. Beef With Red Onion Marmalade

Preparation time: 10 minutes
Cooking time: 20 minutes
Servings: 2
Ingredients:

- 4 x 4oz beef steaks, 1" thick
- 1 large red onion, sliced into rings
- 2 tbsp. honey
- 2 tbsp. red wine vinegar
- 1 tsp thyme
- ½ tsp salt
- ¼ tsp ground black pepper
- 1 tbsp. olive oil

Directions:

1. Warm oil in a large frying pan at medium to high heat
2. Add onion and cook for 3 minutes
3. Add vinegar, honey and ¼ tsp salt to the pan and reduce heat
4. Simmer, occasionally stirring for 7 to 9 minutes until thickened slightly and remove from heat
5. Turn grill on high
6. Mix remaining salt, pepper, and thyme with a little olive oil and rub over beef
7. Cook steaks under the grill for 4 to 6 minutes each side
8. Serve with onion mixture and a choice of potatoes, salad or both

Nutrition: Calories: 289 Fat: 11.4g Protein: 32.5g Carbohydrate: 12.6g Fiber: 0.8g

400. Greek Fish

Preparation time: 10 minutes
Cooking time: 55 minutes
Servings: 2
Ingredients:

- 5 small potatoes, cleaned and sliced into wedges
- 1 onion, sliced
- 2 cloves garlic, roughly chopped
- 2 fresh cod or white fish fillets, de-skinned, around 100g each
- 2 large tomatoes, cut into wedges
- ½ lemon, cut into wedges
- 2 tbsp. olive oil
- ½ tsp dried oregano
- Fresh parsley, roughly chopped to garnish

Directions:

1. Preheat oven to 200°c
2. Mix olive oil, garlic, and oregano
3. Toss potato wedges and onion in the mixture and spread onto a baking tray
4. Bake for 30 minutes.
5. Add lemon and tomatoes and cook for a further 10 minutes
6. Place fish fillets on top and continue to cook for a further 10 to 15 minutes until fish is cooked through
7. Sprinkle with parsley and serve

Nutrition: Calories: 388 Fat: 13g Protein: 23g Carbohydrate: 42g Fiber: 6g

401. Lentil & Aubergine Bake

Preparation time: minutes
Cooking time: minutes

Servings: 2

Ingredients:

- 2 aubergines, sliced lengthways, ½ cm thick
- 140g lentils
- 2 onions, finely chopped
- 3 garlic cloves, finely chopped
- 300g butternut squash, cooked
- 400g chopped tomato
- 125g mozzarella, torn
- 3 tbsps. extra virgin olive oil
- Small handful fresh basil, chopped
- Pinch of salt & pepper
- ½ cup water

Directions:

1. Preheat oven to 200°c
2. Using 2 tbsp. olive oil, brush aubergines slices, (both sides) with olive oil and spread onto a baking tray
3. Sprinkle with salt & pepper and bake for 15 to 20 minutes
4. Cook lentils, (follow instructions on the packet)
5. Heat 1 tbsps. olive oil in a large frying pan over a medium to high heat
6. Add onions & garlic and cook for 2 to 3 minutes
7. Stir in squash, tomatoes, and water and simmer for 10 to 15 minutes until thickened
8. Stir in lentils, basil and another pinch of salt & pepper then remove from heat
9. Spread a layer of the lentil mixture into a small baking dish and top with aubergine slices
10. Continue to layer until all mixture and aubergines have been used
11. Sprinkle with mozzarella and bake for a more 15 minutes

Nutrition: Calories: 359 Fat: 16g Protein: 19g Carbohydrate: 34g Fiber: 10g

402. Courgette & Tomato Stew

Preparation time: 10 minutes
Cooking time: 60 minutes
Servings: 4

Ingredients:

- 3 courgettes, cut into chunks
- 1 onion, roughly chopped
- 2 garlic bulbs, finely chopped
- 800g canned chopped tomatoes
- 25g parmesan, grated
- 1 tbsp olive oil
- 1 bunch fresh basil, torn

Directions:

1. Using a large frying pan, warm olive oil in medium heat
2. Add onions and cook until they begin to brown, (5 to 10 minutes)
3. Add garlic and cook for a further 5 minutes, stirring occasionally
4. Add courgettes and cook for an additional 5 minutes
5. Stir in tomatoes and bring to a fast boil
6. Lower the heat temperature and simmer for 35 to 40 minutes
7. Stir in parmesan and basil
8. Remove from heat and serve

Nutrition: Calories: 114 Fat: 5g Protein: 6g Carbohydrate: 10g Fiber: 3g

403. Chana Masala

Preparation time: 5 minutes
Cooking time: 15 minutes
Servings: 4

Ingredients:

- 1 medium onion, chopped
- 1 clove garlic, finely chopped
- 75g quick cook basmati rice, brown
- 400g canned chopped tomatoes
- 400g canned chickpeas drained and rinsed
- 220g baby leaf spinach
- 1cm ginger, peeled and grated
- Juice of half a lemon
- ½ red chilli pepper, deseeded and finely chopped
- 1 tbsp extra virgin olive oil
- 1 tsp cumin seed
- 1 tsp ground coriander
- 1 tsp cumin
- 1 tsp paprika
- 1 tsp garam masala
- 1 tsp turmeric
- 200ml water

Directions:

1. Cook rice and set aside
2. Place cumin seeds into a large frying pan and heat (no oil), over medium heat until popped. Remove from pan and set aside
3. Add oil to the frying pan and heat
4. Add onion, ginger, chilli, and garlic and cook for 3 minutes
5. Reduce to low heat and stir in garam masala, turmeric, coriander, cumin, and paprika and cook for 2 minutes
6. Stir in tomatoes, chickpeas, and water
7. Increase heat temperature then place to the boil before reducing to a simmer for 10 minutes
8. Stir in lemon juice, and spinach then remove from the heat
9. Serve over brown rice

Nutrition: Calories: 420 Fat: 12g Protein: 20g Carbohydrate: 60g Fiber: 12g

404. Salmon & Salsa Salad

Preparation time: 5 minutes
Cooking time: 10 minutes
Servings: 2

Ingredients:

- 2 salmon fillets
- 1 clove garlic, finely chopped
- Juice of 1 lime
- (Using same lime, grate zest then quarter)
- 1 tsp chilli powder
- ½ tsp ground coriander
- ¼ tsp cumin
- 2 tsp olive oil

Salsa Ingredients:

- 1 red onion, finely chopped
- 1 clove garlic, finely chopped
- 1 avocado, peeled, de-stoned and chopped
- 1 corn on the cob
- 1 red bell pepper, seedless and finely chopped
- 1 red chilli, halved, deseeded and finely chopped
- Handful of fresh coriander, finely chopped

Salmon Directions:

1. In a small bowl, put and mix garlic, 1 tsp lime juice, and olive oil, cumin, coriander, and chilli powder
2. Rub the mixture into both sides of salmon fillets
3. Heat a little oil in a frying pan over a medium heat
4. Cook salmon fillets for 2 minutes per side
5. Serve with salsa salad

Salsa Directions:

1. Boil corn on the cob for around 7 to 8 minutes until soft
2. Remove corn from the cob and place in a large mixing bowl
3. Add remaining lime juice, lime zest, red onion, garlic, avocado, chilli, and bell pepper and stir together
4. To serve, add lime wedges and sprinkle with fresh coriander

Nutrition: Calories: 530 Fat: 32g Protein: 29g Carbohydrate: 27g Fiber: 9g

405. Turkish Escalope With Sage, Caper And Parsley And Pickled Cauliflower

Preparation time: 5 minutes
Cooking time: 10 minutes
Servings: 2

Ingredients:

- 150 grams of cauliflower, roughly chopped
- 1 clove garlic, finely chopped
- 40 grams purple onion, finely chopped diagram
- 1 bird's eye chili, finely chopped *
- 1tsp fresh ginger, finely chopped
- Vegetable oil
- 2tsp ground turmeric
- 30g sun-dried tomatoes, finely chopped
- 10g parsley
- 150g turkey escalope
- 1tsp dry sage
- 1/2 lemon Juice
- 1tbsp capers

Directions:

1. 2-second Place the cauliflower on a kitchen appliance and pulse while it bursts. Finely chop until it resembles couscous. Cancel. Fry garlic, red onion, chili, and ginger in 1tsp oil till it becomes soft but not colored. Add turmeric and cauliflower and cook for 1 minute. Remove from heat and add sun-dried tomatoes and half parsley.
2. Coat the turkey escalope within 2 remaining oil and sage and then fry for 5-6 minutes, turning regularly. When cooked, add juice, remaining parsley, capers, and 1tbsp water the pan make the sauce, then serve.

Nutrition: Calories: 449 kcal Protein: 19.95 g Fat: 36.9 g Carbohydrates: 9.94 g

406. Vietnamese Turmeric Fish With Herbs And Mango Sauce

Preparation time: 15 minutes
Cooking time:
25 minutes + 1 hour Marinate
Servings: 4-6

Ingredients:

- 1 ¼ lb. of fresh codfish, boneless and skinless,
- 2-inch piece full that about half an inch-thick digging
- 2 tablespoons copra oil for pan-frying Fish (at most one pair of spoons if necessary)
- Small pinch of sea salt taste the
- Fish: (Marinate for at least 1 hour or until overnight)
- 1 tbsp. turmeric powder
- 1 tsp Sea salt
- 1 Tbsp. sugar. Cooking Wine (Alt Dry Sherry)
- 2 tsp Minced Ginger
- 2 Tablespoons Vegetable Oil
- Infused Scallion and Dill Oil:
- 2 cups Scallion (long thin slices)
- 2 cups fresh dill
- Pinch of sea salt taste.
- Mango Dipping Sauce:
- 1 medium-sized ripe mango
- 2 tablespoons rice vinegar of lemon juice
- 1 clove
- 1 tablespoon dry red chili (before serving)
- Shake Topping:
- Fresh Cetaphil (as you like)
- Sauce as You want a lot)
- Nuts (Cashew or Pine Nuts)

Directions:

1. Marinate the fish for at least 60 minutes or overnight.
2. Place all ingredients in a kitchen appliance under "Mango Dipping Sauce" and mix until desired consistency.
3. Pan-fry the fish: 1.
4. 2 tablespoons of large spoon oil during a sizeable non-stick frypan during high heat. When hot, add pre-marinated fish. * Note: Place the fish slices individually in the pan and, if necessary, separate the 2 or more batches from frying the pan.
5. You should hear a loud sigh, after which you will reduce the heat from medium-high.
6. Do not shake and stir the fish until you see a golden-brown color for about 5 minutes. Season with a pinch of sea salt. Add more copra oil pan-fry the fish if necessary.
7. Once the fish turns golden brown, flip the fish carefully fry it in the opposite direction. Once throne, transfer an outer plate. * Note: Some oil must be left within the frying. We use the remaining oil to make flasks and use oil.
8. Make scallion and dill infused oil:
9. Use the remaining oil within frying over medium-high heat, add 2 cups of scallion and a few cups of dill. Once you've done added the scallions and dill, turn off the heat. Give them only a light toss until the scallions and dill about 15 seconds. Season with a touch of sea salt.
10. Pour crust, dill, and infected oil over the fish and serve with a mango dipping sauce with fresh cilantro, lime, and nuts.

Nutrition: Calories: 990 kcal Protein: 139.69 g Fat: 43.95 g Carbohydrates: 9.31 g

407. Beef Chewed With A Wine Juice, Onion Rings, Garlic, Bananas, And Herb-Roasted Potatoes

Preparation time: 15 minutes
Cooking time: 1 hour and 15 minutes
Servings: 2

Ingredients:

- 100g potatoes, peeled and dug 2cm dice
- 1 tablespoon extra-virgin vegetable oil
- 5g parsley, finely chopped cut into
- 50g purple onion rings.
- 50g Cabbage, chopped
- 1 clove, finely chopped
- 120-150g x 3.5cm thick meat fillet steak or 2cm thick beefsteak
- 40ml alcohol
- 150ml beef broth
- 1 tsp tempura

- 1 tsp corn flour
- 1 tsp water

Directions:

1. Heat 220°C oven/gas 7.
2. Put potatoes in a saucepan of boiling water, boil Undo, and cook for 4-5 minutes, then drain. Place during roasting tin with 1 teaspoon of oil and fry for 35–45 minutes within a hot oven. Flip the potatoes every 10 minutes to ensure cooking. Once cooked, take it off from the oven, sprinkle with chopped parsley, and mix well.
3. Put and fry the onion in 1 teaspoon of oil over medium heat for 5 7 minutes, until soft and well caramelized. Keep safe. Steam black for 2-3 minutes, then drain. Slowly fry the garlic in oil for 1 minute, until it is soft Add the spoon and cook for 1 2 minutes, until tender. Keep safe.
4. Warm an ovenproof frying pan over high heat until smoked. And coat the meat in a teaspoon of oil and fry it with a medium-high heat within the hot grill depending on how you want your meat to do. If you want your meat to be medium, then it would be better baking the beef then move the pan. An oven set at 220 ovens/gas 7 and completes the cooking time.
5. Take off the meat from the pan then set aside rest. Add alcohol. A recent pan mentions any meat residue. Let the bubble cook the wine back in half, until syrup and with a concentrated flavor.
6. Add the stock and tempura the steak pan and allow boil, then add the cornflour paste thicken your sauce, cook it one at a time until you find the consistency you need. Stir in any juice from the rest of the steak and serve with roasted potatoes, bananas, onion rings, and wine sauce.

Nutrition: Calories: 591 kcal Protein: 51.51 g Fat: 24.2 g Carbohydrates: 45.05 g

408. Fresh Saag Paneer

Preparation time: 5 minutes
Cooking time: 15 minutes
Servings: 2

Ingredients:

- 2 teaspoons rape oil
- 200 gm cheese. Digging cubes
- Salt and freshly ground black pepper
- 1 purple onion, sliced
- 1 small thumb ginger, peeled and diced
- Cream 1 clove garlic, peeled and finely chopped
- 1 green chili, deseeded and finely chopped
- 100 grams Cherry Tomatoes, half.
- 2 teaspoon ground coriander
- 1/21/2 teaspoon cumin seeds
- 1/4 teaspoon ground turmeric
- 1/2 teaspoon light chili powder
- 1/2 teaspoon salt
- 100 grams fresh spinach leaves
- Small handful (10 grams) parsley, chopped
- Small handful (10 g) coriander, chopped

Directions:

1. Heat oil during a large lidded frypan over high heat. Pour the cheese generously with salt and pepper and toss in the pan. Fry for a few minutes until golden, stirring often. Remove from the pan with a chopped spoon and keep aside.
2. Reduce heat and add the onion. Fry for five minutes before adding ginger, garlic, and chili. Cook for a few minutes before adding cherry tomatoes. Put the lid on the pan and cook for 5 minutes.
3. Add 3 spices and salt, then stir. Return the cheese the pan and shake until coated. Add the spinach along with the parsley and coriander the pan and cover. Allow the spinach wilt for 1-2 minutes, then add the dish. Serve immediately.

Nutrition: Calories: 142 kcal Protein: 6.35 g Fat: 8.2 g Carbohydrates: 13.29 g

409. Bang-Bang Chicken Noodle Stir-Fry Recipe

Preparation time: 10 minutes
Cooking time: 1 hour and 10 minutes
Servings: 4

Ingredients:

- 1 tablespoon sunflower oil
- 750g package chicken thighs, boned, any surplus skin trimmed
- 250g frozen chopped mixed peppers
- Inch courgette, peeled into ribbons, seeded center chopped
- 1 chicken stock cube
- 250g pack moderate egg yolks
- 4 garlic cloves, finely chopped
- 1/2 tsp crushed chilies, and additional to serve (optional)
- 4 tablespoons reduced-salt soy sauce
- 2 tsp caster sugar
- 1 lime, zested, 1/2 juiced, 1/2 slice into wedges to function

Directions:

1. Warm the oil in a skillet at medium-low warmth. Fry the chicken skin-side down to 10 minutes or until your skin is emptied. Flip and simmer for 10 minutes, or until cooked. Transfer to a plate cover loosely with foil.
2. Reheat the wok over a high temperature, add the peppers and sliced courgette; simmer for 5 minutes. Meanwhile, bring a bowl of water to the boil, crumble in the stock block, and add the noodles. Simmer for 45 minutes until cooked, then drain well.
3. Insert the garlic and crushed chilies into the wok; simmer for two minutes. In a bowl, mix the soy sugar and the lime juice and zest. Enhance the wok, bubble 2 minutes; you can add the courgette noodles and ribbons. Toss using tongs to coat in the sauce.
4. Cut the chicken into pieces. Divide the noodles between 4 bowls and top with the chicken. Serve with the lime wedges along with extra crushed chilies, in case you prefer.

Nutrition: Calories 718kcal Fat 36g Saturates 12g Sugars 8g Salt 2.4gram Carbohydrate 55g Protein 41.3gram Fiber 5.7gram

410. Cajun Steak And Veg Rice Jar

Preparation time: 10 minutes
Cooking time: 25 minutes
Servings: 4

Ingredients:

- 1 tablespoon vegetable oil
- 1 celery stick, finely chopped
- 3 large carrots, sliced into rounds
- 250g frozen chopped mixed peppers
- 4 spring onions, chopped, then split the green and white part
- 500g 5 percent beef mince
- 2 teaspoon seasoning

- 1 teaspoon tomato purée
- 2 x 250g packs ready-cooked long-grain rice

Directions:

1. Warm the oil in a big shallow skillet over moderate heat. Add the carrots, celery, peppers, and snowy areas of the nuts. Cook for 10 mins before the veg is beginning to soften.
2. Insert the mince, season liberally, and cook for 10 mins before mince is browned and start to go crispy.
3. Insert the Cajun seasoning and tomato purée; stir fry to coat the mince. Hint inside the rice combined with 4 tablespoons of plain water. Stir to completely unite heat and heat until the rice is hot. Scatter on the rest of the spring onion before serving.

Nutrition: Calories 456kcal Fat 12g Saturates 3g Sugar 13g Salt 1g Carbohydrate 53.1gram Protein 32.8gram Fiber 8.3gram

411. Chicken Liver Along With Tomato Ragu Recipe

Preparation time: 10 minutes
Cooking time: 30 minutes
Servings: 4

Ingredients:

- 2 tablespoon olive oil
- 1 onion, finely chopped
- 2 carrots, scrubbed and simmer
- 4 garlic cloves, finely chopped
- 1/4 x 30g pack fresh ginger, stalks finely chopped, leaves ripped
- 380g package poultry livers, finely chopped, and almost any sinew removed and lost
- 400g tin Grower's Harvest chopped berries
- 1 chicken stock cube, created around 300ml
- 1/2 tsp caster sugar
- 300g penne
- 1/4 Suntrail Farms lemon, juiced

Directions:

1. Warm 1 tablespoon oil in a big skillet, over a low-medium heating system. Fry the onion and carrots to 10 mins, stirring periodically. Stir in the ginger and garlic pops and cook 2 mins more. Transfer into a bowl set aside.
2. Twist the pan into high heat and then add the oil. Bring the chicken livers and simmer for 5 minutes until browned. Pour the onion mix to the pan and then stir in the tomatoes, sugar, and stock. Season, bring to the boil, and then simmer for 20 minutes until reduced and thickened, and also the liver is cooked through. Meanwhile, cook pasta to package Direction.
3. Taste the ragu and put in a second pinch of sugar more seasoning, if needed. Put in a squeeze of lemon juice to taste and stir in two of the ripped basil leaves. Divide the pasta between four bowls, then spoon across the ragu and top with the rest of the basil.

Nutrition: Calories 469kcal Fat 12g Saturates 2g Sugars 12g Salt 1.8gram Carbohydrate 69.1gram Protein 25.8gram Fiber 3.3gram

412. Minted Lamb With A Couscous Salad

Preparation time: 15 minutes
Cooking time: 15 minutes
Servings: 4

Ingredients:

- 75g Couscous
- 1/2 chicken stock block, composed to 125ml
- 30g pack refreshing flat-leaf parsley, sliced
- 3 mint sprigs, leaves picked and sliced
- 1 tablespoon olive oil
- 200g pack suspended BBQ minted lamb leg beans, De-frosted
- 200g lettuce berries, sliced
- 1/4 tsp, sliced
- 1 spring onion, sliced
- Pinch of ground cumin
- 1/2 lemon, zested and juiced
- 50g reduced-fat salad cheese

Directions:

1. Bring the couscous into a heatproof bowl then pour on the inventory. Cover and set aside for 10 minutes, then fluff with a fork and stir in the herbs.
2. Meanwhile, rub a little oil within the lamb steaks and season. Cook to package Direction, then slit.
3. Mix the tomatoes, cucumber and spring onion into the couscous with the oil, the cumin, and lemon juice and zest. Crumble on the salad and serve with the bunny.

Nutrition: Calories 463kcal Fat 19g Saturates 8g Sugars 11g Salt 2.2gram Carbohydrate 41.1gram Protein 33.8gram Fiber 4.1gram

413. Jack Fruit Tortilla Bowls

Preparation time: 5 minutes
Cooking time: 15 minutes
Servings: 2

Ingredients:

- 2 Sweet Corn cobettes
- 1 red chili, finely chopped
- 2 teaspoon olive oil
- 1 lime, juiced
- 15g fresh coriander, chopped, and additional for garnish
- 150g package stained Jack Fruit in Texmex sauce
- 210g tin kidney beans, drained
- 125g roasted red peppers (in the jar), drained and chopped
- 2 whitened tortilla packs
- 1/2 round lettuce, ripped

Directions:

1. Heat a griddle Pan on a high temperature (or light a barbecue). Griddle that the cobettes to get 10-12 minutes turning until cooked and charred throughout. Remove from the pan and also stand upright onto a plank. Use a sharp knife to carefully reduce the Span of this corn, stay near the heart, and clear away the kernels. Mix that the kernels with the eucalyptus oil, half of the carrot juice along with half an hour of the coriander.
2. Heating the Jack fruit and sauce in a saucepan with the legumes, peppers, staying lime Coriander and juice on medium-low heating for 3-4 minutes until heated through; now.
3. Griddle the wraps for 10 20 secs each side to char. Tear into pieces and serve together with all the Jack Fruit lettuce and sweet corn salsa.

Nutrition: Calories 354kcal Fat 10g Saturates 1g Sugars 10g Salt 1.3gram Carbohydrate 51.4gram Protein 13.7gram Fiber 9.8gram

414. Carrot, Courgette And Halloumi Hamburgers Recipe

Preparation time: 20 minutes
Cooking time: 10 minutes
Servings: 4

Ingredients:

- 1 big carrot, grated
- 1 large courgette, grated

- 225g halloumi, grated
- 2 spring onions, finely chopped
- 90g Bread Crumbs
- 1 tablespoon ground cumin
- 1 tablespoon ground coriander
- 1/2 teaspoon salt
- 2 tbsp
- 2 tablespoons flour
- 4 brioche buns, halved
- 50g baby spinach leaves
- 1 big tomato, sliced
- 1 small red onion, chopped
- 1/2 pineapple, peeled into ribbons
- Tzatziki, to function

Directions:

1. Place the courgette into a clean tea towel and squeeze to eradicate any liquid. Hint into a big bowl and then add the carrot, halloumi, onion, bread crumbs, cumin, coriander, eggs, salt, and flour. Stir well to mix.
2. Put simply over half the mix in a food processor and pulse until the mixture starts to stay. Reunite back this into the booked mix and mix well.
3. Divide the mix into 4 and then form into patties. Heat a grill or griddle pan into a moderate heat. Cook the hamburgers for 45 minutes each side until golden and cooked through.
4. Insert the hamburger buns into the grill till lightly toasted. To assemble the burgers, put lettuce leaves on the base of each bun. Top with all the hamburger, a piece of tomato, pineapple ribbon along with a spoonful of tzatziki.

Nutrition: Calories 523kcal Fat 24g Saturates 12g Sugars 12g Salt 3.1gram Carbohydrate 54g Protein 28.2gram Fiber 7.2gram

415. Rita's 'Rowdy' Enchiladas Recipe

Preparation time: 20 minutes
Cooking time: 1 hour and 20 minutes
Servings: 4

Ingredients:

- 2large chicken breasts (about 400g)
- 2 red peppers, thinly chopped
- 1 tablespoon olive oil
- 3/4 tsp mild chili powder
- 1 teaspoon 1/2 tsp ground cumin
- 3/4 tsp smoked paprika
- 80g grated mozzarella
- 8 Plain Tortilla Wraps
- 65g ripe Cheddar, grated
- 10g fresh coriander, roughly sliced
- The sauce
- 1 tablespoon olive oil
- 1/2 onion, finely chopped
- 2 tsp cloves, crushed
- 500g tomato passata
- 1 tablespoon chipotle chili paste
- 400g tin black beans drained and rinsed
- 1/2 lime, juiced

Directions:

1. Pre heats the oven to gas 5, 190°C, buff 170°C. Set the chicken at a 20 x 30cm skillet with all the peppers olive oil, chili powder, cumin, and paprika. Mix to coat, then cover with foil. Roast for 25-30 minutes before the chicken is cooked and tender with no pink meat remains. Take out the chicken from the dish and then shred with two forks. Reserve in a bowl.
2. Meanwhile, make the sauce. Heat the oil in a saucepan on a low heat and cook the garlic and onion for 10 minutes. Stir from the passata and chipotle chili glue; increase heat to moderate, bring to a simmer and cook for a further 10 minutes, stirring periodically. Bring the beans and carrot juice season.
3. Mix one-third of this sauce plus half of the mozzarella to the cultured broccoli and chicken.
4. To gather, spoon 4 tablespoons of this sauce in exactly the exact baking dish before. Spoon a bit of the chicken mixture down the middle of each tortilla, roll up, and then put it from the dish. Repeat with the tortillas and filling, then placing them alongside so that they do not shatter. Put the remaining sauce on the top and then scatter within the Cheddar and remaining mozzarella. Bake in the oven for 20-25 minutes until the cheese has melted and begun to brownish. Scatter together with all the coriander to function.
5. Freezing And defrosting recommendations
6. Cook As educated and let it cool completely. Subsequently, move to an airtight, freezer-safe container, seal, and freeze up to 1-3 weeks. Guarantee the meatballs are underwater in the sauce since they are going to freeze far better. To serve, defrost thoroughly in the refrigerator overnight before reheating. To serve, put in a bowl over moderate heat, occasionally stirring until the dish is heated throughout.

Nutrition: Calories757kcal Fat 24g Saturates 10g Sugars 14g Salt 2.8gram Carbohydrate 81.5gram Protein 50.1gram Fiber 12.7gram

416. Fusilli Salad With Buckwheat, Pesto, Tomatoes, And Pine Nuts

Preparation time: 10 minutes
Cooking time: 15 minutes
Servings: 4

Ingredients:

- 200g buckwheat fusilli
- Sixteen cherry tomatoes
- 80g dried tomatoes
- 40g pine nuts
- Salt and pepper
- 4 tbsp. basil pesto
- Basil Pesto:
- One bunch of basil
- 2 tbsp. olive oil
- 50g parmesan
- 60g pine nuts
- 1 clove of garlic all mixed

Directions:

1. Cook the pasta for ten minutes, add salt to taste. Drain and let it cool.
2. Cut the cherry tomatoes in half, chop the dried tomatoes into thin strips and lightly toast the pine nuts in a pan for one minute.
3. In a large bowl, gently mix the pasta and pesto. Add the dried tomatoes, half of the chopped basil and the pine nuts. Carefully stir the entire mixture and add seasoning to taste.
4. Arrange the cherry tomatoes and the rest of the chopped basil on the salad.

Nutrition: Calories: 352 kcal Protein: 12.27 g Fat: 26.39 g Carbohydrates: 20.64 g

417. Salmon Salad And Fresh Mint

Preparation time: minutes
Cooking time: minutes
Servings:

Ingredients:

- Salad leaves
- 200 g of fresh salmon
- 6 mint leaves
- 3 tablespoons of white cheese
- 2 limes
- Salad dressing
- 1 large cucumber

Directions:

1. Peel the cucumber and remove the seeds. Cut the cucumber into thin rings and put it in a colander.
2. Steam your salmon for 8 minutes. Mash the salmon in a bowl and mix in the cottage cheese with the lemon, salt, and pepper
3. Add the chopped mint, mix well, and refrigerate.
4. Place the salad in strips on a plate and add in the cucumber salmon and enjoy!

Nutrition: Calories: 352 kcal Protein: 12.27 g Fat: 26.39 g Carbohydrates: 20.64 g

418. Granola With Hazelnut And Chocolate

Preparation time: 15 minutes
Cooking time: 30 minutes
Servings: 4

Ingredients:

- Four small oatmeal packs
- 2 tbsp. coconut oil
- 2 whole hazelnut packs
- 200 bar of dark chocolate
- 4 tbsp. maple syrup

Directions:

1. Preheat your oven to 150°C
2. Cut your hazelnuts and chocolate bar into small pieces.
3. In a medium-sized bowl, mix the oats, coconut oil, hazelnut chips, and the maple syrup to give a paste.
4. Spread the paste over a sheet of baking paper. Keep the thickness at half a centimeter at most.
5. Bake halfway and cook for about thirty minutes until the mixture is slightly brown.
6. Take off the baking pan from the oven, using a zester or a cheese grater, grind the whole four squares of chocolate you have kept whole. Make it right out of the oven when the dough is still hot.
7. Allow to cool and mix your granola with the chocolate chips.

Nutrition: Calories: 346 kcal Protein: 6.82 g Fat: 28.88 g Carbohydrates: 19.76 g

419. Chicken Tangine With Squash And Medjool Dates

Preparation time: 10 minutes
Cooking time: 35 minutes
Servings: 6-8

Ingredients:

- 1 large chicken cut into eight pieces
- 4 tbsp. extra virgin olive oil
- 2 tbsp. flaked almonds
- 2 chopped onions
- 1.5 tsp ground cumin
- 1 tsp coriander seeds
- 1 tbsp. ground cinnamon
- 2 garlic cloves (chopped)
- 2 slices of fresh ginger
- 1 sachet of saffron
- Salt and pepper to taste
- 500 ml chicken broth
- 750g peeled squash
- Six large pitted dates cut in half
- 1bunch of fresh coriander
- Orange zest

Directions:

1. Leniently toast the almonds in your frying pan and set aside.
2. Proceed by heating a little fraction of oil in a Dutch oven and fry the onions for about five-to-six minutes, continue stirring until they are slightly brown.
3. Add in the cumin, previously crushed coriander seeds, cinnamon, and garlic. Now cook for roughly two minutes, then add the chicken, ginger and saffron, salt, and pepper.
4. Cover the entire mixture using a chicken broth and bake in a covered oven for One hour.
5. Add the squash, dates, and orange zest. Continue cooking for about 20-25 minutes.
6. Remove the ginger and serve on a bed of couscous. Add in the cooking broth and garnish with chopped fresh coriander and toasted almonds.

Nutrition: Calories: 230 kcal Protein: 26.51 g Fat: 7.41 g Carbohydrates: 14.7 g

420. Shrimp And Arrabiatta Sauce

Preparation time: 15 minutes
Cooking time: 30 minutes
Servings: 4

Ingredients:

- 1 onion, chopped
- 1 tsp crushed hot pepper flakes
- 5 tbsp. Extra Virgin Olive Oil
- 2 garlic cloves, chopped
- 60 ml white wine
- 28 oz. crushed Italian tomatoes
- 375g pasta
- 454g large raw shrimp (peeled)
- 2 tbsp. Chopped parsley
- 1 cup grated Parmesan Cheese
- Salt and pepper

Directions:

1. Get a saucepan, then add the three tablespoons of oil, sauté the onion and the pepper in the oil, then heat. You should also add some pepper and salt to taste.
2. Add the garlic and continue cooking for One minute. Deglaze with white wine.
3. Add the tomatoes and continue cooking for about ten minutes.
4. Boil your pasta. Add in a little salt and oil. Drain and serve.
5. In a big skillet heated over high heat, heat the shrimp in hot oil. Add salt and pepper to taste.
6. Put the sauce and let the mixture boil.
7. Add the pasta and parsley and season to taste.
8. Serve warm. You can also shower it with Parmesan cheese if desired.

Nutrition: Calories: 451 kcal Protein: 29.28 g Fat: 18.31 g Carbohydrates: 43.76 g

421. Turmeric Salmon And Coconut Milk

Preparation time: 10 minutes
Cooking time: 20 minutes
Servings: 2

Ingredients:

- 2 skinless salmon steaks
- 1 onion
- 1 garlic clove
- 1 tsp. turmeric
- 10 cl coconut milk
- 10 cl of fish stock
- 4 tbsp. Extra Virgin Olive oil
- Salt and pepper to taste

Directions:

1. Peel and chop the onion and garlic. Fry on low heat for 3 minutes in a saucepan with two tablespoons of olive oil.
2. Add the turmeric, cook for 30 seconds, and then pour the coconut milk and the fish stock.
3. Add in pepper and salt to taste and cook over very low heat for 10 minutes.
4. Cook the salmon steaks over high heat in a pan with two tablespoons of olive oil. Cook each side for One to 2 minutes.
5. Serve the fish with the sauce.

Nutrition: Calories: 187 kcal Protein: 4.61 g Fat: 15.19 g Carbohydrates: 8.77 g

422. Coronation Chicken Salad With Cheese

Preparation time: 20 minutes
Cooking time: 40 minutes
Servings: 4

Ingredients:

- 200g chicken cutlet
- 175g of spelled flour
- 75g cottage cheese
- 50g ground almonds
- 3 eggs
- 1 onion
- 1/2. Baking powder
- 2 tbsp. Extra Virgin Olive Oil
- 10 cl whole milk
- 1 tbsp. pepper
- 1 tsp. nutmeg

Directions:

1. Warm by using the extra virgin olive oil in a non-stick pan, add the minced onions and the diced chicken and allow the mixture to fry until slightly brown.
2. Melt the cheese in a bowl, add the eggs, flour, yeast, oil, and warm milk.
3. Add the mixture to the chicken. Sprinkle in the pepper, nutmeg, and finally, the powdered almonds.
4. Mix well, then pour the dough into a mold and bake for about 40 minutes in an oven preheated to One80 ° C.
5. Serve warm with a salad.

Nutrition: Calories: 469 kcal Protein: 28.33 g Fat: 20.82 g Carbohydrates: 41.38 g

423. Baked Potatoes And Chickpea Stew

Preparation time: 20 minutes
Cooking time: 1 hour and 10 minutes
Servings: 4

Ingredients:

- 4-6 baking potatoes
- 1 tbsp. canola oil
- 1 tbsp. cumin seeds
- 1 red onion (finely chopped)
- 5 garlic cloves (minced)
- 1 tbsp. ground coriander seeds
- 1 can of chickpeas (drained)
- 1 cup of water
- 1 red potato (diced)
- 2 tsp. chopped fresh cilantro
- Half tsp. salt
- Half tsp. coarsely ground pepper
- 1 tomato (diced)

Directions:

1. Preheat your oven to 200°C, and add in your baking potatoes for an hour.
2. By using a medium-high heat settings for the saucepan, heat the oil in it to fry the cumin seeds for 10 seconds till they are slightly brown, then add the onion and garlic and stir till they are slightly brown too. Finally, add the coriander and stir for another thirty seconds.
3. Add the chickpeas, water, potato, and one tsp. of fresh cilantro. Add in salt and pepper to taste.
4. Lower the heat and boil the entire mixture. Cover then simmer for fifteen minutes till the potato is soft.
5. Proceed by adding the diced tomatoes then increase the heat slightly. Allow cooking for One-to-two minutes.
6. Garnish with the leftover fresh cilantro and serve with the baked potatoes.

Nutrition: Calories: 467 kcal Protein: 14.41 g Fat: 6.38 g Carbohydrates: 89.96 g

424. Chicken Salad With Sesame Seeds

Preparation time: 20 minutes
Cooking time: 20 minutes
Servings: 4

Ingredients:

- 2 chicken strips
- Mixed salad (Californian style)
- 1 onion (finely chopped)
- 1 tbsp. sesame seeds
- 1 tsp. Almonds
- 1 tbsp. Dijon's mustard
- 2 tbsp. Extra Virgin Olive oil
- 1 tbsp. Balsamic vinegar
- 1 Lemon
- Bacon (to taste)

Directions:

1. Warm by using the extra virgin olive oil in a non-stick pan over high heat.
2. Fry the chicken breasts in the pan with a little mustard to add flavor.
3. Prepare the vinaigrette with oil, balsamic vinegar, finely chopped onions, and a little mustard. Stir the mixture thoroughly and leave to marinate.
4. Wash and cut the salad leaves, and then mix the salad and the vinaigrette.
5. Cut the chicken strips into thin slices.
6. Peel the bacon and place everything on the salad.
7. Sprinkle in the almonds and sesame seeds. Add fresh lemon zest to taste.

Nutrition: Calories: 624 kcal Protein: 99.8 g Fat: 18.86 g Carbohydrates: 8.06 g

425. Chicken With Kale, Red Onions And Chili Salsa

Preparation time: 5 Minutes
Cooking time: 70 Minutes
Servings: 2

Ingredients:

- For the salsa:
- 130g tomatoes
- 1 Thai chili, finely chopped
- 1 tablespoon capers, finely chopped
- 5 g parsley, finely chopped
- Juice of a quarter of a lemon
- For the rest:
- 150g chicken breast
- 2 teaspoons turmeric
- Juice of a quarter of a lemon
- 1 tablespoon of olive oil
- 50g kale, chopped
- 20g red onions, sliced
- 1 teaspoon chopped ginger
- 50g buckwheat

Directions:

1. It is best to prepare the salsa first: remove the stalk of the tomato, chop it finely and mix it well with the other ingredients.
2. Preheat the oven to 425 °. In the meantime, marinate the chicken breast in some olive oil and a teaspoon of turmeric.
3. Heat an ovenproof pan on the stove and sauté the marinated chicken for one minute on each side. Then bake in the oven for about 10 minutes, take out and cover with aluminum foil.
4. In the meantime, briefly steam the kale. In a small saucepan, heat the red onions and ginger with olive oil until they become translucent, then add the kale and heat again.
5. Prepare buckwheat according to package Directions, serve with meat and vegetables.

Nutrition: Calories 330 Total Fat 18.9 g Saturated Fat 1.9 g Cholesterol 64 mg

426. Tomato & Goat's Cheese Pizza

Preparation time: 5 Minutes
Cooking time: 50 Minutes
Servings: 2

Ingredients:

- 225g 8ozbuckwheat flour
- 2 teaspoons dried yeast
- Pinch of salt
- 150mls 5fl oz. slightly water
- 1 teaspoon olive oil
- For the Topping:
- 75g 3ozfeta cheese, crumbled
- 75g 3ozpassata or tomato paste
- 1 tomato, sliced
- 1 red onion, finely chopped
- 25g 1oz rocket arugula leaves, chopped
- 562 calories per serving

Directions:

1. In a bowl, combine all the ingredients for the pizza dough then allow it to stand for at least an hour until it has doubled in size. Roll the dough out to a size to suit you. Spoon the passata onto the base and add the rest of the toppings. Bake in the oven at 200C/400F for 15-20 minutes or until browned at the edges and crispy and serve.

Nutrition: Calories: 269 kcal Protein: 9.23 g Fat: 23.76 g Carbohydrates: 5.49 g

427. Tofu With Cauliflower

Preparation time: 5 Minutes
Cooking time: 45 Minutes
Servings: 2

Ingredients:

- 60g red pepper, seeded
- 1 Thai chili, cut in two halves, seeded
- 2 cloves of garlic
- 1 teaspoon of olive oil
- 1 pinch of cumin
- 1 pinch of coriander
- Juice of a 1/4 lemon
- 200g tofu
- 200g cauliflower, roughly chopped
- 40g red onions, finely chopped
- 1 teaspoon finely chopped ginger
- 2 teaspoons turmeric
- 30g dried tomatoes, finely chopped
- 20g parsley, chopped

Directions:

1. Preheat oven to 400 °. Slice the peppers and put them in an ovenproof dish with chili and garlic. Pour some olive oil over it, add the dried herbs and put it in the oven until the peppers are soft about 20 minutes). Let it cool down, put the peppers together with the lemon juice in a blender and work it into a soft mass.
2. Cut the tofu in half and divide the halves into triangles. Place the tofu in a small casserole dish, cover with the paprika mixture and place in the oven for about 20 minutes.
3. Chop the cauliflower until the pieces are smaller than a grain of rice.
4. Then, in a small saucepan, heat the garlic, onions, chili and ginger with olive oil until they become transparent. Add turmeric and cauliflower mix well and heat again. Remove from heat and add parsley and tomatoes mix well. Serve with the tofu in the sauce.

Nutrition: Calories: 101 kcal Protein: 4.22 g Fat: 4.7 g Carbohydrates: 12.38 g

428. Chicken With Kale And Chili Salsa

Preparation time: 5 Minutes
Cooking time: 45 Minutes
Servings: 1

Ingredients:

- 50g of buckwheat
- 1 teaspoon of chopped fresh ginger
- Juice of ½ lemon, divided
- 2 teaspoons of ground turmeric
- 50g of kale, chopped
- 20g red onion, sliced
- 120g of skinless, boneless chicken breast
- 1 tablespoon of extra-virgin olive oil
- 1 tomato

- 1 handful parsley
- 1 bird's eye chili, chopped

Directions:

1. Start with the salsa: Remove the eye out of the tomato and finely chop it, making sure to keep as much of the liquid as you can. Mix it with the chili, parsley, and lemon juice. You could add everything to a blender for different results.
2. Heat your oven to 220 degrees F. Marinate the chicken with a little oil, 1 teaspoon of turmeric, and the lemon juice. Let it rest for 5-10 minutes.
3. Heat a pan over medium heat until it is hot then add marinated chicken and allow it to cook for a minute on both sides until it is pale gold). Transfer the chicken to the oven if pan is not ovenproof place it in a baking tray and bake for 8 to 10 minutes or until it is cooked through. Take the chicken out of the oven, cover with foil, and let it rest for five minutes before you serve.
4. Meanwhile, in a steamer, steam the kale for about 5 minutes.
5. In a little oil, fry the ginger and red onions until they are soft but not colored, and then add in the cooked kale and fry it for a minute.
6. Cook the buckwheat in accordance to the packet Directions with the remaining turmeric. Serve alongside the vegetables, salsa and chicken.

Nutrition: Calories 330 Total Fat 18.9 g Saturated Fat 1.9 g Cholesterol 64 mg

429. Sirt Salmon Salad

Preparation time: 5 Minutes
Cooking time: 30 Minutes
Servings: 1

Ingredients:

- 1 large Medjool date, pitted then chopped
- 50g of chicory leaves
- 50g of rocket
- 1 tablespoon of extra-virgin olive oil
- 10g of parsley, chopped
- 10g of celery leaves, chopped
- 40g of celery, sliced
- 15g of walnuts, chopped
- 1 tablespoon of capers
- 20g of red onions-sliced
- 80g of avocado-peeled, stoned, and sliced
- Juice of ¼ lemon
- 100g of smoked salmon slices alternatives: lentils, tinned tuna, or cooked chicken breast

Directions:

1. Arrange all the salad leaves on a large plate then mix the rest of the ingredients and distribute evenly on top the leaves.

Nutrition: Calories: 143 Fat: 5.4g. Sodium: 37.4mg. Carbohydrates: 0g. Fiber: 0g. Sugars: 0g. Protein: 17g.

430. Mussels In Red Wine Sauce

Preparation time: 5 Minutes
Cooking time: 50 Minutes
Servings: 2

Ingredients:

- 800g 2lb mussels
- 2 x 400g 14 oz. tins of chopped tomatoes
- 25g 1oz butter
- 1 tablespoon fresh chives, chopped
- 1 tablespoon fresh parsley, chopped
- 1 bird's-eye chili, finely chopped
- 4 cloves of garlic, crushed
- 400 ml 14fl. oz. red wine
- Juice of 1 lemon
- 364 calories per serving

Directions:

1. Wash the mussels, remove their beards and set them aside. Heat the butter in a large saucepan and add in the red wine. Reduce the heat and add the parsley, chives, chili and garlic whilst stirring. Add in the tomatoes, lemon juice and mussels. Cover the saucepan and cook for 2-3 minutes. Remove the saucepan from the heat and take out any mussels which haven't opened and discard them. Serve and eat immediately.

Nutrition: Calories: 180 kcal Protein: 7.46 g Fat: 7.5 g Carbohydrates: 22.58 g

431. Roast Balsamic Vegetables

Preparation time: 5 Minutes
Cooking time: 45 Minutes
Servings: 2

Ingredients:

- 4 tomatoes, chopped
- 2 red onions, chopped
- 3 sweet potatoes, peeled and chopped
- 100g 3½ oz. red chicory or if unavailable, use yellow
- 100g 3½ oz. kale, finely chopped
- 300g 11oz potatoes, peeled and chopped
- 5 stalks of celery, chopped
- 1 bird's-eye chili, de-seeded and finely chopped
- 2 tablespoons fresh parsley, chopped
- 2 tablespoons fresh coriander cilantro chopped
- 3 tablespoons olive oil
- 2 tablespoons balsamic vinegar 1 teaspoon mustard
- Sea salt
- Freshly ground black pepper
- 310 calories per serving

Directions:

1. Place the olive oil, balsamic, mustard, parsley and coriander cilantro into a bowl and mix well. Toss all the remaining ingredients into the dressing and season with salt and pepper. Transfer the vegetables to an ovenproof dish and cook in the oven at 200C/400F for 45 minutes.

Nutrition: Calories 330 Total Fat 18.9 g Saturated Fat 1.9 g Cholesterol 64 mg

432. Ginger Prawn Stir-Fry

Preparation time: 5 Minutes
Cooking time: 50 Minutes
Servings: 1

Ingredients:

- 6 prawns or shrimp peeled and deveined
- ½ package of buckwheat noodles called Soba in Asian sections
- 5-6 leaves of kale, chopped
- 1 cup of green beans, chopped
- 5 g Lovage or celery leaves
- 1 garlic clove, finely chopped
- 1 bird's eye chili, finely chopped
- 1 tsp. fresh ginger, finely chopped
- 2 stalks celery, chopped
- ½ small red onion, chopped
- 1 cup chicken stock or vegetable if you prefer
- 2 tbsp. soy sauce

- 2 tbsp. extra virgin olive oil

Directions:

1. Cook prawns in a bit of the oil and soy sauce until done and set aside about 10-15 minutes).
2. Boil the noodles according to the directions, usually 6-8 minutes). Set aside.
3. Sauté the vegetables, then add the garlic, ginger, red onion, chili in a bit of oil until tender and crunchy, but not mushy. Add the prawns, and noodles, and simmer low about 5-10 minutes past that point.

Nutrition: Calories: 330 Carbohydrates: 57g Fat 10g Protein: 23 g

433. Hot Chicory & Nut Salad

Preparation time: 5 Minutes
Cooking time: 40 Minutes
Servings: 2

Ingredients:

- For the salad:
- 100g 3½oz green beans
- 100g 3½oz red chicory, chopped if unavailable use yellow chicory
- 100g 3½oz celery, chopped
- 25g 1oz macadamia nuts, chopped
- 25g 1oz walnuts, chopped
- 25g 1oz plain peanuts, chopped
- 2 tomatoes, chopped
- 1 tablespoon olive oil
- For the dressing:
- 2 tablespoons fresh parsley, finely chopped
- ½ teaspoon turmeric
- ½ teaspoon mustard
- 1 tablespoon olive oil
- 25mls 1fl oz. red wine vinegar
- 438 calories per serving

Directions:

1. Combine the ingredients for the dressing then set them aside. Heat a tablespoon of olive oil in a frying pan then add the green beans, chicory, and celery. Cook until the vegetables have softened, then add in the chopped tomatoes and cook for 2 minutes. Add the prepared dressing, and thoroughly coat all of the vegetables. Serve onto plates and sprinkle the mixture of nuts over the top. Eat immediately.

Nutrition: Calories 262 Total Fat 12 g Saturated Fat 1.6 g Cholesterol 63 mg

434. Honey Chili Squash

Preparation time: 5 Minutes
Cooking time: 50 Minutes
Servings: 2

Ingredients:

- 2 red onions, roughly chopped 2.5cm
- 1-inch chunk of ginger root, finely chopped
- 2 cloves of garlic
- 2 bird's-eye chilies, finely chopped
- 1 butternut squash, peeled and chopped
- 100 ml 3½ fl. oz. vegetable stock broth
- 1 tablespoon olive oil
- Juice of 1 orange
- Juice of 1 lime
- 2 teaspoons honey
- 118 calories per serving

Directions:

1. Warm the oil into a pan and add in the red onions, squash chunks, chilies, garlic, ginger, and honey. Cook for 3 minutes. Squeeze in the lime and orange juice. Pour in the stock broth), orange and lime juice, and cook for 15 minutes until tender.

Nutrition: Calories: 403 kcal Protein: 16.15 g Fat: 15.28 g

435. Serrano Ham & Rocket Arugula

Preparation time: 5 Minutes
Cooking time: 60 Minutes
Servings: 2

Ingredients:

- 175g 6ozSerrano ham
- 125g 4oz rocket arugula leaves
- 2 tablespoons olive oil
- 1 tablespoon orange juice

Directions:

1. Pour the oil and juice into a bowl and toss the rocket arugula in the mixture. Serve the rocket onto plates and top it off with the ham.

Nutrition: Calories: 403 kcal Protein: 16.15 g Fat: 15.28 g Carbohydrates: 50.87 g

436. Parsnip Fries

Preparation time: 15 minutes
Cooking time: 25 minutes
Servings: 4

Ingredients:

- 8 oz. parsnip, peeled
- ½ teaspoon white pepper
- 1 tablespoon avocado oil

Directions:

1. Cut the parsnip into the French fries' shape and sprinkle with avocado oil.
2. Then line the baking tray using baking paper and put the parsnip fries inside in one layer.
3. Bake the parsnips fries for 25 minutes at 355F. Flip them on another side after 15 minutes of cooking.
4. Sprinkle the cooked parsnip fries with white pepper.

Nutrition: Calories 48 Fat 0.6 Fiber 3 Carbs 10.6 Protein 0.8

437. Fried Shrimps

Preparation time: 5 minutes
Cooking time: 10 minutes
Servings: 2

Ingredients:

- 6 oz. shrimps, peeled
- 1 teaspoon avocado oil
- 1 teaspoon cayenne pepper

Directions:

1. Pour the avocado oil in the skillet and heat it.
2. Add shrimps.
3. After this, sprinkle the shrimps with cayenne pepper and stir well.
4. Cook the shrimps for 10 minutes on the medium heat.

Nutrition: Calories 107 Fat 1.9 Fiber 0.3 Carbs 1.9 Protein 19.5

438. Lemon Tapenade

Preparation time: 10 minutes
Cooking time: 0 minutes
Servings: 6

Ingredients:

- ½ cup black olives, pitted
- ¼ cup green olives, pitted
- 1 tablespoon capers
- 1 tablespoon fresh parsley
- 1 tablespoon lemon zest
- 2 tablespoons olive oil

- 1 teaspoon garlic, chopped
- 2 tablespoons lemon juice

Directions:

1. Place the black olives and green olives in the blender.
2. Blend them until you get a smooth mixture.
3. After this, add capers, fresh parsley, lemon zest, olive oil, garlic, and lemon juice.
4. Blend the mixture until smooth.
5. Transfer it in the serving bowl.

Nutrition: Calories 70 Fat 7.4 Fiber 0.8 Carbs 1.3 Protein 0.3

439. Collard Greens Rolls

Preparation time: 15 minutes
Cooking time: 40 minutes
Servings: 6

Ingredients:

- 6 collard green leaves (appx 1 cup)
- 1 cup ground chicken
- 1 teaspoon salt
- 1 tablespoon shallot, chopped
- ¼ cup chicken broth
- ½ teaspoon cayenne pepper

Directions:

1. In the mixing bowl, combine ground chicken, salt, shallot, and cayenne pepper.
2. Then fill the collard greens with ground chicken mixture and roll them.
3. Place the collard greens rolls in the baking mold.
4. Put chicken broth.
5. Bake the rolls for at least 40 minutes at 365F.

Nutrition: Calories 50 Fat 1.9 Fiber 0.3 Carbs 0.8 Protein 7.2

440. Eggplant Italiano

Preparation time: 1 minute
Cooking time: 25 minutes
Servings: 8

Ingredients:

- 2½ lbs. eggplant, cubed
- 4 celery stalks, cut into 1-inch pieces
- 2 sliced onions
- 7½ oz. canned tomato sauce
- 2 cans (16 ounces) diced tomatoes with its juice
- 2tbsps. olive oil, divided
- 1 c. olives pitted and halved
- 4tbsps. balsamic vinegar
- 2tbsps. drained capers
- 1 tbsp. maple syrup
- 2 tsp. Dried basil
- Salt
- Pepper
- Basil leaves to garnish

Directions:

1. Add all the ingredients into the Instant Pot. Stir to mix well.
2. Close the lid. Click "Manual" then cook over high pressure for 4 minutes.
3. When the cooking is complete, do quick release pressures.
4. Garnish with fresh basil and serve over rice or noodles.

Nutrition: Calories: 127 Fat: 5.8 g Carbs: 11.6 Protein: 3 g

441. Quinoa With Mushrooms And Peppers

Preparation time: 10 minutes
Cooking time: 25 minutes
Servings: 8

Ingredients:

- 2½ c. quinoa, rinsed
- 2 chopped onions
- 20 diced button mushrooms
- 1 minced red chili
- 2 red bell peppers, sliced
- 2 sliced green bell peppers
- 4tbsps. miso paste
- 4tbsps. soy sauce
- 2½ c. vegetable broth
- 6tbsps. olive oil
- Salt
- 4 cloves garlic, grated and chopped
- 2tbsps. tomato paste
- 2tbsps. lemon juice
- A handful fresh cilantro, chopped

Directions:

1. Press the SAUTÉ button. Add oil. When the oil is heated, add onion, mushroom, salt, and chili and sauté until onion turns translucent.
2. Add the quinoa along with the remaining ingredients and stir. Press "Cancel."
3. Close the lid. Select "Manual" and cook at high pressure for 5 minutes.
4. When the cooking is complete, do a natural pressure release for 10 minutes. Quick-release it the remaining pressure.
5. Fluff with a fork garnished with cilantro, and serve.

Nutrition: Calories: 348 Fat: 14.5 g Carbs: 39.2 Protein: 11.5 g

442. Turkey Escalope With Saga

Preparation time: 5 minutes
Cooking time: 5 minutes
Servings: 1

Ingredients:

- For the turkey escalope
- 1 x 150g/5½oz piece turkey bosom
- 1 tbsp. olive oil
- 3 crisp sage leaves
- For the sauce Vierge
- 1 tbsp. olive oil
- ½ lemons
- 1 tomato, seeds expelled, cleaved
- Bunch new parsley, cleaved
- Bunch new chives, cleaved
- Salt and newly ground dark pepper

Directions:

1. For the turkey escalope, place the turkey bosom between two sheets of stick film and level with a moving pin or the base of a griddle.
2. Warmth the oil in a skillet at medium heat temperature, cook the escalope with the savvy leaves for 3-4 minutes on each side, or totally cook through. Expel the turkey from the dish and put aside to keep warm.
3. For the sauce verge, in a similar container, heat the staying olive oil with the lemon juice, cleaved tomato, and herbs until stewing.
4. Season it with salt and ground dark pepper.
5. To serve, place the turkey escalope onto a serving plate and shower over the sauce Verge.

Nutrition: Calories: 340 Total Fat: 20 g Total Carbohydrates: 15 g Protein: 22 g

443. Baked Asparagus With Mushrooms, Tomatoes, And Mozzarella

Preparation time: 20 minutes
Cooking time: 30 minutes
Servings: 2
Ingredients:

- 500 g asparagus
- 150 g mushrooms
- 2-3 tomatoes
- 200 g mozzarella
- Butter flakes at will
- 150 ml white wine
- 1 tsp. vegetable broth powder
- 1 lemon / lime (squeezed)
- Salt and pepper

Directions:

1. Wash and peel asparagus, clean and slice mushrooms, sliced tomatoes.
2. Place the finished asparagus in a baking dish, distribute the mushrooms and tomatoes evenly over them and season well with salt and pepper, top with the sliced mozzarella. Spread thin flakes of butter evenly over the top.
3. Mix white wine, vegetable broth, and lemon juice and pour over it.
4. Place the casserole into the oven then bake at 220 ° C for at least 30 minutes.

Nutrition: Calories: 113.7 Total Fat: 7.3 g Total Carbohydrates: 8.7 g Protein: 5.2 g

444. Toasted Sardines With Parsley

Preparation time: 10 minutes
Cooking time: 15 minutes
Servings: 4
Ingredients:

- 400 g fresh sardines already cleaned
- 2 lemons zest
- Salt
- 50 g chopped parsley
- 1 teaspoon black pepper
- 1 crushed clove garlic
- 2 tbsp. white wine
- 1 tablespoon extra-virgin olive oil

Directions:

1. Prepare the sauce by mixing the parsley, pepper, garlic clove, and thinly grated lemon zest. Then add the white wine, lemon juice, and oil.
2. Cook the sardines in a non-stick pan for 1 minute each side.
3. When serving, pour a small amount of sauce on the plate, put the sardines on top and season with other sauce. Complete with a pinch of salt and lemon zest cut into strips.

Nutrition: Calories: 300 Fat: 16.9g Protein: 20.3g Carbohydrate: 6.9g Fiber: 0.9g

445. Savory Crêpes With Vegetables

Preparation time: 5 minutes
Cooking time: 15 minutes
Servings: 12
Ingredients:

- For the crepes batter
- 2 eggs
- 90 g 00 flour
- 150 ml partially skimmed milk
- 1 pinch salt
- 1/2 teaspoon extra virgin olive oil
- For the stuffing
- 500 g spinach
- 10 g parmesan
- Salt
- Pepper
- For the dressing
- 300 g cherry tomatoes
- 1 clove garlic
- 1 teaspoon extra virgin olive oil
- Salt
- Basil leaves

Directions:

1. Start preparing the crepes batter: beat the eggs in a bowl with the help of a whisk, add the milk, a pinch of salt, and beat again.
2. Add the sifted flour, little by little, constantly stirring with the whisk to create a smooth and homogeneous, lump-free batter.
3. Heat half a teaspoon of oil in a non-stick pan or a crepe pan with a sheet of absorbent paper and remove the excess oil.
4. When it is hot, pour a ladle of batter and cook for about 2 minutes on low heat. Turn the crepes over and cook for 1-2 minutes. Repeat the operation until the batter runs out.
5. Boil the spinach in boiling water, when they are soft, drain, squeeze them, and cool. Season them with salt, pepper, and grated Parmesan.
6. Prepare the dressing by heating the teaspoon of oil with the clove of garlic, split in two in a pan.
7. Add the previously cut cherry tomatoes, salt, pepper, and leave to boil for about 5 minutes.
8. Fill the crepes with the spinach filling, season with the sautéed cherry tomatoes, and serve with fresh basil leaves.

Nutrition: Calories: 150 Fat: 7g Protein: 10.3g Carbohydrate: 5.4g Fiber: 0.7g

446. Chicken Skewers With Peppers And Pineapple

Preparation time: 5 minutes
Cooking time: 15 minutes
Servings: 8
Ingredients:

- For the skewers
- 600 g chicken breast
- 400 g peppers
- 320 g fresh or canned natural pineapple
- 3 tablespoons extra virgin olive oil
- 4 garlic cloves
- 2 teaspoons lemon juice
- Salt
- Kitchen skewers
- For the sauce
- 400 ml sugar-free pineapple juice
- 4 teaspoons of corn starch
- 4 tablespoons of tomato puree
- 4 teaspoons balsamic vinegar

- Chili pepper powder
- Salt
- Pepper

Directions:

1. First, prepare the sauce: place all the ingredients in a saucepan, put the corn starch with a sieve and cook over low heat, stirring to prevent lumps from forming.
2. Once the sauce is smooth, season with salt and pepper and turn off the heat. In the meantime, chopped the chicken breast, peppers, and pineapple into coarse cubes and alternate on the skewers.
3. Prepare a marinade with crushed garlic, lemon juice, a pinch of salt, and extra virgin olive oil. Allow it to flavor for a few minutes, brush the skewers, and rest for 5-10 minutes.
4. Brown the skewers in a non-stick pan cover them and cook for 15 minutes, turning them on one side and the other to cook them well. Arrange the skewers on a platter, sail with the prepared sauce, and serve on the table. Chicken skewers with peppers and pineapple lend themselves to be eaten hot or cold.

Nutrition: Calories: 315 Fat: 20.9g Protein: 15.8g Carbohydrate: 5.4g Fiber: 0.4g

447. Light Tuna And Bread Salad

Preparation time: 5 minutes
Cooking time: 15 minutes
Servings: 2

Ingredients:

- 4-5 slices of bread cut not too thin
- 3 boxes of natural tuna
- 4-5 not too ripe tomatoes for a salad
- Salt and pepper
- 4 spoons of olive oil
- A pinch of oregano

Directions:

1. Heat a non-stick pan and, in the meantime, cut the slices of bread into coarse cubes. Add the bread to the pan, leaving it toasted well from all sides and then turning it often.
2. As soon as the bread is ready, let it cool.
3. In a salad bowl or four smaller bowls, put the bread, drain the tuna, distribute it on the bread, and add a pinch of oregano.
4. We cut the tomatoes into not too regular cubes and put them in the salad.
5. We can choose to season the salad with oil, salt, and pepper (I recommend it if we have opted for a large bowl) and mix well, or use the condiments separately (I recommend it in case of using bowls)
6. Let's serve!

Nutrition: Calories: 216 Fat: 16.9g Protein: 13.3g Carbohydrate: 3.4g Fiber: 0.9g

448. Zucchini Carpaccio With Natural Mackerel

Preparation time: 5 minutes
Cooking time: 15 minutes
Servings: 12

Ingredients:

- 240 g of mackerel fillets
- 400g of Courgettes
- 80 ml of extra virgin olive oil
- The juice of one lemon
- Parsley
- A few mint leaves
- Some grain of pink pepper
- Salt

Directions:

1. Cut the Zucchini into thin slices, place it in a tray, and add the salt. Leave the Courgettes to rest for 10 minutes; in this way, they will take out all the liquids contained and become softer.
2. We prepare the dressing - In a bowl, we put the extra virgin olive oil and the juice of a lemon, add the salt and begin to mix quickly with a whisk to create an emulsion.
3. We combine the finely chopped parsley and some crushed pink pepper; we mix again until everything is mixed.
4. We prepare the zucchini Carpaccio - take the slices of zucchini, dry them with kitchen paper, and place them in a bowl. Pour over the dressing and mix until everything is mixed.
5. We serve in a single serving dish, arranging the Carpaccio as a base, and on top, we have the Grilled Mackerel Fillets adding a drizzle of oil.

Nutrition: Calories: 216 Fat: 16.9g Protein: 13.3g Carbohydrate: 3.4g Fiber: 0.9g

449. Couscous With Vegetables Au Gratin

Preparation time: 5 minutes
Cooking time: 15 minutes
Servings: 12

Ingredients:

- 150g of couscous
- 250ml of hot water
- Half a red pepper
- Half a yellow pepper
- A medium courgette
- 2 medium potatoes
- Parsley to taste
- Extra virgin olive oil to taste
- Salt and pepper
- 20-30g of parmesan already grated

Directions:

1. Cut the peppers and courgette into small cubes. Steam the vegetables for 5-10 minutes depending on the quantity, taste before removing from the steamer.
2. Take the hot water and pour it over the couscous, taking into consideration the brand's instructions. Cover the bowl containing the couscous and leave it for 10-15 minutes, until the water has been completely absorbed.
3. Take the ready-made couscous and shell it with a fork, add the vegetables, salt and pepper, chopped parsley, and a drizzle of oil.
4. Take the potatoes, cut them finely with the mandolin, lay them half on the bottom of an oiled oven pan, fill with the couscous, spread another row of chopped potatoes like chips, and a drizzle of oil and finally the parmesan. Bake at 200 ° until the surface is golden brown and then for about 20-25 minutes.

Nutrition: Calories: 219 Fat: 16.9g Protein: 13.3g Carbohydrate: 3.4g Fiber: 0.9g

450. Steamed Spelled With Salmon And Tomatoes

Preparation time: 5 minutes
Cooking time: 15 minutes
Servings: 12

Ingredients:

- 200g spelled

- 3 long salad tomatoes
- 100g of Fjord salmon
- A small fennel
- A little chopped parsley
- A drizzle of extra virgin olive oil
- Salt and pepper

Directions:

1. Soak the spelled for 12 hours, and read the directions on the package here because times vary depending on the brand. Steam the spelled with the steamer in very small holes or with a colander to be placed on a pan, perhaps the one for the pasta without letting the colander touch the water. Here too times vary according to the brand of spelled used, they are longer than normal cooking, and sometimes they can double. You must use two parts of water and one of the cereal to regulate cooking. The advantage, in this case, is that the spelled will have a better flavor and texture.
2. When the spelled is cooked, chop the salmon, add it to the steamer, leave it for 2-3 minutes maximum with the lid closed, or add the salmon cold.
3. Take the spelled with salmon, put it in a bowl and add two-three diced salad tomatoes, add a drizzle of oil, a little chopped parsley, the cubed fennel, and season with salt and pepper.

Nutrition: Calories: 345 Fat: 21.9g Protein: 13.3g Carbohydrate: 3.4g Fiber: 0.9g

451. Fettuccini Alfredo Healthy Version

Preparation time: 5 minutes
Cooking time: 15 minutes
Servings: 12

Ingredients:

- 350 g of spaghetti or other pasta
- 300 g of cauliflower
- Salt and Pepper To Taste
- A little bit of oil
- 40 g of parmesan
- Chopped parsley to taste

Directions:

1. Put the water for the pasta. Blanch the cauliflower and chop it with the blender or mixer by adding a little cooking water to obtain a soft cream. Salt and pepper.
2. Cook the spaghetti or fettuccine and drain them al dente. Add them to the cauliflower cream and mix well.

Nutrition: Calories: 298 Fat: 16.9g Protein: 14.6g Carbohydrate: 4.5g Fiber: 0.9g

452. Parmesan Cauliflower

Preparation time: 5 minutes
Cooking time: 15 minutes
Servings: 12

Ingredients:

- A medium cauliflower
- 3 eggs
- 200g of flour
- 100g of breadcrumbs
- 100g of grated Parmesan
- Chopped fresh parsley
- Salt and pepper

Directions:

1. We blanch the cauliflower in salted water for about ten minutes and immediately drain it and pass it under cold water to stop cooking. Let's dry it well.
2. Obtain many small cauliflower flowers from the cauliflower, trying to dissect it with your hands. We pass the cauliflower pieces in the flour, then in the beaten eggs and then in the breading made of breadcrumbs, parmesan, finely chopped parsley, salt, and pepper.
3. Heat the oil and fry our cauliflowers with Parmesan until they become golden brown. Drain and salt.

Nutrition: Calories: 386 Fat: 16.9g Protein: 13.3g Carbohydrate: 6.9g Fiber: 0.5g

453. Bbq Tempeh Sandwiches

Preparation time: 10 minutes
Cooking time: 45 minutes
Servings: 4

Ingredients:

- 8 ounces Tempeh, sliced into long strips
- 75 cup Barbecue sauce
- 5 teaspoon Liquid smoke
- 1.5 cups Red cabbage, shredded
- 5 cup Carrots, shredded
- 5 cup Red onion, diced
- 5 teaspoon Date sugar
- 1.5 teaspoons sea salt
- 1 tablespoon Apple cider vinegar
- 5 teaspoon Garlic powder
- 2 tablespoons Mayonnaise
- 25 teaspoon Black pepper, ground
- 4 Whole wheat buns

Directions:

1. Place the sliced tempeh in a glass baking dish and coat it in the barbecue sauce and the liquid smoke. While you don't have to add the liquid smoke, it is a great addition that makes it taste like it has come fresh off the grill. Allow the dish to marinate for at least forty-five minutes.
2. When the tempeh is nearly done marinating, begin to preheat your oven to Fahrenheit four-hundred and fifty degrees.
3. Cover the tempeh in a sheet of aluminum, bake it for the first thirty minutes, and then remove the aluminum and bake it for an additional five minutes.
4. Meanwhile, prepare the slaw by combining the remaining ingredients (except for the buns) in a bowl. Once combined, cover the bowl and allow it to meld in the fridge until the tempeh is done cooking. It is best to make the slaw when you first put the tempeh in the oven, rather than near the end, as it gives the flavors longer to meld.
5. To serve, divide the tempeh strips between the buns and then top them off with the slaw.

Nutrition: Calories 382kcal 17g fat 22g carbohydrates 26g protein

454. Tofu Tikka Masala

Preparation time: 5 minutes
Cooking time: 30 minutes
Servings: 4

Ingredients:

- 14 ounces Tofu, extra-firm, sliced into bite-sized cubes
- 1 teaspoon Cumin
- 2 teaspoons ginger, peeled and grated
- .5 teaspoon Sweet paprika
- .5 teaspoon Turmeric
- 2 cloves Garlic, minced
- 1.5 teaspoons Garam masala
- 5 teaspoon Coriander powder
- 25 teaspoon Cayenne
- 1 cup Tomato passata (if not available use puree)

- 14 ounces Coconut milk, full-fat
- 2 tablespoons Olive oil
- 1 Red onion, diced
- 1 teaspoon Sea salt

Directions:

1. Add the olive oil, red onion, and salt to a skillet and cook over medium until the onions have become soft for about five minutes. Add in the grated ginger and minced garlic, cooking for a minute before adding in all the spices. Cook for an additional two minutes, until the spices are fragrant. Keep a close eye on the spices, constantly stirring to avoid burning.
2. Stir the tomato passata or puree into the skillet and allow it to continue cooking until thickened and reduced, about ten to fifteen minutes.
3. Add the tofu and canned coconut milk to the skillet and bring the pan to a boil. Reduce the stove to low and allow the tikka masala to simmer for ten minutes. Serve warm over brown rice or buckwheat.

Nutrition: Calories 344 kcal, 17g fat,22g carbohydrates, 26g protein

455. Tempeh Vegan Chili

Preparation time: 10 minutes
Cooking time: 20 minutes
Servings: 3

Ingredients:

- 8 ounces Tempeh, roughly grated
- 2 tablespoons extra virgin olive oil
- 1Red onion, diced
- 1 rib Celery, diced
- 1 Bell pepper, diced
- 4 cloves Garlic, minced
- 15 ounces Black beans, drained and rinsed
- 15 ounces Kidney beans, drained and rinsed
- 75 cup Tomato sauce
- 1.25 cups Water
- 1 tablespoon Chili powder
- .25 teaspoon Crushed red pepper flakes
- 2 teaspoons Cumin, ground
- 1 teaspoon Sea salt
- 1 tablespoon Cocoa powder

Directions:

1. Add the extra virgin olive oil and grated tempeh to a large pot and brown over medium heat for five minutes.
2. Add the celery, garlic, bell pepper, and onions to the pot, cooking until slightly tender, about five more minutes.
3. Stir in the remaining ingredient and allow the chili to simmer and the flavors to meld for approximately fifteen minutes. Serve warm with your favorite chili toppings.

Nutrition: Calories 455 kcal 17g fat 22g carbohydrates 26g protein

456. Spicy Garlic Soba Noodles With Bok Choy

Preparation time: 10 minutes
Cooking time: 10 minutes
Servings: 4

Ingredients:

- 6 ounces Soba noodles
- 6 ounces Baby bok choy
- 1 cup Bean sprouts
- 3 Green onions, diced, whites and greens separated
- 3 cloves Garlic, minced
- 3 teaspoons Sesame seed oil, divided
- 2 tablespoons Tahini paste
- 1 tablespoon Rice wine vinegar
- 1 tablespoon Chili garlic sauce
- 1 tablespoon Sriracha sauce
- 3 tablespoons Tamari sauce
- 25 cup Peanuts, roasted, chopped
- 25 teaspoon Red pepper, flakes

Directions:

1. In a bowl, create a sauce for the soba by whisking together the tahini paste, tamari sauce, chili garlic sauce, sriracha sauce, red wine vinegar, and two teaspoons sesame seed oil. After combining, set the sauce aside.
2. Bring a large steel pot of water to a boil. Once boiling, add the soba noodles to the pot, and cook until tender, about seven minutes. Drain the boiling water then rinse the noodles with cold water.
3. While the noodles cook, prepare the bok choy by adding it to a large skillet along with the sesame seed oil and red pepper flakes. Cook over medium-high heat while frequently flipping until the bok choy has begun to wilt. Remove the bok choy from the pan and set aside.
4. Add the whites of the green onions and the garlic to the skillet, cooking for thirty seconds until fragrant.
5. Pour the bean sprouts and half of the prepared sauce into the skillet with the onion and garlic, heating for an additional thirty seconds.
6. Lower the heat to medium-low, then put the remaining sauce and cooked noodles. Toss until the soba noodles are coated in the garlic sauce and then add the bok choy back to the pan, continuing to cook until all the ingredients are heated through.
7. Top the dish with the greens of the onions and the peanuts before serving.

Nutrition: Calories 313 kcal, 17g fat, 22g carbohydrates, 26g protein

457. Quinoa Nut And Radicchio Meatballs

Preparation time: 20 minutes
Cooking time: 25 minutes
Servings:

Ingredients:

- 120 grams of white quinoa;
- 2 tufts of late-growing radicchio di Treviso PGI;
- 80 grams of walnut kernels;
- 2 teaspoons of turmeric;
- 1 cup of foil flour;
- 2 teaspoons of marjoram;
- Extra virgin olive oil;
- Salt and pepper to taste

Directions:

1. Wash the quinoa and boil it in lightly salted water until the seeds open and are soft;
2. When the quinoa is cooked, squeeze it well, add the turmeric and pepper and keep it aside;
3. In a centrifuge, add the nuts, salt, pepper, and radicchio previously washed, blanched and dried well, and add a drizzle of oil. Blend everything until a cream is obtained. Add the quinoa cream;
4. With floured hands, form balls from the dough and roll them into a mix of flour and chives;
5. Crush the meatballs at the ends. If the dough is too soft, leave it to rest for half an hour or thicken it with a little flour;

6. Place the meatballs on a sheet of baking paper sprinkled with oil and bake at 180° for twenty minutes. Halfway through cooking, turn the meatballs to the other side;
7. Take them out of the oven then put them on an absorbent sheet to remove excess oil. Serve them hot.

Nutrition: Calories: 385 kcal Protein: 12.52 g Fat: 16.78 g Carbohydrates: 48.09 g

458. Vegan Broccoli And Tofu Flan With Mandarin Flavoring

Preparation time: 15 minutes
Cooking time: 30 minutes
Servings: 4

Ingredients:

- Broccoli
- An orange carrot
- Tofu 125 gr
- 2 seedless tangerines
- Pepper and salt to taste
- Extra virgin olive oil
- 1 teaspoon of marjoram
- A glass of soy-based vegetable drink
- Quinoa;
- Olive oil for frying.
- Ingredients for the milk cream:
- 250 ml of natural soymilk
- Curcuma
- Nutmeg and salt to taste

Directions:

1. Put the soy drink with turmeric, a pinch of nutmeg, and salt on the stove in a kettle. Let it season until it starts to boil, take it off the heat, let it cool and put it in the fridge;
2. Clean the broccoli by removing the outer leaves, cut it into pieces, and cook in hot water with the peeled and chopped. After ten minutes, drain it and sauté it in a pan with a drizzle of oil, it must cook until soft;
3. Wash and dry the tofu, cut it into pieces, blend it with the thickened vegetables, and add salt, pepper, and a little marjoram;
4. Add the juice from the mandarins and, if necessary, a few tablespoons of soy milk, until you get a smooth, creamy mixture;
5. Fill the single-portion stencils with flour and flour and bake the flans at 180° for about 20 minutes, until they are golden brown;
6. Heat a few tablespoons of oil for frying and add a couple of handfuls of quinoa, let it brown and drain well when ready.
7. For Cream:
8. Take a bowl, cool it under running water, and dry it well;
9. Pour the soy drink together with the turmeric and a drizzle of oil into the bowl, mix everything until you get a frothy mixture;
10. Assemble the dish, pouring the cream in the center, and placing the flan and quinoa sofrito on top.

Nutrition: Calories: 114 kcal Protein: 7.3 g Fat: 7.88 g Carbohydrates: 5.38 g

459. Chicken Paprika And Vegetables

Preparation time: 10 minutes
Cooking time: 50 minutes
Servings: 4

Ingredients:

- 60 gr of extra virgin olive oil
- 40 grams of paprika
- 2 orange carrots
- Half celeriac
- 3 turnips
- 300 gr Chicken wings
- 1 liter Vegetable broth
- Thyme and rosemary;
- 2 leaves Fresh bay
- Pepper and salt to taste
- Lemon;
- 1 cap of chopped cabbage.

Directions:

1. Clean and chop celeriac, turnip, and carrot;
2. In a large pan, warm a drizzle of olive oil, put the chicken wings, paprika, and chopped vegetables, and cook for a few minutes;
3. Add salt and pepper, thyme and rosemary on the chicken wings and add a spoon of vegetable stock, cover the pan and let it boil;
4. When the broth dries add another spoon, and continue cooking the chicken on a low flame for about 40 minutes;
5. In the meantime, remove the cabbage's outer leaves, wash it, chop it up, put it in the pan with the paprika chicken, and continue to cook with the stock's help until the cabbage is cooked;
6. Put out the fire, cover, and let it rest for a few minutes before serving.

Nutrition: Calories: 211 kcal Protein: 20.13 g Fat: 11.55 g Carbohydrates: 8.93 g

460. Courgette Tortillas

Preparation time: 10 minutes
Cooking time: 30 minutes
Servings: 4

Ingredients:

- Butter in chunks 20 gr, or 2 spoons of coconut oil;
- 2 green zucchini;
- 4 whole eggs;
- Pepper and salt to taste
- Parsley or chives.

Directions:

1. Wash and slice the zucchini;
2. In a high pot, melt the butter or heat the oil. When it is ready, pour in the freshly cut zucchini and stir well until they soften;
3. In a bowl break the four eggs, beat them adding salt, pepper, parsley, or chives. Pour the mixture over the zucchini and almost finish cooking;
4. Cook until the eggs are almost cooked. Before finishing cooking put the pot in the oven and turn on the grill to toast the tortillas;

Nutrition: Calories: 185 kcal Protein: 12.14 g Fat: 13.7 g Carbohydrates: 3.33 g

461. Sea Bream With Hot Walnut Sauce

Preparation Time: 5 Minutes
Cooking time: 40 minutes
Servings: 6-8

Ingredients:

- Walnut sauce;
- 1.5 kg of sea bream (frozen is also good);
- Shell less walnuts 300 gr;
- Parsley 5/6 branches;
- Garlic 9 wedges;

- Extra virgin olive oil 140 ml;
- 2 fresh chillies;
- 2 lemons;
- Salt.

Directions:

1. Clean and dry the sea bream, taking care to remove the skin and bones, then place the sea bream fillets on a baking tray with baking paper;
2. Mince together and put the parsley, chilli peppers, and walnuts in a bowl, crush the garlic cloves. Put the oil, lemon juice, and a pinch of salt.
3. With the emulsion obtained, you stuff the sea bream. If there's any leftover, pour it on top too;
4. Bake at 180° for 30/40 minutes;
5. Spicy sea bream can be eaten either hot or cold at will;
6. Extra idea: in pomegranate season, squeeze the juice from half a pomegranate and add it to the emulsion.

Nutrition: Calories: 662 kcal Protein: 16.24 g Fat: 42.65 g Carbohydrates: 61.96 g

462. Braised Pork Belly And Avocado Skewer

Preparation time: 5 minutes
Cooking time: 15 minutes
Servings:
Ingredients:

- 1 1/2 pounds pork belly
- 1 tablespoon samba
- 6 cups of water
- 2 tablespoons sugar
- 2 tablespoons whole-grain mustard
- 1/2 tablespoon salt
- 1 teaspoon cayenne
- 3 tablespoons sherry vinegar
- 2 avocados, cubed
- 8 skewers

Directions:

1. Preheat oven to 300°F. Place samba, water, sugar, mustard, salt, cayenne, and sherry vinegar in a small saucepan, heat just until sugar and salt dissolve. Place pork in a baking dish and cover with braising liquid. Cover dish with plastic wrap, followed by aluminum foil. Braise in the oven and cook for approximately 3 1/2 hours, or until tender. Remove pork belly and let cool. While the pork belly is cooling, drain liquid and place in a small saucepot. Reduce until consistency has developed, then remove from heat. Once the abdomen is cold, slice into one 1/2-inch cube. Skewer one piece of pork and one piece of avocado on a skewer. Grill while basting with the sauce, and serve.

Nutrition: 72 calories; 50 g complete fat; 21 mg cholesterol; 20mg sodium.65 mg potassium; 8g starches; 69 mcg folate; 29 mg calcium; 55 mg magnesium.

463. Pastalaaya

Preparation time: 10 minutes
Cooking time: 35 minutes
Servings:
Ingredients:

- 1 tbsp. vegetable oil
- 1/2 lb. smoked sausage (ideally Andouille)
- 2 cloves garlic
- 10 Oz pack solidified "flavoring mix"*
- 15 Oz can dice tomatoes
- 1/2 Tbsps. Creole seasoning
- 1/2 tsp oregano
- 1/2 tsp smoked paprika
- 1/4 tsp thyme
- Crisply split pepper
- 2 cups chicken stock
- 1 cup of water
- 1 lb. penne pasta
- 2 Tbsps. creamer or cream
- 1/2 pack crisp parsley
- 1/2 pack green onions

Directions:

1. Cut the smoked sausage into slight rounds; at that point, cut any more significant parts down the middle. Include the hotdog and vegetable oil to an enormous pot and cook over medium warmth until the meat is all around sautéed (around 5 min). Sauté for one moment, or until the garlic is delicate and fragrant. Include the sack of solidified flavoring blend and sauté until warmed through (3-5 minutes). Include the container of diced tomatoes (with juices), Creole flavoring, oregano, smoked paprika, thyme, crisply split pepper (around 20 wrenches of a pepper factory), and pasta to the pot. Last, include the chicken stock and 1 cup of water and mix until everything is equally consolidated. Spot a cover on the Pan and turn the warmth up to medium-high. Let the pot reach boiling point. When it arrives at a bubble, mix quickly, supplant the top, turn the heat down to low, and let the pot stew for 10-12 minutes, or until the pasta is delicate. Mix the pot once at regular intervals as it stews to keep the pasta from staying. Supplant the top as fast as conceivable to keep up a stew. If the blend, despite everything, appears to be soupy at around 8 minutes, let the pot stew without a cover throughout the previous couple of moments. A tad of thick sauce at the base of the pot is excellent. While the pasta is stewing, cleave the parsley and cut the green onions. Mood killer the warmth and mix in the half and half or cream. Mix in the more significant part of the cleaved parsley and green onions, saving some to sprinkle over top of each bowl. Serve hot.

Nutrition: 39 g complete fat; 3.8 g immersed fat; 12 mg cholesterol; 15mg sodium. 55 mg potassium; 6g starches; 51 mcg folate; 27 mg calcium; 50 mg magnesium.

464. Goulash

Preparation time: 15 minutes
Cooking time: 45 minutes
Servings:
Ingredients:

- 2 tbsp. extra-virgin olive oil
- 1 medium yellow onion, chopped
- 2 cloves garlic
- 1 lb. Beef
- Kosher salt
- Black pepper
- 1 tbsp. tomato paste
- 1 1/4 c. low-sodium beef broth
- 1 (15-oz.) can tomato sauce
- 1 (15-oz.) can diced tomatoes
- 1 tsp. Italian seasoning
- 1 tsp. paprika
- 1 1/2 c. elbow macaroni, uncooked
- 1 c. shredded cheddar
- Freshly chopped parsley, for garnish

Directions:

1. In a large skillet, heat oil. Put onion and cook for about 5 min. Add garlic and cook about 1 min more. Add ground beef and cook about 6 min. Season with salt and pepper. Add tomato paste, then pour in the broth, tomato sauce, and diced tomatoes. Bring to a simmer and cook, occasionally stirring, until pasta is tender, about 15 minutes. Stir in cheese and remove from heat. Garnish with parsley before serving.

Nutrition: 12 g complete fat; 6.8 g immersed fat; 22 mg cholesterol; 8mg sodium.75 mg potassium; 5g starches; 70 mcg folate; 25 mg calcium; 57 mg magnesium.

465. Garlic Shrimp Ramen

Preparation time: 5 minutes
Cooking time: 20 minutes
Servings: 4

Ingredients:

- 3 packages instant ramen, flavor pack discarded
- 1 tbsp. vegetable oil
- 1 lb. shrimp
- Kosher salt
- Cracked black pepper
- 1 tbsp. sesame oil
- 2 garlic cloves, minced
- 1 tsp. minced ginger
- 1/2 c. soy sauce
- 1/4 c. brown sugar
- 1 lime Juice
- 2 tsp. sriracha
- 1 c. vegetable broth
- 1 large head broccoli, cut into florets
- 1 red bell pepper, cut into thin
- 2 green onions, cut into thin

Directions:

1. Cook ramen noodles according to package instructions. In a large skillet heat vegetable oil. Put sesame oil and stir in garlic and ginger. Cook until fragrant about 1 min. Add soy sauce, brown sugar, lime juice, and Sriracha. Bring mixture to a boil. Add broccoli and peppers and cover the skillet cook vegetables for about 5 min. Return shrimp to skillet and stir until coated in sauce. Mix in cooked ramen noodles and green onions. Serve with Sriracha.

Nutrition: 52 calories 42 g complete fat 32 mg cholesterol 25mg sodium. 65 mg potassium 5g starches 69 mcg folate 29 mg calcium 55 mg magnesium.

466. Chicken And Onion Tagine

Preparation time: 15 minutes
Cooking time: 60 minutes
Servings: 4

Ingredients:

- 1 tbsp. legitimate salt, in addition to additional to taste
- Six cloves garlic, generally cleaved
- 2 tsp. cumin seeds, squashed
- 1 tsp. paprika
- 1 tsp. ground turmeric
- 5 tbsp. olive oil
- 4 skinless bone-in chicken thighs
- 4skinless bone-in chicken drumsticks
- 1 tsp. squashed saffron strings
- 4 medium yellow onions, chopped into 12 wedges
- Crisply ground dark pepper, to taste
- 1 lemon, daintily cut transversely, seeds expelled
- 1 1⁄4 cups pitted green olives
- 1⁄3 cup finely cleaved cilantro

Directions:

1. Make a flavor glue: Using the flat side of your blade, slash and pound garlic together on a cutting board into a paste; move paste to a huge bowl and mix in cumin, paprika, and turmeric. Mix in 3 tbsp. Oil, and afterward include chicken thighs and drumsticks; hurl until equitably covered. Spread bowl with saran wrap, and marinate in the fridge for 4 hours. Warmth remaining oil in an 8-qt. Dutch stove or large tagine over medium-high heat. Working in clumps, include chicken pieces, and cook, turning once, until brilliant darker on the two sides, around 10 minutes; move to a plate and put in a safe spot. Add saffron and onions to the pot, season with salt and pepper, and cook, mixing once in a while, until delicate, around 15 minutes. Return chicken to pot alongside lemon cuts and 1 cup water, and heat to the point of boiling; diminish warmth to medium-low, cook, and secure until chicken is cooked through around 40 minutes. Expel from warmth, and disperse olives and cilantro over chicken; present with rice.

Nutrition: 58 calories; 12 g complete fat 3.8 g immersed fat 42 mg cholesterol 15mg sodium. 5 mg potassium 9g starches 67 mcg folate 20 mg calcium; 53 mg magnesium.

467. Sliced Potato Cake

Preparation time: 15 minutes
Cooking time: 45 minutes
Servings:

Ingredients:

- 2 lbs. potatoes
- 3/4 tsp. salt
- 3/4 tsp. pepper
- 1 tsp. dried Italian herbs
- 3 tbsp. olive oil
- 1 cup destroyed Parmesan cheddar

Directions:

1. Wash and strip the potatoes. Cut them into meager cuts (ideally with a mandolin). Spot the vegetables into an enormous blending bowl. Include the oil, salt, pepper, and Italian herbs. Utilizing your hands, blend tenderly, ensuring the entirety of the cuts is prepared. Include the Parmesan and blend delicately. Spot material paper onto an enormous heating sheet and spot a 10" Springform Pan without the base on top. Include the potato blend inside and spread it pleasantly. Evacuate the Spring form Pan ring. Prepare in a preheated stove at 375°F for around 50-55 minutes, until the potatoes look brilliant dark-colored and are cooked through.

Nutrition: 19 calories; 40 g complete fat; 12 mg cholesterol; 23mg sodium.55 mg potassium; 4g starches; 50 mcg folate; 25 mg calcium; 25 mg magnesium.

468. Smothered Green Beans

Preparation time: 10 minutes
Cooking time: 60 minutes
Servings: 2

Ingredients:

- 5 (15-oz) jars green beans, depleted
- 1 lb. bacon
- 2/3 cup dark colored sugar
- 1/4 cup margarine, dissolved
- 1/4 cup low-sodium soy sauce
- 1-1/2 tsp garlic powder

Directions:

1. Preheat grill to 350 degrees. Pour depleted green beans in an ungreased 9x13-inch container. In a large skillet, fry

bacon until about to done yet not very firm. Expel from skillet, a channel on a paper towel, and leave. Sprinkle cooked bacon over green beans. Whisk together dark colored sugar, dissolved margarine, soy sauce, and garlic powder. Pour over green beans. Heat revealed for 40 minutes.

Nutrition: 12 g complete fat; 12 mg cholesterol; 15mg sodium.25 mg potassium; 3g starches; 29 mcg folate; 19 mg calcium; 20 mg magnesium.

469. White Beans With Garlic, Sage, And Tomatoes

Preparation time: 15 minutes
Cooking time: 2 hours
Servings:

Ingredients:

- 1 cup dried cannellini beans
- 1/4 cup olive oil
- 4 cloves garlic, minced around 2 tbsp.
- 4 new sage leaves, cleaved around 1 tbsp.
- 1/4 cup dry white wine
- 1 28 Oz can San Maranon tomatoes depleted
- Genuine salt and crisply ground dark pepper to taste

Directions:

1. Spread the beans with water in a huge pot and let drench medium-term. Channel beans and re-load up with a new pool in the same Pan. Heat to the boiling point and cook for 1/2 to 2 hours, or until beans are delicate. Channels beans, saving around 1 cup of fluid. In a large skillet over medium warmth, warm the olive oil. Include the garlic and sage and cook until daintily brilliant, around 2 minutes. Include the wine and cook until almost dissipated about 3 minutes. Include the beans and the press the tomatoes into the seeds with your hands. Season with a sound touch of salt and pepper. Stew for 15 minutes, including saved fluid if getting dry. Move to a serving bowl and serve without a moment's delay, or serve at room temperature.

Nutrition: 12calories; 40 g complete fat; 30 mg cholesterol; 21mg sodium. 68mg potassium; 3g starches; 60 mcg folate; 19 mg calcium; 40 mg magnesium.

470. Red Wine Marinated Grilled Tuna Steaks

Preparation time: 10 minutes
Cooking time: 30 minutes
Servings: 3

Ingredients

- 4 (5 ounces) fresh tuna steaks, 1 inch thick
- ¼ cup soy sauce
- ½ cup dry red wine
- ¼ cup extra virgin olive oil
- 1 tablespoon freshly squeezed lime juice
- 1 clove garlic, minced

Directions:

1. Set the tuna steaks in a shallow baking dish.
2. In a medium bowl, mix soy sauce, red wine, olive oil, lime juice, and garlic.
3. Pour the soy sauce mixture over the tuna steaks and turn to coat. Cover, and refrigerate for at least one hour.
4. Preheat grill for high heat.
5. Lightly oil the grill grate and place tuna steaks on the grill, discarding remaining marinade.
6. Grill for 3 to 6 minutes per side, or to desired firmness.

Nutrition: Calories 306, Fat 8.9,Fiber 11.1,Carbs 23.8, Protein 14.5

471. Matcha Green Tea Salmon

Preparation time: 10 minutes
Cooking time: 20 minutes
Servings: 3

Ingredients:

- 4 (5 oz.) salmon fillets
- 2 tablespoons of extra virgin olive oil
- 2 tablespoons of fresh-squeezed lemon juice
- 1 teaspoon of Matcha green tea powder
- ½ cup of wholegrain breadcrumbs
- Salt and pepper to taste

Directions:

1. Preheat the oven to 350 degrees F.
2. Once the oven is heating, put the olive oil, lemon juice, Matcha green tea powder, wholegrain breadcrumbs, salt, and pepper to the large bowl, and knead all the ingredients together using your hands.
3. Place the salmon fillets in the large bowl and cover them with the breadcrumb mixture, pressing or patting into the fillet as needed.
4. Bring the salmon fillets on a baking tray and bake them for 20 minutes.

Nutrition: Calories 207.4; Carbs: 31g; Protein: 5.1g; Fat: 7g

472. Tuscan Garlic Chicken

Preparation time: 10 minutes
Cooking time: 40 minutes
Servings: 3

Ingredients:

- 2 tablespoons extra virgin olive oil
- ¼ teaspoon dried parsley
- ¼ teaspoon dried oregano
- ¼ teaspoon dried lovage
- 1 teaspoon garlic powder
- ½ cup Parmesan cheese
- 1 cup arugula, chopped
- ½ cup sundried tomatoes
- 1/3 cup capers, drained

Directions:

1. On a medium heat temperature, warm the oil in a large pan. Then put the chicken and cook for 3-5 minutes until brown all over.
2. When the chicken is no longer pink in the center, remove it from heat and set aside on a plate.
3. Add the chicken broth, heavy cream, garlic powder, parsley, oregano, lovage, and Parmesan cheese to the pan. Whisk on medium heat until it thickens.
4. Add the arugula, sundried tomatoes and capers, allowing them to simmer, until the arugula starts to wilt.
5. Then add the chicken back to the mixture in the pan to reheat for 1 minute before serving.

Nutrition: Calories 285 Carbs: 46.2g Protein: 8.5g Fat: 7.4g

473. Baked Walnut Chicken Breast

Preparation time: 10 minutes
Cooking time: 50 minutes
Servings: 3

Ingredients:

- ¼ cup of walnuts, chopped
- 2 tablespoons of extra virgin olive oil.
- 2 boneless, skinless chicken breasts

Directions:

1. Preheat the oven to 350 degrees F.

2. Slice a deep groove into the middle of each chicken breast using a sharp knife and place the chopped walnuts in this groove, pouring the olive oil over the top.
3. Put the chicken breasts on a baking tray and bake for 20 minutes.

Nutrition: Calories per Serving: 202; Carbs: 21.1g; Protein: 7.9g; Fat: 10.2g

474. Roast Duck With Apple Dressing

Preparation time: 10 minutes
Cooking time: 70 minutes
Servings: 3

Ingredients:

- 1 (4 pound) whole duck
- Salt and pepper to taste
- 1 teaspoon poultry seasoning
- 2 tablespoon extra-virgin olive oil
- 3 tablespoons red onion, chopped
- 5 stalks celery, chopped
- 3 cups, chopped
- 3 cups cornbread crumbs

Directions:

1. Preheat oven to 350 degrees F.
2. Rinse the duck and pat dry. Rub with salt, pepper, and poultry seasoning, to taste.
3. Warm half (1 tablespoon) of the olive oil in a small skillet over medium heat. Sauté onion and celery until tender.
4. In a medium bowl, combine with apple and cornbread crumbs with the onion-celery mixture. Mix to make the stuffing, adding a little water to moisten if necessary.
5. Fill the duck's cavity with the stuffing and sew shut with kitchen twine. Rub the outside of bird lightly with the remaining tablespoon of olive oil, and place in a shallow roasting pan or 9x13 inch baking dish.
6. Bake in preheated oven for 60 to 80 minutes, or until internal temperature reaches 180 degrees F.

Nutrition: Calories 282, Fat 18.6, Fiber 4, Carbs 9.2, Protein 18.5

475. Bacon And Egg Fried

Preparation time: 5 minutes
Cooking time: 30 minutes
Servings: 4

Ingredients:

- 350g long-grain rice, well rinsed
- 1 1/2 tablespoon olive oil
- 100g streaky bacon, diced
- Two peppers, finely chopped
- 2 red onions, finely chopped
- 200g carrots, peeled and coarsely grated
- 2 garlic cloves, crushed
- 5cm slice ginger, peeled and grated
- 1 red chili, finely chopped (optional)
- 2 eggs
- 2 tsp soy sauce

Directions:

1. Cook the rice in a big bowl of warm water for 10 mins until not quite tender. Drain, rinse with warm water and drain. Set aside.
2. Meanwhile, warm 1/2 tablespoon oil in a skillet on a high heat and fry the bacon for 5 7 mins until golden and crispy. Take off from the pan using a slotted spoon and place aside. Add 1 tablespoon oil and fry the peppers for 10 minutes until lightly bubbling. Add the carrots, onions, ginger, garlic, and chili and fry over a moderate-high temperature for 5 minutes more.
3. Insert the rice and bacon and simmer for 5 minutes, stirring often. Push the rice mix to a single side of this pan and then crack the eggs to the gap. Beat the eggs with a wooden spoon, then stir throughout the rice. Cook for 2 minutes, then add the soy sauce and then remove from heat. Split between 4 shallow bowls to function.

Nutrition: Calories: 506kcal Fat: 13g Saturated fat: 4g Sugars: 12g Sodium: 1.9gram Carbohydrate 87.7gram Protein 1405g Fiber 5.3gram

476. Chilli With Meat

Preparation time: 20 minutes
Cooking time: 40 minutes
Servings: 4

Ingredients:

- 0.5 ounce oil
- 0.16 ounce heaped hot chili powder (or 1 level tbsp if you only have mild)
- 0.166 ounce paprika
- 1 large onion
- 1 red pepper
- 2 garlic cloves
- 0.166 ounce ground cumin
- 17.63 ounce lean minced beef
- 1 beef stock cube
- Take 0.166 ounce sugar (or add a thumbnail-sized piece of dark chocolate along with the beans instead)
- 1 ounce tomato purée
- 14.46 ounce can red kidney beans
- 1 Ounce can chopped tomatoes
- ½ tsp dried marjoram
- Plain boiled long grain rice, to serve
- Soured cream, to serve

Directions:

1. Get your vegetables ready. Chop into tiny dice one big onion, around 5 mm long. Cut the onion from root to tip in half, peel it and slice it lengthwise into thick matchsticks every half, not cutting it to the root end, so they're still held together. Round into tidy dice over the match sticks.
2. Break one red pepper in half lengthwise, cut base, wash off the seeds, then chop. Peel and chop 2 cloves of garlic.
3. Kick-off cooking. Place your pan over medium heat onto the hob. Apply 0.5 ounce of oil and keep on for 1-2 minutes before heated (on an electric hob a little longer).
4. Cook for 5 minutes after placing onion, stirring fairly often, or until the onion is soft, squidgy, and slightly translucent.
5. Tip the garlic, red pepper, one heaped tsp of hot chili powder or 0.5 ounce of soft chili powder, 0.166 ounce of paprika, and 0.166 ounce of cumin ground.
6. Offer it a quick swirl, then leave for another 5 minutes to cook, stirring periodically.
7. Brown 500 g lean beef. Turn the heat up a little, put the meat to the saucepan, and break it with your spatula or spoon. When you add the slimming, the mix should sizzle a little bit.
8. For 5 minutes, Keep stirring and prodding for at least 5 minutes, until all thinness is in uniform, thin lumps and no pink bits are left. Making sure you hold fire high enough to cook the meat and turn orange rather than just stewing.

9. Make some sauce. Crumble one cube of the beef reserve into 300ml of hot water. Pour it in the slimming mixture into the oven.
10. Add chopped tomatoes to a 14 ounce can. Cover with 1/2 tsp of dried marjoram, 0.166 ounce of sugar, and give a strong salt and pepper shake. Sprinkle with some 1 ounce of tomato purée and mix well the sauce.
11. Simmer softly around it. Bring the whole thing to the boil, stir well, and put a lid on the saucepan. Turn heat down and leave for 20 minutes.
12. Occasionally check on the pan to stir it and make sure that the sauce does not stick to the pan or dry out. If it sticks, add a few tablespoons of water and ensure that the heat is very small enough. The saucy, thin mixture should look thick, moist, and juicy after gently simmering.
13. Drain and rinse in a sieve a 410 g can of red kidney beans, then mix them into the chili pot. Carry to the boil again, and steam softly for another 10 minutes without the cap, adding more water if it seems too cold.
14. Taste a bit of the season and Chilli. Possibly, it would require far more seasoning than you thought.
15. Now lift the lid, turn the heat down, and leave your Chilli to stand before serving for 10 minutes.
16. Serve long grain rice with soured milk and simple boiled rice.

Nutrition: Calories: 312 kcal Protein: 30.8 g Fat: 16.29 g Carbohydrates: 12.66 g

477. Thai Red Curry

Preparation time: 10 minutes
Cooking time: 50 minutes
Servings: 4

Ingredients:

- Pinch of salt, more to taste
- Add 0.5 ounce finely grated fresh ginger (about a 1-inch nub of ginger)
- Add 2 cloves garlic, pressed or minced
- ¼ cups long-grain brown rice or brown jasmine rice, rinsed
- 0.5 ounce coconut oil or olive oil
- 1 small white onion, chopped (about 8 ounce)
- 1 red bell pepper, sliced into thin 2-inch long strips
- 1 yellow, orange or green bell pepper, sliced into thin 2-inch long strips
- ½ cup of water
- Take 1 ½ cups packed thinly sliced kale (tough ribs removed first), preferably the Tuscan/lacinato/dinosaur variety
- Add 1 ½ teaspoon coconut sugar or turbinado (raw) sugar or brown sugar
- 0.5 ounce tamari or soy sauce
- 2 teaspoons rice vinegar or fresh lime juice
- 3 carrots, peeled and sliced on the diagonal into ¼-inch thick rounds (about 8 ounces)
- 1 ounce Thai red curry paste
- 1 can (14 ounces) regular coconut milk
- Garnishes: a handful of chopped fresh basil or cilantro, optional red pepper flakes, optional sriracha or chili garlic sauce

Directions:

1. To cook rice, boil a large pot of water. Add the rinsed rice and proceed to boil for 30 minutes to prevent overload, decreasing heat as required. Remove the rice from fire, drain and place the rice back in the bowl. Let the rice rest until you're ready to serve for 10 minutes or longer. Just before eating, sauté the rice with salt and fluff it with a fork to try.
2. To render the curry, fire up a broad skillet over medium heat with deep sides. When it's dry, then add the oil. Attach the onion and a sprinkle of salt and fry, stirring regularly for around 5 minutes until the onion has softened. Add the ginger and garlic and simmer for approximately 30 seconds, while constantly stirring, until fragrant.
3. Add chilies and carrots to the whistle. Cook, stirring regularly until the bell peppers are fork-tender, 3 to 5 more minutes. Then, apply the curry paste and cook for 2 minutes, stirring frequently.
4. Add milk, tea, kale, and sugar to the coconut and stir to combine. Carry the mixture over medium heat to a simmer. Reduce heat as necessary to keep a gentle simmer and cook until the peppers, carrots, and kale have softened to your liking, occasionally stirring for about 5 to 10 minutes.
5. Remove the pot from heat and add tamari and rice vinegar to season. Add salt (for optimal flavor, I added 1/4 teaspoon) to taste. If the curry needs a bit more punch, add 0.083 ounces more tamari, or add 1/2 teaspoon rice vinegar for more acidity. Divide rice and curry into two bowls and garnish, if you like, with chopped cilantro and a sprinkling of red pepper flakes. Serve with sriracha sauce on the floor, whether you enjoy spicy curries.
6. If you want to add Tofu, bake it first and add it in phase 4 with coconut milk. If you add raw Tofu, the liquid will soak up too much, and baking it will improve the texture considerably, anyway.

Nutrition: Calories: 152 kcal Protein: 4.55 g Fat: 7.09 g Carbohydrates: 19.58 g

478. Pulled Chicken In Salad Tacos

Preparation time: 20 minutes
Cooking time: 10 minutes
Servings: 4

Ingredients:

- 300 g cooked chicken breast fillet
- 1 carrot
- 1 tomato
- 1 red onion
- Salt
- Pepper
- Chili flakes
- 200 g Greek yogurt
- 1 tsp. lemon juice
- 2 sticks celery
- 8 radicchio leaves
- 2 stems parsley

Directions:

1. Pluck chicken breast fillets with a fork. Clean, wash and grate the carrot. Clean, wash, and chopped the tomato into small cubes. Peel the onion, chopped in half, and cut into fine strips. Mix everything and season with salt, pepper, and chili flakes.
2. Mix the yogurt with lemon juice and season with salt, pepper, and chili flakes. Clean, wash and chop the celery. Wash radicchio leaves and parsley and shake dry; roughly chop parsley.
3. Spread the chicken mix into the lettuce leaves, pour celery and parsley over it and drizzle with yogurt sauce.

Nutrition: Calories 198 Protein 22 g, Fat 9 g, Carbs 6 g, Fiber 2.6 g

479. Fish Cakes With Potato Salad

Preparation time: 70 minutes
Cooking time: 10 minutes
Servings: 4
Ingredients:

- 800 g stuck potatoes
- 100 g sugar snap
- ⅓ Cucumber
- 200 g cherry tomatoes
- 10 g dill (0.5 bunch)
- 1 red onion
- 4 tbsp. olive oil
- 2 tbsp. apple cider vinegar
- 1 tsp. honey
- Salt
- Pepper
- 400 g cod fillet
- 2 tbsp. lemon juice
- 1 clove of garlic
- 50 g herbs (parsley, chives)
- 1 egg
- 50 g whole grain bread crumbs

Directions:

1. Wash potatoes and cook in boiling water over medium heat for 20–25 minutes. Then pour off and let cool.
2. In the meantime, clean and wash the sugar snap peas and cook them in a sieve over the steam of the boiling potatoes for 3–5 minutes. Quench and cut into fine strips. Clean and wash the cucumber and cut it into slices. Wash and halve tomatoes. Wash the dill, shake it dry and chop it roughly.
3. Peel the onion and cut into fine strips. Mix 2 tablespoons of oil with vinegar, honey and onion strips, salt, and pepper. Peel and slice potatoes. Fold in the sugar pods, cucumber slices, tomatoes, and dill and mix with the vinaigrette.
4. Rinse cod fillet, pat dry, cut into small pieces, puree with lemon juice. Peel, chop and add garlic. Wash herbs, shake dry and chop. Mix everything with egg, crumbs, salt, and pepper. Shape 8 meatballs with wet hands. Warm the remaining oil in a huge pan. Fry meatballs in it on both sides over medium heat for 10 minutes and serve with the potato salad.

Nutrition: Calories 421 Protein 27 g, Fat 13 g, Carbs 48 g, Added Sugar 1 g, Fiber 6.2 g

480. Vegetarian Lasagna - Smarter With Seitan And Spinach

Preparation time: 15 minutes
Cooking time: 40 minutes
Servings: 4
Ingredients:

- 225 g spinach leaves (frozen)
- 300 g seitan
- 2nd small carrots
- 2 sticks celery
- 1 onion
- 1 clove of garlic
- 2 tbsp. olive oil
- Salt
- Pepper
- 850 g canned tomatoes
- 200 ml classic vegetable broth
- 1 tsp. fennel seeds
- 30 g parmesan (1 piece)
- Nutmeg
- 225 g ricotta
- 16 whole-grain lasagna sheets
- Butter for the mold
- 150 g mozzarella

Directions:

1. Let the spinach thaw. Chop the seitan finely or put it through the middle slice of the meat grinder.
2. Wash and peel carrots. Wash, clean, remove, and finely dice the celery. Peel and chop the onion and garlic.
3. Heat the oil in a saucepan and braise the carrots, celery, onions, and garlic for 3 minutes over medium heat. Add since then and braise for 3 minutes while stirring. Season with salt and pepper.
4. Put the canned tomatoes and broth in the saucepan and cover and cook over medium heat for 20 minutes, stirring occasionally. Crush the fennel seeds, add and season the sauce with salt and pepper.
5. Meanwhile, finely grate the Parmesan. Rub off some nutmeg. Squeeze the spinach vigorously, roughly chop and stir in a bowl with the ricotta, parmesan, salt, pepper, and nutmeg.
6. Lightly grease a baking dish (approx. 30 x 20 cm). Cover the bottom of the mold with a little sauce and smooth it out. Place 4 sheets of lasagna next to each other, if necessary, cut to size.
7. Add 1/3 of the spinach mixture and smooth out. Spread 1/4 of the sauce above. Layer 4 lasagna sheets, 1/3 spinach, and 1/4 sauce repeat the process.
8. Put the last lasagna sheets on top and spread the rest of the sauce over them.
9. Drain the mozzarella and tear it into large pieces. Spread on the lasagna. Bake vegetarian lasagna in a preheated oven at 180 ° C (fan oven: 160 ° C, gas: levels 2–3) on the middle shelf for 35–40 minutes. Let the vegetarian lasagna rest for about 5 minutes before serving.

Nutrition: Calories 633 Protein 50 g, Fat 25 g, Carbs 48 g, Fiber 7.5 g

481. Spaghetti With Salmon In Lemon Sauce

Preparation time: 10 minutes
Cooking time: 30 minutes
Servings: 3
Ingredients:

- 150 g salmon fillet (without skin)
- 100 g leek (1 thin stick)
- 100 g small carrots (2 small carrots)
- ½ organic lemon
- 2 stems parsley
- 150 g whole grain spaghetti
- Salt
- 2 tbsp. olive oil
- Pepper
- 100 ml of fish stock
- 150 ml of soy cream

Directions:

1. Wash salmon, pat dry, and cut into 2 cm cubes.
2. Clean the leek, wash it, and cut it into thin rings. Peel the carrots and cut them into thin strips.
3. In the meantime, rinse the lemon half hot and rub dry. Peel the lemon peel thinly and cut into very fine strips.

Squeeze lemon juice. Wash parsley, shake dry, pluck leaves and chop finely.

4. Cook the pasta bite-proof in salt water according to the package instructions.
5. Heat oil in a pan. Season the salmon with pepper and fry all over in the hot oil for 3-4 minutes.
6. Take out the salmon, braise the leek rings, and carrot strips in the pan over medium heat for 3-4 minutes.
7. If necessary, salt the salmon, put it back in the pan, and heat briefly. Mix in the parsley.
8. Drain the pasta in a sieve then combine gently with the sauce. Season with salt and pepper and serve the spaghetti with salmon immediately.

Nutrition: Calories: 215 kcal Protein: 12.19 g Fat: 11.33 g Carbohydrates: 17.36 g

482. Baru Nut Bowl

Preparation time: 10 minutes
Cooking time: 30 minutes
Servings: 4

Ingredients:

- 300 g red cabbage
- Salt
- ¼ cucumber
- 2 tomatoes
- 2 zucchini
- ½ romaine lettuce
- 15 Baru nuts
- ½ lemon
- 4 tbsp. olive oil
- ½ tsp. mustard
- 1 tsp. honey
- Pepper
- 2 stems parsley

Directions:

1. Clean the red cabbage, remove the stem, wash and cut the remaining cabbage into fine strips. Place in a bowl, salt, and knead vigorously for 3 minutes.
2. Clean and wash the cucumber, tomato, and zucchini. Halve the cucumber lengthways and cut into fine slices, dice the tomatoes, and turn the zucchini into pasta with a spiral cutter. Clean, wash and cut Romana into strips.
3. Squeeze the lemon and stir the juice together with three tablespoons of oil, mustard, honey, salt, and pepper into a dressing. Finely chop the Baru nuts and add about half to the dressing. Wash the parsley, shake dry and also add to the salad dressing.
4. Cook/Fry the zucchini in a pan with the remaining oil for about 5 minutes over medium heat. Season with salt and pepper.
5. Arrange the salad and vegetables in bowls, sprinkle with the remaining Baru nuts and drizzle the dressing over them.

Nutrition: Calories 188 Protein 6 g,Fat 13 g, Carbs 12 g, Added Sugar 0.9 g,Fiber 5.7 g

483. Spinach And Mushroom Salad

Preparation time: 30 minutes
Cooking time: 15 minutes
Servings: 4

Ingredients:

- 1 cup baby spinach – fresh
- ¼ cup – mandarin - sections
- ¼ cup red onion – diced
- 8 medium mushrooms - halved
- 1 tablespoon extra-virgin olive oil
- Salt to taste

Directions:

1. Warm a small pan at medium heat then add a tablespoon of oil. Toss in halved mushrooms and cook for only a couple of minutes until mushrooms are moderately softened and lightly browned. Take a salad bowl and toss in dry fresh baby spinach. Add the mushrooms, onions, and mandarin. Toss to combine, then add some salt and serve.

Nutrition: Calories: 56 Sugar: 6 grams Fat: 1 gram Carbs: 10 grams Fiber: 2 grams Protein: 3 grams

484. Sweet Pepper Mix

Preparation time: 30 minutes
Cooking time: 0 minutes
Servings: 4

Ingredients:

- 1/8 cup green bell pepper
- ¼ cup red bell pepper
- 1/8 cup yellow pepper
- 1/8 cup red onion
- ¼ cup rocket salad
- 1 tablespoon parsley – chopped
- Sprinkle of salt
- ¼ lemon - juiced

Directions:

1. Dice the bell peppers, onion, and parsley and combine with rocket salad. Mix to combine in a salad bowl then dress with lemon juice.

Nutrition: Calories: 34 Sugar: 0.5 grams Fat: 0 grams Carbs: 5 grams Fiber: 0.8 grams Protein: 0.5 grams

485. Veggie Chef Salad

Preparation time: 20 minutes
Cooking time: 5 minutes
Servings: 4

Ingredients:

- 2 eggs – hard-boiled
- 1 tablespoon light low-calorie mayonnaise
- 1 teaspoon apple cider vinegar
- 50 grams rocket salad
- 5 grams parsley – chopped
- 50 grams lettuce – shredded
- 6 cherry tomatoes – halved
- 1 cucumber - diced

Directions:

1. Whisk the mayonnaise with apple cider vinegar and set aside. Cut the eggs into wedges and combine them with the rest of the ingredients in a salad bowl. Toss the dressing over the salad and enjoy!

Nutrition: Calories: 268 Sugar: 8 grams Fat: 12 grams Carbs: 16 grams Fiber: 3 grams Protein: 16 grams

486. Zucchini Latkes

Preparation time: 10 minutes
Cooking time: 10 minutes
Servings: 1

Ingredients:

- 1 tablespoon chickpea flour
- 2 egg whites
- 1 small zucchini squash
- 1 tablespoon milk
- 1 tablespoon extra-virgin olive oil
- ½ teaspoon turmeric – ground
- Salt to taste

Directions:

1. First, prepare the zucchini by shredding the entire veggie – skin included. Drain zucchini of excess water then beat the egg whites with milk with turmeric and salt. Add the zucchini and the chickpea flour to the bowl and whisk to combine everything. Make sure that the shredded zucchini is well coated in the mixture. Heat a frying pan on medium heat then add a tablespoon of olive oil. Heat the oil then add the mixture to the pan like you are making a pancake.
2. The meal is best served with sour cream. Enjoy.

Nutrition: Calories: 209 Sugar: 4.4 grams Fat: 15 grams Carbs: 8 grams Fiber: 1.5 grams Protein: 10 grams

487. Ratatouille

Preparation time: 15 minutes
Cooking time: 40 minutes
Servings: 4

Ingredients:

- 1 cup eggplant – cubed
- 1/8 cup red onion – diced
- ½ cup yellow bell pepper – chopped
- 1 garlic clove – chopped
- 1 cup zucchini – chopped
- 3 plum tomatoes
- 2 tablespoons extra virgin olive oil
- ½ teaspoon basil – dry
- ½ teaspoon parsley – dry
- ½ teaspoon oregano -dry
- Salt to taste

Directions:

1. Heat a large skillet then put the olive oil. Heat up on medium heat then add onions and peppers to the skillet. Sauté for 5 minutes with occasional stirring, then add the rest of the veggies except for tomatoes. Add salt to the skillet and mix well to combine. Cover using the lid, cook at low temperature for 30 minutes, or until vegetables are soft to your preference. Add plum tomatoes and herbs to the skillet and stir in to combine. Cook for another 5 minutes, then serve and enjoy.

Nutrition: Calories: 246 Sugar: 14 grams Fat: 14 grams Carbs: 26 grams Fiber: 7 grams Protein: 4 grams

488. Almond And Crab Salad

Preparation time: 20 minutes
Cooking time: 10 minutes
Servings: 4

Ingredients:

- 100 grams of crab meat
- 1 tablespoon slivered almonds
- ½ tablespoon milk
- 1/8 cup sour cream – reduced fat
- ½ cup rocket salad
- 1 teaspoon chives
- 1/8 cup red bell pepper
- ½ tablespoon lemon juice – freshly squeezed
- ¼ cup tomatoes – chopped
- 1/8 cup red onion
- 1 tablespoon low-fat mayonnaise – low-calorie

Directions:

1. Take a mixing bowl and combine mayonnaise, sour cream, red onion, milk, and lemon juice. You will make a sauce for the salad by whisking these ingredients together. Combine the sauce with crab meat, then serve on the rocket salad with slivered almonds and crushed chives sprinkled over the sauced crab meat. Enjoy your dinner!

Nutrition: Calories: 215 Sugar: 6 grams Fat: 2 grams Carbs: 22 grams Fiber: 2 grams Protein: 14 grams

489. Lemon Salmon

Preparation time: 5 minutes
Cooking time: 20 minutes
Servings: 2

Ingredients:

- 200 grams wild salmon - fillet
- 1 tablespoon extra-virgin olive oil
- 1/8 lemon
- 1 tablespoon lemon juice
- Salt and pepper

Directions:

1. Use the lemon juice to sprinkle the salmon together with sprinkling both sides of the fillet with salt and pepper. Place a skillet on the stove and set the temperature to medium-high. Once the skillet is hot, add the oil and coat the bottom of the skillet. Place the salmon fillet in the skillet and cook it for 4 minutes on each side. Take off from the heat then serve with lemon.

Nutrition: Calories: 287 Sugar: 0.3 grams Fat: 15 grams Carbs: 1.3 grams Fiber: 0. 3 grams Protein: 33 grams

490. Broccoli Patties

Preparation time: 10 minutes
Cooking time: 30 minutes
Servings: 4

Ingredients:

- 500 grams broccoli florets – steamed
- 2 eggs
- ½ cup shredded parmesan cheese
- 1 garlic clove – minced
- 1 tablespoon extra-virgin olive oil
- Salt to taste
- Pepper to taste

Directions:

1. Steam the broccoli florets and chop them into tiny pieces afterward. You can steam the broccoli by adding larger chunks of broccoli to the pot of water. Add salt to the boiling water with broccoli and cook until fork-tender. Drain the broccoli and chop the florets into tiny pieces. Add salt, pepper, parmesan, garlic, and two whole eggs. Stir to combine into a homogenous mass. You can bake or fry the patties, but we recommend baking as a healthier option. Grease up the baking pan with a tablespoon of extra virgin olive oil. Scoop up 2 to 3 tablespoons of broccoli mixture and slightly flatten the patties onto the greased baking pan. Arrange the patties across the baking pan with a little space in between each patty. Set the oven to 425°F. Bake the broccoli patties for 10 to 13 minutes. Serve warm. You can also top the patties with yogurt, bird's eye chili, and parsley.

Nutrition: Calories: 81 Sugar: 1 gram Fat: 1.5 grams Carbs: 13 grams Fiber: 2 grams Protein: 3.5 grams

491. Lemon Rosemary Fish Fillets

Preparation time: 10 minutes
Cooking time: 15 minutes
Servings: 4

Ingredients:

- 4 white fish fillets
- 1 tbsp. dried rosemary
- 4 tbsp. breadcrumbs
- 2 tbsp. lemon zest
- 1 tsp garlic powder

- 2 tbsp. extra virgin olive oil
- 1 tsp salt

Directions:

1. Combine the rosemary, breadcrumbs, lemon zest, garlic powder, and salt in a food processor and blend until well mixed.
2. Put the fish fillets, skin-side up, on a lined baking tray. Grill for 3-4 minutes.
3. Turn the fish over and press a quarter of the breadcrumb mixture over the top of each fillet.
4. Drizzle with olive oil and grill for 4 min until the crust is golden and the fish is cooked through.
5. Serve with steamed spinach or baked potatoes.

Nutrition: Calories: 199 kcal Protein: 28.45 g Fat: 8.25 g Carbohydrates: 1.18 g

492. Salsa Fresca Chicken

Preparation time: 15 minutes
Cooking time: 35 minutes
Servings: 4

Ingredients:

- 1/4 tsp. dark pepper
- 1/4 tsp. Cumin
- 1/4 tsp. garlic powder
- 1/4 tsp. salt
- 2 lbs. chicken bosom boneless skinless

Directions:

1. The initial step is to preheat the stove to 375°F. And afterward, Lay the chicken level in a large heating dish and sprinkle equally with the cumin, garlic, salt, and pepper.

Nutrition: Calories: 12 Fat: 32 Calcium: 27

493. Moroccan Leeks Snack

Preparation time: 10 minutes
Cooking time: 0 minute
Servings: 4

Ingredients:

- 1 bunch radish, sliced
- 3 cups leeks, chopped
- 1 ½ cups olives, pitted and sliced
- Pinch turmeric powder
- 2 tablespoons essential olive oil
- 1 cup cilantro, chopped

Directions:

1. Take a bowl and mix in radishes, leeks, olives, and cilantro.
2. Mix well.
3. Season with pepper, oil, turmeric, and toss well.
4. Serve and enjoy!

Nutrition: Calories: 120 Cal Fat: 1g Carbohydrates: 1g Protein: 6g

494. Mozzarella Cauliflower Bars

Preparation time: 10 minutes
Cooking time: 40 minutes
Servings: 4

Ingredients:

- 1 cauliflower head, riced
- 12 cup low-fat mozzarella cheese, shredded
- ¼ cup egg whites
- 1 teaspoon Italian dressing, low fat
- Pepper to taste

Directions:

1. Spread cauliflower rice in a lined baking sheet.
2. Preheat your oven to 375 degrees F.
3. Roast for 20 minutes.
4. Transfer to a bowl and spread pepper, cheese, seasoning, egg whites, and stir well.
5. Spread in a rectangular pan and press.
6. Transfer to oven and cook for 20 minutes more.
7. Serve and enjoy!

Nutrition: Calories: 140 Cal Fat: 2g Carbohydrates: 6g Protein: 6g

495. Salmon & Capers

Preparation time: 5 minutes
Cooking time: 40 minutes
Servings: 3

Ingredients:

- 75g (3oz) Greek yogurt
- 4 salmon fillets, skin removed
- 4 tsp Dijon mustard
- 1 tbsp. capers, chopped
- 2 tsp fresh parsley
- Zest of 1 lemon

Directions:

1. In a bowl, blend together the yogurt, mustard, lemon zest, parsley, and capers. Thoroughly coat the salmon in the mixture. Place the salmon under a hot grill (broiler) and cook for 3-4 minutes on each side or until the fish is cooked. Serve with mashed potatoes and vegetables or a large green leafy salad.

Nutrition: Calorie: 430 Fat: 24 g Carbs: 3 g Sodium: 860 mg Protein: 45 g

496. Moroccan Chicken Casserole

Preparation time: 5 minutes
Cooking time: 20 minutes
Servings: 3

Ingredients:

- 250g (9oz) tinned chickpeas (garbanzo beans) drained
- 4 chicken breasts, cubed
- 4 Medjool dates halved
- 6 dried apricots, halved
- 1 red onion, sliced
- 1 carrot, chopped
- 1 tsp ground cumin
- 1 tsp ground cinnamon
- 1 tsp ground turmeric
- 1 bird's eye chili, chopped
- 600ml (1 pint) chicken stock (broth)
- 25g (1oz) corn flour
- 60ml (2fl oz.) water
- 2 tbsp. fresh coriander

Directions:

1. Place the chicken, chickpeas (garbanzo beans), onion, carrot, chili, cumin, turmeric, cinnamon, and stock (broth) into a large saucepan. Place it to the boil, lower the heat and simmer for 25 minutes. Add in the dates and apricots and simmer for 10 minutes. In a cup, mix the cornflour together with the water until it becomes a smooth paste. Pour the mixture into the saucepan and stir until it thickens. Add in the coriander (cilantro) and mix well. Serve with buckwheat or couscous.

Nutrition: Calorie: 381.8 kcal Fat: 10.3 g Carbs: 40.6 g Sodium: 2147 mg Protein: 32.3 g

497. Beef Broth

Preparation time: 5 minutes
Cooking time: 40 minutes
Servings: 3

Ingredients:

- 4-5 pounds beef bones and few veal bones

- 1 pound of stew meat, cut into 2-inch chunks
- Olive oil
- 1-2 medium red onions, peeled and quartered
- 1-2 large carrots, cut into 1-2-inch segments
- 1 celery rib, cut into 1-inch segments
- 2-3 cloves of garlic, unpeeled
- A handful of parsley stems and leaves
- 1-2 bay leaves
- 10 peppercorns

Directions:

1. Heat oven to 375F. Rub olive oil in the stew meat pieces, carrots, and onions. Put the stew meat or beef scraps, stock bones, carrots, and onions in a large roasting pan. Roast in the oven for around 45 minutes, turning everything halfway through the cooking. Put everything from the oven in a large stockpot. Put some boiling water in the oven pan, scrape up all of the browned bits, and pour it all in the stockpot. Put the parsley, celery, garlic, bay leaves, and peppercorns to the pot. Fill the pot with cold water, to 1-inch over the top of the bones. Bring the stockpot to a regular simmer and then reduce the heat to low, so it barely simmers. Cover the pot loosely, then let it simmer in low and slow for at least 3-4 hours. Ladle away the fat and any scum that rises to the surface once in a while. After cooking, take off the bones and vegetables from the pot. Strain the broth. Allow it to cool at room temperature and then put it in the refrigerator. The fat will solidify once the broth has chilled. Discard the fat (or reuse it), then place the broth into a jar and freeze it.

Nutrition: Calorie: 86 kcal Fat: 2.9 g Protein: 6 g

498. Prawn & Coconut Curry

Preparation time: 5 minutes
Cooking time: 35 minutes
Servings: 3

Ingredients:

- 400g (14oz) tinned chopped tomatoes
- 400g (14oz) large prawns (shrimps), shelled and raw
- 25g (1oz) fresh coriander (cilantro) chopped
- 3 red onions, finely chopped
- 3 cloves of garlic, crushed
- 2 bird's eye chilies
- ½ tsp ground coriander (cilantro)
- ½ tsp turmeric
- 400ml (14fl oz) coconut milk
- 1 tbsp olive oil
- Juice of 1 lime

Directions:

1. Place the onions, garlic, tomatoes, chilies, lime juice, turmeric, ground coriander (cilantro), chilies and half of the fresh coriander (cilantro) into a blender and blitz until you have a smooth curry paste. Using a frying pan, heat and put the olive oil, then add the pasta and cook for 2 minutes. Stir in the coconut milk and warm it thoroughly. Add the prawns (shrimps) to the paste and cook them until they have turned pink and are completely cooked. Stir in the fresh coriander (cilantro). Serve with rice.

Nutrition: Calorie: 239.6 kcal Fat: 10.7 g Carbs: 9.2 g Sodium: 186.4 g Protein: 25.3 g

499. Chicken & Bean Casserole

Preparation time: 5 minutes
Cooking time: 40 minutes
Servings: 3

Ingredients:

- 400g (14oz) chopped tomatoes
- 400g (14oz) tinned cannellini beans or haricot beans
- Chicken thighs, skin removed
- 2 carrots, peeled and finely chopped
- 2 red onions, chopped
- 4 sticks of celery
- 4 large mushrooms
- 2 red peppers (bell peppers), de-seeded and chopped
- 1 clove of garlic
- 2 tbsp. soy sauce
- 1 tbsp. olive oil
- 1.75 liters (3 pints) chicken stock (broth)

Directions:

1. In a saucepan pan, put olive oil then heat it. Put the garlic and onions and cook for 5 minutes. Put in the chicken, cook for 5 minutes, then add the carrots, cannellini beans, celery, red peppers (bell peppers), and mushrooms. Pour in the stock (broth) soy sauce and tomatoes. Place it to the boil, lower the heat and simmer for 45 minutes. Serve with rice or new potatoes.

Nutrition: Calorie: 209.1 kcal Fat: 6.6 g Carbs: 6.2 g Sodium: 667.9 mg Protein: 31 g

500. Risotto With Broccoli And Chili Pepper

Preparation time: 5 minutes
Cooking time: 55 minutes
Servings: 2

Ingredients:

- 1 broccoli
- 1 chili pepper
- 1 shallot white wine
- Spicy oil
- Meat or vegetable broth
- Salt
- Pepper
- Butter
- Grated cheese
- 350 g carnaroli rice

Directions

1. Cut the broccoli into small pieces. Chop the shallot.
2. In a saucepan, heat the oil, then brown the shallot, add the rice, toast for a few minutes, salt, and blend with the white wine.
3. Start pouring the broth and broccoli, continuing to mix.
4. Add a chopped red pepper and cook. Stir in butter and grated cheese.
5. Complete with a minced pepper and a drizzle of spicy oil.

Nutrition: Calories: 141 kcal Protein: 4.59 g Fat: 4.82 g Carbohydrates: 20.3 g

501. Chickpea Balls With Yogurt Sauce

Preparation time: 5 minutes
Cooking time: 35 minutes
Servings: 2

Ingredients:

- 400 g of chickpeas
- 1 onion or 2 shallots
- 1/2 teaspoon ground cumin
- 1/2 teaspoon ground coriander
- 1/4 teaspoon of chili powder
- 2 spoons of chopped parsley
- Flour

- 3 eggs
- Oil
- Salt
- Pepper
- For the sauce:
- 250 g of yogurt
- 150 g of cucumbers
- 1/2 teaspoon kummel
- 1/4 teaspoon ground chili
- 1 spoonful of chopped parsley
- Salt
- Pepper

Directions:

1. Soak overnight the chicken, then drain them, place them in a saucepan, cover them with water, bring it to the boil, and cook for about an hour. Drain the chickpeas and blend them with the chopped onion, eggs, and spices. Withdraw, add enough flour, parsley, salt, and pepper to the smoothie. Taking a little mixture at a time, form small balls like a walnut, pass them in flour, fry them in hot oil and dry them on absorbent paper.
2. For the sauce: bring the yogurt into a bowl, add the peeled and diced cucumbers, the spices, parsley, salt, and pepper, mix and keep in the fridge until ready to serve with the balls (falafel in local language).

Nutrition: Calories: 1184 kcal Protein: 75.91 g Fat: 31.3 g Carbohydrates: 157.69 g

502. Sweet And Sour Onions

Preparation time: 5 minutes
Cooking time: 55 minutes
Servings: 2

Ingredients:

- 1 shallot
- 1 clove of garlic
- 40 g of butter
- 3 tablespoons of granulated sugar
- 2 dl of white wine vinegar
- Salt
- Black pepper
- 800 g of onions

Directions:

1. To prepare the glazed onions, begin to peel them and soak them in cold water for 30 minutes. Melt the butter in a huge enough saucepan and add the sugar, the diced shallot, and the minced garlic. After 2-3 minutes, when the sugar has completely melted, add the drained onions and mix them.
2. Salt, pepper, turn up the heat and sprinkle with the vinegar. Let it evaporate partially then lower the heat, cover and simmer for 30 minutes. Check occasionally and wet with a few spoonfuls of hot water if necessary. At the end of cooking, rest the sweet and sour onions for about ten minutes then transfer them to the serving dish and serve.

Nutrition: Calories: 320 kcal Protein: 3.47 g Fat: 16.55 g Carbohydrates: 42.68 g

503. Baked Vegetables

Preparation time: 5 minutes
Cooking time: 25 minutes
Servings: 2

Ingredients:

- 3 white onions
- 3 large fleshy tomatoes
- 4 spoons of stale breadcrumbs
- Origan
- Extra virgin olive oil
- Salt
- 4 large potatoes

Directions:

1. Prepare the vegetables in the oven by starting to peel and wash the potatoes. Dry them and cut them into slices about one centimeter thick. Peel the onions and cut them into slices of the same thickness. Also, wash and slice the tomatoes.
2. Brush a round baking pan with oil and arrange the vegetables in concentric circles, alternating slices of potatoes, onions, and tomatoes. Sprinkle with breadcrumbs and oregano, season with a drizzle of oil and salt. Bake in a hot oven at 170-180 ° for 30 minutes or until the surface has a light crust.
3. Withdraw vegetables in the oven, let them settle for about ten minutes, and serve immediately on the table.

Nutrition: Calories: 724 kcal Protein: 22.33 g Fat: 4.41 g Carbohydrates: 154.96 g

504. Pesto Salmon Pasta Noodles Recipe

Preparation time: 15 minutes
Cooking time: 30 minutes
Servings: 4

Ingredients:

- 350g penne
- 2 x 212g tins cherry salmon, drained
- 1 lemon, zested and juiced
- 190g jar green pesto
- 250g package cherry tomatoes halved
- 100g bunch spring onions, finely chopped
- 125g package reduced-fat mozzarella

Directions:

1. Preheat the oven to windows 7, 220°c, buff 200°c. Boil the pasta for 5 mins. Drain, reserving 100ml drinking water.
2. Meanwhile, at a 2ltr ovenproof dish, then mix the salmon, lemon zest, and juice, then pesto (booking two tablespoons)berries and half of the spring onions; season.
3. Mix the pasta and reserved cooking water to the dish. Mix the allowed pesto using one tablespoon water and then drizzle on the pasta. Gently within the mozzarella, top with the rest of the spring onions and bake for 25 mins until golden.

Nutrition: Calories 669kcal Fat 25g Saturates 6 g Sugars 7g Salt 2 g Carbohydrate 72.2gram Protein 43.2gram Fiber 2.6gram

505. Sri Lankan-Style Sweet Potato Curry

Preparation time: 10 minutes
Cooking time: 45 minutes
Servings: 4

Ingredients:

- 1/2 onion, roughly sliced
- Three garlic cloves, roughly sliced
- 25g sliced ginger, chopped and peeled
- 15g fresh coriander stalks and leaves split leaves sliced
- 2 1/2 tablespoon moderate tikka curry powder
- 60g package cashew nuts
- 1 tablespoon olive oil
- 500g sweet potatoes, peeled then cut into 3cm balls
- 400ml tin isle sun coconut-milk

- 1/2 vegetable stock block, created as much as 300ml
- 200g grower's harvest long-grain rice
- 300g frozen green beans
- 150g RedMere farms lettuce
- One sun trail farms lemon, 1/2 juiced, 1/2 cut into wedges to function

Directions:

1. Set the onion, ginger, garlic, coriander stalks, tikka powder along with half of the cashew nuts in a food processor. Insert two tablespoons water and blitz to a chunky paste.
2. At a large skillet, warm the oil over moderate heat. Insert the paste and cook, stirring for 5 minutes. Bring the sweet potatoes, stir, then pour into the coconut milk and stock. Bring to the simmer and boil for 25-35 minutes before the sweet potatoes are tender.
3. Meanwhile, cook the rice pack directions. Toast the rest of the cashews at a dry skillet.
4. Stir the beans into the curry and then simmer for two minutes. Insert the lettuce in handfuls, allowing each to simmer before adding the following; simmer for 1 minute. Bring the lemon juice, to taste, & the majority of the coriander leaves. Scatter on the remaining coriander and cashews, then use the rice and lemon wedges.

Nutrition: Calories 544kcal Fat 20g Saturates 8g Sugars 14g Salt 1g Carbohydrate 84.2gram Protein 12.1gram Fiber 8.4gram

506. Full-Of-Veg Hash Recipe

Preparation time: 10 minutes
Cooking time: 30 minutes
Servings: 4

Ingredients:

- 750g potatoes, pared and grated
- 2 tablespoon olive oil
- 100g streaky bacon, roughly sliced
- 2 red onions, finely chopped
- 300g carrots, peeled and diced
- 2 courgettes, diced
- 2 garlic cloves, crushed
- 4 eggs
- 5g refreshing flat-leaf parsley, sliced
- 1 red chili, chopped (optional)
- 1/2 x 340g jar pickled red cabbage

Directions:

1. Preheat the oven to windows 7, 220°c, buff 200°c. Place a bowl of soapy water to the boil, simmer the potatoes for 5 minutes, and then drain and put aside.
2. Heat 1 tablespoon oil in a large, ovenproof skillet on a high heat and fry the bacon for 5 minutes until crispy. Add the carrots, onions, courgettes, onions, and garlic; season and then cook for 5 minutes Take the pan into the oven and bake for 25-30 minutes before the veg is tender and gold.
3. Meanwhile, heat the remaining oil into a skillet on medium-high heating and fry the eggs 2-3 minutes or until cooked to your liking.
4. Split the hash between two plates and top each with lettuce. Scatter with parsley and simmer, then function with the pickled red cabbage onto both.

Nutrition: Calories 387kcal Fat 17g Saturates 4g Sugars 11g Salt 1.4gram Carbohydrate 44.5gram Protein 16.3gram Fiber 7.2gram

507. Baked Chicken Breasts

Preparation time: 10 minutes
Cooking time: 30 minutes
Servings: 2

Ingredients:

- For the pesto
- 15g parsley
- 15g walnuts
- 15g Parmesan
- 1tbsp extra virgin olive oil
- Juice 1/2 lemon
- For the chicken
- 150g skinless chicken breast
- 20g red onions, finely sliced
- 1tsp red wine vinegar
- 35g rocket
- 100g cherry tomatoes halved
- 1tsp balsamic vinegar

Directions:

1. Heat the oven 220 ° C/200oC to a fan/gas limit of 7.
2. To make pesto, blend in a food processor the parsley, walnuts, parmesan, olive oil, half the lemon juice, and 1 tbsp. of water until you have done
3. Paste smooth. Gradually add more water until you get the consistency you prefer.
4. In the refrigerator, marinate the chicken breast in 1 tbsp. Of pesto and the remaining lemon juice for 30 minutes or longer, if possible.
5. Fry the chicken in its marinade for 1 minute on either side in an oven-proof frying pan over medium-high heat, then move to the oven and cook for 8 minutes, or until cooked through.
6. Marinate the red wine vinegar with the onions for 5-10 minutes, then drain the liquid.
7. Remove the chicken from the oven, spoon over 1 tbsp. of pesto and let the heat from the chicken melt. Make a cover with foil and leave for 5 minutes to rest before serving.
8. Combine the balsamic with the rocket, tomatoes, and onion and drizzle over it. Serve with the chicken and spoon the rest of the pesto.

Nutrition: Calories: 846 kcal Protein: 120.87 g Fat: 31.31 g Carbohydrates: 14.55 g

508. Beef Burritos

Preparation time: 10 minutes
Cooking time: 20 minutes
Servings: 6

Ingredients:

- ¼ cup white onion, chopped
- ¼ cup green bell pepper, chopped
- 1-pound ground beef
- ¼ cup tomato puree, low-sodium
- ¼ teaspoon ground black pepper
- ¼ teaspoon ground cumin
- 6 flour tortillas, burrito size

Directions:

1. Take a skillet pan, place it over medium heat and when hot, add beef and cook for 5 to 8 minutes until browned.
2. Drain the excess fat, then transfer beef to a plate lined with paper towels and serve.
3. Return pan over medium heat, grease it with oil and when hot, add pepper and onion, cook for 5 minutes, or soften it.
4. Switch to low heat, return beef to the pan, season with black pepper and cumin, pour in tomato puree, stir until mixed and cook for 5 minutes until done.

5. Distribute beef mixture equally on top of the tortilla, roll them in burrito style by folding both ends, and then serve.

Nutrition: Calories: 265 kcal Total Fat: 9 g Saturated Fat: 0 g Cholesterol: 37 mg Sodium: 341 mg Total Carbs: 31 g Fiber: 1.6 g Protein: 15 g

509. Broccoli And Beef Stir-Fry

Preparation time: 5 minutes
Cooking time: 18 minutes
Servings: 4

Ingredients:

- 12 ounces frozen broccoli, thawed
- 8 ounces sirloin beef, chopped into thin strips
- 1 medium Roma tomato, chopped
- 1 teaspoon minced garlic
- 1 tablespoon cornstarch
- 2 tablespoons soy sauce, reduced-sodium
- ¼ cup chicken broth, low-sodium
- 2 tablespoons peanut oil
- 2 cups cooked brown rice

Directions:

1. Take a frying pan, place it over medium heat, add oil and when hot, add garlic and cook for 1 minute until fragrant.
2. Add vegetable blend, cook for 5 minutes, then transfer vegetable blend to a plate and set aside until needed.
3. Add beef strips into the pan, and then cook for 7 minutes until cooked to the desired level.
4. Prepare the sauce by putting cornstarch in a bowl, and then whisking in soy sauce and broth until well combined.
5. Returned vegetables to the pan, add tomatoes, drizzle with sauce, stir well until coated, and cook for 2 minutes until the sauce has thickened.
6. Serve with brown rice.

Nutrition: Calories: 373 kcal Total Fat: 17 g Saturated Fat: 0 g Cholesterol: 42 mg Sodium: 351 mg Total Carbs: 37 g Fiber: 5.1 g Sugar: 0 g Protein: 18 g

510. Meatballs With Eggplant

Preparation time: 15 minutes
Cooking time: 60 minutes
Servings: 6

Ingredients:

- 1-pound ground beef
- ½ cup green bell pepper, chopped
- 2 medium eggplants, peeled and diced
- ½ teaspoon minced garlic
- 1 cup stewed tomatoes
- ½ cup white onion, diced
- 1/3 cup canola oil
- 1 teaspoon lemon and pepper seasoning, salt-free
- 1 teaspoon turmeric
- 1 teaspoon Mrs. Dash seasoning blend
- 2 cups of water

Directions:

1. Take a large skillet pan, place it over medium heat, add oil in it and when hot, add garlic and green bell pepper and cook for 4 minutes until saute.
2. Transfer green pepper mixture to a plate, set aside until needed, then eggplant pieces into the pan and cook for 4 minutes per side until browned, and when done, transfer eggplant to a plate and set aside until needed.
3. Take a medium bowl, place beef in it, add onion, season with all the spices, stir until well combined, and then shape the mixture into 30 small meatballs.
4. Place meatballs into the pan in a single layer and cook for 3 minutes, or until browned.
5. When done, place all the meatballs in the pan, add cooked bell pepper mixture in it along with eggplant, stir in water and tomatoes and simmer for 30 minutes at low heat setting until thoroughly cooked.
6. Serve straight away.

Nutrition: Calories: 265 kcal Total Fat: 18 g Saturated Fat: 0 g Cholesterol: 47 mg Sodium: 153 mg Total Carbs: 12 g Fiber: 4.6 g Protein: 17 g

511. Slow-Cooked Lemon Chicken

Preparation time: 20 minutes
Cooking time: 7 hours
Servings: 4

Ingredients:

- 1 teaspoon dried oregano
- ¼ teaspoon ground black pepper
- 2 tablespoons butter, unsalted
- 1-pound chicken breast, boneless, skinless
- ¼ cup chicken broth, low sodium
- ¼ cup water
- 1 tablespoon lemon juice
- 2 cloves garlic, minced
- 1 teaspoon fresh basil, chopped

Directions:

1. Mix oregano and ground black pepper in a small bowl. Rub mixture on the chicken.
2. Melt the butter in a medium-sized skillet over medium heat. Brown the chicken in the melted butter then take the chicken to the slow cooker.
3. Put chicken broth, water, lemon juice, and garlic in the skillet. Place it to a boil, so it loosens the browned bits from the skillet. Pour over the chicken.
4. Cover set the slow cooker on high for 2½ hours or low for 5 hours.
5. Add basil and baste the chicken. Cover, cook on high for an additional 15–30 minutes or until chicken is tender.

Nutrition: Calories: 197 kcal Total Fat: 9 g Saturated Fat: 5 g Cholesterol: 99 mg Sodium: 57 mg Total Carbs: 1 g Fiber: 0.3 g Sugar: 0 g Protein: 26 g

512. Smothered Pork Chops And Sautéed Greens

Preparation time: 20 minutes
Cooking time: 60 minutes
Servings: 6

Ingredients:

- Smothered Pork Chops:
- 6 pork loin chops ("natural" center-cut, bone-in)
- 1 tbsp. black pepper
- 2 tsp. paprika
- 2 tsp. granulated onion powder
- 2 tsp. granulated garlic powder
- 1 cup & 2 tablespoons flour
- ½ cup canola oil
- 2 cups low-sodium beef stock
- 1 ½ cups fresh onions, sliced
- ½ cup fresh scallions, sliced
- Sautéed Greens:
- 8 cups fresh collard greens, chopped
- 2 tbsp. olive oil
- 1 tbsp. unsalted butter
- ¼ cup onions, finely diced

- 1 tbsp. fresh garlic, chopped
- 1 tsp. crushed red pepper flakes
- 1 tsp. black pepper
- 1 tsp. vinegar (optional)

Directions:

1. Set oven to 350° F.
2. Pork Chops:
3. Mix the black pepper, paprika, onion powder, and garlic powder together. Use half of the mixture to season both sides of the pork chops then mix the other half with 1 cup flour.
4. Reserve 2 tbsp. of flour mix for later.
5. Lightly coat pork chops with seasoned flour.
6. Using a Dutch oven or oven-ready sauté pan (no rubber handles), warm the oil at medium-high.
7. Fry pork chops for 2–4 minutes on every side or until desired crispness. Take off from pan then put all 2 tablespoons of oil.
8. Cook onions until translucent, about 4–6 minutes. Mix in 2 tablespoons of reserved flour and mix well with onions for about 1 minute.
9. Slowly, put beef stock then stir until thickened.
10. Return pork chops to the pan then coat with sauce. Cover or wrap using foil, then cook in the oven for at least 30–45 minutes at 350° F.
11. Take it out from the oven and let rest at least 5–10 minutes before serving.
12. To blanch greens, put the greens to a pot of boiling water. Strain boiling water off and quickly bowl of ice and water.
13. Let cool, then strain and dry. In large sauté pan on medium-high heat, melt butter and oil together. Place onions and slightly browned about 4–6 minutes.
14. Add collard greens, black and red pepper, then cook for 5–8 minutes on high heat, stirring constantly. Remove from heat; add vinegar if desired and stir.

Nutrition: Calories: 464 kcal Total Fat: 28 g Saturated Fat: 5 g Cholesterol: 71 mg Sodium: 108 mg Total Carbs: 26 g Fiber: 1.3 g Sugar: 0 g Protein: 27 g

513. Pasta With Cheesy Meat Sauce

Preparation time: 10 minutes
Cooking time: 30 minutes
Servings: 6

Ingredients:

- ½ box large-shaped pasta
- 1-pound ground beef
- ½ cup onions, diced
- 1 tablespoon onion flakes
- 1½ cups beef stock, lower or no sodium
- 1 tbsp. better than Bouillon beef, no salt
- 1 tbsp. tomato sauce, no salt
- ¾ cup Monterey or pepper jack cheese, shredded
- 8 ounces cream cheese, softened
- ½ teaspoon Italian seasoning
- ½ teaspoon ground black pepper
- 2 tablespoons French's® Worcestershire sauce, reduced-sodium

Directions:

1. Cook pasta noodles based on the directions on the box.
2. In a huge sauté pan, cook ground beef, onions, and onion flakes until the meat is browned.
3. Drain then put stock, bouillon, and tomato sauce.
4. Bring to a simmer, stirring occasionally. Stir in cooked pasta, turn off heat, then put softened cream cheese, shredded cheese, and seasonings (Italian seasoning, black pepper, and Worcestershire sauce). Mix pasta mixture until cheese is melted throughout.

TIP: You can replace the ground turkey for beef.

Nutrition: Calories: 502 kcal Total Fat: 30 g Saturated Fat: 14 g Cholesterol: 99 mg Sodium: 401 mg Total Carbs: 35 g Fiber: 1.7 g Sugar: 0 g Protein: 23 g

514. Aromatic Herbed Rice

Preparation time: 10 minutes
Cooking time: 15 minutes
Servings: 6

Ingredients:

- 2 tablespoons olive oil
- 3 cups cooked rice (don't overcook)
- 4–5 cloves fresh garlic, sliced thin
- 2 tablespoons fresh cilantro, chopped
- 2 tablespoons fresh oregano, chopped
- 2 tablespoons fresh chives, chopped
- ½ teaspoon red pepper flakes
- 1 teaspoon red wine vinegar

Directions:

1. In a large sauté pan, heat olive oil on medium-high heat and lightly sauté garlic. Add rice, herbs, and red pepper flakes and continue to cook for 2–4 minutes or until well-mixed.
2. Turn off heat, add vinegar, mix well, and serve.

Nutrition: Calories: 134 kcal Total Fat: 5 g Saturated Fat: 1 g Cholesterol: 0 mg Sodium: 6 mg Total Carbs: 21 g Fiber: 1.8 g Sugar: 0 g Protein: 2 g

515. Herb-Crusted Roast Leg Of Lamb

Preparation time: 10 minutes
Cooking time: 45 minutes
Servings: 12

Ingredients:

- 1 4-pound leg of lamb
- 3 tablespoons lemon juice
- 1 tablespoon curry powder
- 2 cloves garlic, minced
- ½ teaspoon ground black pepper
- 1 cup onions, sliced
- ½ cup dry vermouth

Directions:

1. Preheat oven to 400° F.
2. Bring leg of lamb on a roasting pan. Sprinkle with 1 teaspoon of lemon juice.
3. Make a paste with 2 teaspoons of lemon juice and the rest of the spices. Rub the paste onto the lamb.
4. Roast lamb in 400° F oven for 30 minutes.
5. Drain off fat and add vermouth and onions.
6. Reduce heat to 325° F and cook for an additional 1¾–2 hours. Baste leg of lamb frequently. When the internal temperature is 145° F, remove from oven and let rest 3 minutes before serving.

Nutrition: Calories: 292 kcal Total Fat: 20 g Saturated Fat: 9 g Cholesterol: 86 mg Sodium: 157 mg Total Carbs: 2 g Fiber: 0 g Sugar: 0 g Protein: 24 g

516. Chicken Fry With Peanut Sauce

Preparation time: 10 minutes
Cooking time: 15 minutes

Servings: 4

Ingredients

- Meat from 4 chicken thighs, cut into bite-size pieces
- 2 tbsp. + ¼ cup peanut oil
- ½ cup peanut butter
- 3 tbsp. toasted sesame oil
- 2 tbsp. soy sauce
- 1 tbsp. lime juice
- 1 clove garlic, minced
- 1 tsp. powdered ginger
- 1-2 tsp. hot sauce, if desired
- 2 red bell peppers, chopped
- 2 tbsp. toasted sesame seeds
- 4 green onions, thinly sliced

Directions:

1. Heat 2 tbsp. Peanut oil in a large frying pan.
2. Put the chicken and cook for about 10 minutes, until no pink remains.
3. Meanwhile, mix together the peanut butter, ¼ cup peanut oil, sesame oil, soy sauce, lime juice, garlic, ginger, and hot sauce.
4. Add more water if needed to achieve a smooth consistency.
5. When the chicken is done, add the red pepper and cook for 1 minute more.
6. Divide the chicken and peppers between four plates and top with peanut sauce, toasted sesame seeds, and green onions.

Nutrition: Calories: 426.9 Sugars: 4.8 g Total Carbohydrate: 16.9 g Protein: 38.7 g

517. Shrimp Fried 'Rice'

Preparation time: 10 minutes
Cooking time: 15 minutes
Servings: 4

Ingredients

- 2 + 2 tbsp. coconut oil
- 3 cups grated cauliflower
- 2 bell peppers, chopped
- 6 green onions, thinly sliced
- 1 lb. shrimp
- 4 eggs, lightly beaten
- 1 tbsp. soy sauce
- 2 tbsp. toasted sesame oil

Directions:

1. In a huge pan, warm the 2 tablespoons of coconut oil at high heat. Add shrimp and cook for 2-4 minutes until opaque and pink.
2. Remove from pan and set aside.
3. Add 2 tbsp. coconut oil and add the cauliflower, peppers, and green onions.
4. Sautee for 4-5 minutes, stirring frequently.
5. Add the eggs and soy sauce to the pan and stir continuously until the eggs are firm.
6. Add the toasted sesame oil and stir, then toss with the shrimp and serve.

Nutrition: Calories 482 Carbs 44.5g Protein 29.5g Fat 15g

518. Pan-Fried Salmon Burgers With Garlic And Greens

Preparation time: 30 minutes
Cooking time: 30 minutes+ 1 hours to chill
Servings: 4

Ingredients:

- 1 lb. boneless Pacific salmon filet, skin removed
- 2 eggs, lightly beaten
- Pinch salt and pepper
- 2 tbsp. onion minced
- ½ cup homemade mayonnaise
- 1 clove garlic, minced
- A handful of fresh cilantro, minced
- 2 tbsp. coconut oil
- 12 oz. greens, such as spinach, arugula, or mixed

Directions:

1. Finely chop the salmon using a sharp chef's knife into ⅛"- ¼" pieces.
2. Mix with the egg, salt, pepper, and onion and form into four patties.
3. Chill for 1 hour.
4. Meanwhile, whisk together the mayonnaise with the garlic and cilantro.
5. Chill.
6. Heat the coconut oil in a large skillet and add the burgers.
7. Cook for 2-3 minutes each side, until opaque throughout.
8. Serve on a bed of greens topped with the garlic

Nutrition: Calories: 439 kcal Protein: 39.15 g Fat: 28.84 g Carbohydrates: 7.31 g

519. Mushrooms Stuffed & Crab Paste

Preparation time: 15 minutes
Cooking time: 20 minutes
Servings: 15

Ingredients

- 20 ounces/566 grams mushrooms (about 20 mushrooms)
- 2 tablespoons parmesan cheese
- 1 tablespoon parsley (fresh, chopped)
- Salt
- For filling
- 4 ounces/100 grams cream cheese
- 4 ounces of crab meat (chopped)
- 5 garlic cloves (minced)
- 1 teaspoon oregano
- ½ teaspoon paprika
- ½ teaspoon pepper
- ¼ teaspoon salt

Directions:

1. Set the oven to 400°F. Put parchment paper over the baking sheet.
2. Remove the stems from the mushrooms. Put the mushroom heads over the baking sheet (not too close to each other). Sprinkle with salt.
3. In a bowl, mix the filling ingredients. (There must be no lumps of cream cheese.) With a teaspoon, carefully stuff the mushroom caps with this cheese mix.
4. Sprinkle parmesan on top of each mushroom head.
5. Bake for half an hour or until the mushrooms are soft, and the parmesan cheese is brownish.

Nutrition: Calories 34.1g Cholesterol 4.7mg Carbohydrate 2.7g Protein 5.0g

520. Taco Pie

Preparation time: 20 minutes
Cooking time: 10 minutes
Servings: 8

Ingredients

- 1-pound ground beef
- 3 tablespoons taco seasoning
- 6 eggs
- 1 cup heavy cream

- 2 garlic cloves (chopped)
- ½ teaspoon salt
- ¼ teaspoon pepper
- 1 cup cheddar cheese (shredded or grated)

Directions:

1. Set the oven to 350°F.
2. Grease a ceramic baking pan.
3. In another pot, cook the beef until it gets brown (medium heat, for seven minutes).
4. Put taco seasoning over the meat and stir well. Lower the heat and let it cook for a couple of minutes. (The sauce should thicken.)
5. Put the beef in the ceramic pan.
6. In another bowl, mix the eggs, cream, salt, pepper, and garlic. Pour this mix over the beef.
7. Top with cheese and bake for half an hour.
8. Once baked, take it out of the oven. Let it sit for a few minutes, then serve.
9. Decorate with sour cream, avocado, or other toppings of your choice.

Nutrition: Calories: 226.6 Total Fat: 9.8 g Protein: 19.0 g Saturated Fat: 3.0 g

521. Shrimp Chowder

Preparation time: 15 minutes
Cooking time: 15 minutes
Servings: 4

Ingredients

- 6 slices bacon (cut in squares)
- 1 turnip (cut in cubes)
- ½ cup onion (chopped)
- 2 garlic cloves (minced)
- 2 cups chicken broth
- 1 cup heavy cream
- 1-pound shrimp
- ½ teaspoon seasoning of your choice
- Salt and pepper
- Parsley

Directions:

1. Using a frying pan, fry the bacon until it is crispy. Set it on a paper towel to drain, and then return the bacon to the pan.
2. Add the onion and turnip to the pan and cook briefly or until the onion is tender. Add garlic and cook for one minute.
3. Put in the chicken broth and allow it all simmer for another 10 minutes.
4. Add the cream and the shrimp and cook until the shrimp is a lovely pink color (about three minutes).
5. Finally, add the seasoning.
6. Serve with bacon and parsley.

Nutrition: 202 calories 8g Fat 169mg Cholesterol 13g Carbohydrate 20g

522. Zucchini Noodles & Chicken Sausage

Preparation time: 10 minutes
Cooking time: 10 minutes
Servings: 4

Ingredients:

- 12 ounces sausage
- 2 medium zucchinis (spiralizer)
- 2 tablespoons butter
- 3 garlic cloves
- 1 cup heavy cream
- ½ cup parmesan
- Salt and pepper

Directions:

1. Use a skillet to fry the sausage for five to ten minutes. Put it in a bowl and allow the grease to drain.
2. Put butter in the skillet and let it melt. Add the garlic and sauté for a minute, add the heavy cream and let it all simmer for five more minutes. (Stir all the time.)
3. Add the parmesan, salt, and pepper and then put the sausage back in. Mix it well.
4. Cook the zucchini noodles in the microwave for a couple of minutes (until they are tender).
5. Serve the zucchini with the sausage sauce and toppings of your choice.

Nutrition: 252 calories 14g fat 10.3g carbohydrates 23g protein 74mg cholesterol 767mg sodium

523. Caprese Chicken

Preparation time: 10 minutes
Cooking time: 20 minutes
Servings: 4

Ingredients:

- 2 tablespoons avocado oil
- 5 chicken thighs (no skin and no bones)
- Salt
- Pepper
- 6 ounces mozzarella (cut in semi-thick circles)
- 1 tomato (cut in slices, the same thickness as the mozzarella)
- ¼ cup basil (chopped, preferably fresh)

Directions:

1. Preheat the oven to 375°F/190°C.
2. Meanwhile, heat the oil in a skillet and put the chicken inside to fry. Season with salt and pepper. Cook for a few more minutes per side.
3. Lay the chicken in a casserole dish and put mozzarella and tomato over each piece of meat.
4. Put the dish in the oven and bake for half an hour, or until the mozzarella is completely melted.
5. Serve while hot and decorate with basil.

Nutrition: 525 calories 34 g fat 139 mg cholesterol 5 g carbohydrate 45g protein

524. Vegetarian Paleo Ratatouille:

Preparation time: 1 hour 10 minutes
Cooking time: 55 minutes
Servings: 2

Ingredients:

- 200 g Tomato cubes (can)
- 1/2 pieces Onion
- 2 cloves Garlic
- 1/4 teaspoon dried oregano
- 1 / 4 TL Chili flakes
- 2 tablespoon Olive oil
- 1 piece Eggplant
- 1 piece Zucchini
- 1 piece hot peppers
- 1 teaspoon dried thyme

Directions:

1. Set the oven to 180 °C then lightly grease a round or oval shape.
2. Finely chop the onion and garlic.
3. Mix the tomato cubes with garlic, onion, oregano and chilli flakes, season with salt and pepper, and put them on the bottom of the baking dish.

4. Use a mandolin, a cheese slicer or a sharp knife to cut the eggplant, zucchini and hot pepper into very thin slices.
5. Put the vegetables in a bowl (make circles, start at the edge and work inside).
6. Drizzle the remaining olive oil on the vegetables and sprinkle with thyme, salt, and pepper.
7. Cover the baking dish with a piece of parchment paper and bake in the oven for 45 to 55 minutes.
8. Enjoy it!

Nutrition: Calories: 273 kcal Protein: 5.66 g Fat: 14.49 g Carbohydrates: 35.81 g

525. Chicken Thighs With Creamy Tomato Spinach Sauce

Preparation time: 45 minutes
Cooking time: 10 minutes
Servings: 2

Ingredients:

- 1 tablespoon olive oil
- 1.5 lb. chicken thighs, boneless skinless
- 1/2 teaspoon salt
- 1/4 teaspoon pepper
- 8 Oz tomato sauce
- 2 garlic cloves, minced
- 1/2 cup overwhelming cream
- 4 Oz new spinach
- 4 leaves fresh basil (or utilize 1/4 teaspoon dried basil)

Directions:

1. The most effective Direction to cook boneless skinless chicken thighs in a skillet: In a much skillet heat olive oil on medium warmth. Boneless chicken with salt and pepper. Add top side down to the hot skillet. Cook for 5 minutes on medium heat, until the high side, is pleasantly burned. Flip over to the opposite side and heat for five additional minutes on medium heat. Expel the chicken from the skillet to a plate. Step by step instructions to make creamy tomato basil sauce: To the equivalent, presently void skillet, include tomato sauce, minced garlic, and substantial cream. Bring to bubble and mix. Lessen warmth to low stew. Include new spinach and new basil. Mix until spinach withers and diminishes in volume. Taste the sauce and include progressively salt and pepper, if necessary. Include back cooked boneless skinless chicken thighs, increment warmth to medium.

Nutrition: Calories: 1061 kcal Protein: 66.42 g Fat: 77.08 g

526. Creamy Shrimp & Mozzarella Pasta

Preparation time: 45 minutes
Cooking time: 10 minutes
Servings: 2

Ingredients:

- 2 cups penne pasta, cooked still somewhat firm
- 2 tablespoons olive oil
- 4 cloves garlic, minced
- 1 pound shrimp, stripped and deveined
- 2 teaspoons salt, partitioned
- 1/2 cups substantial cream
- 1 cup destroyed mozzarella
- 1/2 cup sun-dried tomatoes
- 2 tablespoons cleaved basil
- 1/2 teaspoon red pepper pieces
- 2 teaspoons lemon juice
- Cleaved basil, to decorate

Directions:

1. In a heavy skillet over medium-high warmth, saute garlic in olive oil until fragrant, around 2 minutes. Include shrimp and cook about 3 minutes on each side. Season with a large portion of the salt, expel from skillet, and put in a safe spot. In a similar skillet, add overwhelming cream and heat to the point of boiling. Diminish to a stew and include mozzarella, sun-dried tomatoes, basil, and red pepper chips. Stew for 5 minutes and lessen to low warmth. Return shrimp to the dish and include lemon squeeze and staying salt. Include cooked pasta and basil and serve.

Nutrition: Calories: 664 kcal Protein: 70.86 g Fat: 20.94 g Carbohydrates: 51.53 g

527. Beef Stroganoff French Bread Toast

Preparation time: 10 minutes
Cooking time: 20 minutes
Servings: 2

Ingredients:

- 4 tablespoons olive oil
- 1/2 cups mushrooms
- 2 teaspoons salt, separated
- 1/2 teaspoon dark pepper
- 2 tablespoons thyme
- 2 tablespoons spread
- 1/2 cup onions, diced
- 2 cloves garlic, minced
- 1 pound ground meat
- 3 tablespoons generally useful flour
- 2 teaspoons paprika
- 1/2 cups meat juices
- 1/2 cup sharp cream
- 1 teaspoon Dijon mustard
- For the toasts:
- 1 portion French bread, inner parts dugout
- 2 cups mozzarella
- 3 tablespoons cleaved Italian parsley

Directions:

1. Preheat stove to 350 degrees, and line a sheet container with material paper. Make the stroganoff: In a large Dutch grill or skillet, heat olive oil over medium warmth. Sauté mushrooms with one teaspoon salt and dark pepper. Include thyme. Cook mushrooms until brilliant, roughly 4 minutes. Expel from a dish and put it in a safe spot. Include margarine, onions, and garlic to the container and sauté 2 minutes. Cook ground hamburger over medium warmth until dark-colored, roughly 4 minutes. Add flour and paprika to cover uniformly. Include meat soup, sour cream, and mustard. Blend entirely and include mushrooms back in. Round the emptied portion with stroganoff and top with mozzarella cheddar. Spot on the readied heating sheet, and prepare for 5 to 10 minutes until cheddar is brilliant and softened. Head with parsley, cut, and serve right away.

Nutrition: Calories: 1007 kcal Protein: 88.04 g Fat: 60 g Carbohydrates: 32.06 g

528. Beef Onion Rings, Garlic Kale, And Herb Roasted Potatoes

Preparation time: 1 hour 30 minutes
Cooking time: 1 hour 10 minutes
Servings: 2

Ingredients

- 100g potatoes, peeled and diced

- 1 tablespoon extra-virgin olive oil
- 5g parsley, finely chopped
- 50g red onion, sliced into rings
- 50g kale, sliced
- 1 garlic clove, finely chopped
- 120–150g x 3.5cm-thick beef fillet steak
- 40ml red wine 150ml beef stock
- 1 teaspoon tomato purée
- 1 teaspoon corn flour
- 1 tablespoon water

Directions:

1. Set the oven to 220°C, then put the potatoes in boiling water and cook for 4–5 minutes, drain. Pour 1 teaspoon oil in a roasting tin and roast the potatoes for 35–45 minutes, turning the potatoes on every side every 10 minutes to ensure they cook evenly.
2. Remove from the oven when fully cooked, sprinkle with chopped parsley, and mix thoroughly.
3. Pour 1 teaspoon of the oil on a saucepan and fry the onion for 5-7 minutes to become soft and neatly caramelized. Keep it warm.
4. Place the kale in a saucepan, steam for 2–3 minutes, and drain. In ½ teaspoon of oil, fry the garlic for 1 minute to become soft though not colored. Add the kale and continue to fry for an extra 1–2 minutes to become tender. Maintain the warmth.
5. Over high heat, place an ovenproof frying pan until it becomes smoking. Then use the ½ a teaspoon of the oil to coat the meat and fry over medium-high heat. Take off the meat then set aside to rest.
6. Pour the wine to the hot pan and bubble to reduce the wine quantity by half to form syrupy and to have a concentrated flavor. Add the tomato purée and stock to the steak pan and boil. Add the corn flour paste little at a time to act as a thickener until the desired consistency is achieved. Put any juices from the rested steak and serve with the kale, onion rings, roasted potatoes, and red wine sauce.

Nutrition: Calories: 244 kcal Protein: 14.26 g Fat: 14.46 g Carbohydrates: 14.69 g

529. Kale & Feta Salad With Cranberry Dressing

Preparation time: 5 Minutes
Cooking Time: 30 Minutes
Servings 2

Ingredients

- 9oz kale, finely chopped
- 2oz walnuts, chopped
- 3oz feta cheese, crumbled
- 1 apple, peeled, cored and sliced
- 4 Medjool dates, chopped
- For the Dressing
- 3oz cranberries
- ½ red onion, chopped
- 3 tablespoons olive oil
- 3 tablespoons water
- 2 teaspoons honey
- 1 tablespoon red wine vinegar
- Sea salt

Directions

1. Set all the ingredients for the dressing into a food processor and process until smooth. If it seems too thick, you can add a little extra water if necessary. Place all the ingredients for the salad into a bowl. Pour on the dressing and toss the salad until it is well coated in the mixture.

Nutrition: Calories: 706 kcal Protein: 15.62 g Fat: 45.92 g Carbohydrates: 70.28 g

530. Tuna, Egg & Caper Salad

Preparation time: 5 Minutes
Cooking time: 20 Minutes
Servings 2

Ingredients

- 3½ozred chicory or yellow if not available
- 5oz tinned tuna flakes in brine, drained
- 3 ½ oz cucumber
- 1oz rocket arugula
- 6 pitted black olives
- 2 hard-boiled eggs, peeled and quartered
- 2 tomatoes, chopped
- 2 tablespoons fresh parsley, chopped
- 1 red onion, chopped
- 1 stalk of celery
- 1 tablespoon capers
- 2 tablespoons garlic vinaigrette see recipe

Directions

1. Place the tuna, cucumber, olives, tomatoes, onion, chicory, celery, parsley, and rocket arugula into a bowl. Pour in the vinaigrette and toss the salad in the dressing. Serve onto plates and scatter the eggs and capers on top.

Nutrition: Calories: 309 kcal Protein: 26.72 g Fat: 12.23 g Carbohydrates: 25.76 g

531. Sesame Chicken Salad

Preparation time: 30 minutes
Cooking time: 12 minutes
Servings: 2

Ingredients

- 1 tablespoon of sesame seeds
- 1 cucumber, peeled, deseeded and sliced
- 100g baby kale, roughly chopped
- 60g pak choi, finely shredded
- ½ red onion, finely sliced
- 20g parsley, chopped
- 150g cooked chicken, shredded
- For the dressing:
- 1 tablespoon of extra virgin olive oil
- 1 teaspoon of sesame oil
- 1 lime
- 1 teaspoon of clear honey
- 2 teaspoons of soy sauce

Directions:

1. In a dry frying pan, put the sesame seeds and toast for 2 minutes to become lightly browned and fragrant. Put in a plate and set aside.
2. Put the olive oil, honey, soy sauce, sesame oil, and lime juice in a small bowl and mix to make the dressing.
3. Put in a large bowl, the kale, cucumber, pak choi, parsley, and red onion and gently mix. Pour the dressing into the mixture and continue mixing.
4. Share the salad in two plates topping them with the shredded chicken. Sprinkle the sesame seeds and serve.

Nutrition: Calories: 478 kcal Protein: 19.53 g Fat: 39.8 g Carbohydrates: 12.52 g

532. Raw Vegan Walnuts Pie Crust & Raw Brownies

Preparation time: 5 Minutes

Cooking time: 40 Minutes
Servings 2
Ingredients

- 1 1/2 cups walnuts
- 1 cup pitted dates
- 1 1/2 tsp. ground vanilla bean
- 1/3 cup unsweetened cocoa powder
- Topping for Raw Brownies:
- 1/3 cup walnut butter

Directions:

1. Add walnuts to a food processor or blender. Mix until finely ground.
2. Add the vanilla, dates, and cocoa powder to the blender. Mix well and optionally add a couple of drops of water to make the mixture stick together.
3. This is a basic Raw Walnuts Pie Crust recipe.
4. If you need a pie crust, then spread it thinly in a 9-inch disc and add the filling.
5. If you want to make Raw Brownies, then transfer the mixture into a small dish and top with walnut butter.

Nutrition: Calories: 899 kcal Protein: 13.83 g Fat: 71.65 g Carbohydrates: 71.67 g

533. Tuna Salad

Preparation time: 30 minutes
Cooking time: 0 minutes
Servings: 2
Ingredients:

- 100g red chicory
- 150g tuna flakes in brine, drained
- 100g cucumber
- 25g rocket
- 6 Kalamata olives, pitted
- 2 hard-boiled eggs, peeled and quartered
- 2 tomatoes, chopped
- 2 tbsp. fresh parsley, chopped
- 1 red onion, chopped
- 1 celery stalk
- 1 tbsp. capers
- 2 tbsp. garlic vinaigrette

Directions:

1. Mix all ingredients in a bowl then serve.

Nutrition: Calories: 308 kcal Protein: 27.13 g Fat: 12.2 g Carbohydrates: 24.6 g

534. Steak And Mushroom Udon

Preparation time: 15 minutes
Cooking time: 45 minutes
Servings: 4
Ingredients:

- 3.5 oz. Chestnut mushrooms, sliced
- 1 Tbsp. Cilantro
- 1-inch chunk ginger, chopped
- 3 oz. Kale, chopped
- 2 Tbsp. Miso paste
- 2 Tbsp. Olive oil
- 1Red chili, sliced
- 1Red onion, chopped
- 3.5 oz. Shitake mushrooms, halved
- 2 Sirloin steaks
- 3 oz. Spinach leaves, chopped
- 1 Star anise
- 5 oz. Udon noodles
- 1.5 pints Warm water

Directions:

1. This recipe is quite savory and will be a hit with anyone that craves umami flavors. Take the water you measured out and pour it into a pan. Toss in your ginger, miso, and star anise. Get this all boiling and then drop the heat. Simmer for a couple of minutes.
2. Review the instructions on the packaging of your udon and prepare them accordingly. Drain them; do not have them sitting in water.
3. Take a pan and oil it up. Place on a burner set to medium-high. Season your steak however you wish and slap it down onto the pan. Brown on each side to get the most flavor. You may want a meat thermometer to figure out how done your steak is here, as steaks vary in thickness. Regardless, cook your steak until you are happy with it. Remove it from the pan and set it off to the side.
4. Grab your veggies, minus the onion and chili, and throw them into the pot. Give them about five minutes of bathing in the miso.
5. Get the pan you used for the steak ready again by placing it on a burner set to medium and warm up the remaining oil in it. Now you will sauté the chili and onion until tender. Transfer noodles into serving bowls with slices of steak on top. Pour in your soup and veggies and enjoy it.

Nutrition: Calories: 317 kcal Protein: 10.59 g Fat: 9.64 g Carbohydrates: 54.61 g

535. Chili Cod Fillets

Preparation time: 5 minutes
Cooking time:
20 minutes
Servings: 2
Ingredients:

- 2 Bird's eye chilies
- 2 Chopped garlic cloves, chopped
- 2 tbsp. Chopped parsley
- 4 Cod fillets
- 4 tbsp. Olive oil

Directions:

1. Here is an easy and low ingredient dinner you can prepare rather quickly. You can try substituting cod with another fish fillet and see how much you like it. Get started by grabbing yourself a large pan and pouring in your oil. Get this ready by placing it on a stovetop burner set to medium-high. Toss in your fish and cook it thoroughly. The amount of time will depend on how thick each fillet is, so watch it and be patient. It should only take about ten minutes or so.
2. When the cod fillets are done, pull the fish out and set it off to the side. You could try keeping it warm in a toaster oven if you have other dishes or sides that you have yet to prepare.
3. Pour in any remaining oil (or more if needed) along with the rest of the ingredients. Stir thoroughly and get the chili nice and warm.
4. Go ahead and serve your fish with a side of noodles, rice, or veggies. Pour the chili over your cod and dig in. Dinner is done in under 20 minutes, and you've got yourself a nice plate of seafood. Not bad.

Nutrition: Calories: 779 kcal Protein: 42.6 g Fat: 60.68 g Carbohydrates: 16.53 g

536. Super-Speedy Prawn Risotto

Preparation time: 5 minutes
Cooking time: 20 minutes
Servings: 2
Ingredients:

- 100g Diced Onion
- 2 X 250g packs whole-grain Rice & Quinoa
- 200g Frozen Garden Peas
- 2 x 150g packs Cooked & Peeled King Prawns
- 1/285g Tote water-cress

Directions:

1. Heating 1 tablespoon coconut oil in a skillet on medium-high heat and then put in 100g Diced Onion; cook 5 minutes. Insert 2 x 250g packs whole-grain Rice & Quinoa along with 175ml hot vegetable stock (or plain water) and a 200g suspended Garden Peas. Gently split using rice using a wooden spoon. Cover and cook 3 minutes, stirring occasionally, you can add two x 150g packs Cooked and Peeled King Prawns. Cook for 12 minutes before prawns, peas, and rice have been piping hot, and the majority of the liquid was consumed. Remove from heat. Chop 1/2 x 85g tote water-cress and stir throughout; up to taste. Top with watercress leaves and pepper to function.

Nutrition: Calories: 103 kcal Protein: 6.54 g Fat: 3.4 g Carbohydrates: 11.89 g

537. Chicken Breast With Asparagus

Preparation time: 15 minutes
Cooking time:
16 minutes
Servings: 5

Ingredients:

- For Chicken:
- ¼ cup extra-virgin olive oil
- ¼ cup fresh lemon juice
- 2 tablespoons maple syrup
- 1 garlic clove, minced
- Salt and ground black pepper, as required
- 5 (6-ounce) boneless, skinless chicken breasts
- For Asparagus:
- 1½ pounds fresh asparagus
- 2 tablespoons extra-virgin olive oil
- 1 tablespoon fresh lemon juice

Directions:

1. For the marinade: in a large bowl, add oil, lemon juice, Erythritol, garlic, salt, and black pepper and beat until well combined.
2. In a large resealable plastic bag, place the chicken and ¾ cup of marinade.
3. Seal the bag and shake to coat well.
4. Refrigerate overnight.
5. Cover the bowl of remaining marinade and refrigerate before serving.
6. Preheat the grill to medium heat. Grease the grill grate.
7. Remove the chicken from the bag and discard the marinade.
8. Place the chicken onto grill grate and grill, covered for about 5-8 minutes per side.
9. Meanwhile, in a pan of boiling water, arrange a steamer basket.
10. Place the asparagus in steamer basket and steam, covered for about 5-7 minutes.
11. Drain the asparagus well and transfer into a bowl.
12. Add oil and lemon juice and toss to coat well.
13. Divide the chicken breasts and asparagus onto serving plates and serve.

Nutrition: Calories: 520 Fat: 29.7g Sat Fat: 6g Cholesterol: 151mg Sodium: 184mg Carbohydrates: 11.2g Fiber: 2.9g Sugar: 7.7g Protein: 52.4g

538. Chicken With Mushrooms & Broccoli

Preparation time: 15 minutes
Cooking time:
25 minutes
Servings: 6

Ingredients:

- 3 tablespoons extra-virgin olive oil
- 1 pound skinless, boneless chicken breast, cubed
- 1 medium onion, chopped
- 6 garlic cloves, minced
- 2 cups fresh mushrooms, sliced
- 16 ounces small broccoli florets
- ¼ cup water
- Salt and ground black pepper, as required

Directions:

1. Heat the oil in a large wok at medium heat and cook the chicken cubes for about 4-5 minutes.
2. With a slotted spoon, transfer the chicken cubes onto a plate.
3. In the same wok, add the onion and sauté for about 4-5 minutes.
4. Add the mushrooms and cook for about 4-5 minutes.
5. Stir in the cooked chicken, broccoli, water, and cook, covered for about 8-10 minutes, stirring occasionally.
6. Stir in salt and black pepper and remove from heat.
7. Serve hot.

Nutrition: Calories: 197 Fat: 10.1g Sat Fat: 2g Cholesterol: 44mg Sodium: 82mg Carbohydrates: 8.5g Fiber: 2.7g Sugar: 2.5g Protein: 20.1g

539. Beef With Kale & Carrot

Preparation time: 15 minutes
Cooking time: 12 minutes
Servings: 4

Ingredients:

- 2 tablespoons coconut oil
- 4 garlic cloves, minced
- 1 pound beef sirloin steak, cut into bite-sized pieces
- Ground black pepper, as required
- 1½ cups carrots, peeled and cut into matchsticks
- 1½ cups fresh kale, tough ribs removed and chopped
- 3 tablespoons low-sodium soy sauce

Directions:

1. Melt the coconut oil in a wok over medium heat and sauté the garlic for about 1 minute.
2. Add the beef and black pepper and stir to combine.
3. Increase the heat to medium-high and cook for about 3-4 minutes or until browned from all sides.
4. Add the carrot, kale, and tamari and cook for about 4-5 minutes.
5. Remove from the heat and serve hot.

Nutrition: Calories: 311 Fat: 13.8g Sat Fat: 8.6g Cholesterol: 101mg Sodium: 700mg Carbohydrates: 8.4g Fiber: 1.6g Sugar: 2.3g Protein: 37.1g

540. Kale Stuffed Steak

Preparation time: 15 minutes
Cooking time: 40 minutes
Servings: 6

Ingredients:

- 1 (1½-pound) flank steak, trimmed

- Salt and ground black pepper, as required
- 1 tablespoon extra-virgin olive oil
- 2 small garlic cloves, minced
- 6 ounces fresh kale, tough ribs removed and chopped finely
- 1 medium green bell pepper, seedless and chopped
- 1 medium tomato, chopped finely

Directions:

1. Preheat the oven to 425 degrees F. Grease a large baking dish.
2. Place the flank steak onto a clean cutting board.
3. Hold a sharp knife parallel to work surface, slice the steak horizontally, without cutting all the way through, that you can open like a book.
4. With a pounder, flatten the steak to an even thickness.
5. Dust the steak with a little salt and black pepper evenly.
6. In a skillet, heat the oil over medium heat and sauté the garlic for about 1 minute.
7. Add the kale and cook for about 3 minutes.
8. Stir in the bell pepper and tomato and immediately remove from heat.
9. Take the spinach mixture into a bowl and set aside to cool slightly
10. Place the filling on top of steak evenly.
11. Roll up the steak to seal the filling.
12. With cotton twine, tie the steak.
13. Place the steak roll into the prepared baking dish.
14. Bake for about 30-35 minutes.
15. Take it out from the oven and let it cool slightly before slicing.
16. With a sharp knife, cut the roll into desired sized slices and serve.

Nutrition: Calories: 264 Fat: 11.9g Sat Fat: 4.3g Cholesterol: 62mg Sodium: 104mg Carbohydrates: 5.3g Fiber: 0.9g Sugar: 1.5g Protein: 32.8g

541. Steak With Mushroom Sauce

Preparation time: 15 minutes

Cooking time:

20 minutes

Servings: 2

Ingredients:

- For Steak:
- 2 teaspoons extra-virgin olive oil
- 2 (4-ounce) strip steaks
- Salt and ground black pepper, as required
- For Mushroom Sauce:
- 2 tablespoons extra-virgin olive oil
- 1/3 cup fresh shiitake mushrooms, sliced
- ½ of shallot, sliced
- 1 garlic clove, peeled
- 1/3 cup red wine
- 1/3 cup homemade beef broth
- 2 tablespoons fresh parsley, chopped

Directions:

1. In a big heavy-bottomed skillet, warm the oil at high heat and cook the steaks with salt and black pepper for about 3-4 minutes per side.
2. With a slotted spoon, transfer the steaks onto a plate.
3. With a piece of foil, cover the steaks to keep warm.
4. In the same sauté pan, heat the remaining oil over medium-low heat and cook the mushrooms, shallot, and garlic for about 5 minutes, stirring frequently.
5. Mix in the wine then cook for about 2-3 minutes, stirring frequently.
6. Add the broth and stir to combine.
7. Stir in the parsley salt and black pepper and remove from the heat.
8. Divide the steaks onto serving plates and serve with the topping of mushroom sauce.

Nutrition: Calories: 335 Fat: 22.7g Sat Fat: 3.1g Cholesterol: 63mg Sodium: 578mg Carbohydrates: 4.5g Fiber: 0.3g Sugar: 2g Protein: 23.1g

542. Lamb Chops With Kale

Preparation time: 15 minutes

Cooking time:

11 minutes

Servings: 4

Ingredients:

- 1 garlic clove, minced
- 1 tablespoon fresh rosemary leaves, minced
- Salt and ground black pepper, as required
- 4 lamb loin chops
- 4 cups fresh baby kale

Directions:

1. Preheat the grill to high heat. Grease the grill grate.
2. In a bowl, add the garlic, rosemary, salt, and black pepper and mix well.
3. Coat the lamb chops with the herb mixture generously.
4. Place the chops onto the hot side of the grill and cook for about 2 minutes per side.
5. Now, move the chops onto the cooler side of the grill and cook for about 6-7 minutes.
6. Divide the kale onto serving plates and top each with 1 chop.
7. Serve immediately.

Nutrition: Calories: 301 Fat: 10.5g Sat Fat: 3.8g Cholesterol: 128mg Sodium: 176mg Carbohydrates: 7.8g Fiber: 1.4g Sugar: 0g Protein: 41.9g

543. Lamb Ribs With Herb Salad

Preparation time: 15 minutes

Cooking time:

25 minutes

Servings: 4

Ingredients:

- For Rack of Lamb:
- 4 garlic cloves, peeled
- 2 tablespoons fresh parsley
- 2 tablespoons extra-virgin olive oil
- 1 (2-pound) rack of lamb, frenched
- Salt and ground black pepper, as required
- For Salad:
- ½ cup fresh parsley, chopped
- ½ cup fresh mint leaves
- 1 tablespoon extra-virgin olive oil
- 1 tablespoon fresh orange juice
- 1 teaspoon raw honey
- Salt and ground black pepper, as required

Directions:

1. For the lamb:
2. In a mini food processor, put the garlic, rosemary and oil, and pulse until well combined.
3. Flavor the rack of lamb using a salt and black pepper and then rub with garlic mixture.
4. Arrange the rack onto a large rimmed baking sheet, fat-side up.
5. Set aside for about 1 hour.
6. Set the oven to 450°F. Prepare the rack in the upper third of the oven.

7. Bring the baking sheet in the oven and roast for about 15 minutes.
8. Flip the rack and roast for about 10 minutes.
9. Remove from oven, place the racks onto a cutting board, stand them upright, and rest for 10 minutes.
10. Meanwhile, for the salad: in a salad bowl, place all ingredients and toss to coat well.
11. With a sharp knife, cut the rack evenly into serving-sized portions.
12. Divide the salad onto serving plates and top each with ribs.
13. Serve immediately.

Nutrition: Calories: 494 Fat: 30.8g Sat Fat: 8.6g Cholesterol: 151mg Sodium: 208mg Carbohydrates: 4.9g Fiber: 1.7g Sugar: 1.8g Protein: 47.2g

544. Salmon With Arugula

Preparation time: 15 minutes
Cooking time: 8 minutes
Servings: 4

Ingredients:

- For Salmon:
- 4 tablespoons extra-virgin olive oil, divided
- 2 tablespoons fresh lemon juice
- 1 teaspoon ground turmeric
- 1 teaspoon ground cumin
- Salt and ground black pepper, as required
- 4 (4-ounce) boneless, skinless salmon fillets
- For Salad:
- 6 cups fresh arugula
- 2 cups cherry tomatoes, halved

Directions:

1. In a bowl, put and mix together 2 tablespoons of oil, lemon juice, turmeric, cumin, salt, and black pepper.
2. Add the salmon fillets and coat with the oil mixture generously. Set aside.
3. In a non-stick wok, heat remaining oil over medium heat.
4. Place salmon fillets, skin-side down, and cook for about 3-5 minutes.
5. Change the side and cook for about 2-3 minutes more.
6. Divide the salmon, arugula, and tomatoes onto serving plates and serve immediately.

Nutrition: Calories: 299 Fat: 21.6g Sat Fat: 3.2g Cholesterol: 50mg Sodium: 104mg Carbohydrates: 5.4g Fiber: 1.8g Sugar: 3.2g Protein: 23.8g

545. Shrimp With Veggies

Preparation time: 15 minutes
Cooking time:
8 minutes
Servings: 5

Ingredients:

- For Sauce:
- 1 tablespoon fresh ginger, grated
- 2 garlic cloves, minced
- 3 tablespoons low-sodium soy sauce
- 1 tablespoon red wine vinegar
- 1 teaspoon brown sugar
- ¼ teaspoon red pepper flakes, crushed
- Ground black pepper, as required
- For Shrimp Mixture:
- 3 tablespoons extra-virgin olive oil
- 1½ pounds medium shrimp, peeled and deveined
- 8 ounces broccoli florets
- 6 ounces carrot, peeled and sliced
- 2 cups fresh kale, tough ribs removed and chopped

Directions:

1. For the sauce: in a bowl, place all the ingredients and beat until well combined. Set aside.
2. In a large skillet, warm oil at medium-high heat and cook the shrimp for about 2 minutes, stirring occasionally.
3. Add the broccoli, carrot, and kale and cook for about 3-4 minutes, stirring frequently.
4. Stir in the sauce mixture and cook for about 1-2 minutes.
5. Serve immediately.

Nutrition: Calories: 297 Fat: 10.7g Sat Fat: 1.3g Cholesterol: 305mg Sodium: 882mg Carbohydrates: 7g Fiber: 2g Sugar: 2.4g Protein: 45.5g

546. Tofu & Veggies Curry

Preparation time: 20 minutes
Cooking time: 30 minutes
Servings: 5

Ingredients:

- 1 (16-ounce) block firm tofu, drained, pressed and cut into ½-inch cubes
- 2 tablespoons coconut oil
- 1 medium yellow onion, chopped
- 1½ tablespoons fresh ginger, minced
- 2 garlic cloves, minced
- 1 tablespoon curry powder
- Salt and ground black pepper, as required
- 1 cup fresh mushrooms, sliced
- 1 cup carrots, peeled and sliced
- 1 (14-ounce) can unsweetened coconut milk
- ½ cup homemade vegetable broth
- 2 teaspoons light brown sugar
- 8 ounces broccoli florets
- 2 cups fresh kale, tough ribs removed and chopped
- 1 tablespoon fresh lime juice
- ¼ cup fresh parsley, chopped

Directions:

1. In a Dutch oven, warm the oil in medium heat and sauté the onion, ginger, and garlic for about 5 minutes.
2. Mix in the curry powder, salt, and black pepper then cook for about 2 minutes, stirring occasionally.
3. Put the mushrooms and carrot then cook for about 4-5 minutes.
4. Stir in the coconut milk, broth, and brown sugar and bring to a boil.
5. Add the tofu, broccoli, and kale and simmer for about 12-15 minutes, stirring occasionally.
6. Mix in the lime juice and parsley, then remove from the heat.
7. Serve hot.

Nutrition: Calories: 364 Fat: 28.8g Sat Fat: 22.4g Cholesterol: 0mg Sodium: 146mg Carbohydrates: 22.2g Fiber: 6.1g Sugar: 7.6g Protein: 13.1g

547. Perfect Cauliflower Mash

Preparation time: 5 minutes
Cooking time: 5 minutes
Servings: 4

Ingredients:

- 1 large head cauliflower, cored and cut in large florets
- 1 cup low-sodium chicken broth
- 3 tablespoons unsalted butter
- ½ tablespoon garlic powder
- Salt to taste
- Pepper to taste

Directions:

1. Add the cauliflower and broth to the Instant Pot. Lock the lid and set the Pressure Release to Sealing. Select the Pressure Cook or Manual setting and set the cooking time to 5 minutes at high pressure.
2. Once the time comes up, use a kitchen towel or oven mitts to protect your hand and move the Pressure Release knob to Venting, to perform a quick pressure release.
3. Drain, reserving any excess broth, and return the cauliflower to the pot. With a potato masher, immersion blender, or fork, mash to your desired consistency, adding broth as needed for more moisture. Stir in the butter and garlic powder, and add salt and pepper to taste.
4. Note: For more flavor, mix in fresh herbs such as thyme or rosemary before serving. You may also mix in a splash of unsweetened original almond milk for a creamier mash.

Nutrition: Calories: 141 Cal Fat: 9.1g (sat 5.5g), Cholesterol: 22.6mg Protein: 5.6g Carbohydrate: 12.6g Fiber: 5.4g Sugar: 5.4g Sodium: 107 mg

548. 10-Minute Balsamic Roasted Beets

Preparation time: 1 minute
Cooking time: 10 minutes
Servings: 6

Ingredients:

- 6 medium beets (about 2 in. in diameter), unpeeled
- 3 tablespoons balsamic vinegar
- 2 tablespoons olive oil
- Salt to taste
- Pepper to taste

Directions:

1. Wash the beets well and remove any leaves. Add 1 cup of water to the Instant Pot and place the trivet on top. Arrange the beets on the trivet.
2. Lock the lid then set the pressure release to sealing. Select the Pressure Cook or Manual setting and set the cooking time to 10 minutes at high pressure.
3. When the timer goes off, use a kitchen towel or oven mitts to protect your hand and move the Pressure Release knob to Venting to perform a quick pressure release.
4. Remove the beets, allow to cool, and peel. The skin should slip off easily. Slice the beets into rounds or chop them into bite-sized pieces. Dress them with the balsamic vinegar, olive oil, and salt and pepper to taste.
5. Serve immediately or allow to marinate for 30 minutes for more flavor.

Nutrition: Calories: 82.1 Cal Fat: 4.6g (sat 0.6g) Cholesterol: 0mg Protein: 1.4g Carbohydrate: 9.2g Fiber: 2.3g Sugar: 6.7g Sodium: 82mg

549. Chicken Pram Lasagna

Preparation time: 5 minutes
Cooking time: 30 minutes
Servings: 3

Ingredients:

- 3 chicken bosoms
- Salt, to taste
- Pepper, to taste
- 1 cup generally useful flour (125 g)
- 5 eggs, separated
- 2 cups Italian bread pieces (230 g)
- Vegetable oil, for broiling
- 2 cups ricotta cheddar
- 24 Oz marinara sauce (680 g)
- ½ cups destroyed mozzarella cheddar
- ½ cups destroyed parmesan cheddar
- New basil, to embellish

Directions:

1. Cut chicken bosoms down the middle (pound slim if fundamental) and season with salt and pepper. Include the flour, four eggs, and bread morsels to 3 separate shallow dishes. Beat the eggs. Coat the chicken in the flour, at that point the eggs, lastly in the bread scraps. Fry the chicken on the two sides until brilliant darker, around 4 minutes on each side. Let channel on paper towels. In a medium bowl, join the ricotta cheddar and the rest of the egg. Preheat the grill to (180°C). Spread about ⅓ of the marinara sauce over the base of a goulash dish. Rehash to make another layer, at that point, finish with the rest of the sauce and mozzarella and Parmesan cheeses. Appreciate!

Nutrition: Calories: 68 Fat: 5g Magnesium: 55g Potassium: 32g

550. Simplest Brothy Beans

Preparation time: 5 minutes
Cooking time: 35 minutes
Servings: 4

Ingredients:

- 1 lb. dried white beans, like great northern, cannellini, or chickpeas
- 1 medium yellow onion, quartered
- 2 celery stalks, cut into 2
- 1 medium carrot, peeled and cut into 2
- 8 cups of water
- Salt to taste
- Freshly ground pepper to taste
- Extra virgin olive oil to taste
- 1 lemon, juiced

Directions:

1. In the Instant Pot, add the beans, onion, celery, carrots, water, and 1 teaspoon salt. Lock the lid then set the Pressure Release to Sealing. Select the Pressure Cook or Manual setting and set the cooking time to 35 minutes at high pressure.
2. When the time comes up, allow it to rest for at least 10 minutes; the pressure will release naturally. Then switch the Pressure Release to Venting to allow any last steam out.
3. Open the Instant Pot and season beans generously with salt and pepper, tasting the broth as you add seasoning until it's to your taste. Serve warm, drizzled with a few drops of olive oil and lemon juice.

Nutrition: Calories: 399 Cal Fat: 1.7g (sat 0.4g) Cholesterol: 0mg Protein: 24.2g Carbohydrate: 74.4g Fiber: 29.1g

551. Parsley Pesto Pasta

Preparation Time: 10 minutes
Cooking Time: 15 minutes
Servings: 5

Ingredients:

- 2 cups Parsley, fresh, packed –
- 3 cloves Garlic
- .25 cup Pine nuts
- 1 tablespoons Sea salt
- 2 teaspoon Lemon juice
- 5 tablespoons Coconut cream
- 3 tablespoons Nutritional yeast
- .25 teaspoon Black pepper, ground
- .5 cup Almonds

- 1 tablespoon Nutritional yeast
- .25 teaspoon Sea salt
- 200 grams Pasta of choice

Directions:

1. In a food processor, put and mix the parsley, garlic, pine nuts, teaspoon of sea salt, lemon juice, coconut cream, three tablespoons of nutritional yeast, and the black pepper create the parsley pesto. Scrape down each side of the food processor as needed.
2. In a blender, combine the almonds and one tablespoon of nutritional yeast until it forms a fine meal. This will be your vegan Parmesan cheese.
3. Meanwhile, cook the pasta based on the instructions on the packaging until it is al dente. Drain the water off of the cooked pasta and return it back to the pot.
4. Pour the pesto over the pasta and allow it to cook together over medium heat while constantly stirring for one to two minutes. Remove the pot from the heat.
5. Serve the pasta, topping it off with the vegan Parmesan cheese you previously prepared.

Nutrition: Calories: 348 Carbohydrates: 7.4 g Cholesterol: 44 mg Fat: 3.2 g

552. Special Enchiladas

Preparation time: 30 minutes
Cooking time: 65 minutes
Servings: 4

Ingredients:

- 2 large chicken breasts (about 400g)
- 2 red peppers, thinly chopped
- 1 tablespoon olive oil
- 3/4 tsp mild chili powder
- 1 teaspoon 1/2 tsp ground cumin
- 3/4 tsp smoked paprika
- 80g grated mozzarella
- 8 plain tortilla wraps
- 65g ripe cheddar, grated
- 10g fresh coriander, roughly sliced
- For the sauce
- 1 tablespoon olive oil
- 1/2 onion, finely chopped
- 2 tsp cloves, crushed
- 500g tomato passata
- 1 tablespoon chipotle chili paste
- 400g tin black beans, drained and rinsed
- 1/2 lime, juiced

Directions:

1. Set the oven 190°c, and buff 170°c. Set the chicken at a 20 x 30cm skillet with all the peppers olive oil, chili powder, cumin, and paprika. Mix to coat, then cover with foil. Roast for 25-30 mins before the chicken is cooked and tender with no pink meat remains. Take out the chicken from the dish and then shred with two forks. Reserve in a bowl.
2. Meanwhile, make the sauce. Heat the oil in a saucepan at low heat and cook the garlic and onion for 10 minutes. Stir from the passata and chipotle chilli glue; increase heat to moderate, place it to a simmer, then cook for around 10 minutes, stirring periodically. Bring the beans and carrot juice season.
3. Mix one-third of this sauce plus half of the mozzarella to the cultured broccoli and chicken.
4. To gather, spoon 4 tablespoons of this sauce in exactly the exact baking dish before. Spoon a bit of the chicken mixture down the middle of each tortilla, roll it up, and then put it from the dish. Repeat with the tortillas and filling, then placing them alongside so that they do not shatter. Put the remaining sauce on the top and then scatter within the cheddar and remaining mozzarella. Bake for around 20-25 minutes up to the cheese has melted and begun to brownish. Scatter together with all the coriander to function.

Nutrition: Calories: 470 Saturated Fat: 12g Cholesterol: 90mg Sodium: 1410mg Total Carbohydrates: 33g

553. Red Wine Chicken

Preparation time: 5 minutes
Cooking time: 40 minutes
Servings: 3

Ingredients:

- 500g chicken
- 500ml red wine
- 1 clove garlic
- 1 tablespoon olive oil
- 10g rosemary

Directions:

1. Warm the extra virgin olive oil at low heat in a saucepan with high edges together with the cloves of a head of garlic left poached and lightly crushed and a small sprig of rosemary. Once the oil begins to sizzle, put the chicken cut into pieces and brown evenly. Add plenty of wine to the well-browned chicken until it almost covers the chicken pieces, cover the saucepan, then cook in alow heat for 50 minutes. If necessary, put a little hot water while the chicken is cooking. When cooked, turn off the heat. And serve the chicken by adding the cooking juices to the wine.

Nutrition: Calories: 253 Fat: 8g Cholesterol: 77mg Sodium: 199mg Carbohydrate: 7g Protein: 35g

554. Pasta With Kale And Black Olive

Preparation time: 10 minutes
Cooking time: 40 minutes
Servings: 3

Ingredients:

- 60 g of buckwheat pasta
- 180 g of pasta
- 6 leaves of washed curly kale
- 20 black olives
- 2 tablespoons of oil
- ½ chili pepper

Directions:

1. Cut the curly kale leaves into strips about 4 cm wide; cook them in salted boiling water for 5 minutes. Also, add the pasta to the pan. When the pasta is cooking, in a non-stick pan, towards the oil and olives. Drain the pasta and cabbage (keeping some cooking water aside) and add them to the olives. Mix well, adding, if needed, a little cooking water. Add the chili pepper and keep everything well.

Nutrition: Calories: 300 Total Fat: 16g Carbohydrates: 9.4g Protein: 12g

555. Coq Au Vin

Preparation time: 10 minutes
Cooking time: 15 minutes
Servings: 8

Ingredients:

- 450g 1lb button mushrooms
- 100g 3½oz streaky bacon, chopped
- 16 chicken thighs, skin removed

- 3 cloves of garlic, crushed
- 3 tablespoons fresh parsley, chopped
- 3 carrots, chopped
- 2 red onions, chopped
- 2 tablespoons plain flour
- 2 tablespoons olive oil
- 750mls 1¼ pints red wine
- 1 bouquet grain

Directions:

1. On a large plate, put the flour and coat the chicken in it. Heat the olive oil, then add the chicken and brown it, before setting aside. Fry the bacon in the pan, then add the onion and cook for 5 minutes. Put in the red wine, then add the chicken, carrots, bouquet grain, and garlic. Transfer it to a large ovenproof dish. Cook at 180C/360F for an hour. Remove the bouquet grain and skim off any excess fat, if necessary. Add in the mushrooms and cook for 15 minutes. Stir in the parsley just before serving.

Nutrition: Calories: 267.0 Saturated Fat: 1.8 g Total Fat: 8.7 g Polyunsaturated Fat: 1.1 g

556. Asian Lord Prawn Pan Sear

Preparation time: 10 minutes
Cooking time: 6 minutes
Servings: 4

Ingredients:

- 150g crude ruler prawns shelled
- 2tsp tamari or soy sauce
- 2tsp additional virgin olive oil
- 1 clove garlic, finely hacked
- 1 10,000 foot stew, finely slashed
- 1tsp new ginger, finely hacked
- 20g red onion, cut 40g celery, cut and cut
- 75g green beans, hacked
- 50g kale, generally hacked 100ml chicken stock
- 75g soba (buckwheat noodles)
- 5g lavage or celery leaves

Directions:

1. In a skillet over high warmth, cook the prawns in 1tsp tamari or soy sauce and 1tsp oil for 2-3 minutes. Move to a plate.
2. Put the rest of the oil to the dish and fry the garlic, stew, ginger, red onion, celery, beans, and kale over medium-high warmth for 2-3 minutes. Put the stock and place it to the bubble, then stew until the vegetables are cooked yet at the same time crunchy.
3. Cook the noodles in bubbling water according to pack directions. Channel and include the lavage or celery leaves, noodles, and prawns to the container. Take back to the bubble, then expel from the warmth and serve.

Nutrition: Calories 600 Protein 29.1g Total fat 35g Saturated fat 10g Carbohydrates 45g

557. Turkey Escalope

Preparation time: 10 minutes
Cooking time: 6 minutes
Servings: 4

Ingredients:

- 150g cauliflower, generally slashed
- 1 clove garlic, finely slashed
- 40g red onion, finely slashed
- 1 superior stew, finely hacked
- 1tsp crisp ginger, finely hacked
- 2tbsp additional virgin olive oil
- 2tsp ground turmeric
- 30g sun-dried tomatoes, finely hacked
- 10g parsley
- 150g turkey escalope
- 1tsp dried sage
- Juice 1/2 lemon
- 1tbsp tricks

Directions:

1. Place the cauliflower in a nourishment processor and heartbeat in 2-second blasts to finely cleave it until it looks like couscous. Put in a safe spot. Fry the garlic, red onion, bean stew, and ginger in 1tsp of the oil until delicate, however not hued. Include the turmeric and cauliflower and cook for 1 moment. Expel from the warmth and include the sun-dried tomatoes and a large portion of the parsley.
2. Coat the turkey escalope in the rest of the oil and sage, then fry for 5-6 minutes, turning normally. When cooked, include the lemon juice, remaining parsley, tricks, and 1tbsp water to the container to make a sauce, then serve.

Nutrition: Calories 106 Total Fat 3.4 g Sodium 109.7 mg Carbohydrate 19.2 Dietary Fiber 1.6 g

558. Fragrant Chicken

Preparation time: 10 minutes
Cooking time: 20 minutes
Servings: 4

Ingredients:

- For the salsa: 1 huge tomato
- 1 10,000 foot bean stew, finely cleaved
- 1 tbsp. tricks, finely cleaved
- 5g parsley, finely hacked
- 1/2 lemon juice
- For the chicken
- 120g skinless, boneless chicken bosom
- 2tsp ground turmeric
- 1/2 lemon juice
- 1tbsp additional virgin olive oil
- 50g kale, hacked
- 20g red onion, cut
- 1tsp new ginger, finely cleaved
- 50g buckwheat

Directions:

1. Heat the stove to 220°C/200°C fan/gas mark 7. To make the salsa, finely slash the tomato, ensuring you keep however much of the fluid as could reasonably be expected. Blend in with the bean stew, tricks, parsley, and lemon juice. Marinate the chicken bosom in 1tsp of the turmeric, lemon juice, and a large portion of the oil for 5-10 minutes. Heat an ovenproof griddle, include the marinated chicken, cook for a moment on each side until brilliant, and then exchange it to the broiler for 8-10 minutes or until cooked through. Expel, spread with foil and leave to rest for 5 minutes. Cook the kale in a steamer for at least 5 minutes. Fry the onion and ginger in the remainder of the oil until delicate yet not shaded, then include the cooked kale and fry for one more moment. Cook the buckwheat according to pack directions with the rest of the turmeric and serve.

Nutrition: Calories: 345.4 Fat: 14.5 g Cholesterol: 44.1 mg Sodium: 419.5 mg Potassium: 84.1 mg Total Carbohydrate: 44.1 g Protein: 9.0 g

559. Sautéed Salmon Serving Of Mixed Greens

Preparation time: 10 minutes

Cooking time: 8 minutes
Servings: 4
Ingredients:

- For the dressing
- 10g parsley
- 1/2 lemon juice
- 1 tbsp. tricks
- 1 tbsp. additional virgin olive oil
- For the serving of mixed greens
- 1/2 avocado, stripped, stoned and diced
- 100g cherry tomatoes, divided
- 20g red onion, meagerly cut
- 50g rocket
- 5g celery leaves
- 150g skinless salmon filet
- 2 tsp darker sugar
- 70g chicory (head), divided lengthways

Directions:

1. Heat the broiler to 220°C/200°C fan/gas mark 7. To make the dressing, whizz the parsley, lemon juice, tricks, and 2tsp oil in a blender until smooth. For the plate of mixed greens, blend the avocado, tomato, and red onion, rocket, and celery leaves together. Rub the salmon with a small amount of oil and singe it in an ovenproof skillet for a moment. Move to a heating plate and cook in the broiler for 5 minutes.
2. Mix the darker sugar with 1tsp oil and brush it over the cut sides of the chicory. Spot chop sides down in a hot skillet and cook for 2-3 minutes, turning normally. Dress the plate of mixed greens and serve together.

Nutrition: Calories: 191.5 Protein: 17.8 g Carbohydrate: 2.9 g Fat: 11.2 g

560. Chargrilled Meat

Preparation time: 20 minutes
Cooking time: 50 minutes
Servings: 2
Ingredients:

- 100g potatoes, stripped and diced into 2cm 3D shapes
- 1tbsp additional virgin olive oil
- 5g parsley, finely cleaved
- 50g red onion, cut into rings
- 50g kale, cleaved
- 1 clove garlic, finely cleaved
- 120-150g 3.5cm-thick meat filet
- Steak or 2cm-thick sirloin steak
- 40ml red wine
- 150ml meat stock
- 1tsp tomato purée
- 1tsp corn flour, broke down in 1tbsp water

Directions:

1. Heat the stove to 220°C/200°C fan/gas mark 7.
2. Place the potatoes in a pan of bubbling water, bring it to the bubble, cook for 4-5 minutes, then channel it. Spot in a simmering tin with 1tsp oil and cook for 35-45 minutes, turning at regular intervals. Expel from the stove, sprinkle with the cleaved parsley and blend well.
3. Fry the onion in 1tsp oil over medium warmth until delicate and caramelized. Keep warm.
4. Steam the kale for 2-3 minutes, then channel. Fry the garlic delicately in 1/2tsp oil for 1 moment until delicate. Include the kale and fry for a further 1-2 minutes, until delicate. Keep warm.
5. Heat an ovenproof griddle until smoking. Coat the meat in 1/2tsp oil and fry according to how you like your meat done. Expel from the dish and put aside to rest. Add the wine to the hot skillet to raise any meat buildup. Air pocket to decrease the wine considerably until it's syrupy with a
6. Put the stock and tomato the pour to the steak container and bring to the bubble, then add the corn flour glue to thicken the sauce a little at once until you have the ideal consistency. Mix in any juice from the refreshed steak and present with the potatoes, kale, onion rings, and red wine sauce.

Nutrition: Calories: 280 Protein: 30 g Carbs: 5 g Fiber: 16 g Fat: 11.8 g

561. Pad Thai

Preparation time: 10 minutes
Cooking time: 30 minutes
Servings: 4
Ingredients:

- 100 grams of rice stick noodles (thin)
- 1 tsp. tamarind sauce
- 1 tbsp. tamari
- 1 tbsp. lemon juice
- 1 tsp. brown sugar
- 300 grams tofu (firm, cut into pieces of 1.5 cm)
- 200 grams prawns (peeled)
- 1 white onion (sliced)
- 3 cloves of garlic (crushed)
- 1 red capsicum (sliced)
- 1 bunch broccolini
- 350 grams carrots (cut into noodle-like shape)
- 1 cup bean sprouts
- 2 tbsps. Peanuts (for serving)

Directions:

1. Take a large bowl and soak the noodles in boiling water for three minutes.
2. Mix tamari, tamarind, sugar, and lemon juice in a bowl.
3. Place a wok then heat oil in it over a high flame. Stir-fry the pieces of tofu for two minutes. Keep it aside.
4. Spray the wok with oil and add prawns to it—Cook for four minutes.
5. Spray the wok with oil once more and add onions to it. Fry for about two minutes. Add garlic, broccolini, and carrots—Cook for four minutes.
6. Add capsicum and stir-fry for one minute.
7. Add prawns, sauce mixture, and tofu to the wok. Add noodles and toss for two minutes.
8. Serve with peanuts and bean sprouts.

Nutrition: Calories: 293 Protein: 26g Fat: 8.3g Carbs: 29.2g Fiber: 10.5g

562. Fennel And Salmon Salad

Preparation time: 30 minutes
Cooking time: 60 minutes
Servings: 4
Ingredients:

- 4 oranges
- 1 lemon (grated rind)
- 2 tbsps. Dijon mustard
- 2 tbsps. Fresh dill (chopped)
- 3 200 grams fillets of salmon (skinless)
- 250 grams of snow peas (sliced)
- 2 fennel bulbs (sliced)
- 150 grams baby spinach

- 120 grams of salad leaves
- 1 tbsp. balsamic vinegar (white)
- 2 tbsps. Pistachios (chopped, for serving)

Directions:

1. Grate the rind of 1 orange then squeeze the juice. Peel the remaining oranges and cut into rounds.
2. Combine orange rind, lemon rind, half of the orange juice, mustard, and one tbsp. dill in a ceramic dish. Add the fillets of salmon and coat properly. Marinate for one hour in the fridge.
3. Preheat a barbecue on medium. Spray the barbecue with olive oil. Drain the marinade and add the salmon to the barbecue. Cook for three minutes on each side. Flake the salmon coarsely.
4. Soak the snow peas in boiling water for one minute.
5. Take a bowl and combine snow peas, salad leaves, fennel, and slices of orange in a bowl. Whisk mustard, vinegar, dill, and orange juice in another bowl.
6. Put half of the dressing to the salad then toss for combining.
7. Serve the salads on a plate and top it with cooked salmon. Drizzle leftover dressing from the top and sprinkle some pistachios.

Nutrition: Calories: 292 Protein: 27g Fat: 14g Carbs: 15g Fiber: 7g

563. Fish Taco And Chipotle Avocado

Preparation time: 10 minutes
Cooking time:
30 minutes
Servings: 4

Ingredients:

- 2 tbsps. Lime juice
- 1 tbsp. olive oil
- 1 tsp. paprika
- 1 clove of garlic (crushed)
- 2 tsp. Chipotle sauce
- 400 grams white fish fillets (firm, fish of your choice)
- 200 grams capsicum (deseeded, halved)
- 2 zucchini (cut into discs)
- Half avocado
- 1 butter lettuce
- 8 corn tortillas (warmed)
- Coriander leaves (for serving)

Directions:

1. Mix one tbsp. Lime juice, paprika, oil, one tsp. chipotle, and garlic in a shallow dish. Add the fillets of fish and coat properly. Marinate for ten minutes.
2. Preheat a barbecue grill or chargrill. Spray zucchini, capsicum, and the fillets of fish with oil.
3. Cook zucchini and capsicum for two minutes or until soft.
4. Cook the fish fillets for two minutes on both sides for two minutes or until browned.
5. Process lime juice, avocado, and chipotle in a blender. Make a fine paste.
6. Divide grilled veggies, lettuce, and fish among the warmed tortillas.
7. Top the tortillas with a dollop of avocado chipotle.
8. Serve with coriander leaves from the top.

Nutrition: Calories: 303 Protein: 27g Fat: 14g Carbs: 32g Fiber: 6g

564. Baked Fish With Parmesan Crumb

Preparation time: 10 minutes
Cooking time: 20 minutes
Servings: 2

Ingredients:

- 1/2 cup breadcrumbs (multi-grain)
- 1/4 cup parsley (chopped)
- 1/3 cup parmesan cheese (grated)
- 1 tsp. lemon rind (grated)
- 1 tsp. olive oil
- 4 thick fish steaks (white)
- Cooking spray (olive oil)
- Green beans (steamed, for serving)
- Boiled potatoes (for serving)

Directions:

1. Preheat your oven to 200 degrees Celsius. Mix parsley, breadcrumbs, lemon rind, parmesan, pepper, and salt in a mixing bowl. Drizzle some oil.
2. Press the mixture of breadcrumbs on the flesh-side of the fish fillets for making an even topping.
3. Take a baking tray and place the fish skin-side down. Spray some oil. Bake for about fifteen minutes or until the crumbs are golden in color.
4. Serve with potatoes and steamed beans.

Nutrition: Calories: 220 Protein: 36g Fat: 6g Carbs: 3g Fiber: 3g

565. Zucchini Tuna Noodle Bake

Preparation time: 10 minutes
Cooking time: 50 minutes
Servings: 4

Ingredients:

- 4 zucchini (cut like noodles)
- 2 tsp. Olive oil
- Half yellow onion (diced)
- 2 cans of flaked tuna
- 1 tbsp. tomato paste
- 1 can diced tomatoes
- 1/2 cup skimmed milk
- 1/2 tsp. kosher salt
- 1 tsp thyme
- 1/4 tsp. black pepper (ground)
- ½ cup cheddar cheese (fat-free, shredded)
- 1/4 cup parmesan (fat-free, shredded)

Directions:

1. Preheat your oven at 200 degrees Celsius.
2. Spray a pan with cooking spray. Spread the zucchini noodles in a layer.
3. Get a skillet and heat oil in it over a medium flame. Start adding onions to the oil. Cook the onions for three minutes. Add tomato paste and tuna. Cook for one minute.
4. Add diced tomatoes, thyme, milk, pepper, and salt. Simmer the mixture and add parmesan. Allow the cheese to melt.
5. Pour the mix of tuna over the noodles of zucchini. Sprinkle cheddar from the top and bake for twenty minutes or until the cheese melts.

Nutrition: Calories: 165 Protein: 17g Fat: 6g Carbs: 0g Fiber: 3g

566. Snapper Taco With Salsa

Preparation time: 5 minutes
Cooking time: 25 minutes
Servings: 2

Ingredients:

- 450 grams of snapper fillet
- Black pepper (ground)
- Cracked kosher salt

- 4 tortillas (corn)
- Cooking spray
- For salad:
- On avocado (peeled, diced)
- 1 cup of grape tomatoes (halved)
- 2 tbsps. Chives
- ½ juice of a lime

Directions:

1. Get a grill pan then heat it over a high flame.
2. Cut some slits on the fillets of the fish. Season with pepper and salt. Coat the fish with cooking spray.
3. Place the fish to the grill and cook for about ten minutes or until grilled properly. Flip the fish then cook for another 10 minutes. Make sure that the fish is flaky and white.
4. Place corn tortillas on the grill and heat until charred.
5. For the salsa, mix grape tomatoes, avocado, lime juice, and chives in a bowl. Season according to taste. Toss well for combining.
6. Divide the cooked fish among the tortillas and top with the salsa.

Nutrition: Calories: 400 Protein: 39g Fat: 1.2g Carbs: 28g Fiber: 5.6g

567. Veggie Beef Pie

Preparation time: 15 minutes
Cooking time:
3 hours and 15 minutes
Servings: 4

Ingredients:

- 2 tbsps. Olive oil (extra virgin)
- 1 kg beef steak (cut in pieces of 3 cm)
- 200 grams mushrooms (halved)
- 1 onion (chopped)
- 2 cloves of garlic (chopped)
- 2 carrots (chopped)
- 1 zucchini (chopped)
- 400 grams canned tomatoes (chopped)
- 1 cup of water
- 3 sprigs of thyme
- 500 grams of cauliflower florets
- 400 grams lentils (rinsed)
- 1 cup peas (frozen)
- 5 pastry sheets

Directions:

1. Using a pan, heat oil then cook the beef. Cook for four minutes and keep aside.
2. Put remaining oil to the pan then cook the mushrooms for five minutes. Keep aside.
3. Add garlic, onion, zucchini, and carrot to the pan—Cook for ten minutes. Add beef to the pan. Mix well. Add tomato and water to the pan. Boil the mixture. Lower the heat temperature and simmer for two hours.
4. Add lentils, cauliflower, and mushrooms and cook for twenty minutes. Cook until the liquid reduces. Add the peas and season.
5. Preheat your oven at 160 degrees Celsius.
6. Transfer the mixture of beef to a deep pie dish. Spray one pastry sheet with olive oil and place over the mixture of beef. Repeat with the other sheets and tuck in the dish edges for sealing. Spray with olive oil from the top.
7. Bake for forty minutes.

Nutrition: Calories: 310 Protein: 37g Fat: 15g Carbs: 17g Fiber: 9.6g

568. Fiery Jerk Pork

Preparation time: 10 minutes
Cooking time:
1 hour and 20 minutes
Servings: 2

Ingredients:

- 2 habanero peppers (chopped)
- 8 scallions (chopped)
- 2 limes (juiced)
- 2tbsp. of canola oil
- 3 cloves of garlic (chopped)
- 1 tsp. of allspice
- 1/2 tsp. nutmeg
- 400 grams pork loin

Directions:

1. Add peppers, lime juice, scallions, garlic, oil, nutmeg, allspice, and a little bit of pepper and salt in a blender. Pulse the ingredients for making a fine paste. You can add some water if the paste is too dry.
2. Marinate the pork with the prepared spice paste. Refrigerate for one hour.
3. Preheat a chargrill or grill pan. Put some oil to the pan then cook the pork. Cook for ten minutes on both sides.

Nutrition: Calories: 220 Protein: 20g Fat: 11g Carbs: 36g Fiber: 6.8g

569. Thai Pork Kebab

Preparation time: 10 minutes
Cooking time: 30 minutes
Servings: 2

Ingredients:

- 1/2 cup coconut milk
- 2 tbsps. Thai curry paste
- 1tbsp. of peanut butter
- 400 grams pork loin (cut into three cm pieces)
- 1 red capsicum (chopped in cubes)
- 1 red onion (chopped in cubes)
- 8 skewers

Directions:

1. Start by preheating the grill pan.
2. Mix curry paste, coconut milk, and peanut butter in a bowl.
3. Keep half of the mix in another bowl.
4. Thread the capsicum, pork, and onion into the skewers. Alternate between veggies and meat.
5. Brush the skewers with the paste.
6. Add the kebab skewers to the preheated pan. Cook for four minutes on each side.
7. Serve by brushing the skewers with the remaining curry paste.

Nutrition: Calories: 220 Protein: 28g Fat: 17g Carbs: 37g Fiber: 5.2g

570. Fresh Chopped Salad With Vinegar

Preparation time: 20 minutes
Cooking time: 20 minutes
Servings: 8

Ingredients:

- 1/2 cup of fresh parsley, coarsely chopped
- 1/2 cup of Kalamata olives, pitted and chopped coarsely
- Freshly ground pepper
- 4 medium seeded and diced tomatoes
- 2 tablespoon of white-wine vinegar
- 1/2 cup of chopped scallions

- 1/2 teaspoon salt
- 2 cup of diced seedless cucumber
- 4 tablespoons of extra-virgin olive oil

Directions:

1. Combine all the entire ingredients in a medium bowl; carefully toss to combine finely. Serve within an hour.

Nutrition: Calories: 113 Net carbs: 5g Fat: 10g Protein: 1g

571. Sesame Soy Chicken Salad

Preparation time: 10 minutes
Cooking time: 12 minutes
Servings: 2

Ingredients:

- 150 grams of cooked chicken, shredded
- Large handful of chopped parsley (20g)
- ½ finely sliced red onion
- 60 grams of pak choi, very finely shredded
- 100 grams of roughly chopped baby kale
- 1 peeled cucumber, slice in half lengthwise, remove seed and cut into slices
- 1 tbsp of sesame seeds
- For the dressing:
- 2 tsp of soy sauce
- 1 tsp of clear honey
- Juice of 1 lime
- 1 tsp of sesame oil
- 1 tbsp of extra virgin olive oil

Directions:

1. Clean your frying pan well, make sure it's dry, and toast the sesame seeds for 2 minutes in the pan until it is fragrant and lightly browned. Set aside in a plate to cool.
2. To Make the Dressing
3. Put and mix together the soy sauce, olive oil, lime juice, sesame oil, and honey in a small bowl.
4. Place the kale, cucumber, parsley, red onion, and pak choi in a large bowl and mix gently. Pour dressing over salad and mix.
5. Serve the salad in two different plates and add shredded chicken on top. Just before serving, sprinkle with sesame seeds.

Nutrition: Calories

572. Salmon Chicory Rocket Super Salad

Preparation time: 10 minutes
Cooking time: 0 minutes
Servings: 1

Ingredients:

- 10 grams of chopped lavage or celery leaves
- 10 grams of chopped parsley
- Juice ¼ lemon
- 1 tbsp. of extra-virgin olive oil
- 1 large Medjool date, pitted and chopped
- 1 tbsp. of capers
- 15 grams of chopped walnuts
- 20 grams of sliced red onion
- 40 grams of sliced celery
- 80 grams of avocado, peeled, sliced
- 100 grams of smoked salmon slices of cooked chicken breast
- 50 grams of chicory leaves
- 50 grams of rocket

Directions:

1. On a large plate, place the salad leaves. Blend together the remaining ingredients then spread mixture over leaves to serve.

Nutrition: Calories: 300 Net carbs: 30g Fat: 21g Fiber: 10g Protein: 20g

573. Chicken Ayam

Preparation time: 10 minutes
Cooking time: 40 minutes
Servings: 3

Ingredients:

- 1 sliced red chili
- 1 teaspoon of ginger
- 1 small red onion, sliced
- 1 teaspoon turmeric
- 1 teaspoon galangal
- 4 cloves of garlic
- 1 pinch black pepper
- 3 tips muscovado sugar
- 3 tsp. shrimp paste
- 1/3 cup coconut milk

Directions:

1. Season the chicken legs. Put on low heat on the grill for about 10 min on one side.
2. Bring all the ingredients together as finely as possible using a mortar and pestle or a blender.
3. Fry in some peanut oil. Put some paste on the chicken.
4. Cook another side for around 5 minutes. Add some glue to the chicken.
5. Take to the hotter side of the grill, flip, baste, and cook for three additional minutes on both sides. Grill the cake on both sides.

Nutrition: Calories: 41 g Fat: 2.3 g Cholesterol: 35mg Sodium: 75 mg Potassium: 7g Starches: 61 mcg Calcium: 45 mg

574. Garbanzo Kale Curry

Preparation time: 10 minutes
Cooking Time: 30 minutes
Servings 8

Ingredients:

- 4 cups dry garbanzo beans
- Curry Paste, but go low on the heat
- 1 cup sliced tomato
- 2 cups kale leaves
- 1/2 cup coconut milk

Directions:

1. Put ingredients in the slow cooker. Cover, & cook on low for 30 minutes.

Nutrition: Calories: 282 Total Fat: 12.6g Carbohydrates: 11.5g Protein: 17.3g

575. Greek Sea Bass Mix

Preparation time: 10 minutes
Cooking time: 22 minutes
Servings: 2

Ingredients:

- 2 sea bass fillets, boneless
- 1 garlic clove, minced
- 5 cherry tomatoes, halved
- 1 tablespoon chopped parsley
- 2 shallots, chopped
- Juice of ½ lemons
- 1 tablespoon olive oil
- 8 ounces baby spinach
- Cooking spray

Directions:

1. Grease a baking dish with cooking oil then add the fish, tomatoes, parsley, and garlic. Drizzle the lemon juice over the fish, cover the dish and place it in the oven at 350 degrees F. Bake for 15 minutes and then divide between plates. In a pan, warm the olive oil in medium heat, add shallot, stir and cook for 1 minute. Add spinach, stir, cook for 5 minutes more, add to the plate with the fish and serve.
2. Enjoy!

Nutrition: Calories: 210 Fat: 3 g Fiber: 6 g Carbohydrates: 10 g Protein: 24 g

576. Cream Of Mushroom Pork Chops

Preparation time: 10 minutes
Cooking time: 20 minutes
Servings: 4

Ingredients:

- 4 thin, bone-in pork chops (½ inch each)
- 2 ½ Tbsp. avocado oil or olive oil, divided
- 1 lb. sliced mushrooms
- 1 Tbsp. onion, minced
- 1 clove garlic, minced
- 1/3 cup dry white wine
- 1/3 cup unsalted chicken broth
- ½ cup heavy cream
- 1/8 tsp. powdered dried sage
- ¼ tsp. fresh thyme leaves, chopped
- Salt, to taste
- Pepper, to taste

Directions:

1. Allow the pork to reach room temperature, then rub both sides of the pork with about 2 tsp. of oil and season with salt and pepper.
2. Place a large pan over medium high heat and add 2 to 3 tsp. of oil to coat the pan's bottom.
3. When heated, add the pork chops to the pan, turn the heat down to medium, and cook for about 3 1/3 minutes each side - If your pork chops are thicker or cold, add more cooking time.
4. Take to a plate and cover with a tent of foil.
5. Put 1 Tbsp. of oil to the pan and swirl to coat the pan.
6. Once heated, add the mushrooms, stir to coat, cook for 2 minutes, and then stir the mushrooms.
7. Put in the onions and garlic, cook for 1 minute and stir, cook for an additional minute.
8. Put the wine and chicken broth scraping all brown bits off the bottom of the pan, allowing it to simmer and reduce by half.
9. Then add the heavy cream, powdered sage, and fresh thyme and cook until the sauce thickens.
10. Season with salt and pepper to taste.
11. Put the sauce in the pork chops and serve with cauliflower mash and green beans.

Nutrition: Calories: 483 Total Fat: 40g Protein: 21g Net Carbs: 5g

DESSERT

577. Fruit Skewers & Strawberry Dip

Preparation time: 10 minutes
Cooking time: 0 minutes
Servings: 4
Ingredients:

- 150g (5oz) red grapes
- 1 pineapple, (approx 2lb weight) peeled and diced
- 400g (14oz) strawberries

Directions:

1. Place 100g (3½ oz) of the strawberries into a food processor and blend until smooth. Pour the dip into a serving bowl. Skewer the grapes, pineapple chunks, and remaining strawberries onto skewers. Serve alongside the strawberry dip.

Nutrition: Calories: 78 kcal Protein: 2.54 g Fat: 1.88 g Carbohydrates: 14.47 g

578. Choc Nut Truffles

Preparation time: 15 minutes+1 hour chilling time
Cooking time: 0 minutes
Servings: 8
Ingredients:

- 150g (5oz) desiccated (shredded) coconut
- 50g (2oz) walnuts, chopped
- 25g (1oz) hazelnuts, chopped
- 4 Medjool dates
- 2 tablespoons 100% cocoa powder or cacao nibs
- 1 tablespoon coconut oil

Directions:

1. Place all of the ingredients into a blender and process until smooth and creamy. Using a teaspoon, scoop the mixture into bite-size pieces then roll it into balls. Place them into small paper cases, cover them, and chill for 1 hour before serving.

Nutrition: Calories: 125 kcal Protein: 2.82 g Fat: 8.66 g Carbohydrates: 11.86 g

579. No-Bake Strawberry Flapjacks

Preparation time: 20 minutes
Cooking time: 0 minutes
Servings: 8
Ingredients:

- 75g (3oz) porridge oats
- 125g (4oz) dates
- 50g (2oz) strawberries
- 50g (2oz) peanuts (unsalted)
- 50g (2oz) walnuts
- 1 tablespoon coconut oil
- 2 tablespoons 100% cocoa powder or cacao nibs

Directions:

1. Place all of the ingredients into a blender and process until they become a soft consistency. Spread the mixture onto a baking sheet or small flat tin. Press the mixture down and smooth it out. Cut it into 8 pieces, ready to serve. You can add an extra sprinkling of cocoa powder to garnish if you wish.

Nutrition: Calories: 175 kcal Protein: 5.43 g Fat: 10.66 g

580. Chocolate Balls

Preparation time: 30 minutes
Cooking time: 0 minutes
Servings: 6
Ingredients:

- 50g (2oz) peanut butter (or almond butter)
- 25g (1oz) cocoa powder
- 25g (1oz) desiccated (shredded) coconut
- 1 tablespoon honey
- 1 tablespoon cocoa powder for coating

Directions:

1. Bring the ingredients into a bowl and mix. Using a teaspoon scoop out a little of the mixture and shape it into a ball. Roll the ball in a little cocoa powder and set aside. Repeat for the remaining mixture. Can be eaten straight away or stored in the fridge.

Nutrition: Calories: 86 kcal Protein: 4.07 g Fat: 4.09 g Carbohydrates: 9.53 g

581. Warm Berries & Cream

Preparation time: 5 minutes
Cooking time: 5 minutes
Servings: 4
Ingredients:

- 250g (9oz) blueberries
- 250g (9oz) strawberries
- 100g (3½ oz) redcurrants
- 100g (3½ oz) blackberries
- 4 tablespoons fresh whipped cream
- 1 tablespoon honey
- Zest and juice of 1 orange

Directions:

1. Place all of the berries into a pan along with the honey and orange juice. Gently heat the berries for around 5 minutes until warmed through. Serve the berries into bowls and add a dollop of whipped cream on top. Alternatively, you could top them off with fromage frais or yogurt.

Nutrition: Calories: 164 kcal Protein: 3.17 g Fat: 4.84 g Carbohydrates: 29.24 g

582. Chocolate Fondue

Preparation time: 15 minutes
Cooking time: 15 minutes
Servings: 4
Ingredients:

- 125g (4oz) dark chocolate (min 85% cocoa)
- 300g (11oz) strawberries
- 200g (7oz) cherries
- 2 apples, peeled, cored and sliced
- 100mls (3½ fl oz) double cream (heavy cream)

Directions:

1. Place the chocolate and cream into a fondue pot or saucepan and warm it until smooth and creamy. Serve in the fondue pot or transfer it to a serving bowl. Scatter the fruit on a serving dish ready to be dipped into the chocolate.

Nutrition: Calories: 9288 kcal Protein: 58.67 g Fat: 976.15 g Carbohydrates: 117.82 g

583. Walnut & Date Loaf

Preparation time: 10 minutes
Cooking time: 45 minutes
Servings: 12
Ingredients:

- 250g (9oz) self-raising flour
- 125g (4oz) Medjool dates, chopped
- 50g (2oz) walnuts, chopped
- 250mls (8fl oz) milk
- 3 eggs
- 1 medium banana, mashed
- 1 teaspoon baking soda

Directions:

1. Strainer the baking soda and flour into a bowl. Add in the banana, eggs, milk, and dates and combine all the ingredients thoroughly. Transfer the mixture to a lined loaf tin and smooth it out. Scatter the walnuts on top. Bake the loaf in the oven at 180C/360F for 45 minutes. Take it to a wire rack to cool before serving.

Nutrition: 3270 kcal Protein: 165.78 g Fat: 172.07 g Carbohydrates: 267.08 g

584. Dark Chocolate Mousse [Vegan]

Preparation time: 10 minutes
Cooking time: 2 hours
Servings: 4
Ingredients:

- 1 (16 ounces) package silken tofu, drained
- ½ cup pure maple syrup
- 1 teaspoon pure vanilla extract
- ¼ cup of soy milk
- ½ cup unsweetened cocoa powder
- Mint leaves (optional and highly encouraged)

Directions:

1. Place tofu, maple syrup, and vanilla in a food processor or blender. Process until well blended.
2. Add remaining ingredients and process until the mixture is fully blended.
3. Pour into small dessert cups or espresso cups. Chill for at least 2 hours.
4. Garnish with fresh mint leaves just before serving.

Nutrition: Calories: 157 kcal Protein: 3.81 g Fat: 3.25 g Carbohydrates: 33.61 g

585. Loaded Chocolate Fudge

Preparation time: 10 minutes
Cooking time: 1 hour
Servings: 16
Ingredients:

- 1 cup Medjool dates, chopped
- 2 tablespoons coconut oil, melted
- 1/2 cup peanut butter
- ¼ cup of unsweetened cocoa powder
- ½ cup walnuts
- 1 teaspoon vanilla

Directions:

1. Soak the dates in boiled water for 20 – 30 minutes
2. Lightly grease an 8" square baking pan with coconut oil.
3. Add dates, peanut butter, cocoa powder, and vanilla to a food processer and blend until smooth.
4. Fold in walnuts.
5. Pack into the greased baking pan and put it in the freezer for 1 hour or until the fudge is solid and firm.
6. Cut into 16 or more bite-sized squares and store in a semi-airtight container in the refrigerator.

Nutrition: Calories: 67 kcal Protein: 1.62 g Fat: 5.33 g Carbohydrates: 4.27 g

586. Maple Walnut Cupcakes With Matcha Green Tea Icing

Preparation time: 20 minutes
Cooking time: 25 minutes
Servings: 4
Ingredients:

- For the Cupcakes:
- 2 cups of All-Purpose flour
- ½ cup buckwheat flour
- 2 ½ teaspoons baking powder
- ½ teaspoon salt
- 1 cup of cocoa butter
- 1 cup white sugar
- 1 tablespoon pure maple syrup
- 3 eggs
- 1 teaspoon maple extract
- 2/3 cup milk
- ¼ cup walnuts, chopped
- For the Icing
- 3 tablespoons coconut oil, thick at room temperature
- 3 tablespoons icing sugar
- 1 tablespoon Matcha green tea powder
- ½ teaspoon vanilla bean paste
- 3 tablespoons cream cheese, softened

Directions:

1. Preheat oven to 350 degrees F.
2. Put paper baking cups into muffin tins for 24 regular-sized muffins.
3. In a medium bowl, blend flours, baking powder, and salt.
4. In a separate large bowl, cream the sugar, butter, syrup, and eggs with a hand or stand mixer.
5. Pause to stir in maple extract.
6. On low speed, alternate blending in dry mixture and milk.
7. Fold in nuts.
8. Pour batter into muffin cup until 2/3 full.
9. Bake for around 20-25 minutes, up to inserted toothpick comes out clean.
10. Cool completely before icing.
11. To Make the Icing: Add the coconut oil and icing sugar to a bowl and use a hand-mixer to cream until it's pale and smooth.
12. Fold in the matcha powder and vanilla.
13. Then put the cream cheese and beat until smooth.
14. Pipe or spread over the cupcakes once they're cool.

Nutrition: Calories: 1124 kcal Protein: 20.07 g Fat: 73.89 g Carbohydrates: 99.39 g

587. Chocolate Maple Walnuts

Preparation time: 15 minutes
Cooking time: 30 minutes
Servings: 2
Ingredients:

- ½ cup pure maple syrup, divided
- 2 cups raw, whole walnuts
- 5 squares of dark chocolate, at least 85%
- 1 ½ tsp. coconut oil, melted
- 1 tbsp. of water
- Sifted icing sugar
- 1 tsp. of vanilla extract

Directions:

1. Line a large baking sheet using parchment paper.
2. In a medium to large skillet, combine the walnuts and ¼ cup of maple syrup and cook over medium heat, stirring

continuously, until walnuts are completely covered with syrup and golden in color 3 – 5 minutes.

3. Put the walnuts onto the parchment paper and separate it into individual pieces with a fork. Allow to cool completely, at least 15 minutes.
4. For a while, melt the chocolate in a double boiler with the coconut oil. Put the remaining maple syrup and mix until thoroughly combined.
5. When walnuts are cooled, take them to a glass bowl and pour the melted chocolate syrup over the top. Use a silicon spatula to mix until walnuts are completely covered.
6. Take back to the parchment paper-lined baking sheet and, once again, separate every of the nuts with a fork.
7. Put the nuts in the fridge for 10 minutes or the freezer for 3 – 5 minutes, up to the chocolate has completely set.
8. Keep in an airtight bag in your fridge.

Nutrition: Calories: 1057 kcal Protein: 15.42 g Fat: 65.45 g Carbohydrates: 113.91 g

588. Matcha And Chocolate Dipped Strawberries

Preparation time: 25 minutes
Cooking time: 25 minutes
Servings: 4

Ingredients:

- 4 tsp. cocoa butter
- 4 squares of dark chocolate, (about 85%)
- ¼ cup of coconut oil
- 1 tsp. Matcha green tea powder
- 20 – 25 large whole strawberries, stems on

Directions:

1. Melt cocoa butter, dark chocolate, coconut oil, and Matcha in a double boiler until nearly smooth.
2. Take off from heat and continue stirring until chocolate is completely melted.
3. Pour into a large glass bowl and continuously stir until the chocolate thickens and starts to lose its sheen, about 2 - 5 minutes.
4. Working one at a time, hold the strawberries by stems and dip into chocolate matcha mixture to coat. Let excess drip back into the bowl.
5. Bring on a parchment-lined baking sheet and chill dipped berries in the fridge until the shell is set, 20–25 minutes.
6. You may need to reheat matcha mixture if it starts to set before you have dipped all the berries.

Nutrition: Calories: 269 kcal Protein: 2.33 g Fat: 26.93 g Carbohydrates: 6.92 g

589. Strawberry Rhubarb Crisp

Preparation time: 10 minutes
Cooking time: 45 minutes
Servings: 6-8

Ingredients:

- 1 cup white sugar
- ½ cup buckwheat flour + 3 tablespoons
- 3 cups strawberries, sliced
- 3 cups rhubarb, diced
- ½ lemon, juiced
- 1 cup packed brown sugar
- 1 cup coconut oil, melted
- ¾ cup rolled oats
- ¼ cup buckwheat groats
- ¼ cup walnuts, chopped

Directions:

1. Preheat oven to 375 degrees F
2. In a large bowl, put and mix the white sugar, 3 tablespoons flour, strawberries, rhubarb, and lemon juice. Put the mixture in a 9x13 inch baking dish.
3. In a separate bowl, mix ½ cup flour, brown sugar, coconut oil, oats, buckwheat groats, and walnuts until crumbly. You may want to use a pastry blender for this. Crumble above the rhubarb and strawberry mixture.
4. Bake for at least 45 minutes in the preheated oven, or until crisp and lightly browned.

Nutrition: Calories: 533 kcal Protein: 4.55 g 8%Fat: 30.74 g Carbohydrates: 69.9 g

590. Apple Date Pudding

Preparation time: 10 minutes
Cooking time: 2-3 hours
Servings: 6-8

Ingredients:

- 4-5 apples, diced
- ¾ cup sugar, or less, to taste
- ½ cup Medjool dates, chopped
- ½ cup walnuts, toasted and chopped
- 2 tablespoons buckwheat flour
- 1 teaspoon baking powder
- 1/8 teaspoon. Salt
- ¼ teaspoon. Nutmeg
- 2 tablespoons coconut oil, melted
- 1 egg, beaten

Directions:

1. In a crockpot, mix apples, sugar, dates, and walnuts.
2. In a large bowl, put and mix the flour, baking powder, salt, and nutmeg and then stir into apple mixture.
3. Drizzle melted coconut oil over the batter and stir again.
4. Mix in beaten egg.
5. Cook on low for 3 - 4 hours. Serve warm.

NOTE: If you prefer crispier nuts, add toasted walnuts at the end of the cooking period.

Nutrition: Calories: 189 kcal Protein: 3.22 g Fat: 8.88 g Carbohydrates: 26.79 g

591. Date Nut Bread

Preparation time: 30 minutes
Cooking time:
4-6 hours + 10 minutes cooling
Servings: 4-6

Ingredients:

- ¾ cup Medjool dates
- 1 ¼ cup All-Purpose flour
- 2 teaspoon baking powder
- ¼ teaspoon baking soda
- ½ teaspoon salt
- ½ cup of sugar
- ¾ cup milk
- 1 egg, slightly beaten
- 1 tablespoon orange peel, grated
- 1 tablespoon coconut oil, melted
- ¼ cup buckwheat flour
- 1 cup walnuts, chopped

Directions:

1. Place the dates on a chopping block and sprinkle 1 tablespoon of All-Purpose flour over them. Dip a knife into the flour and chop the dates finely. Flour the knife often to keep the cut-up fruit from sticking together.
2. Sift the remaining All-Purpose flour, baking powder, baking soda, salt, and sugar into a large bowl.

3. In a separate bowl, put and combine the milk, egg, orange peel, and oil.
4. Add the buckwheat flour to the flour mixture, mix well and gently fold in the dates, along with any flour left on the cutting block and the walnuts.
5. Pour in the liquid ingredients and mix until just combined.
6. Transfer dough into a well-greased and floured baking unit. Cover and place in the slow cooker
7. Use a toothpick or small amount of twisted aluminum foil to prop the crockpot lid open a tiny fraction to allow steam to escape.
8. Cook on high for 4 to 6 hours. Cool on a rack for 10 minutes. Serve warm or cold.
9. Do NOT lift the crockpot lid while the bread is baking.

Nutrition: Calories: 471 kcal Protein: 13.42 g Fat: 22.49 g Carbohydrates: 56.51 g

592. Chocolate Coffee Cake

Preparation time: 15 minutes
Cooking time: 35-40 minutes
Servings: 6-8

Ingredients:

- 3 cups All-Purpose flour
- 2 cups of sugar
- 1 cup coconut oil, cold and solid
- 4 teaspoons unsweetened cocoa powder
- 1 teaspoon baking soda
- ½ teaspoon baking powder
- 3 teaspoons cinnamon
- ½ teaspoon ground nutmeg
- 1/8 teaspoon salt
- ½ cup Medjool dates, chopped
- ½ cup mixed nuts or walnuts, chopped
- 2 cups buttermilk

Directions:

1. Preheat oven to 350°F.
2. In a large mixing bowl, put and combine the flour and sugar.
3. Using a pastry knife, cut in the solid coconut oil until your mixture is crumbly. Save 1 cup of the crumbled mixture for topping.
4. To the remaining mixture, add cocoa powder, baking soda, baking powder, cinnamon, nutmeg, and salt and stir until well combined.
5. Fold in dates and nuts.
6. Make a well and place it in on the center of the cake mix and slowly pour the buttermilk into the hole. Stir until everything is just moist.
7. Pour into a greased 13-in. x 9-in. x 2-in. baking pan. Sprinkle with reserved crumb mixture.
8. Bake for 35-40 minutes or until a toothpick inserted near the center comes out clean.

Nutrition: Calories: 580 kcal Protein: 8.67 g Fat: 32.45 g Carbohydrates: 66.98 g

593. Cinnamon Coffee Cake

Preparation time: 30 minutes
Cooking time: 1 hour and 10 minutes + 10 cooling time
Servings: 6-8

Ingredients:

- 1 cup coconut oil, room temperature
- 2 ¾ cups white sugar
- 4 eggs
- 2 teaspoons baking powder
- 1 teaspoon baking soda
- 1 teaspoon salt
- 2 cups sour cream
- 1 ½ cups chopped walnuts
- 2 tablespoons ground cinnamon
- 2 teaspoons vanilla extract
- 4 cups All-Purpose flour

Directions:

1. Preheat oven to 350 degrees F.
2. In a large mixing bowl, put and cream together coconut oil and 2 cups of the sugar until fluffy.
3. Add the vanilla and the eggs, one at the time, beating the mixture well after each egg.
4. In a separate bowl, combine flour with baking powder and baking soda.
5. Alternatively, add on the dry ingredients and the sour cream to the egg mixture, beating just enough after each addition to keep batter smooth.
6. In another bowl, combine walnuts, cinnamon, and remaining 3/4 cup of sugar.
7. Spoon 1/3 of the batter into well-greased, 10" tube pan.
8. Sprinkle using 1/3 of the walnut mixture.
9. Repeat layers two more times.
10. Bake at least 70 minutes or until a toothpick inserted near the center comes out clean.
11. Let cake cool in the pan for 10 minutes, then remove pan and let the cake continue cooling on a wire rack.

Nutrition: Calories: 874 kcal Protein: 18.1 g Fat: 62.59 g Carbohydrates: 64.7 g

594. Thai Cucumber Salad

Preparation time: 50 minutes
Cooking time: 30 minutes
Servings: 8

Ingredients:

- ½ small red onion
- 1 minute, fresh jalapeno, seeds removed
- 3 medium cucumbers
- 2 or 3 cloves fresh garlic, crushed Two tablespoons grated fresh ginger
- ½ cup (120 ml) rice vinegar ½ teaspoon salt ¼ teaspoon pepper
- 2 tablespoons Splenda

Directions:

1. Using a food processor with the S blade, place the onion and syrup solution in the food and press to crush both fine.
2. Remove the S blade and place it on the cutting disc. Rotate the cucumbers and then pass them through the processor. (If you do not use a food processor, you want to fry the onion and run the jelly, then chop the cucumber evenly.)
3. Put onions, pumpkins, and cucumbers in a large bowl. In a separate bowl, put and combine the garlic, ginger, vinegar, salt, pepper, and splendor. Pour the vegetables and mix well.
4. Chill several hours before serving to get the best taste.

Nutrition: Calories: 18 kcal Protein: 1.13 g Fat: 0.81 g Carbohydrates: 1.66 g

595. Mushroom "Risotto"

Preparation time: 10 minutes
Cooking time: 2 to 3 minutes.
Servings: 5

Ingredients:

- ½ head cauliflower
- 3tablespoons butter

- 1 cup sliced mushrooms
- ½ medium onion, diced
- 1 teaspoon minced garlic
- 2 tablespoons dry vermouth
- 1 tablespoon chicken bouillon granules
- ¼ cup grated Parmesan cheese
- Guar or xanthan
- 2 tablespoons chopped fresh parsley

Directions:

1. Run the cauliflower using a food processor with a razor blade. Put the cauliflower in a microwave oven, add a few tablespoons of water, and cover the microwave for 7 minutes over high heat.
2. While the cauliflower cooks, it melts
3. Put the butter in a large fish over medium heat and add the mushrooms, onion, and garlic and mix.
4. Once the cauliflower is ready, pull it out from the microwave and drain it. When the mushrooms have changed and appear, add the cauliflower to the fish and mix everything. Mix in Vermouth, boil, and cheese and cook for 2 to 3 minutes.
5. Simply sprinkle some guar or xanthan on the "risotto," always mixing to give it a creamy texture. Stir in parsley and serve.

Nutrition: Calories: 123 kcal Protein: 3.8 g Fat: 9.84 g Carbohydrates: 5.8 g

596. Cauliflower-Olive Salad

Preparation time: 20 minutes
Cooking time: 10 minutes.
Servings: 5

Ingredients:

- ½ head cauliflower, broken into small florets
- ½ cup diced red onion
- 1 can slice ripe olives, drained
- ½ cup chopped fresh parsley
- ¼ cup lemon juice ¼ cup olive oil
- ¼ cup (mayonnaise
- ½ teaspoon salt or Vege-Sal
- About a dozen cherry tomatoes Lettuce (optional) and parsley in a bowl.

Directions:

1. Combine lemon juice, olive oil, mayonnaise, and salt in a separate bowl. Pour the vegetables and pour well.
2. It cools down for at least an hour - a whole day doesn't hurt. When the salad is ready, cut the cherry tomatoes in half and add them to the mixture. Serve on a bed with salad, if you like, but it's great.

Nutrition: Calories: 72 kcal Protein: 2.87 g Fat: 5.19 g Carbohydrates: 4.24 g

597. Zucchini-Crusted Pizza

Preparation time: 30 minutes
Cooking time: 15-30 minutes
Servings: 4

Ingredients:

- 3 ½ cups shredded zucchini
- 3eggs
- 1 ½ cup rice protein powder or soy powder
- 1½ cups shredded mozzarella, divided
- ½ cup grated Parmesan cheese
- A pinch or two of dried basil
- ½ teaspoon salt
- ¼ teaspoon pepper Oil
- 1 cup sugar-free pizza sauce
- Toppings as desired (sausage, pepperoni, peppers, mushrooms, or whatever you like)

Directions:

1. Preheat oven to 180 ° C.
2. Sprinkle the pumpkin with a little salt and let stand 15-30 minutes. Put it in a straightener and press for extra moisture. Multiply the chopped pumpkin, eggs, protein powder, 2 cups of mozzarella, parmesan, basil, salt, and pepper. Spray a 9 13 13-inch (23 33 33 cm) pan with a non-stick cooking spray and spread the pumpkin mixture—Bake for about 25 minutes or until firm. Wash the pumpkin peel with a little oil and cook for 5 minutes until golden. Then spread the pizza sauce and add 1 cup Mozzarella and other tops. (If you use vegetables as a topping, you may want to smooth them a bit at first.) Bake for another 25 minutes, then cut into squares and serve.

Nutrition: Calories: 363 kcal Protein: 54.3 g Fat: 12.84 g Carbohydrates: 7.08 g

598. Broccoli Salad

Preparation time: 20 minutes
Cooking time: 15-20 minutes
Servings: 6

Ingredients:

- ½ cup (120 ml) olive oil ¼ cup (60 ml) vinegar
- 1 clove garlic, crushed
- ½ teaspoon Italian seasoning herb blend
- ½ teaspoon salt or Vege-Sal
- ½ teaspoon pepper
- 4 cups frozen broccoli "cut"

Directions:

1. Multiply the olive oil, vinegar, garlic, herbs, salt, and pepper.
2. They don't even bother you
3. Broccoli - Put it in a bowl and pour the olive oil mixture over it. Stir well and let it sit in the refrigerator for a few hours. If you think and serve it as vegetables or vegetables, mix it.
4. Feel free to try fresh broccoli for this salad. You have to peel the stalks, cut and steam for about 5 minutes. And at that moment, it will melt just like frozen broccoli! I follow the easy way.

Nutrition: Calories: 48 kcal Protein: 4.11 g Fat: 1.32 g Carbohydrates: 5.81 g

599. Not-Quite-Middle-Eastern Salad

Preparation time: 20 minutes
Cooking time: 15-20 minutes
Servings: 6

Ingredients:

- ½ head cauliflower
- 2/3 cup sliced stuffed olives
- 7 scallions, sliced
- 2 cups triple-washed fresh spinach, finely chopped
- 1 stalk celery, diced
- 1 small ripe tomato, finely diced
- 4 tablespoons chopped parsley
- ¼ cup olive oil
- 1 teaspoon minced garlic or two cloves garlic, crushed
- 1 tablespoon red wine vinegar
- 2 tablespoons mayonnaise
- Salt and pepper

Directions:

1. Run cauliflower using a food processor knife, place in a microwave oven, add a few tablespoons (30 ml) of water, cover the pan, and cook for only 5 minutes.
2. While cooking, place the olives, onions, spinach, celery, tomatoes, and parsley in a large salad bowl.
3. When the cauliflower has come out of the microwave, pour it into a rectifier and run it for a moment or two in cold water to cool. (You can refrigerate the cauliflower instead, but it will take a long time.) Drain the cauliflower well and sprinkle with other vegetables. Add oil, garlic, vinegar and mayonnaise, and pot. Add salt and pepper to taste, bake and serve again.

Nutrition: Calories: 148 kcal Protein: 2.89 g Fat: 13.42 g Carbohydrates: 5.58 g

600. Halloween Desserts

Preparation time: 30 minutes
Cooking time: 50 minutes
Servings: 6

Ingredients:

- 210 g whole meal spelled flour
- 7 tbsp. entire natural sweetener
- 40 g spread
- 280 g dull chocolate (in any event 70% cocoa)
- 1 l milk (3.5% fat)
- 1 vanilla bean
- 1 map. Orange strip
- 6 egg yolks
- 2 tbsp. food starch
- 5 tsp cocoa powder

Directions:

1. For the bread rolls, rapidly manipulate 50 g of flour, 1 tbsp of entire unadulterated sweetener, and 25 g of margarine into a smooth shortcrust baked good. Chill enveloped by stick film for around 30 minutes.
2. Roughly slash chocolate. Expel 10 tablespoons from the milk and put it in a safe spot. Cut the vanilla case lengthways and scratch out the mash.
3. Put the rest of the milk in a pan with 240 g chocolate, vanilla mash, case, and orange pizzazz and warmth while blending. In a bowl, mix the egg yolks with 4 tablespoons of entire unadulterated sweetener until foamy, mix in the cornstarch and the milk put in a safe spot.
4. Stir in the hot cocoa drain and take back to the bubble in the pot and let it thicken. Expel the blend from the oven, keep beating quickly, evacuate the vanilla case, and let the pudding cool in glasses.
5. Sprinkle scone mixture with 1 tsp cocoa powder and work in as a marbling. Reveal the batter and cut out headstones with an oval shaper. Spot treats on a heating sheet secured with preparing paper and prepares for 10–15 minutes in a preheated stove at 180 ° C (constrained air 160 ° C; gas: setting 2-3). Take out and let cool.
6. To enhance, blend the rest of the fixings (cocoa powder, flour, margarine, entire natural sweetener) and disintegrate. Dissolve the keep going 40 g of dull chocolate, fill it into a little funneling sack and name it with the treats.
7. Sprinkle the pudding with the chocolate morsels, embed the named treats as a 'tombstone' and enhance them with blossoms as you like

Nutrition: Calories: 392 kcal Protein: 9.81 g Fat: 8.3 g Carbohydrates: 70.83 g

601. Cottage Cheese With Raspberry Sauce

Preparation time: 20 minutes
Cooking time: 30 minutes
Servings: 6

Ingredients:

- 400 g flour-bubbling potatoes (2-3 potatoes)
- 300 g raspberries
- 2 tbsp nectar
- ½ vanilla bean
- 250 g low-fat quark
- 50 g coconut sugar
- 150 g spelled flour type 1050
- 1 egg cinnamon
- 15 g margarine (3 tsp)
- 30 g planed almond bits (2 tbsp.)

Directions:

1. For the quark legs, strip, wash, slash the potatoes and cook delicately in bubbling water in around 15 minutes over medium warmth. At that point, pour off and let cool for 10 minutes.
2. In the interim, wash the raspberries cautiously and puree them with a hand blender. Push the mash through a sifter, blend in with nectar, and keep cool.
3. In the interim, divide the vanilla case lengthways and scratch out the vanilla mash with a blade.
4. Press potatoes through a potato press into a bowl. Include the curd, sugar, flour, egg, vanilla mash, and 1 spot of cinnamon to the potatoes and work everything into a smooth batter; if it is excessively damp, include some flour—structure 12 little treats out of the batter.
5. Fry the quark balls in progression. Warmth 1 teaspoon margarine in a dish. Include 4 balls and prepare brilliant earthy colored on each side in around 3-4 minutes; Bake remaining cups similarly.
6. Toast the almonds in a hot container without fat over medium warmth for 3 minutes. Orchestrate the quark drumstick with the raspberry sauce and almonds.

Nutrition: Calories: 512 kcal Protein: 19.94 g Fat: 8.98 g Carbohydrates: 89.2 g

602. Spelled Semolina Porridge With Elderberry Sauce And Roasted Hazelnuts

Preparation time: 10 minutes
Cooking time: 30 minutes
Servings: 6

Ingredients:

- 300 ml elderberry juice
- 1 tbsp. food starch
- 800 ml oat drink (oat milk)
- 1 squeeze salt
- 120 whole meal spelled semolina
- 100 g hazelnut bits
- 2 tbsp. beet syrup

Directions:

1. Bring elderberry juice to a bubble except for 2 tablespoons. Mix the rest of the juice with cornstarch until smooth, add to the pot, and mix. Stew for 5 minutes on a low to medium warmth and put in a safe spot.
2. In the interim, put the oat drink with 1 touch of salt in a different pot and warmth. Mix in the spelled semolina with a whisk and bring it to the bubble. Lessen warmth

and stew on low warmth with blending for around 5 minutes until it thickens.

3. Roast the hazelnut pieces in a container without oil over medium warmth for 3-4 minutes. Take out, let cool, and cleave generally.
4. Stir the syrup under the semolina porridge and separate it into four dishes. Shower elderberry sauce over it and serve sprinkled with hazelnuts.

Nutrition: Calories: 139 kcal Protein: 3.56 g Fat: 11.15 g Carbohydrates: 8.41 g

603. Red Wine Chocolate Cake

Preparation time: 15 minutes
Cooking time: 32 minutes
Servings: 8

Ingredients:

- 1 3/4 cups (228g) generally useful flour
- 2 cups (414g) sugar
- 3/4 cup (85g) characteristic unsweetened cocoa powder
- 2 1/4 tsp preparing pop
- 1/2 tsp preparing powder
- 1 tsp salt
- 1 cup (240ml) milk
- 1/2 cup (120ml) vegetable oil
- 1/2 tsp vanilla concentrate
- 2 huge eggs
- 1/2 cups (360ml) red wine, separated, room temperature
- 1 cup (240ml) improved dense milk
- 3/4 cup (127g) semi-sweet chocolate chips

Directions:

1. Preheat grill to 350°F (176°C) and set up a 9×13-inch cake skillet with a non-stick preparing shower. Include the flour, sugar, cocoa, heating pop, preparing powder, and salt to an enormous blender bowl and join. Put in a safe spot.
2. Include the milk, vegetable oil, vanilla concentrate, and eggs to a medium measuring bowl and join. Add the wet fixings to the dry fixings and beat until very much united.
3. Gradually include one cup of red wine to the player and blend at low speed until very much consolidated. Scratch down the sides of the bowl varying to ensure everything is all around joined. Pour the player into the readied cake container and heat for 29-32 minutes, or until a toothpick turns out with a couple of soggy morsels.
4. Expel cake from stove and jab gaps everywhere.

Nutrition: Energy (calories): 401 kcal; Protein: 8.23 g; Fat: 18.92 g; Carbohydrates: 54.03 g

604. Glaze

Preparation time: 10 minutes
Cooking time: 15 minutes
Servings: 10

Ingredients:

- 11/2cups powdered sugar
- 3tbsp lemon juice
- Zest of one lemon

Directions:

1. Preheat the oven to 375 degrees f.
2. In a medium bowl, put and combine the flour, baking powder, and salt then set aside.
3. From the big bowl, blend the butter and the sugar. With an electric mixer, beat the sugar and butter until light and fluffy, about three minutes. Put the eggs one at a time, beating until incorporated.
4. Insert the ricotta cheese, lemon juice, and lemon zest. Beat to blend. Stir in the dry ingredients.
5. Line two baking sheets with parchment paper. Spoon the dough (approximately 2 tablespoons of each cookie) on the baking sheets. Bake for at least 15 minutes, until slightly golden at the borders. Remove from the oven and allow the cookies to remain on the baking sheet for about 20 minutes.

Nutrition: Energy (calories): 216 kcal; Protein: 0.03 g; Fat: 0.02 g; Carbohydrates: 55.52 g

605. Home-Made Marshmallow Fluff

Preparation time: 10 minutes
Cooking time: 10 minutes
Servings: 10

Ingredients:

- 3/4cup sugar
- 1/2cup light corn syrup
- 1/4cup water
- ⅛tsp salt
- 3little egg whites
- 1/4tsp cream of tartar
- 1teaspoon 1/2 tsp vanilla extract

Directions:

1. In a little pan, mix together sugar, corn syrup, salt, and water. Attach a candy thermometer into the pan's side, but make sure it will not touch the underside of the pan.
2. From the bowl of a stand mixer, combine egg whites and cream of tartar. Begin to whip on medium speed with the whisk attachment.
3. Meanwhile, turn a burner on top and place the pan with the sugar mix onto heat. Pout mix into a boil and heat to 240 degrees, stirring periodically.
4. The aim is to have the egg whites whipped to soft peaks and also the sugar heated to 240 degrees at near the same moment. Simply stop stirring the egg whites once they hit soft peaks.
5. Once the sugar has already reached 240 amounts, turn heat low allowing it to reduce. Insert a little quantity of the popular sugar mix and let it mix. Insert still another little sum of the sugar mix. Add mix slowly, and that means you never scramble the egg whites.
6. After all of the sugar was added into the egg whites, then decrease the mixer's speed and keep mixing concoction for around 7- 9 minutes until the fluff remains glossy and stiff. At roughly the 5-minute mark, then add the vanilla extract.

Nutrition: Energy (calories): 84 kcal; Protein: 1.08 g; Fat: 0.08 g; Carbohydrates: 20.71 g

606. Guilt Totally Free Banana Ice-Cream

Preparation time: 10 minutes
Cooking time: 0 minutes
Servings: 3

Ingredients:

- 3 quite ripe banana - peeled and chopped
- A couple of chocolate chips
- 2tbsp skim milk

Directions:

1. Set all the ingredients into a food processor and blend until creamy.

Nutritional: Energy (calories): 288 kcal; Protein: 6.78 g; Fat: 8.8 g; Carbohydrates: 48.96 g

607. Perfect Little Pb Snack Balls

Preparation time: 10 minutes
Cooking time: 0 minutes

Servings: 2

Ingredients:

- 1/2cup chunky peanut butter
- 3tbsp flax seeds
- 3tbsp wheat germ
- 1tbsp honey or agave
- 1/4cup powdered sugar

Directions:

1. Mix the dry ingredients then add from the honey and peanut butter.
2. Stir well and roll into chunks and then conclude by rolling into wheat germ.

Nutritional: Energy (calories): 381 kcal; Protein: 9.81 g; Fat: 19.35 g; Carbohydrates: 45.2 g

608. Dark Chocolate Pretzel Cookies

Preparation time: 10 minutes
Cooking time: 17 minutes
Servings: 1

Ingredients:

- 1cup yogurt
- 1/2tsp baking soda
- 1/4teaspoon salt
- 1/4tsp cinnamon
- 4tbsp butter (softened/0
- 1/3cup brown sugar
- 1egg
- 1/2tsp vanilla
- 1/2cup dark chocolate chips
- 1/2cup pretzels, chopped

Directions:

1. Preheat oven to 350 degrees.
2. In a medium bowl, put the sugar, butter, vanilla, and egg then whisk together.
3. In another bowl, put the flour, baking soda, and salt then stir together.
4. Stir the bread mixture in, using all the wet components, along with the chocolate chips and pretzels until just blended.
5. Drop a large spoonful of dough on an unlined baking sheet.
6. Bake for at least 15-17 minutes, or until the bottoms are somewhat all crispy.

Nutritional Value: Energy (calories): 508 kcal; Protein: 11.35 g; Fat: 32.73 g; Carbohydrates: 43.06 g

609. Mascarpone Cheesecake With Almond Crust

Preparation time: 10 minutes
Cooking time: 1-2 minutes
Servings: 1

Ingredients:

Crust:

- 1/2cup slivered almonds
- 8tsp -- or 2/3cup graham cracker crumbs
- 2tbsp sugar
- 1tbsp salted butter melted

Filling:

- 1(8-ounce) packages cream cheese, room temperature
- 1(8-ounce) container mascarpone cheese, room temperature
- 3/4cup sugar
- 1tsp fresh lemon juice (I needed to use imitation lemon-juice)
- 1tsp vanilla extract
- 2large eggs, room temperature

Directions:

1. For the crust: Set the oven to 350°F. You will need a 9-inch pan (I had a throw off). Finely grind the almonds, cracker crumbs sugar in a food processor (I used my Magical Bullet). Add the butter and process until moist crumbs form.
2. Press the almond mixture on the base of the prepared pan (maybe not on the edges of the pan). Bake the crust until it's set and start to brown, about 1-2 minutes. Cool. Decrease the oven temperature to 325°F.
3. For your filling: with an electric mixer, beat the cream cheese, mascarpone cheese, and sugar in a large bowl until smooth, occasionally scraping down the sides of the jar using a rubber spatula. Beat in the lemon juice and vanilla. Add the eggs one at a time, beating until combined after each addition.
4. Pour the cheese mixture on the crust from the pan. Put the pan into a big skillet or Pyrex dish pour enough hot water to the roasting pan to come halfway up the sides of one's skillet. Bake until the middle of the filling moves slightly when the pan is gently shaken, about 1 hour (the dessert will get hard when it's cold). Transfer the cake to a stand; cool for 1 hour. Refrigerate until the cheesecake is cold, at least eight hours.

Nutrition: Energy (calories): 532 kcal; Protein: 6.82 g; Fat: 14.84 g; Carbohydrates: 93.11 g

610. Marshmallow Popcorn Balls

Preparation time: 10 minutes
Cooking time: 1-2 minutes
Servings: 1

Ingredients:

- 2bag of microwave popcorn
- 1 12.6ounces. Tote M&M's
- 3cups honey roasted peanuts
- 1pkg. 16 ounces. Massive marshmallows
- 1cup butter, cubed

Directions:

1. In a bowl, mix the popcorn, peanuts and M&M's.
2. In a big pot, combine marshmallows and butter.
3. Cook using medium-low heat. Insert popcorn mix, blend thoroughly
4. Spray muffin tins with non-stick cooking spray.
5. When cool enough to handle, spray hands together with non-stick cooking spray and then shape into chunks and put into the muffin tin to shape.
6. Add Popsicle stick into each chunk and then let cool.

Nutrition: Energy (calories): 116 kcal; Protein: 39.83 g; Fat: 19.53 g; Carbohydrates: 21.27 g

611. Home-Made Ice-Cream Drumsticks

Preparation time: 10 minutes
Cooking time: 0 minutes
Servings: 4

Ingredients:

- Vanilla ice cream
- 2 Lindt hazelnut chunks
- 100 g Magical shell - out chocolate
- 50% of Sugar levels
- 2 Nuts (I mixed crushed peppers and unsalted peanuts)
- Parchment paper

Directions:

1. Soften ice cream and mixing topping - I had two sliced Lindt hazelnut balls.
2. Fill underside of Magic shell with sugar and nuts and top with ice-cream.
3. Wrap parchment paper round cone and then fill cone over about 1.5 inches across the cap of the cone (the paper can help to carry its shape).
4. Sprinkle with magical nuts and shells.

Nutritional Value: Energy (calories): 170 kcal; Protein: 0.54 g; Fat: 0.33 g; Carbohydrates: 16.28 g

612. Ultimate Chocolate Chip Cookie N' Oreo Fudge Brownie Bar

Preparation time: 10 minutes
Cooking time: 55 minutes
Servings: 1

Ingredients:

- 1cup (2 sticks) butter, softened
- 1cup granulated sugar
- 3/4cup light brown sugar
- 2large egg
- 1tablespoon pure vanilla extract
- 2 ½cups all-purpose flour
- 1tsp baking soda
- 1tsp lemon
- 2cups (12 oz.) milk chocolate chips
- 1package double stuffed Oreo
- 1family-size (9×1 3) brownie mixture
- 1/4cup hot fudge topping

Directions:

1. Preheat oven to 350 degrees F.
2. Cream the butter and sugars in a huge bowl using an electric mixer at medium speed for 35 minutes.
3. Add the vanilla and eggs and mix well to combine thoroughly. In another bowl, whisk together the flour, baking soda and salt, and slowly incorporate in the mixer everything is combined.
4. Stir in chocolate chips.
5. Spread the cookie dough at the bottom of a 9×1-3 baking dish that is wrapped with wax paper and then coated with cooking spray.
6. Shirt with a coating of Oreos. Mix brownie mix, adding an optional 1/4 cup of hot fudge directly into the mixture.
7. Stir the brownie batter within the cookie-dough and Oreos.
8. Cover using a foil and bake at 350°F for 30 minutes.
9. Remove foil and continue baking for another 15- 25 minutes.

Nutrition: Energy (calories): 454 kcal; Protein: 5.92 g; Fat: 21.75 g; Carbohydrates: 60.15 g

613. Fruit Cake Without Sugar

Preparation time: 10 minutes
Cooking time: 30 minutes
Servings: 4

Ingredients:

- 400 g dried fig
- 400 g dried natural product as an example b. plums, apricot, raisins
- 400 g nuts z. b. hazelnuts, almonds, pecans
- 5 eggs
- 125 g spread
- 200 g spelled flour type 1050
- 1 tbsp. cinnamon
- 1 tsp clove stripped

Directions:

1. Roughly cleave the figs, dried organic products, and nuts. Separate the egg and whisk the egg whites until solid. Beat the spread until cushy; at that point, include the egg yolks and flour and make a smooth batter. Ply in organic products, nuts, and flavors. Cautiously crease within the protein.
2. Fill the batter into a heating tin fixed with preparing the paper, smooth, and prepare within the broiler at 175 ° C (fan stove 150 ° C; gas: level 2) for around hour. Play out a stick test.
3. Take off the cake from the stove and let it cool.

Nutrition: Calories: 1426 kcal Protein: 41.79 g Fat: 82.49 g Carbohydrates: 147.53 g

614. Chocolate Fruit Cake

Preparation time: 15 minutes
Cooking time: 40 minutes
Servings: 6-8

Ingredients:

- 300 g prunes
- 300 g dried fig
- 200 g prepared organic product
- 200 g almond portions
- 150 g hazelnuts
- 5 eggs
- 125 g spread
- 1 tbsp. nectar
- 200 g spelled flour
- 1 squeeze ground carnation
- ½ tsp ground ginger
- 1 tbsp. cinnamon
- 100 g dim chocolate
- 20 g coconut oil

Directions:

1. Roughly slash plums, figs, and heated organic products. Slash nuts with a blade or quickly put them during a Blitz hacker. Separate eggs then whisk the egg whites with a hand blender to a firm day off. Whisk the margarine and nectar until cushioned; at that point, include the ingredient and flour and blend to a smooth mixture. Ply the natural products, nuts, and flavors under the mixture and cautiously overlap within the egg whites.
2. Line a heating tin with preparing paper and pour it within the batter. Heat during a preheated broiler at 175 ° C (fan stove: 150 ° C; gas: speed 2) for around an hour.
3. Take the cake out of the broiler and let it cool. Within the interim, hack the chocolate and soften alongside coconut oil over a boiling water shower. Twist the cake with the chocolate.

Nutrition: Calories: 668 kcal Protein: 21.84 g Fat: 34.88 g Carbohydrates: 74.7 g

615. Avocado Mousse

Preparation time: 20 minutes+ chilling time
Cooking time: 0 minutes
Servings: 2-4

Ingredients:

- 2 ready avocados
- 2 tbsp. coconut milk
- 40 g chocolate
- 40 ml of nectar

- ½ tsp vanilla powder
- ½ tsp chia seeds (ground)
- 12 raspberries
- 1 tsp ground coconut

Directions:

1. Halve the avocados, stone them and spoon them into a blender.
2. Add coconut milk, chocolate, nectar, vanilla powder, and ground chia seeds.
3. Puree to a smooth mass.
4. Chill in any event half-hour or overnight before serving. Select the raspberries, wash, and pat dry. Topping the avocado and mousse with raspberries and coconut chips.

Nutrition: Calories: 216 kcal Protein: 4.07 g Fat: 16.61 g Carbohydrates: 15.55 g

616. Avocado Mint Dessert With Chocolate

Preparation time: 30 minutes+ chilling time
Cooking time: 0 minutes
Servings: 4

Ingredients:

- 400 ml coconut milk (can)
- 3 ready avocados
- 10 g mint (0.5 pack)
- 2 tbsp. juice
- 50 g agave syrup
- 100 g chocolate drops produced using dim chocolate (cocoa content at any rate of 70%)

Directions:

1. Get the coconut milk the open it and spoon out the strong part at the very best - don't shake the can previously - and place it during an enormous bowl. Whisk the firm coconut milk with a hand blender and afterward empty it into a cake or heating dish.
2. Halve the avocados, expel the stones, evacuate the mash, and put during a blender. Wash mint, shake dry and pluck leaves. Puree the avocado mash with juice, agave syrup, and mint to a velvety and smooth mass.
3. Pour the avocado blend onto the foamy coconut milk, sprinkle with chocolate drops and blend the blend cautiously yet equitably. The surface of the mass got to be moderately smooth.
4. Place stick film on the yogurt mass and depress delicately so as that there is no air between the film and thus the dessert mass. Spot the ice within the cooler for, at any rate, 2 hours. 5. Let it defrost quickly and appreciate it.

Nutrition: Calories: 402 kcal Protein: 6.36 g Fat: 24.66 g Carbohydrates: 44.85 g

617. Cottage Cheese With Plums

Preparation time: 10 minutes
Cooking time: 60 minutes
Servings: 6

Ingredients:

- 700 g potatoes
- 6 plums
- 45 g margarine (3 tbsp.)
- 30 g nectar (2 tbsp.)
- 2 squeezes cinnamon
- 250 g quark (20% fat in dry issue)
- 50 g coconut sugar
- 30 g raisins (2 tbsp.)
- 150 g spelled flour type 1050
- 1 egg
- 1 squeeze cardamom powder
- 1 squeeze clove powder

Directions:

1. For the quark legs, strip, wash, hack the potatoes and cook delicately in bubbling water around a quarter-hour over medium warmth. At that point, pour off and let cool for 10 minutes.
2. Within the interim, wash the plums, cut them down the middle, expel the stones, and cut the plums into cuts. Warmth 1 tablespoon of margarine during a touch pot. Include the plums and braise for 3 minutes over medium warmth. Include nectar and let it caramelize for five minutes—season with a spot of cinnamon.
3. Press potatoes through a potato press into a bowl. Include the curd, sugar, raisins, flour, egg, and flavors to the potatoes and ply everything into a smooth mixture; on the off chance, it's excessively soggy and includes some flour—structure 18 little treats out of the batter.
4. Fry the quark balls in progression. Warmth 1 teaspoon margarine during a container. Include 4-5 batter heaps and prepare until brilliant on all sides in around 3-4 minutes over medium warmth; spend the rest of the mixture. Organize the quark drumstick with the plums.

Nutrition: Calories: 698 kcal Protein: 7.9 g Fat: 50.65 g Carbohydrates: 55.43 g

618. Coconut Milk Cake With The Chocolate Base

Preparation time: 20 minutes + chilling time
Cooking time: 30 minutes
Servings: 4

Ingredients:

- 2 eggs
- 1 squeeze salt
- 80 g agave syrup
- 125 g margarine
- 220 g flour type 1050 or spelled flour 1050
- ½ parcel heating powder
- 30 g chocolate (vigorously oiled)
- 1 parcel custard powder
- 400 ml coconut milk (9% fat)
- 30 g coconut sugar
- 40 g coconut drops
- 4 sheets gelatin
- 150 ml topping
- 100 g dim chocolate
- 20 g coconut oil

Directions:

1. Separate the eggs and egg whites, beat the egg whites, and put salt. Mix agave syrup with spread and ingredient until foamy. Blend the flour, heating powder, and cocoa and sifter to the ingredient froth, at that point procedure to a smooth mixture and overlap within the egg whites cautiously.
2. Line or oil the springform dish with heating material. Include the mixture, smooth and heat at 180 ° C (convection 160 ° C; gas: level 2) for around 25-30 minutes (make a stick test). At that point, let the cake cool within the form.
3. Within the interim, mix the pudding powder with 5–6 tablespoons of coconut milk until smooth. Put the rest of the coconut milk, coconut bloom sugar, and 30 g coconut pieces during a pan and convey it to the bubble. Mix within the blended pudding powder and convey to the bubble while mixing and afterward let it cool.

4. Soak the gelatin in chilly water. Whip 100 ml of cream until solid. Warm the rest of the cream during a pot marginally and hack the all-around communicated gelatin in it. Mix in 4 tablespoons of the coconut milk and afterward increase the remainder of the coconut milk. Include the cream and smooth the cream on the chocolate base. Chill for at any rate hour.
5. Roughly cleave the dull chocolate and dissolve with the coconut oil over the water shower, let cool marginally. Meanwhile, cautiously expel the cake from the shape. Spread the cake with the chocolate icing. Sprinkle with outstanding coconut pieces and let it set. Serve dig pieces.

Nutrition: Calories: 660 kcal Protein: 12.68 g Fat: 32.38 g Carbohydrates: 80.06 g

619. Zucchini Mint Popsicles

Preparation time: 20 minutes + chilling time
Cooking time: 0 minutes
Servings: 4

Ingredients:

- 2 zucchini
- 10 g ginger (1 piece)
- 30 g coconut bloom sugar (3 tbsp.)
- 5 g mint (1 bunch)
- 50 ml of juice
- 2 tbsp. nectar

Directions:

1. Clean, wash, and finely grind zucchini. Strip and finely grind the ginger.
2. Mix zucchini with coconut bloom sugar and ginger. Wash the mint leaves, shake dry, blend in with the zucchini blend, and spread quite 8 dessert molds.
3. Mix juice with 450 ml of water and nectar. Fill in ice forms and let freeze for around hour. At that point, embed wooden sticks and permit them to freeze for an extra 3 hours. Expel from the molds to serve.

Nutrition: 47 kcal Protein: 1.98 g Fat: 2.18 g Carbohydrates: 4.98 g

620. Currant Skyr Popsicles

Preparation time: 30 minutes + chilling time
Cooking time: 0 minutes
Servings: 4

Ingredients:

- 250 g red currants
- 1 natural lemon (pizzazz)
- 3 tbsp syrup
- 200 g skyr
- 100 g Greek yogurt
- 100 g topping

Directions:

1. Pluck currants from the panicles, wash and finely puree alongside the lemon get-up-and-go, and a few tbsp syrup. Spread the blend through a fine strainer into a bowl.
2. Mix the Skyr with yogurt in another bowl. Add 1/3 of it to this puree and blend.
3. Stir the remainder of the syrup into the remainder of the Skyr yogurt blend. Whip the cream until hardened and spread half over all of the two masses and crease incautiously.
4. Fill the blend on the other hand in 6 yogurt forms and blend delicately with a spoon. Freeze for around hour. At that point embed wooden sticks and permit them to freeze for an extra 3 hours.
5. To serve, expel ice from the molds and fill in as wanted on a soothing record plate.

Nutrition: Calories: 176 kcal Protein: 5.81 g Fat: 5.07 g Carbohydrates: 28.92 g

621. Pineapple Popsicles

Preparation time: 30 minutes + chilling time
Cooking time: 0 minutes
Servings: 4

Ingredients:

- 600 g new pineapple mash
- 100 g raspberries
- 200 g coconut milk (without sugar)
- 50 g rice syrup
- 1 lime (juice)

Directions:

1. Cut the pineapple mash into pieces, set 100 g aside. Wash the raspberries cautiously and pat them dry.
2. Mix coconut milk with rice syrup. Acknowledged the pineapple with the coconut milk and thus the lime squeeze during a blender and crush finely.
3. Fill the blend into 8 yogurt molds, include 4-5 raspberries each, and let freeze for around hour. At that point embed wooden sticks and let it freeze for an extra 3 hours. To serve, expel ice from the molds and organize with the pineapple pieces put during a secure spot.

Nutrition: Calories: 181 kcal Protein: 2.84 g Fat: 1.8 g Carbohydrates: 41.77 g

622. Coconut And Chocolate Dessert With Chia Seeds

Preparation time: 15 minutes + freezing time
Cooking time: 20 minutes
Servings: 8

Ingredients:

- 400 ml of coconut milk
- 4 tbsp. syrup
- 15 g chocolate (2 tbsp.; vigorously oiled)
- 2 packs chai tea
- 12 g white chia seeds (2 tbsp.)
- 250 g soy yogurt
- 30 g dim chocolate (in any event 70% cocoa)

Directions:

1. Put coconut milk during a pan. Include syrup and chocolate and warmth, however, don't bring back the bubble. Hang the tea sack in, spread, expel from the warmth, and let steep for a half-hour. At that point, remove the tea sack, pressing out the fluid. Blend in 1 1/2 tbsp chia seeds and yogurt.
2. Fill the mass in 8 ice shapes and let freeze for around hour. At that point embed wooden sticks and permit them to freeze for an extra 3 hours.
3. Chop the chocolate and dissolve over a warm water shower. Expel the dessert from the molds and brighten with the chocolate and, thus, the remaining chia seeds.

Nutrition: Calories: 82 kcal Protein: 3.99 g Fat: 1.4 g Carbohydrates: 14.49 g

623. Sesame Vanilla Dessert

Preparation time: 20 minutes + chilling time
Cooking time: 15 minutes
Servings: 4

Ingredients:

- 130 g dark sesame
- 1 favorer
- 300 ml milk (3.5% fat)
- 200 g topping
- 4 eggs
- 40 g coconut sugar

Directions:

1. Roast 120 g sesame seeds during a hot container without fat for five minutes over medium warmth. Expel from the container and let cool for five minutes. At that point, pound finely with a processor or mortar.
2. Within the interim, split the vanilla case lengthways and cut out the mash with a blade. Carry rock bottom sesame to the overflow with vanilla mash, milk, and cream. Expel from the warmth and let cool for five minutes.
3. Within the interim, separate the eggs (utilize the proteins somewhere else). Beat egg yolks with coconut bloom sugar until feathery. Mix within the recent cream blend and warmth during a metal bowl over a high temp water shower with mixing to around 75 ° C until the blend thickens, this may take approximately 10 minutes. At that point, let cool for approximately 20 minutes, blending every so often.
4. Then let the mass freeze smooth during a yogurt producer for around 40 minutes. Or on the other hand, fill a holder and freeze within the cooler for 3-4 hours. Mix at regular intervals.
5. For serving, cut balls out of the ice and sprinkle with the rest of the sesame seeds.

Nutrition: Calories: 388 kcal Protein: 25.24 g Fat: 21.59 g Carbohydrates: 24.61 g

624. Exotic Vegan Pancakes With Mango

Preparation time: 10 minutes
Cooking time: 10 minutes
Servings: 4
Ingredients:

- 120 g spelled flour (type 630)
- 50 g coconut flour
- 2 tsp tartar preparing powder
- 1 squeeze salt
- 2 tbsp. coconut sugar
- 450 ml of rice drink (rice milk) with coconut
- 4 tsp rapeseed oil
- ½ mango
- 200 g coconut yogurt
- 2 tsp chia seeds

Directions:

1. Place every single dry element for the batter during a bowl and blend. Include the rice-coconut drink and blend it into a homogeneous mixture. On the off chance that the batter is excessively firm, include a scramble of rice and coconut drink.
2. Heat 2 teaspoons of oil during a covered container, add 1 tablespoon of spread to the skillet, and prepare 4 to 6 hotcakes in around 3-4 minutes over medium warmth on the two sides until brilliant earthy colored.
3. Peel the mango, disengage from the center, and dig 3D squares. Spread the hotcakes on three plates, spread the yogurt elective produced using coconut on top, and present with the mango and chia seeds.

Nutrition: Calories: 197 kcal Protein: 5.15 g Fat: 6.44 g Carbohydrates: 29.3 g

625. Matcha Mochi

Preparation time: 10 minutes
Cooking time: 20 minutes
Servings: 2
Ingredients:

- 1 cup Superfine White Rice Flour
- 1 cup of coconut milk
- 2 tablespoons matcha powder
- 1/2 cup sugar
- 2 tablespoons butter melted
- 1 teaspoon baking powder

Directions:

1. Preheat the oven to 325.Spray baking dish with non-stick spray. (we use a coconut oil spray.). Mix all dry ingredients, including sugar. Whisk to blend. Add melted butter and coconut milk. Stir well. Put into a baking dish. Used an 8x8 pan. Bake for at least 20 minutes, until done in the middle.

Nutrition: Calories: 170 Fat: 4,3g Fiber: 3.9g Carbs: 34g Protein: 4.9g

626. Choco-Matcha Cupcakes

Preparation time: 15 minutes
Cooking time: 15-18 minutes
Servings: 12pcs
Ingredients:

- 150g coconut flour or almond flour
- 1/2 cup dates
- 60g cocoa
- ½ tsp salt
- ½ tsp fine espresso coffee, decaf if preferred
- 120ml milk
- ½ tsp vanilla extract
- 50ml vegetable oil
- 1 egg
- 120ml boiling water
- 1 tsp baking powder
- For the icing:
- 50g substitute sweetener
- 1 tbsp. matcha green tea powder
- ½ tsp vanilla bean paste
- 50g chilled coconut cream, whipped

Directions:

1. Preheat the oven to 350° F/320° F fan. Line a cupcake tin with paper or silicone cake cases.
2. Place the flour, dates, cocoa, salt, and espresso powder in a large bowl and mix thoroughly.
3. Put the milk, vanilla extract, vegetable oil, and egg to the dry ingredients and use an electric mixer to mix until well combined.
4. Gently pour in the boiling water slowly and beat on low speed until fully combined.
5. Use high speed to mix for a more minute to put air to the batter.
6. The batter is more liquid than a normal cake mix.
7. Scoop the batter evenly between the cake cases. Every cake case should be no more than ¾ full. Bake in the oven for at 15-18 minutes, until the mixture, bounces back when tapped.
8. Take it out from the oven and allow to cool completely before icing.
9. To make the icing, whip the coconut cream and icing sugar together until it's pale and smooth.
10. Put the matcha powder, and vanilla then mix again. Pipe or spread over the cakes.

Nutrition: Calories: 100 Fat: 2.6g Fiber: 1.4g Carbs: 21.6g Protein: 3.1g

627. Quinoa Date Cookies

Preparation time: 10 minutes
Cooking time: 10-12 minutes
Servings: 12pcs
Ingredients:

- ½ cup almond flour

- ½ cup cooked quinoa
- 1/3 cup brown sugar
- ½ cup butter
- 4 tbsp. tahini
- Dates, pitted and chopped
- 1 tsp baking soda
- ½ tsp vanilla extract

Directions:

1. Preheat oven to 350°F.
2. Combine sugar, tahini, and butter stirring until creamy. Add in remaining ingredients. Mix very well. Spoon rounded teaspoonful of dough onto cookie sheets. Bake for 10-12 minutes, or until cookies start to turn golden brown.

Nutrition: Calories: 176 Fat: 1.5g Fiber: 0.9g Carbs: 27g Protein: 1,5g

628. Dark Chocolate Fondue

Preparation time: 10 minutes
Cooking time: 10 minutes
Servings: 2
Ingredients:

- 125g (4oz) dark chocolate (min 85% cocoa)
- 300g (11oz) strawberries
- 200g (7oz) cherries
- 2 apples, peeled, cored and sliced
- 100ml (3½ fl oz) double cream (heavy cream)

Directions:

1. Place the chocolate and cream into a fondue pot or saucepan and warm it until smooth and creamy. Serve in the fondue pot or transfer it to a serving bowl. Scatter the fruit on a serving dish ready to be dipped into the chocolate.

Nutrition: Calories: 129 Fat: 3.1g Fiber: 3.5g Carbs: 28.5g Protein: 3g

629. Pistachio Fluff Salad

Preparation time: 5 minutes
Cooking time: 4 hours
Servings: 4
Ingredients:

- 2 boxes (3.4 Oz each) JELL-O Instant Pistachio pudding blend
- 1 can (20 Oz) squashed pineapple
- 16 Oz Cool Whip, defrosted
- 1 sack (10 Oz) smaller than usual marshmallows
- Maraschino fruits, for embellish

Directions:

1. In an enormous bowl, join pudding blend in with squashed pineapple. Blend in with a wooden spoon until the pudding blend is mixed with pineapple fluids. Include Cool Whip and smaller than normal marshmallows. Cover and refrigerate 4 hours, or medium-term. Present with maraschino fruits as an embellishment. Or then again, whenever wanted, add fruits to lighten directly before serving.

Nutrition: Calories: 2743 kcal Protein: 21.3 g Fat: 84.99 g Carbohydrates: 489.87 g

630. Watergate Salad Recipe

Preparation time: 10 minutes
Cooking time: 60 minutes
Servings: 4
Ingredients:

- 2 (8-ounce) jars squashed pineapple in juice, undrained
- 1 (3.4-ounce) bundle pistachio moment pudding
- 1 (8-ounce) tub solidified whipped beating, defrosted
- 1 cup smaller than usual marshmallows
- 1/2 cup toasted walnuts, hacked

Directions:

1. In a medium bowl, put the pineapple jars' full substance and the pudding then blend until smooth. Overlay in whipped fixing and marshmallows. Cover and refrigerate in any event 60 minutes. Sprinkle walnuts on top before serving.

Nutrition: Calories: 641 kcal Protein: 5.77 g Fat: 68.47 g Carbohydrates: 4.97 g

631. Strawberry Pretzel Salad

Preparation time: 45 minutes
Cooking time: 10 minutes
Servings: 4-6
Ingredients:

- Pretzel Crust
- 3 1/2 cups pretzels, squashed
- 1/4 cup sugar
- 1/2 cup unsalted spread, dissolved
- Cream Cheese Filling
- 8 Oz cream cheddar, mellowed
- 1/2 cup sugar
- 8 Oz cool whip, or whipped cream (solidly whipped)
- Strawberry Jell-O Topping
- 1 lb. new strawberries, hulled and cut
- 2 cups bubbling water
- 6 Oz strawberry jelly powder

Directions:

1. Preheat stove to 350°F. Put aside a 9x13 inch glass preparing dish. Spot pretzels in a ziplock sack, seal, and pound with a moving pin to smash daintily. In a medium bowl, mix the liquefied margarine and sugar. Include the squashed pretzels and blend to cover. Press the pretzel blend into the preparing dish, and afterward heat for 10 minutes. Expel from broiler. In a medium bowl, consolidate jello powder with bubbling water. Mix gradually for one moment until broke down and put in a safe spot. In a huge bowl, beat the cream cheddar and sugar until soft. Utilizing a huge spatula, crease in the cool whip until equitably mixed. When the prepared pretzels are cool, spread the cream cheddar blend equitably on top until level over the dish. At that point, chill for at any rate 30 minutes. While chilling, you can wash, body, and cut the strawberries. Tenderly spot the cut strawberries onto the filling in a solitary layer. Include any residual strawberries top as a fractional second layer. When the jello blend is room temperature, spill over the strawberries utilizing the rear of a spoon for even dispersion. Chill for in any event two hours. Serve and appreciate it!

Nutrition: Calories: 888 kcal Protein: 13.43 g Fat: 40.16 g Carbohydrates: 121.75 g

632. Sheet Pan Apple Pie Bake

Preparation time: 20 minutes
Cooking time: 15 minutes
Servings: 6-8
Ingredients:

- 8 flour tortillas, 8 inch
- 4 tbsp unsalted spread
- 8 Granny Smith apples, stripped, cored and cleaved
- 3/4 cup sugar, partitioned
- 3 tsp cinnamon, partitioned

- 1 tbsp lemon juice, new pressed
- Serving thoughts - discretionary
- Whipped cream
- Frozen yogurt
- Caramel sauce

Directions:

1. Preheat stove to 400°F. Put aside a medium preparing sheet. On a medium-prepared sheet, orchestrate 6 tortillas in a blossom petal design with a few creeps outside the dish and a few crawls of cover. Spot a seventh tortilla in the center. Spot an enormous skillet on medium-high warmth. Include spread, slashed apples, 1/2 cup sugar, and 2 tsp cinnamon. Sauté the apples for 8-10 minutes until they begin to relax, normally mixing with a wooden spoon. Spoon apple blend from skillet over tortillas on prepared sheet. Spread out to make an even layer. Overlay the folds of tortilla outside the dish over the apples. Spot the eighth tortilla in the center to cover the hole. Blend staying 1/4 cup sugar with 1 tsp cinnamon. Sprinkle equally over the tortillas. Spot another preparing dish on top to hold the tortillas set up and heat for 20 minutes. Expel from the stove and permit to cool for 5-10 minutes. Present with discretionary frozen yogurt, whipped cream, and caramel sauce. Appreciate!

Nutrition: Calories: 335 kcal Protein: 5.37 g Fat: 9.61 g Carbohydrates: 57.06 g

633. Heaven On Earth Cake

Preparation time: 20 minutes
Cooking time:
5 hours
Servings: 6-8

Ingredients:

- 1 box Angel nourishment cake or 1 arranged Angel Food Cake
- 1 bundle (3.4 ounces) moment vanilla pudding
- 1/2 cups milk
- 1 cup harsh cream
- 1 can (21 ounces) cherry pie filling
- 1 tub (8 ounces) Cool Whip
- 1 tablespoon almond bits, toasted

Directions:

1. Heat fluffy cake as indicated by bundle's bearings. Permit to cool and cut into 3D shapes. In a bowl, consolidate pudding blend, milk, and acrid cream and beat until smooth. Put in a safe spot. In a 9x13 preparing dish, organize 1/2 of cake solid shapes layer. Spoon 2/3 of cherry over cake. Spot the staying 1/2 of the cake over pie filling. Spoon pudding over cake and spread equally. Spoon and spread whipped besting over the pudding layer. Embellishment cake with the rest of the pie filling and toasted almonds. Chill for around 4 to 5 hours.

Nutrition: Calories: 284 kcal Protein: 4.69 g Fat: 7.69 g Carbohydrates: 48.5 g

634. Lemon Tofu Cheesecake

Preparation time: 5 minutes
Cooking time: 35 minutes
Servings: 8

Ingredients:

- 24 ounces Silk tofu, drained
- 2 tablespoons Almond butter
- 1 cup Date sugar
- 1 teaspoon Lemon zest
- .5 teaspoon Sea salt
- .5 teaspoon Vanilla extract
- 2 tablespoons Lemon juice
- 3 tablespoons Cornstarch
- 1 Crust, 8-inch (optional)

Directions:

1. Preheat the oven to Fahrenheit three-hundred and fifty degrees. If you are preparing the lemon tofu cheesecake without a crust, I recommend preparing eight individual ramekins to divide the filling between. Otherwise, prepare an eight-inch crust of your choice.
2. Whisk together the lemon juice with the cornstarch to form a slurry.
3. In a food processor or blender, combine the cornstarch slurry and remaining ingredients until fully mixed, smooth, and creamy. You don't want any lumps.
4. Pour the lemon tofu cheesecake filling into the prepared crust or ramekins if baking with the crust allows the cheesecake to cook until set, about thirty minutes. If you are using individual ramekins, the cheesecake will only take fifteen to twenty-two minutes, depending on the ramekins' size.
5. Let the cheesecake cool to room temperature, and then transfer it to the fridge until completely chilled through.

Nutrition: Calories: 428 kcal Protein: 16.81 g Fat: 26.89 g Carbohydrates: 34.55 g

635. Blueberry Walnut Crisp

Preparation time: 10 minutes
Cooking time: 35 minutes
Servings: 6

Ingredients:

- 25 cup Walnuts, chopped
- 5 cup Rolled oats
- 2 tablespoons Date sugar
- 5 teaspoon Cinnamon, ground
- 25 teaspoon Sea salt
- 2 tablespoons butter, cut into cubes
- 4 cups Blueberries
- 1 tablespoon Cornstarch
- 2 tablespoons Date sugar
- 5 teaspoon Lemon zest
- 1 teaspoon Vanilla extract

Directions:

1. Begin by preheating your oven to Fahrenheit three-hundred and fifty degrees and preparing six individual ramekins with non-stick cooking spray. Set the ramekins on a baking sheet to avoid spilling.
2. In a bowl, toss together the blueberries with the cornstarch, date sugar, lemon zest, and vanilla. Once combined, divide the blueberries between the ramekins.
3. To make the crispy topping combine the remaining ingredients with a fork or pastry cutter. It will be crumbly. Top the blueberries in the ramekins with the crumble.
4. Set the baking sheet of ramekins in the oven and bake until golden-brown, about twenty-five to thirty minutes. Remove the blueberry walnut crisp from the oven and allow the crisps to cool slightly before serving.

Nutrition: Calories: 1543 kcal Protein: 25.24 g Fat: 41.24 g Carbohydrates: 300.74 g

636. Red Wine Poached Pears

Preparation time: 10 minutes
Cooking time: 35 minutes
Servings: 6

Ingredients:

- 6 Bosc pears
- 5 cup Cherries, pitted (optional)

- 2 cups Red wine
- 5 cup Orange juice
- 2 teaspoons Vanilla extract
- 5 cup Date sugar
- 1 Cinnamon stick
- 8 Cloves, whole
- .5 teaspoon Orange zest

Directions:

1. Add all of your red wine poached pear ingredients, except for the Bosc pears, into a large Dutch oven. You need a large/big pot enough to fit all six whole hears. You want them to fit snugly so that the pears are fully covered in the liquid, but still have a slight wiggle room. But, remember, don't add the pears yet.
2. Allow the wine mixture to reach a simmer in the pot while stirring to dissolve the date sugar.
3. Wait until the poaching liquid has reached a simmer and then peel the pears. This will help avoid discoloration. Place the pears into the poaching liquid, arranging them so that they are submerged.
4. Allow the pears to continue simmering on medium-low for about twenty to twenty-five minutes. But, while the pears poach rearrange and rotate them every five minutes. Don't skip this, as it will ensure they poach evenly on all sides. You want to ensure even the tops of the pears are well poached.
5. Once the pears are done poaching, keep the pears upright in the wine mixture. Remove the pot from the heat of the stove, and allow both the pears and poaching liquid to cool down together.
6. While you can serve the poached pears once cooled to room temperature, I recommend first chilling them in the fridge.
7. When chilling the pears in the fridge, keep them stored in the liquid.
8. Once you are ready to serve the pears, remove them from the liquid and set them on serving dishes. Meanwhile, add the poaching liquid into a saucepan and allow it to simmer to heat until it forms a slightly thickened syrup.
9. Pour the red wine syrup over the cold pears and serve.

Nutrition: Calories: 72 kcal Protein: 1.75 g Fat: 1.06 g Carbohydrates: 13.6 g

637. Dark Chocolate Walnut No-Bake Cookies

Preparation time: 10 minutes
Cooking time: 25 minutes
Servings: 24

Ingredients:

- 25 cups Walnuts, chopped
- 3 tablespoons Coconut oil
- 25 cup Cocoa powder
- 5 cup Dark chocolate chips
- 2 cups shredded coconut, unsweetened
- 5 cup Almond butter
- 33 cup Honey
- 1 teaspoon Vanilla extract
- 25 teaspoon Sea salt

Directions:

1. Prepare an aluminum baking sheet by covering it with kitchen parchment, wax coated paper, or a silicone mat.
2. Melt the coconut oil with the almond butter and honey over low heat in a saucepan. Once melted, stir in the remaining ingredients.
3. Use a tablespoon to scoop out portions of the chocolate walnut dough and roll each portion into a ball in your hands. Place the dark chocolate walnut no-bake cookie balls on the prepared baking sheet.
4. Freeze the cookies for ten minutes to set up. Enjoy immediately, or store the leftovers in a container in the freezer.

Nutrition: Calories: 78 kcal Protein: 0.75 g Fat: 6.49 g Carbohydrates: 5.25 g

638. Quick Soft-Serve Cherry Sorbet

Preparation time: 5 minutes
Cooking time: 5 minutes
Servings: 6

Ingredients:

- 2 cups Cherries, frozen
- 2 Bananas, frozen
- 1 cup Coconut milk, full-fat

Directions:

1. Add all of the sorbet ingredients to a blender, and combine until it is completely smooth without any chunks. It should be the consistency of soft-serve.
2. Enjoy the sorbet alone, or consider topping it with toasted coconut, roasted walnuts, or dark chocolate shavings.

Nutrition: Calories: 68 kcal Protein: 2.97 g Fat: 2.42 g Carbohydrates: 9.22 g

639. Honey-Roasted Plums With Ricotta

Preparation time: 10 minutes
Cooking time: 20 minutes
Servings: 4

Ingredients:

- 4Plums halved and pitted
- 1 tablespoon butter, melted
- 25 cup Honey
- 1 cup Ricotta, part-skim, ideally fresh

Directions:

1. Set the oven to 400°F then prepare a baking dish or skillet that can fit all eight plum halves. Add the melted butter into the dish.
2. Arrange your plum halves in the prepared dish, with the cut side facing upward. Drizzle the honey over the plums and bake until the plums are soft and release the juices, about fifteen minutes.
3. If you want to char the plums slightly, you can turn the broiler on for the last minute of baking.
4. Divide the roasted plums between serving dishes and top them with the ricotta. Serve while still warm.

Nutrition: Calories: 252 kcal Protein: 8.93 g Fat: 11.54 g Carbohydrates: 30.04 g

640. No-Bake Triple Berry Mini Tarts

Preparation time: 10 minutes
Cooking time: 20 minutes
Servings: 16

Ingredients:

- 1 cup frozen mixed berries, defrosted
- 5 cup Honey
- 5 tablespoons cacao butter, melted
- 33 cup Coconut cream
- 2 cups Walnuts, raw
- 1 cup Dates

Directions:

1. In a food processor, place and combine the walnuts with the dates until it forms a crumbly mixture that can hold together when you press it. Scrape down the sides as needed.
2. Prepare a mini muffin tin for the crust to make the mini-tarts. Spray the pan with non-stick cooking spray.
3. Press the prepared crust into the mini muffin tin, forming mini tarts with crust pressed both on the bottom and the sides of the muffin cups.
4. In a blender, mix the berries and other remaining ingredients until completely smooth. Divide the berry mixture between the crusts.
5. Place the filled muffin tin in the fridge, allow it to chill for six hours, or set it.
6. Use a kitchen knife to run around the edges of each tart to release them from the pan. Use a fork and take each tart out of the pan. Serve or store in a container in the fridge or freezer.

Nutrition: Calories: 191 kcal Protein: 2.72 g Fat: 12.64 g Carbohydrates: 19.67 g

641. Mocha Buckwheat Pudding

Preparation time: 7 minutes
Cooking time: 0 minutes
Servings: 6

Ingredients:

- 5 cup Buckwheat groats
- 3 tablespoons Cocoa powder
- 2 scoops Chocolate soy protein powder
- 1 teaspoon instant espresso powder
- 2 tablespoons Almond butter
- 5 cup Soy milk, unsweetened
- 1 Banana
- 2 Dates, pitted

Directions:

1. Cover the buckwheat groats in water and allow them to soak overnight to soften. The following day (or at least six hours later) drain the water off of the buckwheat. Rinse it well.
2. Add the prepared buckwheat and the remaining ingredients all into a blender together, and blend on high speed until completely smooth.
3. Serve the pudding immediately, or allow it to chill first.

Nutrition: Calories: 144 kcal Protein: 11.1 g Fat: 6.8 g Carbohydrates: 11.45 g

642. Fudgy Buckwheat Brownies

Preparation time: 10 minutes
Cooking time: 30 minutes
Servings: 14

Ingredients:

- 1 cup Buckwheat flour
- 66 cup Cocoa powder
- 1.33 cup Date sugar
- 25 teaspoon Sea salt
- 25 cup Baking powder
- 75 cup Olive oil, light
- 1 tablespoon Vanilla extract
- 3 Eggs
- 1 teaspoon instant espresso powder
- 1 cup Dark chocolate chips

Directions:

1. Begin by lining a square baking dish (eight-by-eight or nine-by-nine inch) with kitchen parchment and setting the oven to Fahrenheit three-hundred and fifty.
2. In a kitchen, bowl whisks together the cocoa powder, baking powder, sea salt, and buckwheat flour.
3. In another bowl, combine the date sugar, espresso powder, and olive oil. Whisk in the eggs one at a time, each until completely combined, and then add in the vanilla last. Add the wet ingredients into the buckwheat mixture and whisk until combined, being careful not to over mix.
4. Gently fold in the chocolate chips.
5. Pour the buckwheat brownie mixture into the prepared baking pan and bake it until set, about twenty minutes. Keep in mind, buckwheat flour takes a little extra time to cook than wheat flour. The brownies are ready when a toothpick is removed cleanly after being inserted into the brownies' center.
6. Let the brownies cool thoroughly before slicing and serving.

Nutrition: Calories: 228 kcal Protein: 4.53 g Fat: 16.1 g Carbohydrates: 18.9 g

643. Dark Chocolate Cranberry Oatmeal Cookies

Preparation time: 15 minutes
Cooking time: 15 minutes
Servings: 15

Ingredients:

- 1 cup Rolled oats
- 1.5 teaspoon Baking powder
- 25 teaspoon Sea salt
- 75 cup Whole wheat flour
- 1 teaspoon Cinnamon, ground
- 1 Eggs
- 2 tablespoons Olive oil, light
- 5 cup Date sugar
- 1 teaspoon Vanilla extract
- 5 cup Fresh cranberries, chopped
- 3 tablespoons Dark chocolate, chopped

Directions:

1. In a kitchen bowl, combine the sea salt, cinnamon, whole-wheat flour, baking powder, and rolled oats.
2. In another bowl, combine the egg, olive oil, vanilla, and date sugar. Once combined, add the wet ingredients to the flour mixture, stirring just until combined.
3. Gently fold the cranberries and dark chocolate into the dough. Cover the bowl and allow the dough to chill for thirty minutes to set up.
4. Meanwhile, allow the oven to preheat to Fahrenheit three-hundred and twenty-five degrees and line a couple of baking sheets with kitchen parchment or a silicone mat.
5. Use a spoon or cookie scoop and divide the dough into fifteen, evenly-sized mounds. Roll each mound between your hands to form a ball and then assemble them on the two baking sheets. Gently press down on every ball with your hand to flatten it about halfway.
6. Bake the cookies until the sides just begin to set, but the middle of the cookies are still soft about nine to twelve minutes. Once removed from the oven, allow the cookies to cool on the baking sheets for five minutes before transferring them to a wire rack to finish cooling.

Nutrition: Calories: 85 kcal Protein: 2.91 g Fat: 3.45 g Carbohydrates: 13.18 g

644. Crunchy Chocolate Chip Coconut Macadamia Nut Cookies

Preparation time: 10 minutes

Cooking time: 20 minutes
Servings: 8
Ingredients:

- 1 cup yogurt
- 1 cup yogurt
- 1/2 tsp baking soda
- 1/2 tsp salt
- 1 tbsp. of butter, softened
- 1 cup firmly packed brown sugar
- 1/2 cup sugar
- 1 large egg
- 1/2 cup semi-sweet chocolate chips
- 1/2 cup sweetened flaked coconut
- 1/2 cup coarsely chopped dry-roasted macadamia nuts
- 1/2 cup raisins

Directions:

1. Preheat the oven to 325°f.
2. Put and whisk together the flour, oats, baking soda, and salt in a little bowl and then place aside.
3. In your mixer bowl, mix together the butter/sugar/egg mix.
4. Mix in the flour/oats mix until just combined and stir into the chocolate chips, craisins, nuts, and coconut.
5. Place outsized bits on a parchment-lined cookie sheet.
6. Bake for 1-3 minutes before biscuits are only barely golden brown.
7. Remove from the oven and then leave the cookie sheets to cool at least 10 minutes.

Nutrition: Calories: 281 kcal Protein: 4.07 g Fat: 11.16 g Carbohydrates: 44 g

645. Peach And Blueberry Pie

Preparation time: 20 minutes
Cooking time:
40 minutes
Servings: 6-8
Ingredients:

- 1 box of noodle dough
- Filling:
- 5 peaches, peeled and chopped (I used roasted peaches)
- 3 cups strawberries
- 3/4 cup sugar
- 1/4 cup bread
- Juice of 1/2 lemon
- 1 egg yolk, beaten

Directions:

1. Preheat oven to 400 degrees.
2. Place dough to a 9-inch pie plate
3. In a big bowl, combine tomatoes, sugar, bread, and lemon juice, then toss to combine. Pour into the pie plate, mounding at the center.
4. Simply take some of the bread and then cut into bits, put a pie shirt, put the dough in addition to pressing on edges.
5. Brush crust with egg wash then sprinkles with sugar.
6. Set onto a parchment paper-lined baking sheet.
7. Bake at 400 for about 20 minutes, until crust is browned at borders.
8. Turn oven down to 350, bake for another 40 minutes.
9. Remove and let sit at least 30minutes.
10. Have with vanilla ice-cream.

Nutrition: Calories: 74 kcal Protein: 1.61 g Fat: 1.53 g Carbohydrates: 14.33 g

646. Pear, Cranberry And Chocolate Crisp

Preparation time: 20 minutes
Cooking time: 40 minutes
Servings: 6-8
Ingredients:

- Crumble topping:
- 1/2 cup flour
- 1/2 cup brown sugar
- 1 tsp cinnamon
- ⅛ Tsp. salt
- 3/4 cup yogurt
- 1/4 cup sliced peppers
- 1/3 cup butter, melted
- 1 teaspoon vanilla
- Filling:
- 1 tbsp brown sugar
- 3 tsp, cut into balls
- 1/4 cup dried cranberries
- 1 teaspoon lemon juice
- 2 handfuls of milk chocolate chips

Directions:

1. Preheat oven to 375°F.
2. Spray a casserole with a butter spray.
3. Put all of the topping ingredients - flour, sugar, cinnamon, salt, nuts, legumes and dried
4. Butter a bowl and then mix. Set aside.
5. In a large bowl, combine the sugar, lemon juice, pears, and cranberries.
6. Once the fully blended move to the prepared baking dish.
7. Spread the topping evenly over the fruit.
8. Bake for about half an hour.
9. Disperse chocolate chips out at the top.
10. Cook for another 10 minutes.
11. Have with ice cream.

Nutrition: Calories: 155 kcal Protein: 2.53 g Fat: 9.19 g Carbohydrates: 15.85 g

647. Japanese Cheesecake

Preparation time: 30 minutes
Cooking time: 1 hour and 20 minutes
Servings: 6-8
Ingredients:

- 80 ml of milk
- 140 g cream cheese
- 40 g butter
- 5 eggs
- 50 g of flour
- 15 g cornstarch
- ½ tsp salt
- 1 untreated lemon or finished lemon peel
- 90 g of sugar

Directions:

1. Preheat the oven to approx. 150 ° C (top and bottom heat).
2. Heat the milk a low heat and add the cream cheese and stir until melted.
3. Now add the butter and let it melt while stirring.
4. As soon as the mass has a smooth consistency, remove from the heat.
5. Separate the eggs and beat the egg yolk smoothly with your hand (this will make the color slightly light yellow).
6. Now stir the milk mixture carefully under the egg yolk.

7. Put the flour and the starch into the mixture through a sieve and mix everything well. Necessary that the dough must be free of lumps!
8. Now the protein in another bowl beat, adding your sugar in small increments.
9. Add the lemon zest to the egg whites and then carefully lift them in portions under the egg yolk mixture.
10. Line a small spring form pan (18 cm) with baking paper and let the paper stand high over the edge at the edges as the cake opens. Grease the baking paper beforehand so that the cake does not tear when it goes up.
11. Then wrap the baking tin twice with aluminum foil so that it is waterproof.
12. Pour in the dough and tap lightly on the work surface several times so that any bubbles come out.
13. Place the spring form pan in a deep baking sheet, which is approximately 2 cm high and filled with hot water.
14. Cook the cake in the oven for about 80 minutes. After that time, remove it and let it cool down. So, when it is cold, you can easily remove it from the mold.
15. If you want to add some icing sugar or apricot jam and serve it either slightly warm or cold.

Nutrition: Calories: 252 kcal Protein: 8.34 g Fat: 15.9 g Carbohydrates: 18.95 g

648. Apple Cheesecake

Preparation time: 15 minutes
Cooking time: 45 minutes
Servings: 12

Ingredients:

- 250g mascarpone
- 250g low-fat curd
- 3 eggs
- 1 pack of custard
- 1 teaspoon Baking powder
- 1 packet of vanilla sugar
- 1 pinch of salt
- 2-3 apples

Directions:

1. Peel, quarter and scratch the apples.
2. Mix the remaining ingredients starting from the dry ones, then the others.
3. Line a 28 cm spring form pan with baking paper. Fill in the dough. Press in the apples.
4. Forty-five minutes at 160 ° C (circulation) baking, allow cooling after that in the oven slightly open.
5. Preparation time without baking 10-15 minutes.
6. Depending on how quickly you can peel apples.

Nutrition: Calories: 95 kcal Protein: 7.95 g Fat: 4.44 g Carbohydrates: 5.89 g

649. Kiwi Yogurt Ice Cream

Preparation time: 30 minutes
Cooking time: 0 minutes
Servings: 6

Ingredients:

- 360 ml of yogurt
- 8 kiwi fruits
- 150 g of sugar
- 45 ml of lemon juice
- 30 ml orange liqueur (e.g., Grand Marnier)

Directions:

1. Peel and roughly cut the kiwi into cubes.
2. Mix the kiwi cubes and sugar and let them steep for 20 minutes.
3. Then puree all ingredients in the blender.
4. Place in the ice maker and allow to freeze according to the instructions.

Nutrition: Calories: 190 kcal Protein: 2.33 g Fat: 1.87 g Carbohydrates: 49.78 g

650. Chocolate Brownies

Preparation time: 15 minutes
Cooking time: 30 minutes
Servings: 14

Ingredients:

- 200g (7oz) dark chocolate (min 85% cocoa)
- 200g (70z) Medjool dates, stone removed
- 100g (3½oz) walnuts, chopped
- 3 eggs
- 25mls (1fl oz) melted coconut oil
- 2 teaspoons vanilla essence
- ½ teaspoon baking soda

Directions:

1. Place the dates, chocolate, eggs, coconut oil, baking soda, and vanilla essence into a food processor and mix until smooth. Stir the walnuts into the mixture. Place the mixture into a shallow baking tray. Transfer to the oven and bake at 180C/350F for 25-30 minutes. Allow it to cool. Cut into pieces and serve.

Nutrition: Calories: 618 kcal Protein: 4.8 g Fat: 60.13 g Carbohydrates: 20.55 g

651. Crème Brûlée

Preparation time: 10 minutes
Cooking time: 5 minutes
Servings: 4

Ingredients:

- 400g (14oz) strawberries
- 300g (11oz) plain low-fat yogurt
- 125g (4oz) Greek yogurt
- 100g (3½oz) brown sugar
- 1 teaspoon vanilla extract

Directions:

1. Divide the strawberries between 4 ramekin dishes. In a bowl, combine the plain yogurt with the vanilla extract. Spoon the mixture onto the strawberries. Scoop the Greek yogurt on top. Sprinkle the sugar into each ramekin dish, completely covering the top. Place the dishes under a hot grill (broiler) for around 3 minutes or until the sugar has caramelized.

Nutrition: Calories: 218 kcal Protein: 9.39 g Fat: 3.1 g Carbohydrates: 39.16 g

652. Pistachio Fudge

Preparation time: 10 minutes
Cooking time: 0 minutes
Servings: 10

Ingredients:

- 225g (8oz) Medjool dates
- 100g (3½ oz.) pistachio nuts, shelled (or other nuts)
- 50g (2oz) desiccated (shredded) coconut
- 25g (1oz) oats
- 2 tablespoons water

Directions:

1. Place the dates, nuts, coconut, oats, and water into a food processor and process until the ingredients are well mixed. Remove the mixture and roll it to 2cm (1 inch) thick. Cut it into 10 pieces and serve.

Nutrition: Calories: 134 kcal Protein: 3.54 g Fat: 5.36 g Carbohydrates: 21.46 g

653. Spiced Poached Apples

Preparation time: 10 minutes
Cooking time: 20 minutes
Servings: 4
Ingredients:

- 4 apples
- 2 tablespoons honey
- 4 star anise
- 2 cinnamon sticks
- 300mls (½ pint) green tea

Directions:

1. Place the honey and green tea into a saucepan and bring to the boil. Add the apples, star anise, and cinnamon. Reduce the heat and simmer gentle for 15 minutes. Serve the apples with a dollop of crème Fraiche or Greek yogurt.

Nutrition: Calories: 147 kcal Protein: 2.1 g Fat: 1.82 g Carbohydrates: 33.79 g

654. Black Forest Smoothie

Preparation time: 5 minutes
Cooking time: 0 minutes
Servings: 1
Ingredients:

- 100g (3½oz) frozen cherries
- 25g (1oz) kale
- 1 medjool date
- 1 tablespoon cocoa powder
- 2 teaspoons chia seeds
- 200mls (7fl oz.) milk or soya milk

Directions:

1. Place all the ingredients in a blender and process until smooth and creamy.

Nutrition: Calories: 21586 kcal Protein: 1419.04 g Fat: 852.7 g Carbohydrates: 2088.94 g

655. Shrimp Muffins

Preparation time: 15 minutes
Cooking time:
45 minutes
Servings: 8
Ingredients:

- 1 spaghetti squash, peeled and halved
- 2 tablespoons avocado mayonnaise
- 1 cup low-fat mozzarella cheese, shredded
- 8 ounces shrimp, peeled, cooked and chopped
- 1 ½ cups almond flour
- 1 teaspoon parsley, dried
- 1 garlic clove, minced
- Black pepper to the taste
- Cooking spray

Directions:

1. Line a parchment paper on a baking sheet and arrange the squash.
2. Bake in the oven at 375°F for 30 minutes.
3. Scrape flesh into a bowl, add pepper, parsley flakes, flour, shrimp, mayo, and mozzarella and stir well.
4. Divide this mix into a muffin tray greased with cooking spray, bake in the oven at 375°F for 15 minutes and serve them cold as a snack.

Nutrition: Calories: 180 kcal Protein: 13.1 g Fat: 12.3 g Carbohydrates: 5.55 g

656. Buckwheat Burgers

Preparation time: 20 minutes
Cooking time: 60 minutes
Servings: 4
Ingredients:

- ¾ cup dry buckwheat
- 1½ cups water
- Salt, as required
- 2 tablespoons olive oil, divided
- ½ of large red onion, chopped finely
- ½ of a large carrot, peeled and grated
- ½ of celery stalk, chopped finely
- 1 fresh kale leaf, tough ribs removed and chopped finely
- 1 large cooked sweet potato, mashed
- 2 tablespoons almond butter
- 2 tablespoons low-sodium soy sauce
- For Serving
- 6 cups fresh baby kale
- 2 cups cherry tomatoes

Directions:

1. Preheat your oven to 350°F. Line a baking sheet with parchment paper. For patties: Heat a nonstick frying pan over medium heat and toast the buckwheat for about 5-6 minutes, stirring continuously.
2. Add the water and salt and bring to a boil over high heat. Adjust the temperature to low and cook, covered for about 15 minutes, or until all the water is absorbed.
3. On the other hand, warm 1 tablespoon of the oil in a skillet over medium heat and sauté the onion for about 4-5 minutes.
4. Add the carrot and celery and cook for about 5 minutes. Stir in the remaining ingredients and remove from the heat.
5. Transfer the mixture into a bowl with buckwheat and stir to combine. Put aside to completely cool.
6. Make 4 equal-sized patties from the mixture. Arrange the patties onto the prepared baking sheet in a single layer.
7. Bake for approximately 20 minutes per side. Divide the greens, tomatoes, cabbage, and bell pepper onto serving plates.
8. Top each plate with 1 patty and serve.

Nutrition: Calories: 342 kcal Protein: 8.88 g Fat: 15.32 g Carbohydrates: 46.7 g

657. Potato Bites

Preparation time: 10 minutes
Cooking time:
20 minutes
Servings: 4
Ingredients:

- 1 potato, sliced
- 2 bacon slices, already cooked and crumbled
- 1 small avocado, pitted and cubed
- Cooking spray

Directions:

1. Spread potato slices on a lined baking sheet, spray with cooking oil.
2. Introduce in the oven at 350°F, bake for 20 minutes, arrange on a platter, top each slice with avocado and crumbled bacon, and serve as a dessert.

Nutrition: Calories: 225 kcal Protein: 6.1 g Fat: 14.07 g Carbohydrates: 20.51 g

658. Cocoa Bars

Preparation time: 20 minutes + 60 minutes chilling time
Cooking time: 0 minutes
Servings: 6
Ingredients:

- 1 cup unsweetened cocoa chips

- 2 cups rolled oats
- 1 cup low-fat peanut butter
- ½ cup chia seeds
- ½ cup raisins
- ¼ cup coconut sugar
- ½ cup coconut milk

Directions:

1. Put 1 and ½ cups oats in your blender, pulse well and transfer this to a bowl.
2. Add the rest of the oats, cocoa chips, chia seeds, raisins, sugar, and milk, stir well.
3. Spread this into a square pan, press well, keep in the fridge for 2 hours, slice into 12 bars, and serve.

Nutrition: Calories: 227 kcal Protein: 12.92 g Fat: 12.05 g Carbohydrates: 37.54 g

659. Pancakes With Apples And Blackcurrants

Preparation time: 30 minutes
Cooking time: 10 minutes
Servings: 4

Ingredients:

- 2 apples cut into small chunks
- 2 cups of quick-cooking oats
- 1 cup flour of your choice
- 1 tsp. baking powder
- 2 tbsp. raw sugar, coconut sugar, or 2 tbsp. honey that is warm and easy to distribute
- 2 egg whites
- ¼ cups of milk (or soy/rice/coconut)
- 3 tsp. extra virgin olive oil
- A dash of salt
- For the berry topping:
- 1 cup blackcurrants, washed and stalks removed
- 1 tbsp. water (may use less)
- 2 tbsp. sugar (see above for types)

Directions:

1. Place the ingredients for the topping in a small pot simmer, frequently stirring for about 10 minutes until it cooks down and the juices are released.
2. Take the dry ingredients and mix them in a bowl. After, add the apples and the milk a bit at a time (you may not use it all), until it is a batter. Stiffly whisk the egg whites and then gently mix them into the pancake batter. Set aside in the refrigerator.
3. Pour a one-quarter of the oil onto a flat pan or flat griddle, and when hot, pour some of the batter into it in a pancake shape. When the pancakes start to have golden brown edges and form air bubbles, they may be ready to be gently flipped.
4. Test to be sure the bottom can leave away from the pan before actually flipping. Repeat for the next three pancakes. Top each pancake with the berries.

Nutrition: Calories: 287 kcal Protein: 11.68 g Fat: 4.97 g Carbohydrates: 56.99 g

660. Sweet And Savory Guacamole

Preparation time: 20 minutes
Cooking time: 0 minutes
Servings: 2

Ingredients:

- 2 large avocados, pitted and scooped
- 2 Medjool dates, chopped into small pieces and pitted
- ½ cup cherry tomatoes cut into halves
- Sprigs of parsley, chopped
- ¼ cup of arugula, chopped
- Sticks of celery washed, cut into sticks for dipping
- Juice from ¼ lime
- Dash of sea salt

Directions:

1. Mash the avocado in a bowl, sprinkle salt, and squeeze of the lime juice. Fold in the tomatoes, dates, herbs, and greens. Scoop with celery sticks, and enjoy!

Nutrition: Calories: 392 kcal Protein: 4.58 g Fat: 29.53 g Carbohydrates: 36.05 g

661. Berry Yogurt Freeze

Preparation time: 1 hour 30 minutes
Cooking time: 0 minutes
Servings: 2

Ingredients:

- 2 cups plain yogurt (Greek, soy or coconut)
- ½ cup sliced strawberries
- ½ cup blackberries
- 1 tsp. Honey (warmed) ½ tsp. chocolate powder

Directions:

1. Blend all of the above ingredients until creamy in a bowl. Place into two glass or in freezer-safe metal bowls, and put into the freezer for 1 hour, remove and thaw just slightly so that it is soft enough to eat with a spoon, makes two servings.

Nutrition: Calories: 264 kcal Protein: 12.86 g Fat: 11.27 g Carbohydrates: 29.54 g

662. Banana & Ginger Snap

Preparation time: 30 minutes
Cooking time: 0 minutes
Servings: 1

Ingredients:

- 2.5cm (1 inch) chunk of fresh ginger, peeled
- 1 banana
- 1 large carrot
- 1 apple, cored
- ½ stick of celery
- ¼ level teaspoon turmeric powder

Directions:

1. Place all the ingredients into a blender with just enough water to cover them. Process until smooth

Nutrition: Calories: 104 kcal Protein: 3.81 g Fat: 3.29 g Carbohydrates: 16.28 g

663. Chocolate, Strawberry & Coconut Crush

Preparation time: 30 minutes
Cooking time: 0 minutes
Servings: 1

Ingredients:

- 100mls (3½fl oz) coconut milk
- 100g (3½oz) strawberries
- 1 banana
- 1 tablespoon 100% cocoa powder or cacao nibs
- 1 teaspoon matcha powder

Directions:

1. Toss all of the ingredients into a blender and process them to a creamy consistency. Add a little extra water if you need to thin it a little.

Nutrition: Calories: 24284 kcal Protein: 248.75 g Fat: 2510.29 g Carbohydrates: 594.43 g

664. Chocolate Berry Blend

Preparation time: 30 minutes

Cooking time: 0 minutes
Servings: 1
Ingredients:

- 50g (2oz) kale
- 50g (2oz) blueberries
- 50g (2oz) strawberries
- 1 banana
- 1 tablespoon 100% cocoa powder or cacao nibs
- 200mls (7fl oz.) unsweetened soya milk

Directions:

1. Put all of the ingredients into a blender with enough water to cover them and process until smooth.

Nutrition: Calories: 21528 kcal Protein: 1419.28 g Fat: 853.01 g Carbohydrates: 2071.99 g

665. Mango & Rocket (Arugula) Smoothie

Preparation time: 30 minutes
Cooking time: 0 minutes
Servings: 1
Ingredients:

- 25g (1oz) fresh rocket (arugula)
- 150g (5oz) fresh mango, peeled, de-stoned and chopped
- 1 avocado, de-stoned and peeled
- ½ teaspoon matcha powder
- Juice of 1 lime

Directions:

1. Bring all of the ingredients into a blender with enough water to cover them and process until smooth. Add a few ice cubes and enjoy.

Nutrition: Calories: 511 kcal Protein: 12.48 g Fat: 36.29 g Carbohydrates: 44.24 g

666. Buckwheat Pancakes With Strawberries And Chocolate Nut Butter

Preparation time: 25 minutes
Cooking time: 25 minutes
Servings: 8
Ingredients:

- 1.5 cups soy milk 1 cup buckwheat flour 1 large egg
- 1 tablespoon extra-virgin olive oil, for cooking
- 1 ½ cups strawberries, chopped
- For the chocolate nut butter:
- 2/3 cup dark chocolate (at least 85%) ¼ cup milk
- 2 tablespoons double cream 1 tablespoon coconut oil ½ cup walnuts

Directions:

1. Place milk, flour, and egg in a blender and blend until smooth. Transfer batter to measuring cup for easy pouring. To make the chocolate nut butter: melt chocolate in a double-boiler, once melted, whisk in the milk, then the double cream and oil. Pour into a blender with your walnuts and blend until smooth. For a saucier mix, add more milk or cream as desired. To make the pancakes: warm a griddle to medium heat, adding a small amount of oil as needed. Pour batter onto griddle and cook until lightly browned on the bottom. Watch for air bubbles. You will know it's time to flip your pancake when the air bubbles pop. Flip your pancakes and cook until lightly browned on the other side. Repeat with the remaining batter. Top pancakes with strawberries and drizzle over with sauce, as desired.

Nutrition: Calories: 139 kcal Protein: 3.82 g Fat: 6.62 g Carbohydrates: 17.96 g

667. Tropical Chocolate Delight

Preparation time: 30 minutes
Cooking time: 0 minutes
Servings: 1
Ingredients:

- 1 mango, peeled & de-stoned
- 75g (3oz) fresh pineapple, chopped
- 50g (2oz) kale
- 25g (1oz) rocket
- 1 tablespoon 100% cocoa powder or cacao nibs
- 150mls (5fl oz) coconut milk

Directions:

1. Place all of the ingredients into a blender and blitz until smooth. You can add a little water if it seems too thick.

Nutrition: Calories: 185 Protein: 525.08 g Fat: 5371.29 g Carbohydrates: 1265.8 g

668. Choc Nut Truffles

Preparation time: 5 minutes
Cooking time: 50 minutes
Servings: 3
Ingredients

- 150g (5oz) desiccated (shredded) coconut
- 50g (2oz) walnuts, chopped
- 25g (1oz) hazelnuts, chopped
- 4 medjool dates
- 2 tablespoons 100% cocoa powder or cacao nibs
- 1 tablespoon coconut oil

Directions:

1. Place all of the ingredients into a blender and process until smooth and creamy. Using a teaspoon, scoop the mixture into bite-size pieces then roll it into balls. Place them into small paper cases, cover them, and chill for 1 hour before serving.

Nutrition: Calories 332, Fat 16.5, Fiber 10.3, Carbs 20.7, Protein 26.5

669. Fruit Skewers & Strawberry Dip

Preparation time: 5 minutes
Cooking time: 20 minutes
Servings: 3
Ingredients:

- 150g (5oz) red grapes
- 1 pineapple, (approx 2lb weight) peeled and diced
- 400g (14oz) strawberries

Directions:

1. Place 100g (3½ oz) of the strawberries into a food processor and blend until smooth. Pour the dip into a serving bowl. Skewer the grapes, pineapple chunks, and remaining strawberries onto skewers. Serve alongside the strawberry dip.

Nutrition: Calories 304, Fat 14,Fiber 5.6,Carbs 12.5,Protein 24

670. Guilt-Free Banana Ice-Cream

Preparation time: 10 minutes
Cooking time:
0 minutes
Servings: 3
Ingredients:

- Three quite ripe banana - peeled and rooted
- A couple of chocolate chips
- 2 tbsp. skim milk

Directions:

1. Set all ingredients into a food processor and blend until creamy.

2. Eat freeze and appreciate afterward.

Nutrition: Calories: 216 kcal Protein: 8.31 g Fat: 5.12 g Carbohydrates: 36.11 g

671. Pineapple Buckwheat Pancake

Preparation time: 15 minutes
Cooking time: 5 minutes
Servings: 4

Ingredients:

- 1 cup buckwheat flour
- 1/4 cup almond flour
- 2 tablespoons hemp seeds, plus more for topping
- 1 teaspoon baking powder
- 1/2 teaspoon allspice
- 2 Ounces' pineapple Muuna cottage cheese
- 1 egg
- 1 teaspoon vanilla extract
- 2 tablespoon of maple syrup, plus more for serving
- 1 tablespoon butter, divided
- 1 cup unsweetened almond milk
- 1 small pineapple, outer layer cut off, sliced into rings and cored, (you can also use canned pineapple rings)
- 1/4 teaspoon salt

Directions:

1. Prepare a medium-heat pancake griddle or skillet.
2. In a wide bowl, mix flours, hemp seeds, baking powder, allspice, and salt, and whisk until mixed.
3. In the bowl, add the cottage cheese, egg, maple syrup, and vanilla. Whisk in as you add the milk gradually until all is well mixed.
4. Add a bit of butter to the saucepan. Place one pineapple ring on top once melted, cook until golden brown and start caramelizing. Flip the slice of pineapple over, spoon pancake batter on top, filling the ring and spills a little over the edges. Cook until set (about 3 minutes), turn carefully on the other side and cook for another 2 minutes.
5. Repeat using the remaining batter and pineapple rings.
6. Serve to top with maple syrup and extra hemp seeds.

Nutrition: Calories: 279 kcal Protein: 10.57 g Fat: 12.06 g Carbohydrates: 34.1 g

672. Sirty Blueberry Pancakes

Preparation time: 20 minutes
Cooking time: 10 minutes
Servings: 4

Ingredients:

- 6bananas
- 6 eggs
- 1 tsp baking powder
- 1 2/3 cups rolled oats
- 1 1/2 cup blueberries
- ¼ teaspoon salt

Directions:

1. In a high-speed blender, pop out the flour, spin for 1 minute, or until it has formed a flour of oats. Tip: make sure your mixer is dry before you do this, or else it's all going to get soggy!
2. Add the bananas, sugar, baking powder, and salt to the blender and pump until forming a smooth batter for 2 minutes.
3. Move the mixture and fold in the blueberries to a large pot. Leave the baking powder to rest for 10 minutes until it activates.
4. To make your pancakes, add a dollop of butter to your frying pan over medium-high heat (this helps to make them very fluffy and crispy!).
5. Add a couple of spoons of blueberry pancake mix and fry on the bottom side until nicely golden. Toss the other side of the pancake to cook. You will Love it!

Nutrition: Calories: 396 kcal Protein: 22.46 g Fat: 19.05 g Carbohydrates: 48.69 g

673. Apricot Oatmeal Cookies

Preparation time: 10 minutes
Cooking time: 30 minutes
Servings: 8

Ingredients:

- 1/2 cup (1 stick) butter, softened
- 2/3 cup light brown sugar packed
- 1 egg
- 3/4 cup all-purpose flour
- 1/2 tsp baking soda
- 1/2 tsp vanilla extract
- 1/2 tsp cinnamon
- 1/4 tsp salt
- 1 teaspoon 1/2 cups chopped oats
- 3/4 cup yolks
- 1/4 cup sliced apricots
- 1/3 cup slivered almonds

Direction

1. Preheat oven to 350°.
2. In a huge bowl, combine with the butter, sugar, and egg until smooth.
3. In another bowl, blend the flour, baking soda, cinnamon, and salt together.
4. Mix the dry ingredients to the butter-sugar bowl.
5. Now stir in the oats, raisins, apricots, and almonds.
6. I heard on the web that in this time, it's much better to cool with the dough (therefore, your biscuits are thicker)
7. Afterward, I scooped my biscuits into some parchment-lined (easier removal and wash up) cookie sheet - around two inches apart.
8. I sliced mine for approximately ten minutes - they were fantastic!

Nutrition: Calories: 354 kcal Protein: 9.08 g Fat: 20.46 g Carbohydrates: 38.47 g

674. Watergate Salad Recipe

Preparation time: 60 minutes
Cooking time: 0
Servings: 1

Ingredients:

- 2 (8-ounce) jars squashed pineapple in juice, undrained
- 1 (3.4-ounce) bundle pistachio moment pudding
- 1 (8-ounce) tub solidified whipped beating, defrosted
- 1 cup smaller than usual marshmallows
- 1/2 cup toasted walnuts, hacked

Directions:

1. In a medium bowl, mix together the full substance of the pineapple jars and the pudding blend until smooth. Overlay in whipped fixing and marshmallows. Cover and refrigerate in any event 60 minutes. Sprinkle walnuts on top before serving.

Nutrition: Calories: 150 Fat: 2 Carbohydrates: 7

675. Strawberry Upside-Down Cake

Preparation time: 15 minutes
Cooking time: 40 minutes

Serving: 1

Ingredients:

- 2 c. new strawberries squashed
- 2 3 Oz strawberry Jell-O
- 3 c. little marshmallows
- 18.25 oz. strawberry cake blend + fixings to get ready cake blend
- Cool Whip

Directions:

1. Take your two cups of strawberries and pound them with a fork. Fill a lubed 9x13 in cake container. Sprinkle strawberry Jell-O over the highest point of the strawberries. At that point, sprinkle the marshmallows over the Jell-O. Plan cake blend, as indicated by bundle headings. Pour over the marshmallows. Heat at 350 degrees for 40-50 minutes or until cake tests are done. Let sit for around 15 minutes and afterward, run a blade around the outside of the cake. Flip onto a serving plate. Refrigerate. Present with Cool Whip. Store scraps in the fridge.

Nutrition: Calories: 250 Fiber: 2 Fats: 1

676. Lemon Blueberry Poke Cake

Preparation time: 30minutes
Cooking time: 60
Serving: 1

Ingredients:

- 1 box vanilla cake blend, in addition to fixings called for on the box
- 2 1/2 c. blueberries
- Juice of 1/2 lemon
- 1 tbsp. granulated sugar
- 1/2 c. whipped besting
- For the frosting and Toppings:
- 1 c. (2 sticks) spread, relaxed
- 2 (8-oz.) squares cream cheddar, mellowed
- 2 1/4 c. powdered sugar
- Get-up-and-go of 1 lemon
- Juice of 1/2 lemon
- 1 tsp. unadulterated vanilla concentrate
- Blueberries, for decorate

Directions:

1. Preheat stove to 350°. Line a 9"- x-13" dish with material paper and oil with cooking shower. Prepare cake as indicated by bundle guidelines. Let cool totally. Make the blueberry sauce: In a little pan over medium warmth, join blueberries, lemon squeeze, and sugar. Bring to a stew and cook until thick and jammy, 5 to 7 minutes. Expel from warm and fill a medium bowl. Let cool for 15 minutes, at that point overlay in a whipped beating. Make icing: In a huge bowl utilizing a hand blender, beat the spread and cream cheddar. Include powdered sugar, lemon get-up-and-go and squeeze, and vanilla and beat until smooth and soft. Utilizing the rear of a wooden spoon, jab openings all over cooled cake at that point pour blueberry blend on top. Spread icing on top at that point embellish cake with more blueberries.

Nutrition: Calories: 235 Fats: 2 Carbohydrates: 8

677. Easy No-Churn Funfetti Ice Cream Cake

Preparation time: 20 minutes
Cooking time: 10 minutes
Serving: 6

Ingredients:

- 2 cups heavy whipping cream, well chilled
- 2 teaspoons vanilla extract
- ¼ teaspoon salt
- 14 Oz sweetened condensed milk
- 2 Tablespoons unsalted butter, melted and cooled
- 1/2 cup rainbow sprinkles
- For the frosting:
- 1 cup semi-sweet chocolate chips
- 1 cup butter

Directions:

1. For the ice cream cake:
2. Place a large bowl or whisk attachment into the freezer to chill for about 10 minutes. Carefully pour condensed milk and melted butter into the bowl, then gently fold into the whipped cream. Then quickly fold in the sprinkles. Spread the ice cream in the prepared pan and freeze for several hours or until firm.

Nutrition: Calories: 260 Fats: 5 Carbohydrates: 9

678. No-Bake Strawberry Flapjacks

Preparation time: 10 minutes
Cooking time: 15 minutes
Servings: 1

Ingredients:

- 75g 3oz porridge oats
- 125g 4oz dates
- 50g 2oz strawberries
- 50g 2oz peanuts unsalted
- 50g 2oz walnuts
- 1 tablespoon coconut oil
- 2 tablespoons 100% cocoa powder or cacao nibs

Directions:

1. Place ingredients into a blender and process until they become a soft consistency. Spread the mixture onto a baking sheet or small flat tin. Press the mixture down and smooth it out. Cut it into 8 pieces, ready to serve. You can add an extra sprinkling of cocoa powder to garnish if you wish.

Nutrition: Calories: 182 Protein: 44.52 g Fat: 84.42 g Carbohydrates: 171.07 g

679. Warm Berries & Cream

Preparation time: 10 minutes
Cooking time: 15 minutes
Servings: 1

Ingredients:

- 250g 9oz blueberries
- 250g 9oz strawberries
- 100g 3½ oz. redcurrants
- 100g 3½ oz. blackberries
- 1 tablespoon honey
- 4 tablespoons fresh whipped cream

Directions:

1. Mix all ingredients into a bowl. Spoon a small amount of mixture and shape it into a ball. Roll the ball in a little cocoa powder and set aside. Repeat for the remaining mixture. Can be eaten straight away or stored in the fridge.

Nutrition: Calories: 115 Protein: 12.69 g Fat: 19.36 g Carbohydrates: 116.95 g

680. Chocolate Fondue

Preparation time: 10 minutes
Cooking time: 15 minutes

Servings: 1

Ingredients:

- 2 apples, peeled, cored and sliced
- 125g 4oz dark chocolate min (85% cocoa)
- 200g 7oz cherries
- 300g 11oz strawberries
- 100mls 3½ FL oz. double cream heavy cream

Directions:

1. In a fondue pot or saucepan, place the chocolate and cream then warm it until smooth and creamy. Serve in the fondue pot or transfer it to a serving bowl. Scatter the fruit on a serving dish ready to be dipped into the chocolate.

Nutrition: Calories: 352 Protein: 79.33 g Fat: 1110.22 g Carbohydrates: 241.8 g

681. Yogurt With Mixed Berries, Dark Chocolate, And Chopped Walnuts

Preparation time: 15 minutes
Cooking time: 0 minute
Servings: 2

Ingredients:

- ¼ cup (chopped) walnuts
- 2 teaspoons grated dark chocolate (85% cocoa solids)
- 1 cup Greek yogurt
- 1 cup mixed berries

Directions.

1. Add your preferred berries into a serving bowl. Pour the yogurt on top. Sprinkle with chocolate and walnuts.

Nutrition: Calories: 115 Protein: 12.12 g Fat: 19.9 g Carbohydrates: 57.84 g

682. Dark Chocolate Protein Truffles

Preparation time: 25 minutes
Cooking time: 0 minute
Servings: 8

Ingredients:

- ¼ cup (chopped) medjool dates
- ¼ cup coconut oil ¼ cup almond milk
- ¼ cup (or soy protein powder for vegans) vanilla whey protein powder
- 2 tablespoon honey or maple syrup
- ⅛ Cup steel-cut oats
- 1 tablespoon coconut flour
- 2 Dark chocolate bars, minimum 85% cacao

Directions:

1. Mix the protein powder, honey, almond milk, dates, coconut flour, and oats in a bowl, then mold the mixture into eight balls. Melt the coconut oil and chocolate over medium heat in a pot. Turn off the heat once melted and allow the chocolate to cool for about five to ten minutes. Dip each of the balls into the melted chocolate until well covered.
2. Place the balls in the freezer to harden.

Nutrition: Calories: 236 Protein: 3.06 g Fat: 18.45 g Carbohydrates: 16.58 g

683. Matcha Granola With Berries

Preparation time: 25 minutes
Cooking time: 0 minute
Servings: 2-4

Ingredients:

- 1 cup rolled oats
- 2 tablespoon coconut oil
- ½ cup (chopped) mixed nuts
- 1 tablespoon pumpkin seeds
- 1 tablespoon matcha powder
- 1 cup (halved or quartered) strawberries
- 1 tablespoon sesame seeds
- ½ teaspoon ground cinnamon
- 3 tablespoons honey or maple syrup
- 2/3 cup blueberries 1 ¾ cups greek yogurt

Directions:

1. Heat your oven to 325 degrees F. place parchment paper on a baking tray.
2. Heat the coconut oil under low heat until it melts. Put off the heat and stir in the seeds, nuts, and oats. Add the cinnamon, matcha powder, and honey, then mix thoroughly.
3. Evenly spread the granola mixture over the lined baking tray and place in the oven to bake for about fifteen minutes, until crisp and toasted – turn it 2 to 3 times.
4. Remove from the oven to cool, then store in an airtight container.
5. To serve, layer the yogurt in the serving dishes, then add the berries and granola.

Nutrition: Calories 250 Fat 2 g Cholesterol 0 mg Sodium 61 mg Carbohydrate 15 g Protein 1 g

684. Potato Cake With Carrots And Rice

Preparation time: 10 minutes
Cooking time: 39 minutes
Servings: 3

Ingredients:

- 1 tablespoon of chopped rosemary
- 250 g of potatoes 1 carrot 1/2 onion
- 50 g of rice Salt and pepper

Directions:

1. Pour the potatoes into a saucepan of cold water along with a pinch of salt, bring to a boil and cook for about 20 minutes or until the potatoes are tender.
2. For a while, cook the rice in abundant lightly salted water, and sauté the onions with a drizzle of oil and the chopped rosemary, adding later also the grated carrots once the onions have become transparent.
3. Spice with salt and pepper and cook for about 15 minutes to soften the vegetables.
4. Prepare the dough
5. Once everything is cooked, drain the rice, then drain the potatoes and mash them with a potato masher in a bowl. Then add the rice and the vegetables and mix well with a spoon.
6. Put the potato cakes in a pan.
7. Warm oil in a non-stick pan and cook your potato cakes for 3-4 minutes on each side over medium heat until they are beautifully golden, then serve immediately hot.

Nutrition: Calories 350 Total Fat 5.4 g Cholesterol 21 mg Sodium 73.5 mg Total Carbohydrate 18.8 g Dietary Fiber 1.5 g

685. Balsamic Plum Ice Cream

Preparation time: 30 minutes
Cooking time: 0 minute
Servings: 4

Ingredients:

- 9 medium-small plums, halved and destoned
- ¼ cup balsamic vinegar
- 1 tablespoon tapioca powder
- ½ cup maple syrup

- Ice Cream Mixture:
- 1 cup raw cashews, pre-soaked and strained
- 1 teaspoon pure vanilla extract
- 1 cup unsweetened dairy-free yogurt
- ½ cup maple syrup
- 1/8 teaspoon ground cardamom
- ¼ teaspoon salt

Directions:

1. Mix all plum mixture ingredients in a medium-small saucepan and place it to a light boil on medium-high heat. When the mixture begins to bubble, continue simmering for 10 minutes, stirring occasionally. Take it from heat and cool on a wire rack until the mixture is at room temperature.
2. Blend all ice cream mixture ingredients and the cooled plum mixture in a high power blender until smooth.
3. Transfer into a freezer-safe container and chill for 5-6 hours or overnight. Thaw out on the counter before serving and enjoy!

Nutrition: Calories 149 Fat 7g Carbohydrates 12.8g

686. Vanilla Cheesecake Popsicles

Preparation time: 30 minutes
Cooking time: 0 minute
Servings: 8

Ingredients:

- 1 vanilla bean, seeds scraped
- 8 oz. light cream cheese
- 1 teaspoon vanilla extract
- ½ cup low-fat milk
- ½ cup non-fat plain or vanilla Greek yogurt
- 2/3 cup powdered sugar

Directions:

1. In a food processor, put all the ingredients.
2. On the other hand, to scrape the seeds from the vanilla bean, cut through one layer vertically with a paring knife and then, using the back of the paring knife, scrape the inside of the bean to pull out the seeds. Put seeds to the mixture and discard the rest of the bean. Pulse until ingredients are completely blended. Divide the mixture into 8 Popsicle molds and add sticks. Freeze for 3-4 hours until solid.
3. To take off from molds, hold mold upside down under warm water and gently tug on the stick until the pop comes out.

Nutrition: Calories 118 Fat 6g Carbohydrates 10g Protein 1.8g

687. Mocha Truffle Cheesecake

Preparation time: 60 minutes
Cooking time: 55 minutes
Servings: 16

Ingredients:

- 6 tablespoons butter, melted
- 1 to 3 tablespoons instant coffee granules
- 1 package devil's food cake mix, regular size
- 1 large egg, room temperature
- Filling/Topping:
- 2 packages (8 oz. each) cream cheese, softened
- 1 can sweeten condensed milk
- 3 to 6 tablespoons instant coffee granules
- 3 large eggs, room temperature, lightly beaten
- 2 cups semisweet chocolate chips, cooled and melted
- 1 cup heavy whipping cream
- ½ teaspoon almond extract
- 1 tablespoon baking cocoa
- ¼ cup confectioners' sugar
- ¼ cup hot water

Directions:

1. In a large bowl, put and blend the cake mix, butter, egg, and coffee granules until well blended. Press onto the bottom and 2 inches up the sides of a greased 10 inch springform pan.
2. In another big bowl, whisk cream cheese until smooth. Beat in milk and melted chips. Dissolve coffee granulates in water. Add to cream cheese mixture. Add eggs. Beat on low speed just until combined. Pour into crust—place pan on a baking sheet.
3. Bake at 325° F until the center is almost set, about 50-55 minutes. Let it cool on a wire rack for 10 minutes. Gently run a knife around edge of pan to loosen. Cool 1 hour longer. Chill overnight
4. Just before serving, in a big bowl, whisk cream up to the soft peaks form. Batter in sugar and extract until stiff peaks form. Spread on the top of cheesecake. Dust with cocoa if desired. Refrigerate leftovers.

Nutrition: Calories 424 Fat 22g Carbohydrates 48g Protein 8g

688. Apple Berry Crumble Pies

Preparation time: 60 minutes
Cooking time: 50 minutes
Servings: 2

Ingredients:

- 2 medium firm apples cut into ¼ inch slices and peeled
- 1 pie crust
- 1 ½ cups frozen berries (tayberries, raspberries, and blueberries)
- 4 teaspoons tapioca flour
- 1 teaspoon cinnamon
- 1/3 cup light brown sugar
- 1/3 cup white sugar
- ¼ teaspoon salt
- Crumble Topping:
- ½ cup rolled oats
- 1/3 cup walnuts, chopped
- ½ cup all-purpose flour
- 6 tablespoons unsalted butter, cut into cubes
- ¼ cup granulated sugar
- ¼ cup light brown sugar

Directions:

1. Preheat oven to 375° F. Line two 4 inch ceramic ramekins with rolled out pie crust. Press crust into ramekins then repairs any tears with extra pie crust. Put in the freezer until ready to fill the pie.
2. For Filling: Use a medium saucepan to blend apples and brown sugar. Cook over medium-low temperature for about 10 minutes, until reduced and bubbling.
3. Drain most juice from apples, then put berries, tapioca flour, sugar, cinnamon, and salt and stir gently to combine. For the crumble: Mix together all ingredients except butter. Add butter and cut into the mixture with pastry cutter or fork until it resembles coarse crumbs. Take off the pie crust from the freezer and add apple-berry filling until ramekin is full. Add a generous handful of crumble topping by packing it on.
4. Bake for at least 25 minutes; the top of the pie should be starting to turn golden brown. Tent using a foil and bake for another 10 to 15 minutes until filling is bubbling. Pull out from the oven and let cool for 15 minutes. Serve warm and enjoy!

Nutrition: Calories 214 Fat 7.9g Carbohydrates 28g Protein 2.7g

689. Raspberry Scones

Preparation time: 5 minute
Cooking time: 20 minutes
Servings: 12

Ingredients:

- 3 Eggs, Beaten
- 1 ½ Cups Almond Flour
- ¾ Cup Raspberries, Fresh
- ½ Cup Stevia
- 2 Teaspoons Vanilla Extract, Pure
- 2 Teaspoons Baking Powder

Directions:

1. Set the oven to 375°F, and then line a baking sheet with parchment paper.
2. Take a bowl, mix your stevia, vanilla, eggs, almond flour, baking powder together, and whisking well.
3. Fold your raspberries in and create mounds with the batter on your baking sheet.
4. Bake for fifteen minutes before allowing cooling.

Nutrition: Calories: 133 Protein: 2 Grams Fat: 8 Grams Net Carbs: 4 Grams

690. Coconut Macaroons

Preparation time: 15 minute
Cooking time: 2 hours
Servings: 4-6

Ingredients:

- 1 ½ Cups Coconut, Shredded & Unsweetened
- ¾ Cup Coconut Milk, Full Fat
- 2 ¼ Teaspoons Stevia

Directions:

1. Mix all ingredients together, and tightly cover using plastic wrap.
2. Leave in the fridge for two hours before scooping into balls to serve.

Nutrition: Calories: 47 Protein: 0.4 Grams Fat: 5 Grams Net Carbs: 2 Grams

691. Banana Fat Bombs

Preparation time: 15 minute
Cooking time: 1 hour and 15 minutes
Servings: 12

Ingredients:

- 1 ¼ Cups Cream Cheese, Room Temperature
- 1 Tablespoon Banana Extract
- 6 Drops Liquid Stevia
- ¾ Cup Heavy Whipping Cream

Directions:

1. Line a baking sheet using parchment paper.
2. Beat your heavy cream, cream cheese, stevia, and banana extract until smooth and thick. This should take roughly five minutes.
3. Put mounds of the batter onto the baking sheet, freezing for an hour before serving.

Nutrition: Calories: 134 Protein: 3 Grams Fat: 12 Grams Net Carbs: 1 Gram

692. Almond Butter Fudge

Preparation time: 10 minute
Cooking time: 2 hours and 10 minutes
Servings: 12

Ingredients:

- 1 Cup Coconut Oil, Room Temperature
- 1 Cup Almond Butter
- 10 Drops Liquid Stevia
- ¼ Cup Heavy Whipping Cream
- Pinch Sea Salt

Directions:

1. Line a six by six-inch pan using parchment paper.
2. Get out a medium bowl, whisking your almond butter, heavy cream, coconut oil, stevia, and salt until smooth.
3. Spoon this mixture into a baking dish and refrigerate for two hours before slicing to serve.

Nutrition: Calories: 204 Protein: 3 Grams Fat: 22 Grams Net Carbs: 2 Grams

693. Vanilla Popsicles

Preparation time: 5 minute
Cooking time: 4 hours and 15 minutes
Servings: 2

Ingredients:

- 1 Cup Coconut, Shredded & Unsweetened
- 2 Cups Almond Milk
- 1 Cup Heavy Whipping Cream
- 1 Vanilla Bean, Halved Lengthwise

Directions:

1. Get out a saucepan, heating it over medium heat. Add together your vanilla bean, heavy cream, and almond milk.
2. Bring it all to a simmer, reducing to low heat. Let it simmer for five minutes, and then let it cool.
3. Take out your vanilla bean, and then scrape the seeds out and back into the mixture.
4. Divide between molds after stirring, allowing it to freeze for four hours before serving.

Nutrition: Calories: 166 Protein: 3 Grams Fat: 15 Grams Net Carbs: 2 Grams

694. Coffee Popsicles

Preparation time: 5 minute
Cooking time:
2 hours and 5 minutes
Servings: 2

Ingredients:

- 2 Cups Coffee, Cold
- ¾ Cup Coconut Cream
- 2 Teaspoons Swerve
- 2 Tablespoons Sugar-Free Chocolate Chips

Directions:

1. Start by blending all ingredients together and then pour into Popsicle molds.
2. Freeze for two hours before serving.

Nutrition: Calories: 105 Protein: 1 Gram Fat: 10 Grams Net Carbs: 2 Grams

695. Raspberry Popsicles

Preparation time: 5 minute
Cooking time: 2 hours
Servings: 4

Ingredients:

- ¼ Cup Sour Cream
- ¼ Cup Heavy Cream
- ½ Teaspoon Guar Gum
- 3 ½ Ounces Raspberries
- ½ Lemon, Juiced
- 1 Cup Coconut Milk
- ¼ Cup Coconut Oil
- 20 Drops Liquid Stevia

Directions:

1. Toss all ingredients in a blender and then push through a mesh strainer, discarding the raspberry seeds.
2. Pour the mixture into a mold, set in the freezer for about two hours before serving.

Nutrition: Calories: 65 Protein: 3 Grams Fat: 1 Gram Net Carbs: 8 Grams

696. Chocolate Bacon

Preparation time: 10 minute
Cooking time: 35 minutes
Servings: 2

Ingredients:

- 2 ¼ Tablespoons Coconut Oil
- 1 ½ Teaspoons Liquid Stevia
- 4 ½ Tablespoons Dark Chocolate, Unsweetened
- 12 Slices Bacon

Directions:

1. Set the oven to 425°F, then skewer your bacon using iron skewers. Arrange your bacon on a baking sheet.
2. Bake until crispy, which should take fifteen minutes.
3. Allow it to cool, getting out a saucepan, putting it over low heat. Melt your coconut oil before stirring in your chocolate.
4. Add in stevia, stirring again.
5. Coat your bacon in the mixture, letting it harden and dry before serving.

Nutrition: Calories: 258 Protein: 7 Grams Fat: 26 Grams Net Carbs: 0.5 Grams

697. Vanilla Pudding

Preparation time: 5 minute
Cooking time: 20 minutes
Servings: 2

Ingredients:

- Sea Salt as Needed
- 2 Egg Yolks, Large
- 1 Cup Heavy Cream, 36%
- 1 ½ Teaspoons Stevia
- 1 Teaspoon Arrowroot Flour
- ½ Teaspoon Vanilla Extract, Pure

Directions:

1. Get out a heavy-duty saucepan, add in egg yolks and whisk in the arrowroot flour, cream, vanilla, and stevia.
2. Season with salt and whisk again.
3. Put over medium heat, stirring until it begins to steam.
4. Lower the heat, continuing to stir for ten minutes.
5. Pour into four containers to cool before serving.

Nutrition: Calories: 135 Protein: 2 Grams Fat: 13 Grams Net Carbs: 2 Grams

698. Poppy Seed Cupcakes

Preparation time: 5 minute
Cooking time: 35 minutes
Servings: 4

Ingredients:

- ¾ Cup Blanched Almond Flour
- 1/3 cup Erythritol
- ¼ Cup Golden Flaxseed Meal
- 2 Tablespoons Poppy Seeds
- 1 Teaspoon Baking Powder
- 3 Eggs, Large
- ¼ Cup Salted Butter, Liquid
- ¼ Cup Heavy Cream
- 2 Lemons, Zested
- 3 Tablespoons Lemon Juice, Fresh
- 25 Drops Liquid Stevia
- 1 Teaspoon Vanilla Extract

Directions:

1. Set the oven to 350°F, then get out a bowl.
2. Mix your Erythritol, almond flour, and poppy seeds, adding in your flaxseed meal stir in melted butter and heavy cream, and then add in your egg. Mix well, pouring into cupcake molds.
3. Bake for twenty minutes, let cool before serving.

Nutrition: Calories: 229 Protein: 6 Grams Fat: 15 Grams Net Carbs: 14 Grams

699. Cheesy Shells

Preparation time: 40 minute
Cooking time: 20 minutes
Servings: 12

Ingredients:

- 3 ounces (85 g) cream cheese, softened
- ½ cup butter softened
- ¼ cup coconut flour
- Mini muffin cups

Directions:

1. Set the oven to 325°F.
2. Mix the cream cheese with the butter in a bowl until well combined then add the flour. Mix until well blended, then put it in the refrigerator to chill for 1 hour.
3. Roll the chilled dough into 24 1-inch (2.5 cm) balls then press each ball into each ungreased mini muffin cups to make a shallow shell. Fill the shell with your desired fillings and bake it for 20 minutes or until the crust is light brown.
4. Serve with your favorite toppings.

Nutrition: Calories: 90 Fat: 9.7g Carbs: 0.4g Protein 0.6g Cholesterol: 27mg Sodium: 97mg

700. Chewy Nutty Chocolate Cubes

Preparation time: 10 minute
Cooking time: 35 minutes
Servings: 12

Ingredients:

- 3.5 ounces (99 g) dark chocolate with a minimum of 80% cocoa solids
- 4 tablespoons butter or coconut oil
- ¼ cup peanut butter
- 1 pinch salt
- ½ teaspoon vanilla extract
- 1 teaspoon licorice powder or ground cinnamon or ground cardamom (green)
- 1.5 ounces (43 g) hazelnuts, finely chopped

Directions:

1. Put the chocolate and butter or coconut oil in a microwave-safe bowl and put it in the microwave to melt. Stir well to make sure it is combined then set aside.
2. Mix in the rest of the ingredients except the hazelnuts until well blended.
3. Grease, a dish, and line with parchment paper, then pour the batter into the dish.
4. Sprinkle the chopped hazelnuts over the batter then place it in the refrigerator to chill.
5. When it has hardened, cut it into cubes and store it in the refrigerator or freezer.
6. Serve cold.

Nutrition: Calories: 139 Fat: 11g Fiber: 2g Net carbs: 3g Protein: 4g

701. Creamy Vanilla Chocolate Bowls

Preparation time: 15 minute
Cooking time: 20 minutes
Servings: 16

Ingredients:

- Dark chocolate cake:

- 9 ounces (255 g) dark chocolate with a minimum of 70% cocoa solids
- 5 ounces (142 g) butter
- 5 eggs
- 1 pinch salt
- 1 teaspoon vanilla extract
- For Serving:
- 8 ounces (227 g) fresh raspberries or fresh blueberries
- 6 tablespoons lime juice
- 1 teaspoon vanilla extract
- 2 cups heavy whipping cream
- 4 ounces (113 g) pecans, chopped
- 1.5 ounces (43 g) roasted unsweetened coconut chips
- A spring form pan

Directions:

1. Set the oven to 325°F.
2. Grease a spring form pan with butter or coconut oil then line it with parchment paper.
3. Cut the chocolate and the butter into smaller pieces and melt it together in a heat-safe bowl in the microwave. Set aside to cool.
4. Break the eggs and remove the yolks from the egg whites and put them in separate bowls. Sprinkle some salt in the egg whites, then whisk until soft peaks form and keep aside.
5. Pour the vanilla extract into the yolks and whisk well.
6. Add the chocolate mixture to the yolks and mix well then fold in the egg whites. Place the mixture into the pan and bake for 15 to 20 minutes or until a toothpick inserted into the cake comes out clean.
7. To Serve:
8. Combine the berries, lime juice, and vanilla in a small bowl then set aside for 5 minutes.
9. Whisk the cream in a large bowl until soft peaks are formed.
10. Cut the chocolate cake into small bite sizes and share it into plates.
11. Put some berries and sprinkle some coconut flakes over it.
12. Serve immediately.

Nutrition: Calories: 356 Fat: 32g Net carbs: 8g Protein: 6g Fiber: 2g

702. Sweet Cinnamon And Pecan Bars

Preparation time: 15 minute
Cooking time: 35 minutes
Servings: 16

Ingredients:

- 1 cup pecans
- 1 teaspoon liquid stevia
- 1 teaspoon ground cinnamon
- ¼ teaspoon ground nutmeg
- 2 tablespoons melted butter
- 4 eggs
- ¼ cup cream cheese
- ¼ cup sour cream
- ¼ teaspoon vanilla extract
- 1 cup unsweetened almond milk
- Syrup:
- 1 cup fresh strawberries
- 1 teaspoon vanilla
- 2 tablespoons erythritol
- Brownie pan

Directions:

1. Set the oven to 350°F.
2. Put and blend the pecans in a food processor until it is smooth. Pour in the stevia, cinnamon, and nutmeg then process for 15 seconds. Pour the mixture into a bowl then mix in the melted butter. Pour it into a brownie pan with the divider removed, then press it so that it sits in the bottom of the pan.
3. In a separate bowl, whip the eggs using a mixer until it is fluffy then add the cream cheese in small quantities until the cream cheese is smooth. Mix in the sour cream, vanilla extract, and almond milk until it is smooth. Pour it over the crust in the pan and place the divider into the pan.
4. In the oven, place the pan then bake for at least 35 minutes or until an inserted toothpick comes out clean.
5. Make the syrup: Place a pot over medium heat and add strawberries, vanilla, and erythritol to the pot to cook for 5 minutes. Stir and crush some of the berries until syrup is formed. Cook until it thickens for 10 minutes.
6. Remove the cheesecake bars and set aside to cool for 1 hour. Pour the syrup over the bars and slice to serve.

Nutrition: Calories: 120 Fat: 10.3g Carbs: 3.1g Protein: 3.8g Cholesterol 165mg Sodium 63mg

703. Sweet Strawberry Sauce

Preparation time: 15 minute
Cooking time: 20 minutes
Servings: 4

Ingredients:

- 1 pint fresh strawberries
- 1 teaspoon vanilla
- ⅓ Cup liquid stevia

Directions:

1. Take off the stems of the strawberries, wash them well, cut them in half, or chop them roughly.
2. Mix the strawberries, vanilla, and stevia in a saucepan over medium-high heat. Stir occasionally. It will sizzle for a while and begin to juice. Continue stirring and mash the berries with a spatula to get syrup. Continue to cook for at least 15 minutes or until the sauce thickens.
3. Remove and pour ⅓ of the sauce in a blender. Puree it, then pour it unto the rest of the sauce. Store in a fridge.

Nutrition: Calories: 77 Fat: 5g Carbs: 8.1g Protein: 1.1g Cholesterol: 0mg Sodium: 1mg

SNACKS

704. Homemade Hummus & Celery

Preparation time: 15 minutes
Cooking time: 0 minutes
Servings: 4

Ingredients:

- Sticks of celery, cut into batons
- 175g (6oz) tinned chickpeas (garbanzo beans), drained
- 2 cloves of garlic, crushed
- 1 tablespoon fresh parsley, chopped
- 1 tablespoon tahini (sesame seed paste)
- Juice of 1 lemon
- 1 tablespoon olive oil

Directions:

1. Place the chickpeas (garbanzo beans) into a blender along with the garlic, tahini paste, and lemon juice. Process until it's smooth and creamy. Transfer the mixture to a serving bowl. Make a small well in the center of the dip and pour in the olive oil. Sprinkle with parsley. Serve the celery sticks on a plate alongside the hummus.

Nutrition: Calories: 140 kcal Protein: 5.57 g Fat: 8.18 g Carbohydrates: 12.2 g

705. Pizza Kale Chips

Preparation time: 15 minutes
Cooking time: 15 minutes
Servings: 6

Ingredients:

- 250g (9oz) kale, chopped into approx. 4cm (2inch)
- 50g (2oz) ground almonds
- 50g (2oz) Parmesan cheese
- 3 tablespoons tomato purée (tomato paste)
- ½ teaspoon mixed herbs
- ½ teaspoon oregano
- ½ teaspoon onion powder
- 2 tablespoons olive oil
- 100mls (3½ fl oz.) water

Directions:

1. Set all of the ingredients, except the KALE, into the food processor and process until finely chopped into a smooth consistency. Toss the kale leaves in the Parmesan mixture, coating it really well. Spread the kale out onto 2 baking sheets. Bake in the oven at 170C/325F for 15 minutes, until crispy.

Nutrition: Calories: 162 kcal Protein: 7.25 g Fat: 12.43 g Carbohydrates: 7.76 g

706. Rosemary & Garlic Kale Chips

Preparation time: 10 minutes
Cooking time: 25 minutes
Servings: 6

Ingredients:

- 250g (9oz) kale chips, chopped into approx 4cm (2inch)
- 2 sprigs of rosemary
- 2 clove of garlic
- 2 tablespoons olive oil
- Sea salt
- Freshly ground black pepper

Directions:

1. Warm the olive oil, rosemary, and garlic over low heat for 10 minutes. Take it out from the heat and set aside to cool. Take the rosemary and garlic out of the oil and discard them. Toss the kale leaves in the oil, making sure they are well coated. Season with salt and pepper. Spread the kale leaves onto 2 baking sheets and bake them in the oven at 170C/325F for 15 minutes, until crispy.

Nutrition: Calories: 75 kcal Protein: 2.91 g Fat: 5.9 g Carbohydrates: 3.98 g

707. Honey Chilli Nuts

Preparation time: 5 minutes
Cooking time: 20minutes
Servings: 20

Ingredients:

- 150g (5oz) walnuts
- 150g (5oz) pecan nuts
- 50g (2oz) softened butter
- 1 tablespoon honey
- ½ bird's-eye chilli, very finely chopped and de-seeded

Directions:

1. Preheat the oven to 180C/360F. Combine the butter, honey, and chilli in a bowl, then put the nuts and mix them well.
2. Spread the nuts into a baking sheet and roast it in the oven for 10 minutes, stirring once halfway through.
3. Take off from the oven and let them cool before eating.

Nutrition: Calories: 126 kcal Protein: 2.17 g Fat: 12.62 g Carbohydrates: 2.93 g

708. Pomegranate Guacamole

Preparation time: 15 minutes + Chilling time
Cooking time: 0 minutes
Servings: 4

Ingredients:

- Flesh of 2 ripe avocados
- Seeds from 1 pomegranate
- 1 bird's-eye chilli pepper, finely chopped
- ½ red onion, finely chopped
- Juice of 1 lime

Directions:

1. Place the avocado, onion, chill and lime juice into a blender and process until smooth. Stir in the pomegranate seeds. Chill before serving. Serve as a dip for chop vegetables.

Nutrition: Calories: 184 kcal Protein: 3.66 g Fat: 16.26 g Carbohydrates: 9.5 g

709. Tofu Guacamole

Preparation time: 10 minutes
Cooking time: 0minutes
Servings: 6

Ingredients:

- 225g (8oz) silken tofu
- 3 avocados
- 2 tablespoon fresh coriander (cilantro) chopped
- 1 bird's-eye chilli
- Juice of 1 lime

Directions:

1. Bring all of the ingredients into a food processor and blend a soft chunky consistency. Serve with crudités.

Nutrition: Calories: 278 kcal Protein: 9.56 g Fat: 23.32 g Carbohydrates: 13.14 g

710. Ginger & Turmeric Tea

Preparation time: 5
Cooking time: 10 minutes
Servings: 1

Ingredients:

- 2.5cm (1 inch) chunk fresh ginger root, peeled
- ¼ teaspoon turmeric
- 1 teaspoon of honey (optional)
- Hot water

Directions:

1. Make incisions in the piece of root ginger, without cutting all the way through. Place the ginger and turmeric in a cup and pour in hot water. Allow it to steep for 7 minutes. Put a teaspoon of honey if you want. Enjoy.

Nutrition: Calories: 106 kcal Protein: 6.5 g Fat: 6.09 g Carbohydrates: 6.39 g

711. Iced Cranberry Green Tea

Preparation time: 5 minutes
Cooking time: 0 minutes
Servings: 1

Ingredients:

- 150mls (5fl oz) light cranberry juice
- 100mls (3½ fl oz) green tea, cooled
- Squeeze of lemon juice
- A handful of crushed ice (optional)
- Sprig of mint

Directions:

1. Pour the green tea and cranberry into a glass and add a squeeze of lemon juice. Top it off with some ice and garnish with a mint leaf.

Nutrition: Calories: 13176 kcal Protein: 25.92 g Fat: 34.88 g Carbohydrates: 3240.95 g

712. Superfoods Raw Vegan Cookies

Preparation time: 10 minutes
Cooking time: 30 minutes
Servings: 4

Ingredients:

- ½ cup of coconut milk
- ½ cup of cocoa powder
- ½ cup of coconut oil
- ½ cup raw honey
- 2 cups finely shredded coconut
- 1 cup large flake coconut
- 2 tsp of ground vanilla bean
- ½ cup chopped almonds or chia seeds (optional)
- ½ cup almond butter (optional)

Directions:

1. Combine the coconut milk, cocoa powder, and coconut oil in a saucepan.
2. I think that it still counts as a raw dessert if you have to warm up the coconut milk and coconut oil.
3. So, warm up the mixture over medium heat because we want the coconut oil to melt and become liquid.

Nutrition: Calories: 212 Cal Fat: 14 g Carbs: 20 g Protein: 4 g

713. Raw Vegan Walnuts Pie Crust And Fresh Brownies

Preparation time: 10 minutes
Cooking time: 30 minutes
Servings: 4

Ingredients:

- 1½ cups walnuts
- 1 cup pitted dates
- 1½ tsp ground vanilla bean
- 2 tsp chia seeds
- 1/3 cup unsweetened cocoa powder
- Topping for raw brownies:
- 1/3 cup almond butter

Directions:

1. Place walnuts to a food processor or blender.
2. Mix until finely ground.
3. Add the vanilla, dates, and cocoa powder to the blender.
4. Mix well and optionally add a couple of drops of water at a time to make the mixture stick together.
5. That is an essential raw walnuts pie crust recipe.
6. You can use almonds or cashews.
7. If you need a pie crust, then spread it thinly in a 9-inch disc and add the filling.
8. If you want to make raw brownies, then transfer the mixture into a small dish and top with almond butter.

Nutrition: Calories: 320 Cal Fat: 32 g Carbs: 6 g Protein: 10 g

714. Raw Vegan Reese's Cups

Preparation time: 10 minutes
Cooking time: 35 minutes
Servings: 4

Ingredients:

- "Peanut" butter filling
- ½ cup sunflower seeds butter
- ½ cup almond butter
- 1 tbsp. raw honey
- 2 tbsp. melted coconut oil
- Superfoods chocolate part:
- ½ cup cacao powder
- 2 tbsp. raw honey
- 1/3 cup of coconut oil (melted)

Directions:

1. Mix the "peanut" butter filling ingredients.
2. Lay a spoonful of the mixture into each muffin cup.
3. Refrigerate.
4. Mix superfoods chocolate ingredients.
5. Put a spoonful of the superfood's chocolate mixture over the "peanut" butter mixture. Freeze!

Nutrition: Calories: 320 Cal Fat: 32 g Carbs: 6 g Protein: 10 g

715. Raw Vegan Coffee Cashew Cream Cake

Preparation time: 10 minutes
Cooking time: 35 minutes
Servings: 4

Ingredients:

- Coffee cashew cream
- 2 cups raw cashews
- 1 tsp of ground vanilla bean
- 3 tbsp melted coconut oil
- ¼ cup raw honey
- 1/3 cup solid coffee or triple espresso shot

Directions:

1. Mix all ingredients for the cream, pour it onto the crust, and refrigerate.
2. Garnish with coffee beans.

Nutrition: Calories: 80 Cal Fat: 5 g Carbs: 6 g Protein: 2 g

716. Raw Vegan Chocolate Cashew Truffles

Preparation time: 10 minutes
Cooking time: 35 minutes
Servings: 4

Ingredients:

- 1 cup ground cashews
- 1 tsp of ground vanilla bean

- ½ cup of coconut oil
- ¼ cup raw honey
- 2 tbsp. flax meal
- 2 tbsp. hemp hearts
- 2 tbsp. cacao powder

Directions:

1. Mix all ingredients and make truffles. Sprinkle coconut flakes on top.

Nutrition: Calories: 65 Cal Fat: 5 g Carbs: 3 g Protein: 1 g

717. Raw Vegan Double Almond Raw Chocolate Tart

Preparation time: 10 minutes
Cooking time: 35 minutes
Servings: 4

Ingredients:

- 1½ cups of raw almonds
- ¼ cup of coconut oil, melted
- 1 tbsp. raw honey or royal jelly
- 8 ounces dark chocolate, chopped
- 1 cup of coconut milk
- ½ cup unsweetened shredded coconut

Directions:

1. Crust:
2. Ground almonds then put melted coconut oil, raw honey, and blend.
3. Use spatula to spread the mixture into the tart or pie pan.
4. Filling:
5. Put the chopped chocolate in a bowl, heat coconut milk and place over chocolate and whip together.
6. Pour filling into tart shell.
7. Put in refrigerator.
8. Toast almond slivers chips and dust over the tart.

Nutrition: Calories: 139 Cal Fat: 10 g Carbs: 9 g Protein: 0 g

718. Raw Vegan Bounty Bars

Preparation time: 10 minutes
Cooking time: 35 minutes
Servings: 4

Ingredients:

- "Peanut" butter filling
- 2 cups desiccated coconut
- 3 tbsp. coconut oil, melted
- 1 cup of coconut cream, full fat
- 4 tbsp. of raw honey
- 1 tsp ground vanilla bean
- Pinch of sea salt
- Superfoods chocolate part:
- ½ cup cacao powder
- 2 tbsp. raw honey
- 1/3 cup of coconut oil (melted)

Directions:

1. Mix the coconut oil, coconut cream, honey, vanilla, and salt.
2. Pour over desiccated coconut and mix well.
3. Mold the coconut mixture into balls, small bars similar to bounty, and freeze.
4. Put the whole mixture into a tray, freeze, and cut into small bars.
5. Make superfoods chocolate mixture, warm it up, dip frozen coconut into the chocolate, put on a tray, and freeze again.

Nutrition: Calories: 68 Cal Fat: 2 g Carbs: 9 g Protein: 1 g

719. Raw Vegan Tartlets With Coconut Cream

Preparation time: 10 minutes
Cooking time: 35 minutes
Servings: 4

Ingredients:

- Pudding:
- 1 avocado
- 2 tbsp. coconut oil
- 2 tbsp. raw honey
- 2 tbsps. Cacao powder
- 1 tsp ground vanilla bean
- Pinch of salt
- ¼ cup almond milk, as needed
- Add ½ tsp cinnamon and whip again.
- Directions:
- Whisk all the ingredients in the food processor up to smooth and thick.
- Spread evenly into tartlet crusts.
- Optionally, add some goji berries above the pudding layer.
- Make the coconut cream, spread it above the pudding layer, and place it back in the fridge overnight.
- Serve with one blueberry on top of every tartlet.

Nutrition: Calories: 87 Cal Fat: 9 g Carbs: 1 g Protein: 1 g

720. Raw Vegan "Peanut" Butter Truffles

Preparation time: 10 minutes
Cooking time: 30 minutes
Servings: 4

Ingredients:

- 1 tbsp. sunflower seed butter
- 1 tbsp. coconut oil
- 1 tbsp. raw honey
- 1 tsp ground vanilla bean
- ¾ cup almond flour
- 1 tbsp. flaxseed meal
- Pinch of salt
- 1 tbsp. cacao butter
- Hemp hearts (optional)
- ¼ cup superfoods chocolate

Directions:

1. Blend until all ingredients are incorporated.
2. Roll the dough into 1-inch balls, put them on parchment paper then refrigerate for around 30 minutes (yield about 14 truffles).
3. Dip every truffle in the melted superfoods chocolate, one at the time.
4. Bring them back on the pan with parchment paper or coat them in cocoa powder or coconut flakes.

Nutrition: Calories: 73 Cal Fat: 5 g Carbs: 7 g Protein: 0 g

721. Raw Vegan Chocolate Pie

Preparation time: 10 minutes
Cooking time: 25 minutes
Servings: 4

Ingredients:

- Crust:
- 2 cups almonds, soaked overnight
- 1 cup pitted dates, soaked overnight
- 1 cup chopped dried apricots
- 1½ tsp ground vanilla bean

- 2 tsp chia seeds
- One banana
- Filling:
- 4 tbsp. raw cacao powder
- 3 tbsp. raw honey
- 2 ripe avocados
- 2 tbsp. organic coconut oil
- 2 tbsp. almond milk (if needed)

Directions:

1. Put almonds and banana to a food processor or blender.
2. Mix until it forms a thick ball.
3. Place the vanilla, dates, and apricot chunks to the blender.
4. Mix well and optionally put a couple of drops of water at a time to make the mixture stick together.
5. Spread in a 10-inch dis.
6. Blend filling ingredients in a blender and add almond milk if necessary.
7. Add filling to the crust and refrigerate.

Nutrition: Calories: 278 Cal Fat: 21 g Carbs: 19 g Protein: 0 g

722. Raw Vegan Chocolate Walnut Truffles

Preparation time: 10 minutes
Cooking time: 35 minutes
Servings: 4
Ingredients:

- 1 cup ground walnuts
- 1 tsp cinnamon
- ½ cup of coconut oil
- ¼ cup raw honey
- 2 tbsp. chia seeds
- 2 tbsp. cacao powder

Directions:

1. Mix all the ingredients needed and make truffles.
2. Coat with cinnamon, coconut flakes, and almonds.

Nutrition: Calories: 130 Cal Fat: 11 g Carbs: 6 g Protein: 2 g

723. Raw Vegan Carrot Cake

Preparation time: 10 minutes
Cooking time: 35 minutes
Servings: 4
Ingredients:

- Crust:
- Four carrots, chopped
- 1½ cups oats
- ½ cup dried coconut
- 2 cups dates
- 1 tsp cinnamon
- ½ tsp nutmeg
- 1½ cups cashews
- 2 tbsp. coconut oil
- Juice from 1 lemon
- 2 tbsp. raw honey
- 1 tsp ground vanilla bean
- Water, as needed

Directions:

1. Put all crust ingredients to the blender.
2. Mix well and optionally put a couple of drops of water at a time to make the mixture stick together.
3. Press in a small pan.
4. Remove and put on a plate, and freeze.
5. Blend frosting ingredients in a blender and add water if necessary.
6. Add frosting to the crust and refrigerate.

Nutrition: Calories: 60 Cal Fat: 3 g Carbs: 10 g Protein: 1 g

724. Frozen Raw Blackberry Cake

Preparation time: 10 minutes
Cooking time: 45 minutes
Servings: 4
Ingredients:

- Crust:
- 3⁄4 cup shredded coconut
- Dried dates soaked in hot water, drained
- 1/3 cup pumpkin seeds
- 1⁄4 cup of coconut oil
- Middle filling
- Coconut whipped cream
- Cream recipes.
- Top filling:
- 1 pound of frozen blackberries
- 3-4 tbsp. raw honey
- 1⁄4 cup of coconut cream
- 2 egg whites

Directions:

1. Grease the cake tin using coconut oil and mix all ingredients in the blender until it gets a sticky ball.
2. Press the bottom mixture in a cake tin then freeze.
3. Make Coconut Whipped Cream.
4. Process berries then add honey, coconut cream, and egg whites.
5. Put middle filling - Coconut Whipped Cream in the tin and spread evenly.
6. Freeze.
7. Put top filling - berries mixture-in the tin, spread, decorate with blueberries and almonds, and return to freezer.

Nutrition: Calories: 12 Cal Fat: 0 g Carbs: 3 g Protein: 0 g

725. Raw Vegan Chocolate Hazelnuts Truffles

Preparation time: 10 minutes
Cooking time: 30 minutes
Servings: 4
Ingredients:

- 1 cup ground almonds
- 1 tsp ground vanilla bean
- ½ cup of coconut oil
- ½ cup mashed pitted dates
- 12 whole hazelnuts
- 2 tbsp. cacao powder

Directions:

1. Blend all ingredients and make truffles with one whole hazelnut in the middle.

Nutrition: Calories: 35 Fat: 3 g Carbs: 1 g Protein: 1 g

726. Raw Vegan Chocolate Cream Fruity Cake

Preparation time: 10 minutes
Cooking time: 45 minutes
Servings: 4
Ingredients:

- 1 avocado
- 2 tbsp. raw honey
- 2 tbsp. coconut oil
- 2 tbsp. cacao powder
- 1 tsp ground vanilla bean
- Pinch of sea salt
- ¼ cup of coconut milk

- 1 tbsp. coconut flakes
- Fruits:
- 1 chopped banana
- 1 cup pitted cherries.

Directions:

1. Arrange the crust and press it at the bottom of the pan.
2. Mix all chocolate cream ingredients, fold in the fruits, and pour in the crust.
3. Whip the top layer, spread, and sprinkle with cacao powder.
4. Refrigerate.

Nutrition: Calories: 68 Cal Fat: 3 g Carbs: 9 g Protein: 0 g

727. Monkey Trail Mix

Preparation time: 1 hour
Cooking time: 30 minutes.
Servings: 5

Ingredients:

- 1teaspoon of vanilla extract
- 3tablespoons of coconut oil
- ⅓ Cup of coconut sugar
- 5 oz. of dried banana
- ½ cup of dark chocolate chips
- 1 cup of coconut flakes, unsweetened
- 1 cup of cashews, raw and unsalted
- 2 cups of walnuts, raw and unsalted

Directions:

1. Add the coconut oil, vanilla extract, coconut sugar, coconut flakes, and nuts into a crockpot.
2. Mix to combine, then cook on high for 1 hour. Stir occasionally to make sure the coconut flakes do not burn.
3. Turn the crockpot temperature to low and continue to cook for another 30 minutes.
4. Pour the mixture out onto parchment paper and allow to dry completely.
5. Allow the mixture to cool before adding the banana and chocolate chips.
6. Store in an airtight container and enjoy it when hungry.
7. Use a combination of raw, unsalted nuts to extend the recipe—this can include Brazil nuts or almonds.

Nutrition: Calories: 151; Total Fat: 10g;Cholesterol: 0mg;Sodium: 16mg; Carbohydrate: 13g; Dietary Fiber: 2g; Sugar: 9g; Protein: 4g

728. Granola With Quinoa

Preparation time: 30 minutes
Cooking time: 20 minutes
Servings: 6

Ingredients:

- 1 pinch of salt
- ¼ cup of maple syrup
- 3 ½ tablespoons of coconut oil
- 1tablespoon coconut sugar
- 1 cup of rolled oats
- 2 cups of almonds, raw and unsalted
- ½ cup of quinoa, uncooked

Directions:

1. Preheat your oven to 340°F and line a baking tray with parchment paper. In a large mixing bowl, add the salt, sugar, oats, almonds, and quinoa and set aside.
2. In a small pan at medium heat, put the maple syrup and coconut oil. Using a whisk, stir regularly until combined, then remove from the heat. Pour the syrup over the mixed nuts and quinoa and give it a thorough stir. Place the mixture onto the baking tray and, using a spatula, spread the ingredients evenly over the dish.
3. Put in the oven and bake for 20 minutes. Remove the tray, give it a shake, and return to the oven to bake for another 10 minutes or until the mixture has turned a golden, brown color.
4. Allow to cool, then serve.
5. As an alternative, you may use muscovado or brown sugar instead of coconut sugar.
6. Feel free to alternate the nut mixture depending on your tastes. You may include cashews, brazil, and pine nuts. Change the maple syrup for agave nectar as another alternative.

Nutrition: Calories: 241; Total Fat: 6g; Fat: 2g; Cholesterol: 95mg; Sodium: 158 mg; Carbohydrate: 33g; Dietary Fiber: 4g Sugar: 1g; Protein: 15g

729. Med-Styled Olives

Preparation time: 10 minutes
Cooking time: 10 minutes
Servings: 6

Ingredients:

- Pinch of salt
- 1 pinch of black pepper
- 1 ½ tablespoon of coriander seeds
- 1 tablespoon of extra-virgin olive oil
- 1 lemon
- 1 oz. of Kalamata olives
- 7 oz. of green queen olives

Directions:

1. Using a pestle and mortar, crush well the coriander seeds and set aside.
2. Using a sharp knife, cut long, thin slices of lemon rind and place it into a bowl with both the green queen and Kalamata olives.
3. Squeeze the juice of one lemon over the top of the olives and add the olive oil.
4. Add the salt, pepper, and coriander seeds, then stir and serve.
5. The longer you allow the olives to rest in the marinade, the more delicious they will taste.

Nutrition: Calories: 477; Total Fat: 9g; Cholesterol: 61mg; Sodium: 795mg; Carbohydrate: 60g; Dietary Fiber: 3g; Sugar: 5g; Protein: 35g

730. Roasted Chickpeas

Preparation time: 10 minutes
Cooking time: 40 minutes
Servings: 6

Ingredients:

- 1 pinch of salt
- 1 pinch of black pepper
- 1pinch of garlic powder
- 1 teaspoon of dried oregano
- 2tablespoons of extra-virgin olive oil
- Juice of 1 lemon
- 2 teaspoons of red wine vinegar
- 2 15 oz. canned chickpeas

Directions:

1. Set the oven to 425°F and put a sheet of parchment paper onto a baking tray.
2. Drain and rinse the chickpeas, then pour them onto the baking tray. Spread them evenly. Place them in the oven and roast them for 10 minutes. Remove from the oven, give the plate a firm shake, then return the plate to the oven for a further 10 minutes. Once roasted, take off from the oven and set aside. Add the remaining ingredients into a mixing bowl. Combine well, then add the roasted chickpeas. Using a spatula ensures that the

chickpeas are evenly coated. Return the chickpeas into the oven and allow to roast for 10 minutes. Take them off from the oven, allow to cool, then serve.

3. Keep checking on the chickpeas while they roast to ensure they do not burn or require longer cooking time.

Nutrition: Calories: 323; Total fat: 15.6g; Cholesterol: 4.9g; Sodium: 333mg; Carbohydrate: 39.5g; Dietary Fiber: 5.3g; Sugar: 11.5g; Protein: 10.4g

731. Baked Root Veg Crisps

Preparation time: 10 minutes
Cooking time: 30 minutes
Servings: 2

Ingredients:

- 1pinch of salt
- 1pinch of black pepper
- 1 pinch of ground cumin
- 1 pinch of dried thyme
- 1 teaspoon of garlic powder
- 2 tablespoons of extra-virgin olive oil
- 1parsnip, finely sliced
- 1 turnip, finely sliced
- 2 red beet, finely sliced
- 1 golden beet, finely sliced
- Ingredients for the dipping sauce:
- 1 pinch of salt
- 1 pinch of black pepper
- 6 tablespoons of buttermilk
- 1 cup of Greek yoghurt
- 1 teaspoon of honey
- 1 teaspoon of lemon zest
- 2 cloves of garlic, minced
- 2 tablespoons of fresh, flat-leaf parsley, minced

Directions:

1. Mix all dipping sauce ingredients into a medium mixing bowl, using a whisk to ensure that the sauce is evenly combined. Set aside in the refrigerator for when needed.
2. Preheat your oven to 400°F.
3. In a small mixing bowl, combine the seasoning, herbs, and olive oil.
4. Rinse your root vegetables and dry them off using a kitchen towel. Remove all the root vegetable skins, and gently use a mandoline slicer, slice the vegetables into thin crisps.
5. Brush each side of the crisp with the olive oil and then place onto an oven-proof wire rack. Place the wire rack onto a baking sheet and put this into the oven to bake for 20 minutes or until the vegetables have crisped up.
6. Allow to cool or enjoy them warm with the sauce.
7. If you notice that a few crisps are turning brown during baking and the time has not ended, remove them from the oven and return the rest to finish baking.

Nutrition: Calories: 457; Total Fat: 31g; Cholesterol: 0mg; Sodium: 478mg; Carbohydrate: 33g; Dietary Fiber: 8g; Sugar: 7g; Protein: 12g

732. Coconut Orange Creamsicle Fat Bombs

Preparation time: 2-3 hours
Cooking time: 0 minutes
Servings: 10

Ingredients:

- ½ cup of coconut oil
- ½ cup heavy whipping cream
- ¼ cup cream cheese
- 1 tsp orange-vanilla Mio
- 10 drops liquid Stevia

Directions:

1. Add the coconut oil to a blender. Pulse it until smooth.
2. Add the whipped cream. Pulse until combined.
3. Add the cream cheese. Pulse it until smooth.
4. Add the orange Milo and Stevia. Pulse it until smooth.
5. Spoon the mixture into a silicon tray mold or ice cube tray. Freeze 3 hours.
6. Pop-out to eat. Store the uneaten bombs in a bag in the freezer.

Nutrition: Calories: 176 Fat: 20g Carbs: 0.7g Protein: 0.8g Fiber: 0g Net Carbs: 0.7g

733. Corndog Muffins

Preparation time: 10 minutes
Cooking time: 15 minutes
Servings: 20

Ingredients:

- ½ cup blanched almond flour
- ½ cup flaxseed meal
- 1 Tbsp. psyllium husk powder
- 3 Tbsp. swerve sweetener
- ¼ tsp salt
- ¼ tsp baking powder
- ¼ cup melted butter
- 1 egg
- ¼ cup of coconut milk
- ⅓ Cup sour cream
- 3 all-beef hot dogs

Directions:

1. Preheat oven to 375F
2. In a bowl, add the almond flour, flaxseed, husk powder, granulated sweetener, salt, and baking powder. Whisk together.
3. In a separate bowl, combine the egg, coconut milk. Whisk together. Add the butter. Stir until combined. Add the sour cream. Stir until combined.
4. Add the dry ingredients to the wet ingredients. Stir until a smooth batter form.
5. Grease a 12 mini muffin tin.
6. Slice the hot dogs into 4 sections.
7. Fill the muffin cup halfway. Add the sliced hot dog to the batter.
8. Bake 12 minutes.
9. Then broil 1-2 minutes until golden brown. Serve.

Nutrition: Calories: 78.5 Fat: 6.8g Carbs: 2.1g Protein: 2.4g Fiber: 1.5g Net Carbs: 0.7g

734. Layered Fried Queso Blanco

Preparation time: 10 minutes
Cooking time: 10 minutes
Servings: multiple

Ingredients:

- ½ cup Queso Blanco
- 1½ Tbsp. olive oil
- Pinch red pepper flakes or salt and pepper

Directions:

1. Cut the cheese into cubes. Chill in the freezer as you heat the oil.
2. In a skillet, heat the olive oil. Once the pan is hot, add the cubes of cheese.
3. As it cooks, it will melt. Once it is golden brown on one side, flip it over. Press down against the cheese to flatten it slightly and push out the oil. When each side is golden brown, tilt the edges against the pan and cook those until golden brown. It will seal the cheese into a square.

4. Remove from pan. Place on paper towel. Pat lightly. Slice into cubes again.
5. Sprinkle red pepper flakes or salt and pepper over the cubes. Serve immediately.

Nutrition: Calories: 525 Fat: 43g Carbs: 4g Protein: 30g Fiber: 2g Net Carbs: 2g

735. Raspberry Lemon Popsicles

Preparation time: 10-15 minutes
Cooking time: 2 hours
Servings: 6

Ingredients:

- 1 cup of raspberries
- Juice from ½ a lemon
- ¼ cup of coconut oil
- 1 cup of coconut milk
- ¼ cup sour cream
- ¼ cup heavy cream
- ½ tsp Guar Gum
- 20 drops liquid Stevia

Directions:

1. Combine all the ingredients in a blender. Pulse it until smooth. Strain the liquid.
2. Pour mixture into Popsicle molds. Freeze 2 hours.
3. If stuck, run the mold under hot water briefly.

Nutrition: Calories: 150.5 Fat: 16.0g Carbs: 3.3g Protein: 0.5 Fiber: 1.3g Net Carbs: 2.0g

736. Neapolitan Fat Bombs

Preparation time: 15-30 minutes
Cooking time: 1 hour
Servings: 24

Ingredients:

- ½ cup butter
- ½ cup of coconut oil
- ½ cup sour cream
- ½ cup cream cheese
- 2 Tbsp. liquid stevia
- 2 Tbsp. cocoa powder
- 1 tsp pure vanilla extract
- 2 strawberries

Directions:

1. In a blender, add the butter, coconut oil, sour cream, cream cheese. Pulse until smooth.
2. Set out 3 bowls. Add cocoa powder to a bowl. Add vanilla extract to another bowl. Add strawberries to a bowl. Mash them.
3. Pour the mixture evenly between the 3 bowls. Stir each mixture until smooth.
4. Pour vanilla mixture into the bottom of the silicon mold or ice cube tray. Freeze for 30 minutes. Place other bowls in the fridge. Pour the chocolate layer in the silicon mold or ice cube tray. Freeze 30 minutes. Pour the strawberry layer into the silicone mold or ice cube tray. Freeze 2 hours. Ready to serve.

Nutrition: Calories: 102.2 Fat: 10.9g Carbs: 0.6g Protein: 0.6g Fiber: 0.2g Net Carbs: 0.4g

737. No Bake Chocolate Peanut Butter Balls

Preparation time: 20 minutes
Cooking time: 0 minutes
Servings: 8

Ingredients:

- ¼ cup of cocoa powder
- 4 Tbsp. Peanut Butter Fit Powder
- 5 tbsp. shelled hemp seeds
- 2 tbsps. Heavy cream
- ½ cup of coconut oil
- 1 tsp pure vanilla extract
- 28 drops liquid stevia
- ¼ cup unsweetened shredded coconut

Directions:

1. In a bowl, crush the hemp seeds. Add the cocoa powder, fit powder. Stir. Add the coconut oil. Stir together until a paste form.
2. Stir in the heavy cream, liquid stevia, and vanilla. Keep mixing until it forms a dough consistency.
3. Pinch off dough to make 1-inch round balls. Roll in unsweetened shredded coconut. Chill 30 minutes. Serve.

Nutrition: Calories: 208.3 Fat: 20.0g Carbs: 3.1g Protein: 4.4g Fiber: 2.4g Net Carbs: 0.8g

738. Kale Pesto Hummus

Preparation time: 5 minutes
Cooking time: 0 minutes
Servings: 12

Ingredients:

- 15 ounces Chickpeas, drained and liquid reserved
- .25 cup reserved chickpea liquid
- .5teaspoon Sea salt
- .5cup Tahini paste
- 2cloves Garlic, minced
- 2.5tablespoons Lemon juice
- .33cup extra virgin olive oil
- .5teaspoon Black pepper, ground
- 2cups Kale, chopped and leaves packed
- 2tablespoons Pine nuts
- 1.25cups Basil leaves, packed
- 4cloves Garlic, minced
- .25cup extra virgin olive oil

Directions:

1. Into a food processor, add the basil, kale, pine nuts, and four cloves of minced garlic. Pulse until the leaves and garlic are finely chopped.
2. Pour in the olive oil, and once again pulse until smooth. Remove the pesto from the bowl of the food processor and set aside.
3. Into the empty food processor, add the remaining ingredients to assemble the hummus, pulsing until creamy. Add in the prepared pesto, and pulse just until the two are combined.
4. Transfer the pesto hummus to a serving bowl or store in the fridge.

Nutrition Facts: Energy (calories): 594 kcal; Protein: 9.69 g; Fat: 44.92 g; Carbohydrates: 43.25 g

739. Parsley Hummus

Preparation time: 7 minutes
Cooking time: 0 minutes
Servings: 6

Ingredients:

- 15 ounces Chickpeas, drained and rinsed
- 1 cup Curly parsley, stems removed
- .5 teaspoon Sea salt
- .5 cup Soy milk, unsweetened
- 3 teaspoons extra virgin olive oil
- 1 tablespoon Lime juice
- .5 teaspoons Red pepper flakes
- .25 teaspoon Black pepper, ground
- 2 tablespoons Pine nuts

- 2 tablespoons sesame seeds, toasted

Directions:

1. In the blender, pulse the parsley and toasted sesame seeds until it forms a fine powdery texture. Mizzle in the extra virgin olive oil while you continue to pulse until it is smooth.
2. Add the chickpeas, lime juice, and seasonings to the food processor and pulse while slowly adding in the soy milk. Continue to pulse the parsley hummus until it is smooth and creamy.
3. Adjust the seasonings to your preference and then serve or refrigerate the hummus.

Nutrition Facts: Energy (calories): 209 kcal; Protein: 6.62 g; Fat: 16.18 g; Carbohydrates: 12.49 g

740. Edamame Hummus

Preparation time: 7minutes
Cooking time: 0 minutes
Servings: 10

Ingredients:

- 2 cups Edamame, cooked and shelled
- 1 teaspoon Sea salt
- 1 tablespoon extra-virgin olive oil
- .25 cup Tahini paste
- .25 cup Lemon juice
- 3 cloves Garlic, minced
- .25 teaspoon Black pepper, ground

Directions:

1. Add the cooked edamame and remaining ingredients to a blender or food processor and mix on high until it forms a creamy and completely smooth mixture. Taste it then add seasoning base on your preference.
2. Serve the hummus immediately with your favorite vegetables or store in the fridge.

Nutrition: Energy (calories): 589 kcal; Protein: 37.16 g; Fat: 30.44 gl Carbohydrates: 50.34 g

741. Edamame Guacamole

Preparation time: 7 minutes
Cooking time: 0 minutes
Servings: 6

Ingredients:

- 1 cup Edamame, cooked and shelled
- 1 Avocado pitted and halved
- .5 cup Red onion, diced
- .25 cup Cilantro, chopped
- 1 Jalapeno, minced
- 2 cloves Garlic, minced
- 2 tablespoons Lime juice
- 3 tablespoons Water
- .5 teaspoon Lime zest
- 2 Roma tomato, diced
- .125 teaspoon Cumin
- .5 teaspoon Sea salt

Directions:

1. Into a blender, put all the ingredients, except for the diced tomato, onion, and jalapeno. Blend the tomato mixture on high speed until it is smooth and creamy, making sure that the edamame has been completely blended.
2. Adjust the seasoning to your preference and then transfer the guacamole to a serving bowl. Stir in the tomato, onion, and jalapeno. Place the bowl in the fridge, allowing it to chill for at least thirty minutes before serving.

Nutrition: Energy (calories): 584 kcal; Protein: 23.94 g; Fat: 38.13 g; Carbohydrates: 49.58 g

742. Eggplant Fries With Fresh Aioli

Preparation time: 5 minutes
Cooking time: 25 minutes
Servings: 4

Ingredients:

- 2 Eggplants
- .25 teaspoon Black pepper, ground
- 2 tablespoons extra virgin olive oil
- 1 tablespoon Cornstarch
- 1 tablespoon Basil, dried
- .25 teaspoon Garlic powder
- .5 teaspoon Sea salt
- .5 cup Mayonnaise, made with olive oil
- 1 teaspoon Garlic, minced
- 1 tablespoon Basil, fresh, chopped
- 1 teaspoon Lemon juice
- .5 teaspoon Chipotle, ground
- .25 teaspoon Sea salt

Directions:

1. Begin by preheating your oven to Fahrenheit four-hundred and twenty-five degrees. Place a wire cooking/cooling rack on a baking sheet.
2. Remove the peel from the eggplants and then slice them into rounds, each about three-quarters of an inch thick. Slice the rounds into wedges one inch in width.
3. Add the eggplant wedges to a large bowl and toss them with the olive oil. Once coated, add the pepper, cornstarch, dried basil, garlic powder, and sea salt, tossing until evenly coated.
4. Arrange the eggplant wedges on top of the wire rack and set the baking sheet in the oven, allowing the fries to cook for fifteen to twenty minutes.
5. Meanwhile, prepare the aioli. To do this, add the remaining ingredients into a small bowl and whisk them together to combine. Cover the bowl of aioli and allow it to chill it in the fridge until the fries are ready to be served.
6. Remove the fries from the oven immediately upon baking, or allow them to cook under the broiler for an additional three to four minutes for extra crispy fries. Serve immediately with the aioli.

Nutrition: Energy (calories): 632 kcal; Protein: 11.64 g; Fat: 37.26 g; Carbohydrates: 73.98 g

743. Eggplant Caponata

Preparation time: 5 minutes
Cooking time: 25minutes
Servings: 4

Ingredients:

- 1 pound Eggplant, sliced into 1.5-inch cubes
- 1 Bell pepper, diced
- .5 cup Green and black olives, chopped
- .25 cup Capers
- 1 teaspoon Sea salt
- 4 Garlic, minced
- 1 Red onion, diced
- 15 ounces diced tomatoes
- 4 tablespoons extra virgin olive oil, divided
- .25 teaspoon Black pepper, ground -
- .25 cup Parsley, chopped

Directions:

1. Preheat your oven to Fahrenheit four-hundred degrees and line a baking sheet with kitchen parchment.

2. Toss the eggplant cubes in half of the olive oil and then arrange them on the baking sheet, sprinkling the sea salt over the top. Allow the eggplant to roast until tender, about twenty minutes.
3. Meanwhile, add the remaining olive oil into a large skillet along with the red onions, bell pepper, diced tomatoes, and garlic. Sauté the vegetables until tender, about ten minutes.
4. Add the roasted eggplant, capers, olives, and black pepper to the skillet, continuing to cook together for five minutes so that the flavors meld.
5. Remove the skillet from the heat, top it off with parsley, and serve it with crusty toast.

Nutrition: Energy (calories): 755 kcal; Protein: 29.98 g; Fat: 29.03 g; Carbohydrates: 116.59 g

744. Buckwheat Crackers

Preparation time: 5 minutes
Cooking time: 45 minutes
Servings: 12

Ingredients:

- 2 cups Buckwheat groats
- .75 cup Flaxseeds, ground
- .33 cup Sesame seeds
- 2 Sweet potatoes, medium, grated
- .33 cup extra virgin olive oil
- 1 cup Water
- 1 teaspoon Sea salt

Directions:

1. Soak the buckwheat groats in water for at least four hours before preparing the crackers. Once done soaking, drain off the water.
2. Preheat the oven to a temperature of Fahrenheit three-hundred and fifty degrees, prepare a baking sheet, and set aside kitchen parchment and plastic wrap.
3. In a kitchen bowl, combine the ground flaxseeds with the warm water, allowing the seeds to absorb the water and form a substance similar to gelatin. Add the buckwheat groats and other remaining ingredients.
4. Spread the cracker dough onto a sheet of kitchen parchment and cover it with a sheet of plastic wrap. Use a rolling pin on top of the plastic wrap (so that it doesn't stick) and roll out the buckwheat cracker dough until it is thin.
5. Peel the plastic wrap off the crackers and transfer the dough-coasted sheet of kitchen parchment to the prepared baking sheet. Allow it to partially bake for fifteen minutes and then remove the tray from the oven.
6. Reduce the oven temperature to Fahrenheit three-hundred degrees. Use a pizza cutter and slice the crackers into squares, approximately two inches in width. Return the crackers to the oven until they are crispy and dry, about thirty-five to forty minutes.
7. Remove the crackers from the oven, allowing them to cool completely before storing them in an air-tight container.

Nutrition: Energy (calories): 91 kcal; Protein: 2.38 g; Fat: 6.27 g; Carbohydrates: 7.37 g

745. Matcha Protein Bites

Preparation time: 5 minutes
Cooking time: 0 minutes
Servings: 12

Ingredients:

- .25 cup Almond butter
- 2 teaspoons Matcha powder
- 1-ounce Soy protein isolate
- .5 cup Rolled oats
- 1 tablespoon Chia seeds
- 2 teaspoons Coconut oil
- 1 tablespoon Honey
- .125 teaspoon Sea salt

Directions:

1. In a blender, blend all of the matcha protein bite ingredients until it forms a mixture similar to wet sand that will stick together when squished between your fingers.
2. Divide the mixture into twelve equal portions. You can do this by eye while estimating, or you can use a digital kitchen scale if you want the portions to be exact. Roll every portion between the palms of your hands to form balls.
3. Chill the bites in the fridge for up to two weeks.

Nutrition: Energy (calories): 34 kcal; Protein: 0.37 g; Fat: 2.88 g; Carbohydrates: 2.74 g

746. Chocolate-Covered Strawberry Trail Mix

Preparation time: 5 minutes
Cooking time: 0 minutes
Servings: 10

Ingredients:

- 1 cup Freeze-dried strawberries
- .66 cup Dark chocolate chunks
- 1 cup Walnuts, roasted
- .25 cup Almonds, roasted
- .25 cup Cashews, roasted

Directions:

1. Mix all of the trail mix ingredients in a bowl, store it in a large glass jar or divide each serving into its transportable plastic bag. Store for up to one month.

Nutrition: Energy (calories): 74 kcal; Protein: 1.69 g; Fat: 7 g; Carbohydrates: 2.32 g

747. Vegan Tofu Omelette

Preparation time: 5 minutes
Cooking time: 15 minutes
Servings: 1

Ingredients:

- 6 ounces silken tofu
- 1 teaspoon Tahini (optional)
- 1 tablespoon Cornstarch
- 1 tablespoon Nutritional yeast
- 1 tablespoon Soy milk, unsweetened
- 125 teaspoon Turmeric, ground
- .25 teaspoon Onion powder
- .25 teaspoon Sea salt
- .125 teaspoon Smoked paprika (optional)
- .25 teaspoon Black salt
- .5 cup Kale, chopped
- .25 cup Button mushrooms, sliced
- 2 tablespoons Onion, diced
- 1 clove Garlic, minced
- 1 tablespoon extra-virgin olive oil, dived

Directions:

1. Into a blender, add the tofu, tahini, cornstarch, yeast, soy milk, turmeric, onion powder, smoked paprika, and both salts. Pulse on high until the mixture is completely blended.
2. In a skillet, add half of the olive oil along with the vegetables and garlic. Saute until they become tender, about five minutes over medium heat.

3. Meanwhile, add the remaining half of the olive oil to a non-stick medium skillet over medium-high heat. Allow this skillet to preheat while you cook the vegetables until it is very hot. Once hot, pour the tofu batter into the skillet, slightly tilting the pan so that the egg forms a circular shape. You may use a spoon to make the top smooth.
4. Sprinkle the cooked vegetables over the tofu "egg" and reduce the skillet's heat to medium-low. Cover the skillet with a lid, allowing it to cook three to five minutes until the tofu "egg" is set and the edges have dried. You can use a spatula to lightly lift the edges of the omelet and ensure it is fully set. The coloring should be golden with some browned spots.
5. When ready, loosen the omelet by lifting it with the spatula and then flip one side over the other. Transfer the tofu omelet to a plate and enjoy while warm.

Nutrition: Energy (calories): 174 kcal Protein: 6.4 g; Fat: 9.47 g; Carbohydrates: 16.52 g

748. Cucumber And Radish Salad With Feta

Preparation time: 15 minutes
Cooking time: 0 minutes
Servings: 4

Ingredients:

- 1½ cucumbers
- 1 pack radish
- 1 pack rocket (80 g)
- 4 gherkins
- 200 g feta
- 4 tbsp. oil
- 3 tbsp. juice
- 1 tsp mustard
- 1 tsp nectar salt pepper

Directions:

1. Clean, wash, and cut cucumber and radishes into dainty cuts. Wash the rocket and shake it dry. Divide the cured gherkins lengthways and dig cuts. Disintegrate the feta.
2. Whisk for the dressing oil with juice, mustard, and nectar, season with salt and pepper. Blend the cucumber, radish, and cured cucumber cuts and blend in with the dressing. Spot on a plate and sprinkle with the feta and rocket.

Nutrition: Calories: 327 kcal Protein: 9.88 g Fat: 26.12 g Carbohydrates: 14.02 g

749. Tacos With Cauliflower Bean Mole And Sour Cream

Preparation time: 15 minutes
Cooking time: 15 minutes
Servings: 4

Ingredients:

- 1 little cauliflower (800 g)
- 2 tbsp. oil
- 2 red onions
- 1 clove of garlic
- 2 tbsp. vinegar
- 800 g thick tomato (glass)
- ½ group parsley (10 g)
- 100 g low-fat quark
- 50 g acrid cream
- 1 sprinkle juice
- Salt
- Pepper
- 240 g dark beans (glass; depleted weight)
- 1 PC dim chocolate (30 g; at any rate 85% cocoa)
- 1 tsp smoked paprika powder
- 8 little wholegrain tortilla shops

Directions:

1. Wash, clean, and partition the cauliflower into little florets. Warmth the oil during a dish and fry the cauliflower over medium warmth for five minutes.
2. Peel the onions and garlic. 1 onion in solid shapes, the other dig rings—hack garlic. Include the onion 3D shapes and garlic to the cauliflower and sauté for 2–3 minutes. Include the vinegar and tomatoes and stew secured over low warmth for around quarter-hour.
3. Within the interim, wash the parsley, shake dry and pluck the leaves. For the sharp cream, finely slash half the parsley leaves and blend in with the quark, acrid cream, and juice—season with salt and pepper.
4. Drain the beans and permit them to channel. Include the cauliflower with chocolate and paprika powder, mix, and warmth the cauliflower bean mole for an extra 5 minutes—season with salt and pepper.
5. Within the interim, a warm tortilla during a container, or within the broiler. Fill the tortilla with the cauliflower bean mole, pour a dab of harsh cream over it and sprinkle with onion rings and remaining parsley leaves.

Nutrition: Calories: 500 kcal Protein: 19.43 g Fat: 18.81 g Carbohydrates: 64.83 g

750. Spring Cloud Bread

Preparation time: 10 minutes
Cooking time: 30 minutes
Servings: 4

Ingredients:

- 3 eggs
- 200 g cream cheddar (60% fat in dry issue)
- 1 tsp preparing powder
- Salt
- 50 ml milk (3.5% fat)
- ½ tsp medium-hot mustard
- Pepper
- ½ pack chives (10 g)
- 100 g sheep's lettuce
- ½ pack radish
- 1 bunch red radish cress

Directions:

1. Separate the eggs and blend the egg yolks in with 100 g cream cheddar and preparing powder. Beat the egg whites with slightly salt until solid and overlay in divides under the cream cheddar cream.
2. Spread the mixture in 8 level parts on a preparing sheet secured with heating paper and heat during a preheated stove at 150 ° C (convection 130 ° C; gas: setting 1-2) for around 20 minutes. Remove and allow to cool for around 10 minutes.
3. Mix the rest of the cream cheddar with milk, mustard, somewhat salt, and pepper. Wash the chives, shake dry, dig folds and blend into the cream.
4. Clean sheep's lettuce, wash, and shake dry. Clean, wash, and cut radishes into meager cuts. Wash the cress and channel well. Spread some cream on the underside of 4 cloud bread each, mastermind sheep's lettuce, radish cuts, remaining cream and cress on top, and spot 1 cloud bread each on top as a cover.

Nutrition: Calories: 248 kcal Protein: 10.97 g Fat: 18.61 Carbohydrates: 10.11 g

751. Cauliflower Nachos

Preparation time: 5 minutes
Cooking time: 30 minutes
Servings: 1-2

Ingredients:

- 2 tablespoons extra virgin olive oil
- ½ teaspoon onion powder
- ½ teaspoon turmeric
- ½ teaspoon ground cumin
- 1 medium head cauliflower
- ¾ cup shredded cheddar cheese
- ½ cup tomato, diced
- ¼ cup red bell pepper, diced
- ¼ cup red onion, diced
- ½ Bird's Eye chili pepper, finely diced
- ¼ cup parsley, finely diced
- Pinch of salt

Directions:

1. Preheat oven to 400 ° F.
2. Mix onion powder, cumin, turmeric, and olive oil. Core cauliflower and slice into ½" thick rounds. Coat the cauliflower using olive oil mixture and bake for 15 – 20 minutes. Top with shredded cheese & bake for an additional 3 – 5 minutes, until cheese is melted. In a bowl, combine tomatoes, bell pepper, onion, chili, and parsley with a pinch of salt.
3. Top cooked cauliflower with salsa and serve.

Nutrition: Calories: 195g Fat: 5.1g Fiber: 5.3 Carbs: 50.9g Protein: 3.6g

752. Cardamom Granola Bars

Preparation time: 5 minutes
Cooking time: 30 minutes
Servings: 18pcs

Ingredients:

- 2 cups rolled oats
- ½ cup raisins
- ½ cup walnuts, chopped and toasted
- 1 ½ teaspoon ground cardamom
- 6 tablespoons cocoa butter
- 1/3 cup packed brown sugar
- 3 tablespoons honey
- Coconut oil, for greasing pan

Directions:

1. Set oven to 350°F. Line a 9-inch square pan using a foil, extending the foil over sides. Grease the foil with coconut oil. Mix the oats, raisins, walnuts, and cardamom in a large bowl. Heat the cocoa butter, brown sugar, and honey in a saucepan until the butter melts and begins to bubble. Bake for a half-hour or until the top is golden brown.
2. Allow cooling for 30 minutes. Using the foil, lift the granola out of the pan and place on cutting board. Cut into 18 bars.

Nutrition: Calories: 95g Fat: 2g Fiber: 1.8g Carbs: 7.8g Protein: 3g

753. Thai-Style Nuts

Preparation time: 5 minutes
Cooking time: 15-20 minutes
Servings: 2

Ingredients:

- ½ cup walnuts
- ½ cup coconut flakes
- ½ tsp soy sauce
- 1 tsp honey
- 1 pinch of cayenne pepper
- 1 dash of lime juice

Directions:

1. Add the above ingredients to a bowl, toss the nuts to coat, and place on a baking sheet, lined with parchment paper. Cook at 250F for 15-20 minutes, checking as not to burn, but lightly toasted. Remove from the oven. Cool first before eating.

Nutrition: Calories: 56 Fat: 0.5g Fiber: 0,8g Carbs: 5.1g

754. Crunchy Potato Bites

Preparation time: 10 minutes
Cooking time: 20 minutes
Servings: 3

Ingredients:

- 1 potato, sliced
- 2 bacon slices, already cooked and crumbled
- 1 small avocado, pitted and cubed
- 1 tbsp of extra virgin olive oil

Directions:

1. Spread potato slices on a lined baking sheet.
2. Toss around with the extra virgin olive oil.
3. Insert in the oven at 350 degrees F.
4. Bake for 20 minutes.
5. Arrange on a platter, top each slice with avocado and crumbled bacon and serve as a snack.

Nutrition: Calories: 91 kcal Protein: 0 g Fat: 10.35 g Carbohydrates: 0 g

755. Dates In A Parma Ham Blanket

Preparation time: 10 minutes
Cooking time: 5 minutes
Servings: 12

Ingredients:

- 12 Medjool dates
- 2 slices of Parma ham, cut into strips

Directions:

1. Wrap each date with a strip of Parma ham. It can be served hot or cold.

Nutrition: Calories: 77 kcal Protein: 1.62 g Fat: 0.67 g Carbohydrates: 18.03 g

756. Mung Beans Snack Salad

Preparation time: 10 minutes
Cooking time: 0 minutes
Servings: 6

Ingredients:

- 2 cups tomatoes, chopped
- 2 cups cucumber, chopped
- 3 cups mixed greens
- 2 cups mung beans, sprouted
- 2 cups clover sprouts
- For the salad dressing:
- 1 tablespoon cumin, ground
- 1 cup dill, chopped
- 4 tablespoons lemon juice
- 1 avocado, pitted, peeled and roughly chopped
- 1 cucumber, roughly chopped

Directions:

1. In a salad bowl, mix tomatoes with 2 cups cucumber, greens, clover, and mung sprouts.
2. In your blender, mix cumin with dill, lemon juice, 1 cucumber, and avocado and blend well
3. Add the blended cream to your salad, toss well, and serve as a snack.

Nutrition: Calories: 122 kcal Protein: 5.46 g Fat: 6.58 g Carbohydrates: 14.22 g

757. Peanut Energy Bars

Preparation time: 5 minutes
Cooking time: 30 minutes
Servings: 16

Ingredients:

- Zest of 1 lemon (washed in hot soapy water to remove the wax first) 50ml light olive oil
- 50g blanched (unsalted) peanuts 200g jumbo oats
- 25g dark brown sugar
- 30g butter
- 50g good-quality (70%) dark chocolate chips
- Heaped tbsp (50g) rice malt syrup Juice of ½ lemon

Directions:

1. A 15 cm square cake pan, finely oil. Oven preheats to 160 ° C (140 ° C fan / Gas 3).
2. Add the almonds, oats, and lemon zest into a wide pot.
3. Apply the olive oil, butter, brown sugar, rice malt syrup, and lemon juice to a medium non-stick plate.
4. Heat gently, stirring continuously until the butter has melted and the ingredients have mixed.
5. Remove from heat and sprinkle over peanut/oat mix. Keep stirring until the oats are filled. Exhale the mixture into the prepared cake tin. Even with spoon back, push tightly down while you move.
6. Bake for 20 minutes until the edges have only been tingling white. Clear from the frying pan, but keep in the pot.
7. Sprinkle the chocolate chips over while the energy bars are still hot and leave to melt for about 10 minutes. Use a knife to evenly spread the dark chocolate over the bars and let it cool down – still in the tin – until the chocolate has set.
8. Remove the entire cake from the tin carefully, and place it on a chopping board. Cut into 16 squares with a very sharp knife—store in an airtight container for up to 5 days, when completely cool.

Nutrition: Calories: 61 kcal Protein: 1.25 g Fat: 4.37 g Carbohydrates: 4.76 g

758. Turmeric Roasted Nuts

Preparation time: 5 minutes
Cooking time: 20 minutes
Servings: 8

Ingredients:

- 1 tbsp. granulated sugar
- 1 tsp. ground cumin
- 250g blanched peanuts 1 tbsp honey
- ½ tsp chili powder
- 1 tsp salt
- ½ tsp smoked paprika
- ½ tsp ground turmeric

Directions:

1. Oven preheats to 160 ° C (140 ° C fan / Gas 3). Line a silicone-plated baking tray or baking parchment.
2. Add the peanuts with the honey in a big tub. Combine the sugar, smoked paprika, salt, chili powder, turmeric, and smoked paprika in a separate, small bowl. Stir in the peanuts with the sugar and spice mixture and toss well to coat evenly. Into the lined baking sheet, scatter the peanuts.
3. Bake every 5 minutes for about 20 minutes, stirring until the coating has started thickening.
4. Remove from the oven and leave onto the tray to cool completely.
5. .Break up any large lumps and keep for up to 2 weeks in an airtight container.

Nutrition: Calories: 175 kcal Protein: 8.96 g Fat: 11.43 g Carbohydrates: 11.75 g

759. Crunchy Kale Seaweed

Preparation time: 2 minutes
Cooking time: 10 minutes
Servings: 2

Ingredients:

- 1 tbsp. extra virgin olive oil
- Sea salt and ground black pepper
- 100g kale washed

Directions:

1. Oven preheats to 200 ° C (180 ° C fan / Gas 6).
2. Cut from the kale the chewy stalks, then cut them roughly. If necessary, sear the kale on kitchen paper and place it on a large baking tray.
3. Spray with the olive oil and brush with a good quantity of kosher salt and a little chili flake.
4. Cook 8–10 minutes in the oven. Remove from the oven and allow the tray to cool to the full. Best eaten the very same day.

Nutrition: Calories: 66 kcal Protein: 5.34 g Fat: 3.5 g Carbohydrates: 4.38 g

760. Wasabi Peas

Preparation time: 5 minutes
Cooking time: 30 minutes
Servings: 4

Ingredients:

- 1 tsp salt
- 250g fresh or frozen soya/edamame beans 6 tsp wasabi powder
- ¼ tsp onion powder 4 tsp water

Directions:

1. If you have soybeans frozen, then you can defrost them completely on paper in the kitchen and pat dry.
2. Oven preheats to 160 ° C (140 ° C fan / Gas 3). Before spreading on a baking tray, dry the soya beans with kitchen paper and cook for 30 minutes.
3. Place the wasabi powder, salt, and onion powder in a bowl five minutes before the end of the cooking time and whisk together with the water to form a smooth paste. Cover, then stop for 5 minutes to relax.
4. Remove from the oven when the beans have cooked and scoop immediately into the wasabi paste.
5. Remove thoroughly so that all bean surfaces are coated and pour back into the baking tray to cool down and dry out. Left in the baking tray for nearly an hour before being moved to an airtight bag.

Nutrition: Calories: 35 kcal Protein: 2.32 g Fat: 1.8 g Carbohydrates: 2.82 g

761. Fried Chili Tofu

Preparation time: 5 minutes
Cooking time: 10 minutes
Servings: 1

Ingredients:

- 1 clove garlic, peeled and crushed
- ½ lemon juice
- 150g firm tofu, cut into cubes
- ½ tsp paprika
- ½ tsp chili flakes
- Salt and ground black pepper
- 1 tsp. oil
- ½ tsp ground turmeric

Directions:

1. Spread the tofu over a kitchen-papered plate. Cover with paper for the kitchen, and set aside to dry.
2. In a wide pot, placed the garlic, lemon juice, spices, and generous salt and pepper seasoning.
3. Mix before inserting the tofu, then mix softly so that the tofu is completely coated. Leave it to stay for 5 to 15 minutes.
4. Heat the oil over the medium-high temperature in a frying pan and wait until the pan is hot before removing the tofu from the marinade and adding it to the pan. Fry for 3–4 minutes turn every minute or so, before all over the tofu is golden colored. Turn off the heat, then add and serve the remaining marinade to the pan.

Nutrition: Calories: 79 kcal Protein: 7.69 g Fat: 4.g Carbohydrates: 2.44 g

762. Olive Tapenade

Preparation time: 5 minutes
Cooking time: 5 minutes
Servings: 4

Ingredients:

- Zest and juice of ½ lemon 1 tbsp capers, drained
- 1 clove garlic, peeled and crushed
- Anchovy fillets drained, and roughly chopped 200g pitted green or black olives, drained
- 1 tbsp extra virgin olive oil

Directions:

1. In a food processor, place the garlic, lemon juice, and zest, capers, and anchovies, and blend until smooth. Stir in the olives and mix again. Don't over-mixture as a few bits of olive allow for a more attractive look.
2. Break the paste out and whisk in the soy sauce. The tapenade will remain in the fridge for a few days. It'll taste better treated at room temperature, as with all olives.

Nutrition: Calories: 108 kcal Protein: 2.18 g Fat: 10.68 g Carbohydrates: 2.3 g

763. Crunchy Fried Olives

Preparation time: 5 minutes
Cooking time: 5 minutes
Servings: 1

Ingredients:

- 50g panko breadcrumbs
- 200g green pitted olives 1 egg, beaten
- ½ tsp paprika 1 tbsp olive oil
- ½ tsp ground turmeric

Directions:

1. Secure the olives on paper for the cooking. Put the pounded eggs in one shallow dish, and add another the breadcrumbs, turmeric, and paprika.
2. Sprinkle the olives first in beaten egg and roll in the chopped breadcrumbs.
3. Heat the oil over low heat in a big frying pan. Attach the coated olives and fry all over until golden brown when dry. Remove with a serving dish and drain before serving onto kitchen paper.

Nutrition: Calories: 385 kcal Protein: 8.61 g Fat: 37.71 g Carbohydrates: 8.69 g

764. Turmeric Apple Chips

Preparation time: 15 minutes
Cooking time: 1 hour and 15 minutes
Servings: 1

Ingredients:

- ¼ tsp ground turmeric
- Juice of ½ lemon
- ½ tsp ground ginger
- 1 large eating apple
- ½ tsp ground cinnamon

Directions:

1. Oven preheats to 120 ° C (100 ° C fan / Gas 1/2). Form two paper baking sheets or silicone papers.
2. In a small pot, put the lemon juice and add in the spices. Cut the apple tip-off. Using a peeler to carve really small apple rings over the edges. Every seed in the middle just drops out. Fall into the lemon juice while each very thin slice is sliced off, then gently sprinkle a little lemon juice over the top to prevent browning. Dispose of the apple foundation.
3. Arrange the apple rings over the baking sheets in one continuous row. Bake 15 minutes for 1 hour, then transform after 45 minutes. Remove from the oven and allow the baking tray to be cool and crisp, before being placed in an airtight jar.

Nutrition: Calories: 96 kcal Protein: 6.69 g Fat: 6.2 g Carbohydrates: 3.89 g

765. Chocolate Shots

Preparation time: 1 minute
Cooking time: 0 minutes
Servings: 1

Ingredients:

- A little boiling water
- 60ml milk
- 20g good-quality Heaped
- 2 tsp Cocoa powder
- 10g granulated sugar

Directions:

1. Place the chocolate and sugar in a small bowl. Apply a bit of kettle water, just enough to create a smooth paste. Pour in the milk, mixing vigorously a little at a time. Pour into two shot glasses, and then appreciate the chocolate blow.

Nutrition: Calories: 10 kcal Protein: 0 g Fat: 0 g Carbohydrates: 2.49 g

766. Frozen Chocolate Grapes

Preparation time: 10 minutes +freezing time
Cooking time: 0 minutes
Servings: 1

Ingredients:

- 150g red seedless grapes
- 50g good-quality (70%) dark chocolate

Directions:

1. Line a silicone-sheet or baking parchment baking tray.
2. Divide the chocolate into tiny chunks and place them in a heat-proof bowl. Heat a small pan of water to a mild simmer and place the chocolate-containing bowl on top. Be sure not to touch the water in the tank.
3. Heat and stir in the chocolate so that it starts to melt slowly and remove a few remaining lumps from the heat. Start swirling the chocolate until all of it is melted (this helps keep white spots of the chocolate from blooming).
4. Cover the grapes one at a time in the chocolate, so that they are half-coated and put directly on the baking tray. Proceed on with the grapes.
5. Leave the chocolate to set before transfer to the freezer at room temperature. Once the grapes have frozen, they can be moved to an appropriate container for the freezer.
6. Come in portions of ten to twelve grapes at a time or only reach in and catch a couple when appropriate.

Nutrition: Calories: 456 kcal Protein: 11.23 g Fat: 21.3 g Carbohydrates: 57.13 g

767. Coconut Brownie Bites

Preparation time: 15 minutes (30 minutes – 2 hours for cooling Time)
Cooking time: 0 Minutes
Servings: 24 – 30 Bites

Ingredients:

- ½ cups walnuts
- ¼ cup almonds
- ½ cups Medjool dates
- ¼ cup unsweetened cocoa powder
- 1 teaspoon vanilla extract
- ¼ teaspoon of sea salt
- ¼ cup unsweetened desiccated or shredded coconut

Directions:

1. Bring all ingredients in a food processor and blend until well combined. Roll into 1" balls. Roll balls in coconut until well-covered and place on a wax paper-lined baking sheet. Freeze for 30 minutes or refrigerate for up to 2 hours.

Nutrition: Calorie: 55 Fat: 6 Carbs: 6 Sodium: 5 mg Protein: 0

768. Tortilla Chips And Fresh Salsa

Preparation time: 10 minutes
Cooking time: 10 Minutes
Servings: 4

Ingredients:

- Whole wheat flour tortillas
- 3 tablespoons extra virgin olive oil
- Roma tomatoes, diced
- 1 small red onion, finely diced
- 1 Bird's Eye chili pepper, finely diced
- 2 teaspoons parsley, finely chopped
- 2 teaspoons cilantro, finely chopped
- 1 lime, juiced
- Salt and pepper to taste

Directions:

1. Set the oven to 350°F. Use a pastry brush to coat every side of the tortilla in olive oil. With a sharp knife or pizza cutter, divide each tortilla into 8 wedges. Spread tortillas over a large baking sheet in a single layer. Use more than one baking sheet if necessary. Bake for 8 – 10 minutes, flipping halfway through until both sides are golden brown, and your chips are crispy. While the chips are baking, combine tomatoes, red onion, chili pepper, parsley, cilantro, and lime juice and mix well. Serve salsa with the chips.

Nutrition: Calorie: 375 Fat: 19 g Carbs: 47 g Sodium: 215 mg Protein: 5g

769. Garlic Baked Kale Chips

Preparation time: 30 minutes
Cooking time: 25 Minutes
Servings: 4

Ingredients

- 1 bunch kale leaves
- ½ tablespoon extra-virgin olive oil
- 1 teaspoon garlic powder
- 1/8 teaspoon cayenne powder
- ¼ teaspoon fine salt

Directions:

1. Preheat oven to 300 degrees F and cover a large baking sheet with parchment paper. Remove the stems from your kale and tear up into large pieces. Wash and spin the leaves until thoroughly dry, using a paper towel to pat dry if necessary. Place kale leaves in a large bowl and massage the olive oil carefully into each leaf. Combine garlic, cayenne, and salt in a small bowl and mix well. Sprinkle seasoning over kale and toss to distribute. Spread kale in a single layer over the baking sheet. Bake for 10 minutes, rotate the pan, and bake for another 12-15 minutes more until the kale just begins to get crispy. The leaves will shrink and need to cool at least 5 minutes after being taken out of the oven to crisp properly.

Nutrition: Calorie: 108 kcal Fat: 9 Carbs: 4 Sodium: 49 Protein: 2

770. Herb Roasted Chickpeas

Preparation time: 5 minutes
Cooking time 45 minutes
Servings: 4

Ingredients

- 1 can of chickpeas, drained
- 1 - 2 tablespoon extra-virgin olive oil
- ½ teaspoon dried lovage
- ½ teaspoon dried basil
- 1 teaspoon garlic powder
- 1/8 teaspoon cayenne powder
- ¼ teaspoon fine salt

Directions:

1. Preheat oven to 400 degrees F and cover a large baking sheet with parchment paper. Spread chickpeas out evenly over the pan in a single layer and roast for 30 minutes. Remove from oven and transfer to a heat-resistant bowl. Add the olive oil and toss to coat each chickpea. Sprinkle with herbs and toss again to distribute. Return to oven for an additional 15 minutes. Let cool for at least 15 minutes before eating.

Nutrition: Calorie: 84 Fat: 1 Carbs: 12 Sodium: 50 Protein: 4

771. The Bell Pepper Fiesta

Preparation time: 5 minutes
Cooking time: 0 minutes
Servings: 3

Ingredients:

- 2 tablespoons dill, chopped
- 1 yellow onion, chopped
- 1 pound multi-colored peppers, cut, halved, seeded and cut into thin strips
- 3 tablespoons organic olive oil
- 2 ½ tablespoons white wine vinegar
- Black pepper to taste

Directions:

1. Take a bowl and mix in sweet pepper, onion, dill, pepper, oil, vinegar, and toss well.
2. Divide between bowls and serve.
3. Enjoy!

Nutrition: Calories: 120 Fat: 3g Carbohydrates: 1g Protein: 6g

772. Hearty Almond Crackers

Preparation time: 10 minutes
Cooking time: 20 minutes

Ingredients:

- 1 cup almond flour
- ¼ teaspoon baking soda
- 1/8 teaspoon black pepper
- 3 tablespoons sesame seeds
- 1 egg, beaten
- Salt and pepper to taste

Directions:

1. Preheat your oven to 350°F
2. Line 2 baking sheets using a parchment paper and keep them on the side.

3. Divide dough into two balls.
4. Roll out the dough in the middle of two pieces of parchment paper.
5. Cut into crackers and transfer them to the prepared baking sheet.
6. Bake for 15-20 minutes.
7. Repeat until all the dough has been used up.
8. Leave crackers to cool and serve.
9. Enjoy!

Nutrition: Total Carbs: 8g Fiber: 2g Protein: 9g Fat: 28g

773. Easy Seed Crackers

Preparation time: 10 minutes
Cooking time: 60 minutes

Ingredients:

- 1 cup boiling water
- 1/3 cup chia seeds
- 1/3 cup sesame seeds
- 1/3 cup pumpkin seeds
- 1/3 cup Flaxseeds
- 1/3 cup sunflower seeds
- 1 tablespoon Psyllium powder
- 1 cup almond flour
- 1 teaspoon salt
- ¼ cup coconut oil, melted

Directions:

1. Preheat your oven to 300 degrees F.
2. Line a cookie sheet using a parchment paper and keep it on the side.
3. Add listed ingredients (except coconut oil and water) to the food processor and pulse until ground.
4. Transfer to a large mixing bowl and pour melted coconut oil and boiling water, mix.
5. Transfer mix to prepared sheet and spread into a thin layer.
6. Cut dough into crackers and bake for 60 minutes.
7. Cool and serve.
8. Enjoy!

Nutrition: Total Carbs: 10.6g Fiber: 3g Protein: 5g Fat: 14.6g

774. Amazing Garlic Aioli

Preparation time: 5 minutes
Cooking time: 0 minutes
Servings: 3

Ingredients:

- ½ cup mayonnaise, low fat and low sodium
- 2 garlic cloves, minced
- Juice of 1 lemon
- 1 tablespoon fresh-flat leaf Italian parsley, chopped
- 1 teaspoon chives, chopped
- Salt and pepper to taste

Directions:

1. Add mayonnaise, garlic, parsley, lemon juice, chives, and season with salt and pepper.
2. Blend until combined well.
3. Pour into refrigerator and chill for 30 minutes.
4. Serve and use it as needed!

Nutrition: Calories: 813 Fat: 88g Carbohydrates: 9g Protein: 2g

775. Snow-Flakes

Preparation time: 5 minutes
Cooking time: 15 minutes
Servings: 8

Ingredients:

- Won ton wrappers
- Oil to frying
- Powdered-sugar

Directions:

1. Cut won ton wrappers just like you'd a snow-flake
2. Heat oil when hot add won-ton, fry for approximately 30 seconds, then reverse over.
3. Drain on a paper towel with powdered sugar.

Nutrition: Calories: 10 kcal Protein: 0.8 g Fat: 0.76 g Carbohydrates: 0 g

776. Lemon Ricotta Cookies With Lemon Glaze

Preparation time: 15 minutes
Cooking time: 30 minutes
Servings: 8

Ingredients:

- 2 1/2 cups all-purpose flour
- 1 tsp baking powder
- 1 tsp salt
- 1 tbsps. Unsalted butter softened
- 2 cups of sugar
- 2 capsules
- 1 teaspoon (15-ounce) container whole-milk ricotta cheese
- 3 tbsps. Lemon juice
- One lemon
- Glaze:
- 11/2 cups powdered sugar
- 3 tbsps. Lemon juice
- One lemon

Directions:

1. Preheat the oven to 375 degrees f.
2. In a medium bowl, put and combine the flour, baking powder, and salt. Set-aside.
3. From the big bowl, blend the butter and the sugar levels. With an electric mixer, beat the sugar and butter until light and fluffy, about three minutes. Add the eggs1 at a time, beating until incorporated.
4. Insert the ricotta cheese, lemon juice, and lemon zest. Beat to blend. Stir in the dry skin.
5. Line two baking sheets with parchment paper. Spoon the dough (approximately two tablespoons of each cookie) on the baking sheets. Bake for fifteen minutes, until slightly golden at the borders. Take it off from the oven and allow the biscuits remaining baking sheet for about 20 minutes.
6. Glaze:
7. Combine the powdered sugar lemon juice and lemon peel in a small bowl and then stir until smooth. Spoon approximately 1/2-tsp on each cookie and make use of the back of the spoon to disperse lightly. Allow glaze harden for about two hours. Pack the biscuits to a decorative jar.

Nutrition: Calories: 532 kcal Protein: 5.05 g Fat: 2.25 g Carbohydrates: 124.98 g

777. Herbed Soy Snacks

Preparation time: 8 minutes
Cooking time: 26 minutes
Servings: 16

Ingredients:

- 2 cups dry roasted soybeans
- 1 ½ teaspoons dried thyme, crushed
- ¼ teaspoon garlic salt
- 1/8 teaspoon cayenne pepper

Directions:

1. In a 15x10 inch baking pan spread roasted soybeans in an even layer.
2. In a small bowl, combine thyme, garlic salt, and cayenne pepper. Sprinkle soybeans with thyme mixture—Bake in a 350° F oven about 5 minutes or until heated through, shaking pan once. Cool completely and enjoy it!

Nutrition: Calories 75 Fat 3g Carbohydrates 4g Protein 7g

778. Mung Beans Snack Salad

Preparation time: 10 minutes
Cooking time: 0 minute
Servings: 6

Ingredients:

- 2 cups tomatoes, chopped
- 2 cups cucumber, chopped
- 3 cups mixed greens
- 2 cups mung beans, sprouted
- 2 cups clover sprouts
- For the salad dressing:
- 1 tablespoon cumin, ground
- 1 cup dill, chopped
- 4 tablespoons lemon juice
- 1 avocado, pitted, peeled and roughly chopped
- 1 cucumber, roughly chopped

Directions:

1. In a salad bowl, mix tomatoes with 2 cups cucumber, greens, clover, and mung sprouts.
2. In your blender, mix cumin with dill, lemon juice, 1 cucumber, and avocado, blend well, add this to your salad, toss well and serve as a snack
3. Enjoy!

Nutrition: Calories: 120 Fat: 0g Fiber: 2g Carbohydrates: 1g Protein: 6g

779. Sprouts And Apples Snack Salad

Preparation time: 10 minutes
Cooking time: 0 minutes
Servings: 4

Ingredients:

- 1 pound Brussels sprouts, shredded
- 1 cup walnuts, chopped
- 1 apple, cored and cubed
- 1 red onion, chopped
- For the salad dressing:
- 3 tablespoons red vinegar
- 1 tablespoon mustard
- ½ cup olive oil
- 1 garlic clove, minced
- Black pepper to the taste

Directions:

1. In a salad bowl, mix sprouts with apple, onion and walnuts.
2. In another bowl, mix vinegar with mustard, oil, garlic, and pepper, whisk well, add this to your salad, toss well and serve as a snack.
3. Enjoy!

Nutrition: Calories: 120 Fat: 2g Fiber: 2g Carbohydrates: 8g Protein: 6g

780. Celery And Raisins Snack Salad

Preparation time: 10 minutes
Cooking time: 0 minutes
Servings: 4

Ingredients:

- ½ cup raisins
- 4 cups celery, sliced
- ¼ cup parsley, chopped
- ½ cup walnuts, chopped
- Juice of ½ lemon
- 2 tablespoons olive oil
- Salt and black pepper to the taste

Directions:

1. In a salad bowl, mix celery with raisins, walnuts, parsley, lemon juice, oil, and black pepper, toss, divide into small cups and serve as a snack. Enjoy!

Nutrition: Calories: 120 Fat: 1g Fiber: 2g Carbohydrates: 6g Protein: 5g

781. Lentil Lovage Salad

Preparation time: 10 minutes
Cooking time: 0 minutes
Servings: 1

Ingredients:

- 1 cup cooked red lentils (prepare in advance, use warmed or at room temperature)
- 1 avocado, pitted, sliced, and scooped out
- 2 cups baby kale, chopped
- 2 celery stalks, chopped or sliced thinly
- ½ small red onion, sliced thinly
- 1 Medjool pitted date, chopped
- ¼ cup red currants
- 1 tsp. turmeric
- 1 tbsp. extra virgin olive oil
- 1/4 of a lemon, juiced
- 5 sprigs of parsley, chopped

Directions:

1. Add ingredients and toss together gently. Serve.

Nutrition: Calories: 116 Fat: 0.4 g Sodium: 2 mg Potassium: 369 mg Carbohydrate: 20 g Protein: 9 g

782. Pumpkin Brownies

Preparation time: 10 minutes
Cooking time: 30 minutes
Servings: 4

Ingredients:

- ¾ cup almond flour
- ½ tsp baking powder
- ½ tsp salt
- ¾ cup of coconut oil, melted
- 1 cups raw honey
- 2 tsp ground vanilla bean
- 3 eggs
- 1 tsp of cocoa powder
- 1 cup pumpkin puree
- ½ cup chopped pecans
- ¾ tsp ground cinnamon
- ½ tsp ground cloves
- ½ tsp ground nutmeg
- Dust with crushed pumpkin and sunflower seeds and hemp hearts

Directions:

1. Preheat oven to 350F and grease a baking pan.
2. Blend the almond flour, baking powder, and salt in a bowl.
3. In another bowl, mix the melted coconut oil, honey, and vanilla bean.
4. Whisk in the eggs one at a time.

5. Slowly put the flour mixture and mix.
6. Put cocoa powder, pumpkin puree, pecans, cinnamon, cloves, and nutmeg.
7. Spread the batter into the base of the baking pan.
8. Bake up to the toothpick inserted comes out clean, 45-50 minutes.
9. Cool in the pan, cut and serve.

Nutrition: Calories: 135.3 Total Fat: 2.7 g Sugars: 14.3 g Saturated Fat: 0.8 g

783. Vegan Sesame Seeds Cookies

Preparation time: 10 minutes
Cooking time: 25 minutes
Servings: 4

Ingredients:

- 1 cup toasted sesame seeds
- 2/3 cup almond flour ¼ cup raw honey
- 1/8 tsp baking powder
- ¼ cup of coconut oil (or tahini)
- ¼ cup of water 1 tbsp lemon juice
- ¼ tsp ground vanilla bean

Directions:

1. Heat oven to 350F. Mix all ingredients until you get a sticky ball.
2. Make cookies and put them on the baking tray.
3. Bake for around 20 minutes at 330F, until the cookies turn slightly brown. Take them out and cool.

Nutrition: Calories: 495 kcal Protein: 7.25 g Fat: 30.54 g Carbohydrates: 56.18 g

784. Coconut Cream Tart

Preparation time: 10 minutes
Cooking time: 30 minutes
Servings: 4

Ingredients:

- Crust:
- 2 cups almonds, soaked overnight
- 1 cup pitted dates, soaked overnight
- 1 cup chopped dried apricots
- 1½ tsp ground vanilla bean
- 1 banana
- Filling:
- 1 cup of flaked coconut
- 1 can of unsweetened coconut milk
- ¾ cup of raw honey
- 3 egg yolks
- 2 tbsp. of arrowroot powder
- 2 tbsp. of coconut oil
- 2 tsp of ground vanilla bean
- 1/8 tsp of salt
- ½ cup of coconut cream

Directions:

1. Heat the coconut milk, honey, salt, and ground vanilla bean over medium heat in a medium-size saucepan.
2. In a separate bowl, put and whisk the egg yolks and arrowroot powder.
3. Add ½ cup of the warm coconut milk mixture to the egg yolks while whisking constantly.
4. Then pour the egg mixture back into the coconut milk mixture and whisk until the mix thickens and then mix for 3 more minutes.
5. Take off of the heat and mix in the coconut oil and flaked coconut.
6. Cool and pour in the tart crust and refrigerate.
7. Decorate with large coconut flakes.

Nutrition: Calories: 143 Total fat: 12.3g Cholesterol: 26mg Sodium: 123mg Potassium: 50mg Carbohydrates: 24.9g Fiber: 0.6g Protein: 2.6g

785. Oatmeal Raisin Cookies

Preparation time: 10 minutes
Cooking time: 25 minutes
Servings: 4

Ingredients:

- 1 cup of coconut oil
- 1 cup of coconut sugar or raw honey
- 1½ cups almond flour 1 tsp salt
- ½ tsp grated nutmeg 1 tsp cinnamon
- 1½ cups raisins 2 large eggs, well beaten
- 1 tbsp. ground vanilla bean
- 3 cups rolled oats ½ cup chopped walnuts

Directions:

1. Heat oven to 350F.
2. Grease cookie sheets with coconut oil or line with waxed or parchment paper.
3. Mix coconut oil, coconut sugar, or raw honey in a large bowl and beat until fluffy.
4. Add vanilla.
5. Beat in eggs.
6. Mix almond flour, salt, cinnamon, and nutmeg in a separate bowl.
7. Stir these dry ingredients into a fluffy mixture.
8. Mix in raisins and nuts. Mix in oats.
9. Spoon out on cookie sheets, leaving 2-inches between cookies.
10. Bake until edges turn golden brown.

Nutrition: Calories 100 Total Fat 2.4 g Cholesterol 16.5 mg Sodium 73.5 mg Total Carbohydrate 18.8 g Dietary Fiber 1.5 g

786. Vegan Cacao Chia Cookies

Preparation time: 10 minutes
Cooking time: 35 minutes
Servings: 4

Ingredients:

- 4 tbsp. of raw cacao powder
- 3 tbsp. of chia seeds
- 1 cup of almonds
- 1 cup of cashews
- 1 cup of buckwheat flour
- 2 tbsps. Of coconut oil
- 1/3 of a cup of honey
- ¼ of a cup of dates
- ¼ of a cup of water

Directions:

1. Heat oven to 350F.
2. Blend all ingredients until it gets a sticky ball.
3. Make cookies and put them on the baking tray.
4. Bake for 20 minutes at 350F, until the cookies turn slightly brown.
5. Take them out and cool.

Nutrition: Calories 96 Total Fat 3.4 g Sodium 109.7 mg Carbohydrate 19.2 Dietary Fiber 1.6 g

787. Sweet Superfoods Pie Crust

Preparation time: 10 minutes
Cooking time: 30 minutes
Servings: 4

Ingredients:

- 1 1/3 cups blanched almond flour
- 1/3 cup tapioca flour
- ½ tsp sea salt

- 1 large egg
- ¼ cup of coconut oil
- 2 tbsp. coconut sugar or raw honey
- 1 tsp of ground vanilla bean

Directions:

1. Place almond flour, tapioca flour, sea salt, and vanilla, egg, and coconut sugar (if you use coconut sugar) in the bowl of a food processor.
2. Process 2-3 times to combine.
3. Add oil and sugar (or raw honey) and pulse with several one-second pulses and then let the food processor run until the mixture comes together.
4. Pour dough onto a sheet of plastic wrap.
5. Wrap and then press the dough into a 9-inch disk.
6. Refrigerate for 30 minutes.

Nutrition: Calories 527 Total Fat 35 g Cholesterol 0 mg Sodium 542 mg Potassium 67 mg Carbohydrate 48 g Protein 6 g

788. Spiced Apples

Preparation time: 10 minutes
Cooking time: 20 minutes
Servings: 8

Ingredients:

- .5 pint Green tea
- 2 Cinnamon sticks
- 4 Star anise
- 2 tbsp. Honey
- 4 Apples

Directions:

1. Place the green tea and the honey into a pan and bring it to a boil.
2. When that reaches a boil, add in the cinnamon, star anise, and apples.
3. Reduce the heat a bit and let it simmer. After 15 minutes of simmering, take the apples out and then serve topped by a dollop of Greek yogurt or crème Fraiche to enjoy.

Nutrition: Calories: 74 kcal Protein: 1.05 g Fat: 0.91 g Carbohydrates: 16.89 g

789. Coffee Bites

Preparation time: 10 minutes
Cooking time: 30 minutes + chilling time
Servings: 4

Ingredients:

- 4 Medjool dates, pitted
- .25 cups Espresso, cold
- .5 cups Almonds
- 2 tbsp. Dark chocolate cocoa powder
- .5 tbsp. Chia seeds
- Salt (a pinch)

Directions:

1. Soak dates in coffee for 20 minutes. Drain dates and save coffee for later.
2. Add dates to the food processor, pulsing quickly until you create a smooth mixture. Then, add in some of the coffee to create a thick paste, starting at 1 tbsp. and working up until you get a thick paste.
3. Add in everything else to the processor and pulse until you get a dough.
4. Create bite-sized balls and refrigerate to set.

Nutrition: Calories: 111 kcal Protein: 2.3 g Fat: 1.8 g Carbohydrates: 23.26 g

790. Zucchini Tots

Preparation time: 15 minutes
Cooking time: 30 minutes
Servings: 4

Ingredients:

- 1 cup Zucchini, shredded and packed
- 1 Egg
- .33 cups Italian cheese blend
- .25 cups Rice cereal, crushed up
- .75 tsp. Italian seasoning
- .25 tsp. Garlic powder
- Salt and pepper to taste

Directions:

1. Turn oven to 400 degrees Fahrenheit.
2. Dry out zucchini with paper towels, squeezing to remove excess moisture
3. Combine zucchini in a bowl with all other ingredients and mix well.
4. Use 2 tsp at a time to create tots. Bake on parchment paper for 25 minutes, turning halfway through.

Nutrition: Calories: 117 kcal Protein: 7.36 g Fat: 8.14 g Carbohydrates: 5.68 g

791. Pancake Skewers With Fruits

Preparation time: 0 minutes
Cooking time: 30 minutes
Servings: 4

Ingredients

- 100 g dark chocolate (70% cocoa)
- 3 bananas
- 200 g buttermilk
- 100 g yogurt (3.5% fat)
- 3 eggs
- 3 tbsp. rapeseed oil
- 100 g 5-grain flakes (or oat flakes)
- 100 g whole meal spelled flour
- ½ tsp. baking soda
- 1 tsp. baking powder
- 1 tbsp. whole cane sugar
- 150 g strawberries
- 2 handfuls blueberries

Direction:

1. Cut the chocolate and melt over a warm water bath. Peel bananas, slice them, pull them through the chocolate and let them dry on baking paper.
2. Mix the buttermilk, yogurt, eggs, and 1 tablespoon of rapeseed oil. Chop the 5-grain flakes very finely in a blender, then add the flour, baking soda, baking powder, and sugar to another bowl and mix. Add liquid ingredients and make a smooth dough. Let it rest for about 10 minutes.
3. In the meantime, clean, wash and slice strawberries. Wash and pat the blueberries dry.
4. Heat some oil in a pan and bake small pancakes with 1 teaspoon of dough each over medium heat.
5. Serve the skewers, skewer a blueberry, then a strawberry slice, a pancake, a chocolate banana, and a pancake.

Nutrition: Calories: 110 Carbs: 25 g Fat: 1 g Protein: 6 g

792. Brain Food Cookies

Preparation time: 0 minutes
Cooking time: 52 minutes
Servings: 4

Ingredients

- 150 g spelled flour type 1050
- 1 tsp. baking powder
- 100 g whole cane sugar
- 1 pinch salt
- 120 g room temperature butter

- 3 ripe bananas
- 1 egg
- 150 g pithy oatmeal
- 60 g donated almonds
- 1 tbsp. cocoa nibs
- 2 tbsp. chocolate drop (made from dark chocolate; 15 g)

Direction:

1. Mix the sugar, flour with the baking powder, and 1 pinch of salt. Add the butter in pieces and mix. Peel the bananas, mash them with a fork and add them to the dough together with the egg and stir well with a hand mixer. Fold in the oatmeal, almonds, cocoa nibs, and half of the chocolate drops.
2. Line a baking sheet using a parchment paper. Place the dough on the baking sheet with a tablespoon, leaving enough space between the cookies. Sprinkle with the remaining chocolate drops and bake in a preheated oven at 200 ° C (fan oven 180 ° C; gas: setting 3) for 10–15 minutes. Then allow it cool on a wire rack.

Nutrition: Calories: 170 Cal Carbs: 8 g Fat: 14 g Protein: 6 g

793. Blueberry And Coconut Rolls

Preparation time: 0 minutes
Cooking time: 55 minutes
Servings: 4

Ingredients

- 150 g whole meal flour
- 150 g spelled flour
- 1½ tsp. baking powder
- 1 pinch salt
- 50 g raw cane sugar
- 4 tbsp. rapeseed oil
- 250 g low-fat quark
- 1 egg
- 5 tbsp. milk (3.5% fat)
- 120 g blueberries
- 4 tbsp. grated coconut

Direction:

1. Put the flour with baking powder and salt in a bowl. Add sugar and mix. Add rapeseed oil, curd cheese, egg and 4 tablespoons of milk and use a hand mixer for kneading into a smooth dough.
2. Wash the blueberries, pat dry, and fold in together with the grated coconut under the dough.
3. Line a baking sheet with parchment paper. Form 9 round rolls with floured hands and place them on the baking sheet. Brush the blueberry and coconut buns with the remaining milk and bake in a preheated oven at 200 ° C (fan oven 180 ° C; gas: setting 3) for 12–15 minutes.

Nutrition: Calories: 140 Cal Carbs: 22 g Fat: 5 g Protein: 2 g

794. Vanilla Energy Balls With Coconut Shell

Preparation time: 0 minutes
Cooking time: 10 minutes
Servings: 4

Ingredients

- 100 g almond kernels
- 200 g dried date (pitted)
- ½ tsp. vanilla powder
- 20 g grated coconut (approx. 2 tbsp.)

Direction:

1. Put almonds, dates, and vanilla powder in a food processor or strong blender and chop into sticky mush.
2. Form balls of equal size from the mass.
3. Put coconut flakes on a flat plate. Roll the vanilla energy balls in the coconut flakes and press them down lightly.
4. Place the vanilla energy balls in an airtight sealable box and keep in the fridge.

Nutrition: Calories: 150 Cal Carbs: 17 g Fat: 7 g Protein: 10 g

795. Wake-Up Energy Balls

Preparation time: 0 minutes
Cooking time: 40 minutes
Servings: 4

Ingredients

- 120 g dried dates (without stone)
- 120 g walnuts
- 6 str. tell cocoa powder (18 g; heavily oiled)
- 1 pinch salt
- 1 pinch vanilla powder
- 2 tbsp. coffee bean (30 g)
- 2 tsp. ground coffee (10 g)
- Chili flakes

Direction:

1. Put the dates together with the nuts, 4 teaspoons of cocoa powder, 1 pinch of salt and vanilla powder in a blender and puree until you get a homogeneous dough.
2. Add the coffee beans and mix briefly. Cut 16 portions of dough with a tablespoon and shape into balls.
3. Mix the remaining cocoa powder with coffee powder and chili flakes and roll the energy balls in it.

Nutrition: Calories: 15 Cal Carbs: 3 g Fat: 0 g Protein: 0 g

796. Kale Avocado And Chili Dip With Crackers

Preparation time: 0 minutes
Cooking time: 25 minutes
Servings: 4

Ingredients

- 75 g linseed
- 75 g pumpkin seeds
- 50 g sesame seeds
- 40 g almond flour (4 fl. el)
- 2 tbsp. slightly liquid coconut oil
- Salt
- 3 avocados
- 200 g kale
- 1 small green chili pepper
- 4 tbsp. olive oil
- 1 organic lemon (zest and juice)
- Pepper
- 1 handful watercress (5 g)

Direction:

1. Place seeds and kernels with almond flour in a bowl, pour 125 ml of hot water and let them steep for 10 minutes. Then add coconut oil, season with salt, and mix everything.
2. Spread the mixture thinly on a baking sheet covered with baking paper, about 5 mm thin. Bake crackers in a preheated oven at 175 ° C top and bottom heat (gas: level 2–3) for 25–30 minutes. Then remove, let cool for 10 minutes and break the crackers into pieces.
3. In the meantime, halve the avocados for the dip, remove the stones, lift the pulp out of the bowl with a spoon, and roughly dice. Clean kale, pluck the green from the stems, wash, shake dry and cut into small pieces. Halve, chop, wash, and chop lengthways. Put the avocado, kale, and chili together with olive oil in a blender and coarsely puree. Season everything with salt, lemon peel and juice,

and pepper. Fill the dip into a bowl, garnish with watercress and serve with the crackers.

Nutrition: Calories: 100 Cal Carbs: 11 g Fat: 5 g Protein: 2 g

797. Crunchy Potato Bites

Preparation time: 10 minutes
Cooking time: 20 minutes
Servings: 5

Ingredients:

- 1 potato, sliced
- 2 bacon slices, already cooked and crumbled
- 1 small avocado, pitted and cubed
- 1 tbsp. of extra virgin olive oil

Directions:

1. Spread potato slices on a lined baking sheet.
2. Toss around with the extra virgin olive oil.
3. Insert in the oven at 350 degrees F.
4. Bake for 20 minutes.
5. Arrange on a platter, top each slice with avocado and crumbled bacon and serve as a snack.

Nutrition: Calories: 230 Total Fat: 14 g Carbohydrates: 25 g Protein: 2 g

798. Shrimp Muffins

Preparation time: 10 minutes
Cooking time: 45 minutes
Servings: 6

Ingredients:

- 1 spaghetti squash, peeled and halved
- 2 tablespoons avocado mayonnaise
- 1 cup low-fat mozzarella cheese, shredded
- 8 ounces shrimp, peeled, cooked and chopped
- 1 and ½ cups almond flour
- 1 teaspoon parsley, dried
- 1 garlic clove, minced
- Black pepper to the taste
- Cooking spray

Directions:

1. Prepare the squash on a lined baking sheet.
2. Insert in the oven at 375 degrees F and bake for 30 minutes.
3. Scrape squash flesh into a bowl and add pepper, parsley flakes, flour, shrimp, mayo, and mozzarella and stir well.
4. Divide this mix into a muffin tray greased with cooking spray.
5. Put it in the oven and bake over 375 °F for 15 minutes.
6. Serve them cold as a snack.

Nutrition: Calories: 321 Total Fat: 16 g Cholesterol: 49 mg Sodium: 393 mg Total Carbohydrates: 35 g Protein: 9 g

799. Cinnamon Apple Chips

Preparation time: 10 minutes
Cooking time: 2 hours
Servings: 4

Ingredients:

- Cooking spray
- 2 teaspoons cinnamon powder
- 2 apples, cored and thinly sliced

Directions:

1. Arrange apple slices on a lined baking sheet, spray them with cooking oil, and sprinkle cinnamon.
2. Put it in the oven and bake at 300 degrees F for 2 hours.
3. Divide into bowls and serve as a snack.

Nutrition: Calories: 110 Total Carbohydrates: 27 g Fiber: 4 g Sugar: 21 g

800. Apple And Pecan Bowls

Preparation time: 10 minutes
Cooking time: 10 minutes
Servings: 4

Ingredients:

- 4 big apples, cored, peeled and cubed
- 2 teaspoons lemon juice
- ¼ cup pecans, chopped

Directions:

1. In a bowl, blend apples with lemon juice and pecans and toss.
2. Put into small bowls and serve as a snack.

Nutrition: Calories: 230 Total Fat: 17 g Total Carbohydrates: 15 g

801. Cheesy Bacon Sticks

Preparation time: 5 minute
Cooking time: 15 minutes
Servings: 2

Ingredients:

- 4 Mozzarella String Cheese Pieces
- 8 Bacon Strips
- Sunflower Oil as Needed

Directions:

1. Start by putting two inches of oil into a skillet, heating it over medium heat.
2. Heat to 350 degrees and halve each string cheese pieces to make eight pieces.
3. Wrap each piece with a strip of bacon, using a toothpick to secure.
4. Cook each one for two minutes until your bacon has browned.
5. Allow to cool before serving.

Nutrition: Calories: 278 Protein: 32 Grams Fat: 15 Grams Net Carbs: 3 Grams

802. Green Salmon Bites

Preparation time: 5 minute
Cooking time: 15 minutes
Servings: 5

Ingredients:

- 1 Cucumber Sliced in 10 1/3 Inch Rounds
- 1 Avocado, Large
- 8 Ounces Cream Cheese
- 1 Tablespoon Lemon Juice, Fresh
- 4 Ounces Red Salmon Cooked & Flaked
- Tabasco Sauce to Taste
- ½ Tablespoon Green Onion, Chopped

Directions:

1. Halve your avocados, removing the seed before scooping out the flesh.
2. Add your cream cheese to the flesh and lemon juice, mixing well before adding Tabasco sauce.
3. Arrange the cucumber slices on a platter, dividing the avocado mixture on top.
4. Season with red pepper flakes and garnish with green onions before serving.

Nutrition: Calories: 277 Protein: 19 Grams Fat: 22 Grams Net Carbs: 5 Grams

803. Dill & Smoked Salmon Spread

Preparation time: 5 minute
Cooking time: 20 minutes
Servings: 8

Ingredients:

- 4 Ounces Smoked Salmon
- 4 Ounces Cream Cheese, Room Temperature

- 2 ½ Tablespoons Mayonnaise
- 2 Tablespoons Dill Fresh & Chopped
- Cucumber & Tomato Wedges for Serving
- Sea Salt & Black Pepper to Taste

Directions:

1. Pulse your cream cheese, salmon and mayonnaise in a food processor
2. Add dill. Mix well, and then serve with tomato or cucumber wedges.

Nutrition: Calories: 70 Protein: 5 Grams Fat: 5 Grams Net Carbs: 2 Grams

804. Parmesan Crackers

Preparation time: 5 minute
Cooking time: 15 minutes
Servings: 8

Ingredients:

- Net Carbs: 1 Gram
- 1 Teaspoon Butter
- 8 Ounces Parmesan Cheese, Full Fat & Shredded

Directions:

1. Put the oven to 400°F and then line a baking sheet using parchment paper. Grease with butter.
2. Spoon your cheese into mounds, and then make sure they're flat.
3. Bake until the edges are browned, which should take five minutes.
4. Allow to cool before serving. If you want to make these in advance, just bake them for one to two minutes to crisp after thawing.

Nutrition: Calories: 133 Protein: 11 Grams Fat: 11 Grams

805. Candied Toasted Coconut Cashews

Preparation time: 10 Minutes
Cooking time: 45 Minutes
Servings: 2

Ingredients:

- 3 cups unsalted cashews
- 1 cup granulated monk fruit sweetener
- 1 Tbsp. cinnamon
- ¼ cup of water
- 1 tsp. vanilla extract
- ½ tsp. salt
- ½ cup toasted coconut flakes

Directions:

1. Preheat oven to 250 degrees F.
2. Line a large baking dish or tray using a parchment paper and set aside.
3. In a large mixing bowl, add the cashews, cinnamon, and salt set aside.
4. In a microwave-safe bowl or stovetop, melt the monk fruit sweetener with water.
5. Pour it over the cashews and mix until all cashews are evenly coated.
6. Spread the cashews in an even layer.
7. Bake for 45 minutes, stirring occasionally.
8. Once the cashews have begun to crystallize, remove, and allow them to cool for 1-2 minutes before stirring again to avoid clusters from forming.
9. Let them cool completely before coating with an extra tbsp or two of monk fruit sweetener.
10. Once they are cooled, toss in the coconut flakes.
11. Serve!
12. Recipe Notes:
13. Keep the remaining cashews in a sealed jar or container. They can be kept for up to two months or in the freezer for up to 6 months.

Nutrition: Calories: 99 Total Fat: 5 g Protein: 6g Net Carbs: 1g

806. Almond Butter Fudge Bars

Preparation time: 25 Minutes
Cooking time: 10 Minutes
Servings: 8

Ingredients:

- 1 cup almond flour
- ½ cup unsalted butter, melted and divided
- 6 Tbsp. powdered erythritol, divided
- ½ tsp. ground cinnamon
- ¼ cup heavy cream
- ½ cup almond butter
- ½ tsp. vanilla extract
- 1/8 tsp. xanthan gum
- 1 oz. 80% dark chocolate or sugar-free chocolate chips

Directions:

1. Preheat the oven to 400 degrees F.
2. Line a 9x13 inch or similar baking dish with parchment paper.
3. Whisk together the almond flour, ¼ cup melted butter, 2 Tbsp. Powdered erythritol and cinnamon until well-combined.
4. Spread the mixture on the lined baking dish.
5. Bake for 10 minutes until golden brown.
6. Whisk together the heavy cream and almond butter with the remaining butter and 4 Tbsp. Powdered erythritol in a mixing bowl.
7. Add the vanilla and xanthan gum, blending until well-combined.
8. Spread the fudge mixture over the cooled almond flour base.
9. Sprinkle with roughly chopped dark chocolate or sugar-free chocolate chips.
10. Freeze overnight and then slice the fudge into 8 bars.
11. Serve.

Nutrition: Calories: 235 Total Fat: 24g Protein: 4.5g Net Carbs: 2g

807. Caprese Meatballs

Preparation time: 10 Minutes
Cooking time: 20 Minutes
Servings: 4

Ingredients:

- 1 lb. ground turkey
- 1 egg
- ¼ cup almond flour
- ½ tsp. Salt
- ¼ tsp. Ground black pepper
- ½ tsp. garlic powder
- ½ cup shredded whole milk mozzarella
- 2 Tbsp. sun-dried tomatoes, chopped
- 2 Tbsp. fresh basil, chopped
- 2 Tbsp. olive oil for frying

Directions:

1. In a medium bowl, place the ground turkey, egg, almond flour, salt, ground black pepper, garlic powder, mozzarella, sun-dried tomatoes, and fresh basil, mix thoroughly.
2. Form into 16 meatballs.
3. Place a large nonstick sauté pan over medium heat, add in the olive oil.
4. Once heated, add in the meatballs about 1 inch apart, cook over low/medium heat for 3 minutes per side, or

until thoroughly cooked - the cheese will melt out, so be careful not to burn them or turn the heat down if they're browning too quickly.

5. Serve alone, with marinara sauce on skewers between fresh mozzarella, basil leaves, and cherry tomatoes.
6. Enjoy!

Nutrition: Calories: 312 Total Fat: 24g Protein: 24g Net Carbs: 2g

808. Avocado Fries

Preparation time: 10 Minutes
Cooking time: 15 Minutes
Servings 2

Ingredients:

- 1 large avocado not too ripe
- ½ cup almond meal
- 1 tsp. Cajun seasoning
- ¼ cup almond milk
- Non- stick baking sheet

Directions:

1. Preheat oven to 450 degrees F.
2. Cut the avocado lengthwise and twist halves to separate, removing the pit and peeling the skin off.
3. Then cut the avocado into wedges.
4. In a shallow bowl, put the almond milk.
5. In a separate bowl, blend the almond meal and Cajun seasoning.
6. Dip avocado slices in almond milk, then press them into the almond meal to thoroughly coat the avocado slices – you can also pour the almond meal over the avocado with a spoon.
7. Place the avocado fries on a nonstick baking sheet.
8. Bake for at least 15 to 18 minutes until it makes lightly golden.
9. Remove from the oven and allow them to cool for 1 to 2 minutes.
10. Serve!

Recipe Notes:

1. To make a quick dipping sauce, add ¼ cup mayonnaise with 2 Tbsp. Plain, full-fat Greek yogurt, and 1 Tbsp. Buffalo sauce in a bowl, mix thoroughly.

Nutrition: Calories: 206 Total Fat: 19.3g Protein: 3.8g Net Carbs: 2.5g

809. Banana & Tortilla Snacks

Preparation time: 5 minutes
Cooking time: 5 minutes
Servings: 1

Ingredients:

- 1 flour tortilla (6 inches)
- 2 tablespoons peanut butter
- 1 tablespoon honey
- 1 banana
- 2 tablespoons raisins

Directions:

1. Lay the tortilla flat.
2. Spread honey and peanut on the tortilla.
3. Put the banana in the middle and sprinkle the raisins. Wrap and serve.

Nutrition: 520 calories 19.3 grams of fat 82.9 g carbohydrates 12.8 g of protein 0 mg of cholesterol 357 mg of sodium.

810. Sugar-Coated Pecans

Preparation time: 15 minutes
Cooking time: 60 minutes
Servings: 12

Ingredients:

- 1 egg white
- 1 tablespoon water
- 1 pound pecan halves
- 1 cup white sugar
- 3/4 teaspoon salt
- 1/2 teaspoon ground cinnamon

Directions:

1. Set the oven to 120 ° C. Grease a baking tray.
2. In a bowl, whisk the egg whites and water until frothy.
3. Put and combine the sugar, salt, and cinnamon in another bowl.
4. Add the pecans to the egg whites then stir to cover the nuts. Remove the nuts and mix them with the sugar until well covered. Spread the nuts on the arrange baking sheet.
5. Bake for 1 hour at 250 ° F (120 ° C). Stir every 15 minutes.

Nutrition: 328 calories 27.2 g fat 22 grams of carbohydrates 3.8 g of protein 0 mg of cholesterol 150 mg of sodium

811. Spooky Spider Snacks

Preparation time: 15 minutes
Cooking time: 0 minutes
Servings: 10

Ingredients:

- 20 buttery round crackers
- 5 tablespoons pressurized canned Cheddar cheese spread
- 60 pretzel sticks
- 20 raisins

Directions:

1. Spread 10 salted crackers evenly with about 1/2 tablespoon of spreadable cheese; cover each cookie with another to make sandwiches.
2. Stick 6 pretzel sticks in the cheese, 3 on each side, to obtain 6 legs. Put two dots of cheese on the sandwich and glue two grape eyes on each snack.

Nutrition: 128 calories 3.9 g fat 19.7 g of carbohydrates 3.1 g of protein 6 mg cholesterol 697 mg of sodium.

812. Pita Chips

Preparation time: 10 minutes
Cooking time: 7 minutes
Servings: 24

Ingredients:

- 12 slices of pita bread
- 1/2 cup of olive oil
- 1/2 teaspoon ground black pepper
- 1 teaspoon garlic salt
- 1/2 teaspoon dried basil
- 1 teaspoon dried chervil

Directions:

1. Set the oven to 400°F.
2. Cut each pita bread into 8 triangles. Place the triangles on the baking sheet.
3. Combine oil, pepper, salt, basil, and chervil in a small bowl. Brush each triangle with the oil mixture.
4. Bake for at least 7 minutes or until light brown and crispy.

Nutrition: 125 calories 5.3 g fat 17.7 g of carbohydrates 3.2 g of protein 0 mg of cholesterol 246 mg of sodium

813. Brown Sugar Smokies

Preparation time: 10 minutes
Cooking time: 15 minutes
Servings: 12

Ingredients:

- 1 pound bacon
- 1 (16 ounces) package little smokie sausages
- 1 cup brown sugar, or to taste

Directions:

1. Set the oven to 175 ° C.
2. Cut the bacon in three and wrap each strip around a little sausage. Place sausages wrapped on wooden skewers, several to one place the kebabs on a baking sheet, and sprinkle generously with brown sugar.
3. Bake up to the bacon is crispy, and the brown sugar has melted.

Nutrition: 356 calories 27.2 g fat 18.9 g of carbohydrates 9 g of protein 49 mg cholesterol 696 mg of sodium

814. Soup and Stew

Preparation time: 10 minutes
Cooking time: 15 minutes
Servings: 8

Ingredients:

- 1 tablespoon extra-virgin olive oil
- 1 large red onion, chopped
- 1 stalk celery, chopped
- 2 carrots, chopped
- 4 cloves garlic, chopped
- 2 tablespoons chili powder
- 1 tablespoon ground cumin
- Salt and pepper to taste
- 4 cups vegetable broth
- 4 (15 ounces) cans black beans
- 1 (15 ounces) can whole kernel corn
- 1 (14.5 ounces) can crushed tomatoes

Directions:

1. In a big casserole, heat oil over medium-high heat. Sauté onion, celery, carrots, and garlic for 5 minutes.
2. Season with chili powder, cumin, and salt and pepper and cook for an additional 1 minute.
3. Stir in vegetable broth, 2 cans of beans, and corn. Bring to a boil.
4. Using a food processor, process the remaining 2 cans beans and tomatoes until smooth. Stir into boiling soup mixture, reduce heat to medium, and simmer for 15 minutes.

Nutrition: Calories: 1054 kcal Protein: 5.16 g Fat: 112.11 g Carbohydrates: 20.32 g

815. Buckwheat Split Pea Soup

Preparation time: 10 minutes
Cooking time: 3 hours
Servings: 6

Ingredients

- 1 tablespoon extra-virgin olive oil
- 2 cups dried split peas
- ½ cup buckwheat groats
- 1 ½ teaspoons salt
- 7 cups of water
- 3 carrots, chopped
- 3 stalks celery, chopped
- 1 red onion, diced
- 3 potatoes, diced
- 1 teaspoon curry powder
- 3 cloves garlic, minced
- ½ cup parsley, chopped
- ½ teaspoon dried oregano
- ½ teaspoon dried thyme
- ½ teaspoon turmeric
- ½ teaspoon black pepper

Directions:

1. In a large pot, sauté the oil, onion, and garlic for 5 minutes on medium heat, up to the garlic is fragrant, and the onions are translucent.
2. Add the peas, buckwheat, salt, and water.
3. Set to a boil and then reduce the heat to low. Simmer for 2 hours, stirring occasionally.
4. Add the carrots, celery, red onion, potatoes, dried oregano and thyme, turmeric, and ground black pepper. Simmer for additional 45 minutes or until the peas and vegetables are tender.
5. Add the parsley, stir well and allow to steep for a final 10 minutes.

Nutrition: Calories: 423 kcal Protein: 20.75 g Fat: 2.24 g Carbohydrates: 83.17 g

816. Hot And Sour Miso Soup

Preparation time: 30 minutes
Cooking time: 10 minutes
Servings: 6

Ingredients:

- 6 dried shiitake mushrooms
- 2 cups hot water
- 3 tablespoons soy sauce
- 5 tablespoons rice vinegar
- 1/4 cup cornstarch
- 1 (8 ounces) container firm tofu, cut into 1/4 inch strips
- 1 (8 ounces) can bamboo shoots, drained
- 1 quart Miso broth
- 1/4 teaspoon chili pepper flakes
- 1 teaspoon ground black pepper
- 1/2 tablespoon chili oil
- 1/2 tablespoon sesame oil
- 1 green onion, sliced

Directions:

1. In a small bowl, place shiitake mushrooms in 1 1/2 cups hot water. Soak for 20 minutes, until rehydrated.
2. Drain, reserving the liquid. Cut stems from the mushrooms and cut into thin strips.
3. In a separate small bowl, mix soy sauce, rice vinegar, and 1 tablespoon cornstarch. Put 1/2 the tofu strips into the mixture.
4. In a medium saucepan, stir the reserved mushroom liquid with the vegetable broth. Set to a boil and stir in the mushrooms and bamboo shoots. Reduce heat, and simmer 3 to 5 minutes—season with chili peppers and black pepper.
5. In a small bowl, blend the remaining cornstarch and the remaining water. Stir into the broth mixture until thickened.
6. Blend soy sauce mixture and remaining tofu strips into the saucepan. Return to boil and stir in the chili oil and sesame oil.
7. Garnish with green onion to serve.

Nutrition: Calories: 161 kcal Protein: 9.4 g Fat: 8.62 g Carbohydrates: 13.24 g

817. Garlic, Spinach, And Chickpea Soup

Preparation time: 10 minutes
Cooking time: 25 minutes
Servings: 6

Ingredients:

- 2 tablespoons olive oil
- 4 cloves garlic, peeled and crushed
- 1 medium yellow onion, coarsely chopped
- 2 teaspoons ground cumin

- 2 teaspoons ground coriander
- 1 1/3 quarts vegetable broth
- 3 medium potatoes, peeled and chopped
- 1 (15 ounces) can chickpeas, drained
- 1 cup heavy cream
- 2 tablespoons tahini
- 2 tablespoons cornmeal
- 3 cups spinach, rinsed and chopped
- 2 teaspoons fresh parsley, chopped
- Chili pepper flakes to taste
- Salt to taste

Directions:

1. In a big casserole, heat the oil over medium heat and stir in garlic and onion. Cook until tender, 2 – 3 minutes. Season with cumin and coriander.
2. Stir vegetable stock and potatoes into the pot and bring to a boil. Lower the heat, and simmer about 10 minutes.
3. Mix in the chickpeas and continue to cook until the potatoes are tender about 5 minutes.
4. In a small bowl, stir the heavy cream, tahini, and cornmeal. Mix into the soup.
5. Stir spinach into the soup—season with parsley, chili pepper flakes, and salt. Continue to cook up to the spinach is heated through, about another 5 minutes.

Nutrition: Calories: 382 kcal Protein: 10.16 g Fat: 17.24 g Carbohydrates: 49.2 g

818. Cajun Shrimp Soup

Preparation time: 10 minutes
Cooking time: 25 minutes
Servings: 6
Ingredients:

- 1 tablespoon extra-virgin olive oil
- 1/2 cup green bell pepper, chopped
- 1/4 cup green onions, sliced
- 1 clove garlic, minced
- 3 cups tomato juice
- 1 (8 ounces) bottle clam juice
- 1/2 cup water
- 1/4 teaspoon dried lovage
- 1/4 teaspoon dried basil
- 1/4 teaspoon chili pepper flakes
- 1 bay leaf
- 1/2 teaspoon salt
- 1/2 cup cooked buckwheat groats
- 3/4 pound fresh shrimp, peeled
- Hot pepper sauce, to taste

Directions:

1. In a big casserole, heat the oil over medium heat. Sauté bell pepper, onions, and garlic until tender.
2. Stir in tomato juice, clam juice, and water—season with lovage, basil, chili pepper flakes, bay leaf, and salt.
3. Put to a boil and stir in buckwheat. Reduce heat and cover. Simmer 15 minutes.
4. Mix in shrimp and cook for 5 minutes or until shrimp are opaque.
5. Take off the bay leaf and season with hot sauce to serve.

Nutrition: Calories: 135 kcal Protein: 14.5 g Fat: 3.28 g Carbohydrates: 12.29 g

819. Tofu Mushroom Soup

Preparation time: 10 minutes
Cooking time: 15 minutes
Servings: 6
Ingredients:

- 500ml vegetable broth (or 500 ml of water and One tbsp. dehydrated vegetable broth)
- 375ml Soy beverage
- 250g button mushrooms ready to use
- 240g herb tofu
- 4 tbsp. tapioca
- 1 medium onion
- 1 tbsp. canola oil
- 1 tbsp. parsley
- Pepper to taste

Directions:

1. Rinse the mushrooms well and cut it into pieces.
2. Peel the onion and dice it.
3. Heat the oil over medium heat in a saucepan. Sauté the onion in the oil for one minute, and then add the mushrooms and cook for five minutes, stirring occasionally.
4. While the mushrooms and onion cook cut the diced tofu, and wash and chop your parsley.
5. Add the vegetable broth and soy beverage to the mixture cooking.
6. Add the tapioca into the mixture, then add the tofu. Continue cooking over low heat for about seven minutes.
7. Sprinkle with chopped parsley and serve.

Nutrition: Calories: 210 kcal Protein: 9.6 g Fat: 12.45 g Carbohydrates: 17.32 g

820. Pichelsteiner Stew

Preparation time: 10 minutes
Cooking time: 25 minutes
Servings: 6
Ingredients:

- 400 g stuck potatoes
- 500 g huge carrots (5 huge carrots)
- 350 g huge onions (5 huge onions)
- 2 garlic cloves
- 500 g savoy cabbage (0.5 head)
- 200 gather sheep (from the leg)
- 200 g pork (from the top shell)
- 150 gathers meat goulash
- salt
- pepper
- 2 branches thyme
- 2 branches rosemary
- 2 stems marjoram
- 2 tbsp. rapeseed oil
- 700 ml exemplary vegetable stock

Directions:

1. Wash, strip and cut potatoes and carrots.
2. Peel the garlic and onions then cut them into fine cuts.
3. Clean and wash savoy cabbage. Evacuate the tail and cut the cabbage into wide strips.
4. Cut a wide range of meat into roughly 2 cm solid shapes and season with salt and pepper. Wash thyme, rosemary, and marjoram and shake dry.
5. Heat the oil in a sealable, ovenproof pot or a little cooking dish and burn the meat completely in divides all around. Remove the oven.
6. Remove 2/3 of the meat from the pan and spot half of the readied vegetables on the meat in the pot—season with salt and pepper.
7. Put 1/3 of the meat put aside back in the pot. Spread the rest of the vegetables on top, salt, and pepper.
8. Put the rest of the meat in the pot and spread the herbs over it. Pour in the stock, cover, and heat to the point of

boiling. Cook the stew in the preheated stove at 175 ° C (fan broiler: 150 ° C, gas: speed 2) on the center rack for an hour and a half. Serve the Pichelstein stew directly from the pan.

Nutrition: Calories: 253 kcal Protein: 13.46 g Fat: 9.64 g Carbohydrates: 30.08 g

821. Chicken Soup The Grandmother's Way

Preparation time: 20 minutes
Cooking time: 45 minutes
Servings: 4-6

Ingredients:

- 1½ kg chicken (1 chicken)
- 3 onions
- 2 inlet leaves
- 12 dark peppercorns
- Salt
- 300 g celeriac (0.5 celeriac)
- 400 g huge carrots (3 enormous carrots)
- 150 g little leek (1 little leek)
- 150 g parsnips (2 parsnips)
- 150 g parsley root (3 parsley roots)
- 200 g Hokkaido pumpkin (1 piece)
- 175 g entire grain vermicelli
- 2 stems lovage

Directions:

1. Wash the chicken, bring it in a pot, and place to the bubble, secured with 3 l of water.
2. Remove the froth rising upwards with a froth trowel.
3. In the interim, unpeel the onions down the middle and meal them enthusiastically in a container on the cut surfaces over high warmth without fat.
4. Add onions with narrows leaves, peppercorns, and somewhat salt to the skimmed stock, stew for 15 minutes on low warmth, skimming if fundamental.
5. Peel and clean 50% of the celery and carrots. Clean and wash half of the leek. Generally, dice everything.
6. Put the readied vegetables in the pot and cook over medium warmth for 1/2 hours.
7. Remaining celery, remaining carrots, cleaning, and stripping the parsnips and parsley roots. Clean and wash the pumpkin and remaining leek. Cut everything into 2 cm 3D shapes or cuts.
8. Take the chicken out of the soup. Expel the skin and segregate the meat from the bones.
9. Cut the meat into 2 cm 3D squares and put it in a safe spot.
10. Pour the chicken soup through a sifter into a subsequent pot, cook the diced vegetables in it over medium warmth for 10-15 minutes. Heat the pasta in salted water, channel, hold quickly under running, cold water (alarm), and add to the chicken soup with the meat and warmth. Wash lovage, shake dry, and pluck the leaves. Serve the chicken soup sprinkled with the leaves.

Nutrition: Calories: 687 kcal Protein: 65.18 g Fat: 24.81 g Carbohydrates: 53.5 g

822. Caldo Verde - Portuguese Kale Soup

Preparation time: 5 minutes
Cooking time: 15 minutes
Servings: 6

Ingredients:

- ½ kg of potatoes or only a couple of medium bits of
- About 2-3 bunches of hacked kale (without thick stalks)
- Less than 1 liter of vegetable stock
- 1 white onion
- 1 clove of garlic
- 1 tablespoon of olive oil
- 1-2 tsp. smoked peppers (for soup and serving)
- Salt, pepper
- Toppings: smoked tempeh, seared tofu, firm roll (discretionary)

Directions:

1. Fry finely cleaved onion in olive oil and ground garlic on a grater.
2. Add the recently stripped and diced potatoes and fry for around 10 minutes along with the onion.
3. Then pour the entire stock and cook until the potatoes are delicate.
4. Pull out a large portion of the potatoes in a steady progression, put aside a bowl for some time, and blend the soup in a pot in with a hand blender. At that point, include the remainder of the potatoes and hacked kale pieces. Cook for a few minutes up to the kale relaxes and has a light green shading.
5. Season the soup with liberal pepper and salt and smoked paprika.
6. Serve with singed tempeh or tofu and eat with a fresh roll.

Nutrition: Calories: 120 kcal Protein: 3.05 g Fat: 3.41 g Carbohydrates: 20.26 g

823. Swabian Beef Stew

Preparation time: 20 minutes
Cooking time: 2 hours and 40 minutes
Servings: 6-8

Ingredients:

- 2 onions
- 600 g bubbled hamburger
- Salt
- 250 g carrots (2 carrots)
- 275 g potatoes
- 200 g celeriac (1 piece)
- 1 stick leek
- 200 g wholegrain spaetzle
- Pepper
- 2 stems parsley

Directions:

1. Halve onions and dish with the chop surfaces looking down in a hot skillet without including fat over medium warmth.
2. Rinse the meat cold. A spot in a pot with the onions and 1 tsp. Salt and spread with approx. 2 l cold water.
3. Bring to the bubble and evacuate the rising dim froth with the trowel. Decrease the warmth and stew the meat over medium warmth for an aggregate of 2 hours.
4. In the interim, wash and strip carrots, potatoes, and celery. Cut everything into 1 cm solid shapes. Put potatoes in chilly water, so they don't change shading.
5. Halve the leek lengthways and wash under running water. Cut into 1 cm wide rings.
6. Remove the onions from the stock 35 minutes before the finish of the cooking time, including the celery and carrots.
7. After an additional 15 minutes, including the depleted potato shapes and the leek.
8. Cook the spaetzle in bubbling salted water as indicated by the bundle directions. Deplete and extinguish cold.

9. At the finish of the cooking time, remove the meat from the stock and cut into reduced down 3D squares.
10. Add the meat solid shapes with the spaetzle to the stock and warmth—season with salt and pepper.
11. Wash the parsley, shake dry, cleave and sprinkle with the stew.

Nutrition: Calories: 316 kcal Protein: 11.84 g Fat: 4.9 g Carbohydrates: 56.28 g

824. Chicken Broth

Preparation time: 20 minutes
Cooking time: 2 hours and 40 minutes
Servings: 8

Ingredients:

- 3 kg poultry bones for the back (ideally natural)
- 1 tsp salt
- 3 onions
- 300 g carrots (3 carrots)
- 250 g leek (1 stick)
- 12 dark peppercorns

Directions:

1. Rinse the poultry bones cold in a colander and let them channel.
2. Roughly slash the bones.
3. Place the bones in an enormous pot, spread with approx. 4 l of water and include salt.
4. Bring poultry stock to a bubble. Skim off the rising froth with a froth trowel.
5. Peel onions and carrots, clean and wash leeks, cut everything into enormous pieces.
6. After skimming, add the vegetables and peppercorns to the pan.
7. Let it cook open for around 2 1/2 hours on low warmth, continually skimming if important. Put the poultry stock through a coarse strainer toward the finish of the cooking time and afterward through a fine one.
8. Chill poultry stock for the time being and evacuate the solidified fat layer the following day.
9. Bring the poultry stock to the bubble once more, skim it and let it come down to 1.2 l.
10. Let cool once more. Presently it remains new in the refrigerator for as long as 3 days. For a longer period of usability, freeze poultry stock in a cooler sack (firmly shut!) Or in the ice 3D shape compartment.
11. Tip: Rinse clean safeguarding containers with bubbling water, flip around them on a kitchen towel, and let them channel. At that point, empty the poultry stock into the containers while bubbling hot, close them and flip around the containers for 5 minutes. The poultry stock will keep going for a couple of months if hand contact within the containers and tops has maintained a strategic distance.

Nutrition: Calories: 805 kcal Protein: 53.72 g Fat: 59.01 g Carbohydrates: 11.36 g

825. Chestnut Soup With Pear And Nut Topping

Preparation time: 10 minutes
Cooking time: 25 minutes
Servings: 6

Ingredients:

- 1 shallot
- 4 parsnips
- 400 g chestnuts (pre-cooked; vacuumed)
- 2 tbsp. olive oil
- 600 ml vegetable stock
- 30 g hazelnut bits (2 tbsp.)
- 1 pear
- 1 tsp. Nectar
- ½ tsp. turmeric powder
- 2 tbsp. squeezed orange
- 200 g whipped cream
- Salt
- Pepper
- 2 stems parsley

Directions:

1. Peel the shallot, clean, strip, and wash the parsnips. Cleave the shallot and one parsnip. Generally cut chestnuts.
2. In a pot, warm 1 tablespoon of oil. Braise shallot in it over medium warmth for 2 minutes, include chestnuts and parsnip pieces and braise for 3 minutes. Pour in the stock and cook over medium warmth for around 15 minutes.
3. Meanwhile, dice the rest of the parsnips—cleave hazelnuts. Wash, quarter, center, and cut the pear into blocks.
4. Heat the rest of the oil in a search for gold garnish. Fry the parsnip 3D shapes for 5-7 minutes. At that point, include nuts, pears, nectar, turmeric, and squeezed orange and caramelize for 2 minutes over medium warmth.
5. Puree the soup with cream and season with salt and pepper. Wash parsley, shake dry and cleave. Pour the fixing over the soup and sprinkle with parsley.

Nutrition: Calories: 299 kcal Protein: 4.54 g Fat: 16.52 g Carbohydrates: 34.03 g

826. Potato Mince Soup With Mushrooms

Preparation time: 10 minutes
Cooking time: 35 minutes
Servings: 6

Ingredients:

- 600 g overwhelmingly hard-bubbled potatoes
- 200 g leek (1 little stick)
- 2 tbsp. rapeseed oil
- 800 ml of vegetable stock
- Salt
- ½ tsp. ground cumin
- 200 g mushrooms
- 400 g ground hamburger
- ½ tsp. dried marjoram
- 200 g whipped cream
- 20 g parsley (0.5 bundles)
- 40 g pecans

Directions:

1. Peel, wash, and cut the potatoes into little blocks. Clean and wash the leek, divide lengthways, and cut into fine rings.
2. In a pan, heat the 1 tablespoon of oil, include the potatoes and the leek and sauté for 3-4 minutes over medium warmth. Pour in the stock then season with salt and caraway and cook for 10-15 minutes.
3. Meanwhile, clean mushrooms, wash if necessary, and cut into cuts. Heat the remaining oil in a skillet, sauté the minced meat for 5 minutes while mixing, including the mushrooms and fry for an additional 3 minutes—season with marjoram, salt, and caraway.
4. Add the cream and the minced mushroom blend to the soup, mix and let it heat up. Wash parsley, shake dry and hack. Generally slash pecans. Serve soup decorated with parsley and pecans.

Nutrition: Calories: 370 kcal Protein: 19.37 g Fat: 22.26 g Carbohydrates: 25.74 g

827. Cold Tomato And Melon Soup

Preparation time: 10 minutes
Cooking time: 20 minutes + 30 minutes cooling time
Servings: 4

Ingredients:

- Beef tomato
- ½ melon
- 1 little bean stew pepper
- 150 g little ringer pepper (1 little chime pepper)
- 1 tbsp. lime juice
- 500 ml tomato juice
- Salt
- Pepper
- 2 spring onions
- 4 stems mint
- 4 tsp. olive oil

Directions:

1. Clean, wash, and diced tomatoes. Divide the melon, evacuate the stones, strip, and cut the mash into shapes, some of them aside. Divide, cleave, wash, and slash lengthways. Divide the pepper, expel the seeds, wash and cut into 3D shapes.
2. Put tomatoes, melon, half of the solid paprika shapes, and bean stew with lime and tomato squeeze in a blender and puree until a soup-like consistency is acquired, including a little water if necessary. Season everything with salt and pepper and refrigerate for around 30 minutes.
3. In the interim, clean, wash and cut the spring onions into fine rings. Wash mint, shake dry, pluck leaves, and generally hack.
4. Divide the soup into 4 dishes, sprinkle with spring onions, remaining peppers, melons and mint, shower with 1 teaspoon of oil.

Nutrition: Calories: 1662 kcal Protein: 74.86 g Fat: 29.66 g Carbohydrates: 351.45 g

828. Lentil Curry Soup With Sheep's Cheese

Preparation time: 10 minutes
Cooking time: 20 minutes
Servings: 6

Ingredients:

- 80 g red focal points
- 600 ml vegetable stock
- 1 tsp. curry powder
- 100 g celery (2 stems)
- Salt
- Pepper
- 150 g sheep cheddar (45% fat in dry issue)
- 2 tsp. olive oil
- 2 cuts entire grain bread

Directions:

1. Bring the lentils and stock to the bubble in a pan. Include the curry powder and spread and cook for 10 minutes over low warmth.
2. In the interim, wash celery, channel, clean, and, if vital, unwind. Put the celery green in a safe spot.
3. Cut the celery into around 5 mm slight cuts, add to the lentils, and spread it for another 3-4 minutes.
4. Season the curry lentil soup with salt and pepper. Disintegrate sheep cheddar. Sprinkle with celery, organize with cheddar and olive oil, and present with the bread.

Nutrition: Calories: 73 kcal Protein: 2.99 g Fat: 4.37 g Carbohydrates: 5.85 g

829. Carrots - Cream Soup

Preparation time: 15 minutes
Cooking time: 15 minutes
Servings: 4

Ingredients:

- 100 g carrots (1 carrot)
- 20 g parsley root (1 piece)
- 100 g potatoes (1 potato)
- 220 ml exemplary vegetable stock
- 6 stems arugula
- Salt
- Pepper
- Nutmeg
- 1 tsp. chipped almonds

Directions:

1. Wash the carrot and parsley root, strip and cut into cuts around 1 cm thick. Strip, wash, and shakers the potato.
2. Bring the vegetable stock to a bubble in a pot. Include the readied vegetables, bring to the bubble, and spread and cook over low warmth for 15 minutes.
3. In the interim, wash the rocket, shake it dry, expel the unpleasant stalks, and cleave.
4. Pour the soup in a blender or with a hand blender. Salt, pepper, and include a little nutmeg.
5. Fill the soup into a soup bowl or a profound plate, sprinkle with rocket, and chipped almonds.

Nutrition: Calories: 36 kcal Protein: 1.13 g Fat: 0.28 g Carbohydrates: 7.87 g

830. Asparagus Soup With Carrots

Preparation time: 15 minutes
Cooking time: 55 minutes
Servings: 6

Ingredients:

- 400 g asparagus
- 1 shallot
- 100 g floury potatoes
- 1 tbsp. spread
- 100 ml of vegetable stock
- 50 g creme fraiche cheddar
- Salt
- Pepper
- 125 g shrimps (8 shrimps; without head and shell)
- ½ lime
- 1 carrot
- 1 stem coriander
- 1 tbsp. rapeseed oil

Directions:

1. Peel asparagus, cut off woody finishes if fundamental. Spot bowls and segments in a pot, spread with 600 ml of water and stew for approx. Ten minutes on low warmth. Include asparagus sticks, delicately salt, cook in the blend for around 20 minutes with a light nibble. Expel the sticks from the blend and let them cool marginally. Mix through a strainer.
2. Peel and dice the shallot, strip, wash and cut the potatoes into pieces. Sauté quickly with the shallot in a hot pan in margarine. Mix in the flour and deglaze with 500 ml asparagus. Cook for around 15 minutes, mixing at times. In the interim, cut the asparagus lances into 3 cm pieces, add to the soup, include crème fraîche, and puree the soup.

3. Rinse the shrimp, pat dry, and spread on a level plate.
4. Squeeze the lime and sprinkle the juice over the prawns.
5. Clean, wash and strip the carrot. First cut into slight cuts, at that point into fine pencils.
6. Wash the coriander, shake dry, pluck the leaves, and put in a safe spot.
7. Heat the rapeseed oil in a container and sauté the carrots for 4–5 minutes.
8. Add shrimp and sauté for 1–2 minutes, blending much of the time. Remove the oven. Topping the soup with carrots, shrimps, and coriander leaves and serve.

Nutrition: Calories: 115 kcal Protein: 8.82 g Fat: 5.89 g Carbohydrates: 7.8 g

831. Mediterranean Vegetable Broth

Preparation time: 10 minutes
Cooking time: 1 hour and 10 minutes
Servings: 6
Ingredients:

- 100 g carrots (2 carrots)
- 250 g fennel bulb (2 fennel bulbs)
- 75 g celery (4 stems)
- 80 g tomatoes (6 tomatoes)
- 50 g red onions (3 red onions)
- 2 garlic cloves
- 2 tbsp. olive oil
- 3 stems basil
- 8th dark peppercorns
- 1 squeeze saffron strings
- 3 narrows leaves

Directions:

1. Wash and clean the carrots, fennel, and celery, expel the celery if necessary, and slash it generally. Wash the tomatoes and cut them into little pieces.
2. Halve onions unpeeled. Strip cloves of garlic and squash them with the rear of a blade.
3. Heat olive oil in a huge pan. Braise the fennel, carrots, celery, tomatoes, onions, and garlic over low warmth, blending as often as possible, for 8-10 minutes.
4. Add 4 liters of water and heat to the point of boiling.
5. Skim off any froth that may happen with a trowel.
6. Rinse the basil, shake it dry and add it to the pot with peppercorns, saffron, and sound leaves. Spread and cook over medium warmth for around 60 minutes.
7. Put the fluid through a fine strainer in a subsequent post. Come down to around 1200 ml over high warmth. Either use it straight away or keep it refrigerated; the stock remains there for as long as 3 days.

Nutrition: Calories: 80 kcal Protein: 2.08 g Fat: 5.68 g Carbohydrates: 6.17 g

832. Anti-Inflammatory Ginger-Turmeric Carrot Soup

Preparation time: 45 minutes
Cooking time: 30 minutes
Servings: 2
Ingredients:

- 32 ounces Carrots
- 4 to 6 cups Water
- 1 tablespoon grated fresh ginger
- 1 tablespoon Turmeric
- 4 tablespoons extra virgin olive oil
- 1 ½ cups Coconut milk
- 6 cloves Garlic (peeled and minced)
- 1Medium yellow onion
- Juice of one lime
- ½ teaspoon Ground cayenne pepper
- 1 ½ teaspoon kosher salt
- To Garnish
- 3 tablespoons extra virgin olive oil
- 2 Large fennel bulbs
- 4 tablespoons finely minced scallions
- ¼ cup Pepitas
- Pinch of salt

Directions:

1. Heat your oven to 375 degrees F or 190 degrees C.
2. Coat your carrots with 2 tablespoons of the extra virgin olive oil and place on a baking sheet. Place the baking sheet into the oven to roast for about one hour until tender but not caramelized.
3. When the carrots are done, take it out of the oven and increase the oven heat to 400 degrees F. Thinly slice the fennel bulbs and slowly saute them in 3 tablespoons of oil and a small amount of salt, until it starts to soften. Now place the skillet into the oven to roast the fennel for about 30 minutes until it becomes caramelized and crispy. Set aside once done.
4. Place a dry pan over medium heat, then add the pepitas and toast until it gets brown – this should take about 4 minutes. Set aside once done.
5. Chop the onions and saute it in a pan with the remaining olive oil, for about 12 minutes, until tender. Put the minced garlic to the pan and cook until the garlic begins to get brown and fragrant.
6. Place the onion and carrots mixture into a blender, add all other ingredients minus the water. Blend until you get a smooth texture. Put a small amount of water to thin the consistency.
7. Transfer the mixture into a pan and allow it to simmer over medium heat. Put some more water if needed to thin the soup.
8. Serve the soup and garnish with the scallion greens, pepitas, and caramelized fennel.

Nutrition Facts: Energy (calories): 483 kcal; Protein: 18.13 g; Fat: 66.46 g; Carbohydrates: 95.12 g

833. Turmeric Zucchini Soup

Preparation time: 5 minutes
Cooking time: 15 minutes
Servings: 2
Ingredients:

- 1 tablespoon extra-virgin olive oil
- ½ teaspoon Sea salt
- 1Large onion (diced)
- 1 teaspoon Mild curry powder
- 3 cloves Garlic (diced)
- 2Medium zucchini (cubed)
- Fresh cilantro or coriander, to garnish
- ¼ teaspoon White pepper
- 2 teaspoons Turmeric powder
- 2 tablespoons Lime juice
- 1 teaspoon Fish sauce
- 1 cup Coconut milk
- 1 cup Vegetable stock

Directions:

1. Bring a medium saucepan over medium heat and add the ghee. Once hot, add the onion and saute for about four to five minutes, occasionally stirring, until golden and soft.

2. Add the garlic, zucchini, and salt. Stir to mix with the onion. Then add the pepper, curry powder, and turmeric and stir for some seconds to release the aromas.
3. Now add the fish sauce, coconut milk, and vegetable stock and stir again. Let it boil then lower the heat. Cover and simmer for 10 minutes.
4. Add the lime juice and stir through.
5. Garnish with a few fresh coriander leaves.

Nutrition: Energy (calories): 475 kcal; Protein: 8.5 g; Fat: 32.64 g; Carbohydrates: 45.53 g

834. Kale And Stilton Soup

Preparation time: 10 minutes
Cooking time: 20 minutes
Servings: 4

Ingredients:

- 100g Stilton Cheese
- 1large potato (peeled and chopped finely)
- 200g chopped kale
- 1 liter vegetable stock
- 3 tablespoons double cream
- Fresh nutmeg

Directions:

1. Add the vegetable stock and the diced potatoes into a large pan, cover with a lid and allow to boil, then cook for 10 minutes until the potato softens.
2. Add the crumbled stilton and chopped kale, cover, and cook for another five minutes.
3. Add the double cream, stir and add a generous amount of grounded fresh nutmeg—season to taste. Utilize the back of your spoon to mash some of the potatoes.
4. Serve with some more crumbled stilton on top.

Nutrition: Energy (calories): 164 kcal; Protein: 4.03 g; Fat: 2.34 g; Carbohydrates: 32.64 g

835. Crockpot Sweet Potato Stew

Preparation time: 15 minutes
Cooking time: 8 minutes
Servings: 4-6

Ingredients:

- 3 cups Chopped sweet potatoes
- 1 Small yellow onion
- 1/4 cup Chopped celery
- 8-ounce bag Mini carrots
- 1 can diced tomatoes (14.5 ounces)
- 1 can Corn (15 ounces)
- 1 cup Water
- 1 pound Stew meat (cut into 1-inch)
- 2 tablespoons Flour
- ½ teaspoon Seasoned salt
- ½ teaspoon Pepper
- 1 teaspoon minced garlic
- 1Bay leaf
- ½teaspoon Paprika
- 2 tablespoons fresh parsley
- 1 teaspoon Worcestershire sauce
- 2 Beef bouillon cubes
- Optional: fresh flat-leaf parsley

Directions:

1. Oil a slow cooker with your non-stick spray.
2. Place the chopped sweet potatoes into the slow cooker.
3. Add in the chopped onion, celery, drained can of corn, undrained can have diced tomatoes and the carrots.
4. Stir the salt, pepper, and flour in a large bowl, then add the cut stew meat and toss until well coated.
5. Now place the coated meat on top of the vegetables in the slow cooker. Add the paprika, minced garlic, fresh parsley, Worcestershire sauce, bay leaf, bouillon cubes, and water.
6. Cook and cover the cooker on low heat for about 7 to 9 hours or on high heat for about 5 to 7 hours or until the veggies and the sweet potatoes are tenderized, and the meat is well cooked.
7. Remove the bay leaf before you serve. Also, slightly mash the sweet potatoes in the pot to give a thicker stew consistency. Top with some fresh parsley if desired.

Nutrition: Energy (calories): 352 kcal; Protein: 32.49 g; Fat: 3.32 g; Carbohydrates: 55.39 g

836. Indian Lentil Soup

Preparation time: 15 minutes
Cooking time: 25 -30 minutes
Servings: 2

Ingredients:

- 3 Cups of lentils
- 1 small red onion, chopped
- 1 celery stalk, finely chopped
- 1 chopped carrot
- Large finely chopped kale leaves or 1 cup chopped kale
- Coriander sprigs, chopped
- Sprigs of chopped parsley
- ¼-1/2 hot pepper, seeded and chopped (use more or less as desired)
- 1 tomato, cut into small pieces
- 1 piece of ginger, chopped
- 1 garlic clove, chopped
- 2 Cups chicken or vegetable broth
- 1 teaspoon of turmeric
- 1 teaspoon extra virgin olive oil ½ teaspoon salt

Directions:

1. Cook the lentils according to the package and remove them from the stove about 5 minutes before finishing.
2. Fry all the vegetables in olive oil in a pan. Then add the chopped vegetables at the end. Then put the ginger, garlic, and chili and the turmeric powder.
3. Put the broth and simmer for 5 minutes. Add the lentils and salt.
4. Add the pre-cooked lentils and cook over low heat for another 25 minutes. Pull it out from the stove and allow it cool.
5. Cut the avocado, remove the hole and cut it, then remove the slices just before eating.
6. Cover with an avocado slice and serve immediately.

Nutrition: Calories: 218 Fat: 2.9g Fiber: 4g Carbs: 56g Protein: 4.8g

837. Sirtified Hummus

Preparation time: 15 minutes
Cooking time: 45-50 minutes
Servings: 4

Ingredients:

- 1 green serrano bean stew, minced
- 1 cup cooked chickpeas
- 1/3 cup tahini
- 3 tablespoons new lime or juice
- Stems of celery, cut and dig
- 1 cm pieces (around 1 cup)
- 2 tablespoons vegetable oil (ideally EV)
- Cases of garlic
- 1 teaspoon salt or to taste
- 1 tablespoon minced parsley

Directions:

1. Place the celery into a heating platter. Top with 2 spoonfuls of oil Place the 2 garlic cases during a plate corner and disperse with the bean stew. Bake for 45 minutes within the broiler. Bringing the chickpeas into the blender. Add with any lingering oil into the blender, within the hot cooked celery and different vegetables. Add the tahini, lime or lemon squeeze, salt and blend well for 3-4 minutes until smooth and sweet. Remove from the blender into a bowl, mix within the staying three tablespoons of vegetable oil, and hacked parsley.

Nutrition: Calories: 199 Fat: 3.8g Fiber: 5g Carbs: 39g Protein: 4.8g

838. Shrimp & Arugula Soup

Preparation time: 10 minutes
Cooking time: 30 minutes
Servings: 4

Ingredients:

- Medium-sized shrimp or 5 large prawns, cleaned, deshelled and deveined
- 1 small red onion, sliced very thinly
- 1 cup arugula
- 1 cup baby kale
- Large celery stalks, sliced very thinly
- Sprigs of parsley, chopped
- Cloves of garlic, minced
- 2 Cups of chicken or fish or vegetable stock
- 1 tbsp. extra virgin olive oil
- Dash of sea salt
- Dash of pepper

Directions:

1. Sauté the vegetables (not the kale or arugula just yet, however), in a stockpot, on low heat for around 2 minutes so that they are still tender and still crunchy, but not cooked quite yet.
2. You will need to save the cooking time for the next step. Add the salt and pepper.
3. Next, clean and chop the shrimp into bite-sized pieces that would be comfortable eating in a soup. Then, put the shrimp to the pot and sauté for 10 more minutes on medium-low heat. Make sure the shrimp is cooked thoroughly and is not translucent.
4. When the shrimp seems cooked through, add the stock to the pot, and cook on medium for about 20 more minutes. Remove from heat and cool before serving.

Nutrition: Calories: 210 Fat: 5.8g Fiber: 7g Carbs: 67g Protein: 7g

839. Chilled Gazpacho

Preparation time: 15-20 minutes
Cooking time: 0 minutes
Servings: 2

Ingredients:

- 2 large, or 6 small tomatoes, chopped
- 1 avocado, pitted, sliced, and scooped out (wait to do this until instructed)
- 1 medium cucumber, chopped
- 1 small red onion, chopped
- 1 cup of arugula, chopped very finely
- ½ stalk of celery chopped very finely
- 1 clove of garlic, minced or pressed
- ½ chili or a dash of cayenne pepper
- 1 tsp lime juice
- Dash of sea salt
- Dash of pepper

Directions:

1. Place the ingredients to a blender or a food processor and pulse gently.
2. You do not want to blend too well, or you will make a liquid instead of a soup.
3. The gazpacho should be chunky. After blending, put into the refrigerator for about 1 hour. You can also let this sit overnight, just before eating, slice, and scoop out the avocado. Ladle half of the gazpacho into a chilled bowl. Add the slices of avocado and serve immediately.

Nutrition: Calories: 239 Fat: 4.3g Fiber: 3.2g Carbs: 54g Protein: 4.8g

840. Cauliflower And Walnut Soup

Preparation time: 10 minutes
Cooking time: 25 minutes
Servings: 4

Ingredients:

- 450g (1lb) cauliflower, chopped
- 8 walnut halves, chopped
- 1 red onion, chopped
- 900mls (1½ pints) vegetable stock (broth)
- 100mls (3½ fl oz) double cream (heavy cream)
- ½ teaspoon turmeric
- 1 tablespoon olive oil

Directions:

1. Heat the oil in a saucepan, put the cauliflower and red onion and cook for around 4 minutes, continuously stirring.
2. Pour in the stock (broth), place to the boil and cook for 15 minutes.
3. Mix in the walnuts, double cream, and turmeric.
4. Using a food processor, process the soup up to smooth and creamy.
5. Serve into bowls and top off with a dash of chopped walnuts.

Nutrition: Calories: 10617 kcal Protein: 93.19 g Fat: 1122.61 g Carbohydrates: 113.24 g

841. Celery And Blue Cheese Soup

Preparation time: 10 minutes
Cooking time: 30 minutes
Servings: 4

Ingredients:

- 125g (4oz) blue cheese
- 25g (1oz) butter
- 1 head of celery (approx 650g)
- 1 red onion, chopped
- 900mls (1½ pints) chicken stock (broth)
- 150mls (5fl oz) single cream

Directions:

1. Heat the butter in a saucepan, put the onion and celery, and cook until the vegetables have softened.
2. Pour in the stock, place to the boil then reduce the heat and simmer for 15 minutes.
3. Pour in the cream and stir in the cheese until it has melted.
4. Serve and eat straight away.

Nutrition: Calories: 187 kcal Protein: 8.64 g Fat: 15.59 g Carbohydrates: 3.3 g

842. Sweet Potato And Kale Soup

Preparation time: 15 minutes
Cooking time: 40 minutes
Servings: 4

Ingredients:

- 1 medium red onion
- 1 garlic clove

- 2 medium carrots
- 1 pound of sweet potatoes
- 1 celery stalk
- 2 tbsp. of extra virgin olive oil
- Chili powder to taste
- Cups of vegetable
- ½ pound of kale
- Walnuts

Directions:

1. Peel and cut in small cubes the onions, garlic, carrots, sweet potatoes, and celery stalk.
2. Heat the oil in the pan. Add the cubed vegetables and simmer for 3 minutes.
3. Add chili and salt, if needed
4. Add the stock and let the soup simmer for 20 minutes
5. In the meantime, wash and destem the kale.
6. Lighten the kale for 1 to 2 minutes in boiling salted water
7. Heat up oil in a pan and add the kale. Fry it for 5 minutes.
8. Cut the walnuts
9. Puree the soup with a stab mixer. Add yogurt and chili powder to taste
10. Spoon the soup in 4 bowls and top each bowl with kale and walnuts.

Nutrition: Calories: 658 kcal Protein: 7.01 g Fat: 59.76 g Carbohydrates: 30.64 g

843. Kale, Apple, And Fennel Soup

Preparation time: 10 minutes
Cooking time: 20 minutes
Servings: 4

Ingredients:

- 450g (1lb) kale, chopped
- 200g (7oz) fennel, chopped
- 2 apples, peeled, cored and chopped
- 2 tablespoons fresh parsley, chopped
- 1 tablespoon olive oil
- Sea salt
- Freshly ground black pepper

Directions:

1. Heat the oil in a saucepan put the kale and fennel, and cook for 5 minutes until the fennel has softened.
2. Stir in the apples and parsley.
3. Cover with hot water, bring it to the boil and simmer for 10 minutes.
4. Use a hand blender or food processor blitz until the soup is smooth.
5. Season with salt and pepper.

Nutrition: Calories: 169 kcal Protein: 7.33 g Fat: 6.21 g Carbohydrates: 26.18 g

844. Spicy Pumpkin Soup

Preparation time: 10 minutes
Cooking time: 45 minutes
Servings: 4

Ingredients:

- 150g (5oz) kale
- 1 butternut squash, peeled, de-seeded and chopped
- 1 red onion, chopped
- Bird's-eye chilies, chopped
- Cloves of garlic
- 2 teaspoons turmeric
- 1 teaspoon ground ginger
- 600mls (1 pint) vegetable stock (broth)
- 2 tablespoons olive oil

Directions:

1. Warm the olive oil in a saucepan, put the chopped butternut squash and onion and cook for 6 minutes until softened.
2. Stir in the kale, garlic, chili, turmeric, ginger, and cook for 2 minutes, stirring constantly.
3. Pour in the vegetable stock (broth) place it to the boil, and cook for 20 minutes.
4. Use a food processor, process until it smooths.
5. Serve on its own or with a swirl of cream or crème Fraiche. Enjoy.

Nutrition: Calories: 117 kcal Protein: 3.74 g Fat: 8.71 g Carbohydrates: 7.43 g

845. French Onion Soup

Preparation time: 10 minutes
Cooking time: 60 minutes
Servings: 4

Ingredients:

- 750g (1¾ lbs.) red onions, thinly sliced
- 50g (2oz) Cheddar cheese, grated (shredded)
- 12g (½ oz.) butter
- 2 teaspoons flour
- 2 slices wholemeal bread
- 900mls (1½ pints) beef stock (broth)
- 1 tablespoon olive oil

Directions:

1. In a big pan, warm the oil and butter.
2. Put the onions and gently cook on a low heat for 25 minutes, stirring occasionally.
3. Add in the flour and stir well. Pour in the stock (broth) and keep stirring.
4. Bring to the boil, reduce the heat and simmer for 30 minutes.
5. Cut the slices of bread into triangles, sprinkle with cheese and place them under a hot grill (broiler) until the cheese has melted.
6. Serve the soup into bowls and add 2 triangles of cheesy toast on top. Enjoy.

Nutrition: Calories: 185 kcal Protein: 5.82 g Fat: 8.93 g Carbohydrates: 21.43 g

846. Creamy Broccoli And Kale Soup

Preparation time: 10 minutes
Cooking time: 35 minutes
Servings: 4

Ingredients:

- 250g (9oz) broccoli
- 250g (9oz) kale
- 1 potato, peeled and chopped
- 1 red onion, chopped
- 600mls (1 pint) vegetable stock
- 300mls (½ pint) milk
- 1 tablespoon olive oil
- Sea salt
- Ground black pepper

Directions:

1. Heat the oil in a saucepan, put the onion, and cook for 5 minutes.
2. Add in the potato, kale, and broccoli and cook for 5 minutes.
3. Pour in the stock (broth) and milk and simmer for 20 minutes.
4. Using a food processor or hand blender, process the soup until smooth and creamy.
5. Season with salt and pepper.

6. Re-heat if necessary and serve.

Nutrition: Calories: 177 kcal Protein: 8.42 g Fat: 5.89 g Carbohydrates: 25.93 g

847. Creamy Asparagus Soup

Preparation time: 10 minutes
Cooking time: 10 minutes
Servings: 2

Ingredients:

- Asparagus spears, trimmed
- 1 avocado, pitted and peeled
- A pinch of salt and white pepper
- 1 yellow onion, peeled and chopped
- Cups water

Directions:

1. In your blender, add the mushrooms with asparagus, avocado, onion, water, salt, and pepper.
2. Pulse well, divide into soup bowls, and serve right away. Heat if desired.

Nutrition: Calories: 134 kcal Protein: 3.06 g Fat: 11.25 g Carbohydrates: 7.09 g

848. Mushroom Creamy Soup

Preparation time: 10 minutes
Cooking time: 15 minutes
Servings: 2

Ingredients:

- 2 tablespoons coconut aminos
- 1 tablespoon lime juice
- A pinch of sea salt
- White pepper
- 1 cup white mushrooms
- 1 garlic clove, peeled
- 1 small yellow onion, chopped
- 2 cups cashew milk, unsweetened

Directions:

1. In your blender, mix mushrooms with garlic, onion, cashew milk, salt, pepper, lime juice, and coconut aminos and pulse well.
2. Divide into soup bowls and serve right away.

Nutrition: Calories: 230 kcal Protein: 13.44 g Fat: 11.3 g Carbohydrates: 20.31 g

849. Creamy Tomato Soup

Preparation time: 10 minutes
Cooking time: 10 minutes
Servings: 2

Ingredients:

- 3 sun-dried tomato sliced
- 2 celery stalks, chopped
- 3 big tomatoes, chopped
- ½ teaspoon powdered onion
- 2 basil springs, chopped
- ½ teaspoon garlic powder
- 1 small avocado, pitted and peeled
- Pinch of sea salt
- White pepper

Directions:

1. In your blender, add the tomatoes with celery, onion powder, garlic powder, basil, avocado, salt and pepper, and pulse well.
2. Add sun-dried tomatoes and blend again until smooth.
3. Divide into soup bowls and serve.

Nutrition: Calories: 281 kcal Protein: 8.48 g Fat: 18.34 g Carbohydrates: 26.16 g

850. Grape Gazpacho

Preparation time: 10 minutes
Cooking time: 10 minutes
Servings: 4

Ingredients:

- 1 cup white grapes, seedless and halved
- 1 teaspoon sesame oil
- 2 cups almond milk, unsweetened
- 1 small cucumber, chopped
- A pinch of salt and white pepper
- 1 tablespoon chives, chopped for garnish
- Ice cubes for serving

Directions:

1. In your blender, mix grapes with cucumber, almond milk, sesame oil, salt, and pepper.
2. Pulse well.
3. Divide into soup bowls, add ice cubes, sprinkle chopped chives all over and serve.

Nutrition: Calories: 140 kcal Protein: 6.2 g Fat: 6.78 g Carbohydrates: 14.61 g

851. Mushroom, Avocado, And Creamy Tomato Soup

Preparation time: 10 minutes
Cooking time: 3 hours
Servings: 3

Ingredients:

- 1 yellow onion
- 1 tablespoon agave nectar
- 1 tablespoon balsamic vinegar
- 3 Tablespoons extra-virgin olive oil
- 1 teaspoon olive oil
- 3 ounces mushrooms, sliced
- 1 tomato, chopped
- 1 avocado, pitted, peeled and roughly chopped
- 1 garlic clove, minced
- A pinch of salt and black pepper
- 1½ cups water

Directions:

1. In a bowl, mix mushrooms with agave, vinegar, garlic, salt, pepper, and 3 tablespoons of olive oil.
2. Toss well, then transfer this to your dehydrator and dehydrate the mushrooms for 3 hours.
3. Pour the mushrooms in your blender, add onion, 1 tablespoon oil, tomato, avocado, salt, pepper, and the water.
4. Pulse very well until smooth.
5. Divide into soup bowls, drizzle 1 teaspoon oil on top and serve.

Nutrition: Calories: 139 kcal Protein: 3.23 g Fat: 11.6 g Carbohydrates: 7.52 g

852. Spicy Shrimp Stew

Preparation time: 1 hour 25 minutes
Cooking time: 40 minutes
Servings: 4

Ingredients:

- 1/3 cup extra virgin olive oil
- 1/2 cup All-Purpose flour
- 1 large yellow onion, diced
- 1 cup small, peeled shrimp
- 3 cups of water
- 2 tablespoons green bell pepper, finely chopped
- 2 tablespoons celery, sliced thinly

- 1 tablespoon fresh parsley, chopped
- Salt and pepper to taste

Directions:

1. Make the Roux:
2. In a heavy-bottomed saucepan, at medium heat, heat oil until hot but not smoking. Put flour all at once and continuously stir until the roux is golden brown, 45 minutes to 1 hour. Do not cook the roux too fast. If burnt, black flecks will appear, and you must discard and start over.
3. Put the onion to the roux and cook, continually stirring, until onion is soft and light brown, about 5 minutes.
4. Put down the heat to simmer and put the shrimp, cooking for about 10 minutes.
5. Slowly stir in the water and increase the heat to medium. Continue cooking until the stew reaches a boil.
6. Mix in the green bell pepper, celery, parsley, salt, and pepper.
7. Turn heat down to a simmer and cook for about 30 to 40 minutes to blend flavors. Taste and adjust seasonings.

Nutrition: Calories: 165 kcal Protein: 4.18 g Fat: 9.44 g Carbohydrates: 16.23 g

853. Spicy Vegetable And Turkey Meatball Stew

Preparation time: 20 minutes
Cooking time: 30 minutes
Servings: 6

Ingredients:

- 2 pounds ground turkey
- 5 tablespoons extra virgin olive oil
- 2 large green bell peppers
- 1 large red bell pepper
- 1 large yellow bell pepper
- 2 large onions, cut into 1/2 inch chunks
- 2 cups sofrito sauce
- 1 (15 ounces) can tomato sauce
- 4 medium potatoes, cut into 1/2 inch chunks
- 4 carrots, sliced
- 2 cups broccoli
- 5 cups of water
- 1 cup fresh salsa
- 16 ounces mozzarella cheese, shredded

Directions:

1. Roll the ground turkey into small meatballs. Warm 1 tablespoon oil in a skillet at medium heat, and cook meatballs for 5 minutes, or until evenly browned. Drain, and set aside.
2. Heat remaining oil in a large pot over medium heat, and cook the green, red and yellow bell peppers, and onions until tender, about 5 minutes.
3. Mix in the sofrito and tomato sauce, and continue cooking until heated through another 3 – 5 minutes.
4. Mix in potatoes, carrots, and broccoli. Pour in the water and salsa and put it to a boil.
5. Put meatballs in the pot. Lower the heat to low, and simmer 30 minutes.
6. Top with mozzarella cheese to serve.

Nutrition: Calories: 1166 kcal Protein: 62.86 g Fat: 74.01 g Carbohydrates: 64.33 g

854. Beef And Buckwheat Stew

Preparation time: 15 minutes
Cooking time: 1 hour 45 minutes
Servings: 6

Ingredients:

- 1 lb. beef meat, cut into 1/2 inch pieces
- 1 tablespoon olive oil
- 2 cups carrots, sliced
- 1 cup yellow onion, sliced
- 1 cup sliced celery
- 2 cloves garlic, minced
- 2 cups baby Portobello mushrooms, sliced
- 1 (14.5 ounces) can stewed tomatoes
- 1 cup of water
- 1 cup dry red wine
- 1 cup beef broth
- 2 bay leaves
- 3/4 teaspoon dried thyme
- Salt and pepper to taste
- 1/3 cup uncooked buckwheat groats
- 1/4 cup All-Purpose flour
- 1/3 cup cold water
- 1 tablespoon balsamic vinegar
- Fresh parsley, minced

Directions:

1. In a Dutch oven, cook beef in oil, frequently stirring, until meat is no longer pink, about 6 – 8 minutes.
2. Add the carrots, onion, celery, and garlic and cook for another 5 minutes.
3. Add the mushrooms, stewed tomatoes, water, wine, broth, bay leaves, thyme, salt, and pepper.
4. Place to a boil, lower down the heat, then cover and simmer for about 1 hour.
5. Add buckwheat, return the cover and simmer 45 minutes longer or until buckwheat and meat are tender.
6. In a small bowl, blend flour and cold water until smooth. Gradually stir into pan. Bring up to a boil and cook, constantly stirring, until thickened, about 2 minutes.
7. Remove from the heat. Discard bay leaves.
8. Stir in balsamic vinegar to serve and garnish with fresh parsley.

Nutrition: Calories: 215 kcal Protein: 20.88 g Fat: 8.42 g Carbohydrates: 13.65 g

855. Lamb And Sirtfood Stew

Preparation time: 15 minutes
Cooking time: 50 minutes
Servings: 6

Ingredients:

- 2 tablespoons extra virgin olive oil
- 1-pound lamb stew meat, cubed
- 1 cup dry red wine
- 2 cups beef broth
- 2 cloves garlic, minced
- 1 tablespoon lovage, chopped
- Salt and pepper to taste
- 1 bay leaf
- 2 cups butternut squash, peeled, seedless, and sliced
- 1 cup carrots, peeled and chopped
- 1 cup sweet potatoes, peeled and cubed
- 1 cup celery, chopped
- 1 yellow onion, diced
- 1/2 cup sour cream
- 3 tablespoons buckwheat flour

Directions:

1. In a large saucepan, warm the oil and brown the cubes of lamb meat on all sides, about 5 – 8 minutes.
2. Drain the fat and stir in the red wine and beef broth.

3. Add the garlic, lovage, salt and pepper, and bay leaf and bring the stew just to a boil. Lower the heat to low, cover, and simmer 20 minutes.
4. Mix in the butternut squash, carrots, sweet potatoes, celery, and onion. Place the stew back to a boil, then once more, reduce the heat to low and simmer for 30 minutes more, or until the vegetables are tender.
5. In a small bowl, whisk the buckwheat flour into sour cream. Gradually stir in 1/2 cup of the hot stew mixture.
6. Combine the sour cream mixture back into the saucepan and mix well.
7. Find and remove the bay leaf and continue to stir until the sauce thickens about 5 minutes.

Nutrition: Calories: 272 kcal Protein: 25.34 g Fat: 12.21 g Carbohydrates: 13.38 g

856. Taco Chili

Preparation time: 10 minutes
Cooking time: 1 hour.
Servings: 6

Ingredients:

- 1 tablespoon extra-virgin olive oil
- 1 pound mushrooms, sliced
- 2 cloves garlic, minced
- 1 small red onion, finely chopped
- 2 stalks celery, chopped
- 1 (29 ounces) can tomato sauce
- 1 (6 ounces) can tomato paste
- 3 (15 ounce) cans kidney beans
- 1 (11 ounces) can corn
- 2 tablespoons cilantro, chopped
- 1 tablespoon parsley, chopped
- Zest of 1 lime

Directions:

1. Using a large pan, heat the olive oil and sauté the mushrooms, garlic, onion, and celery until tender, 3 – 5 minutes.
2. Transfer them to a stockpot or slow cooker. Stir in the tomato sauce, tomato paste, beans, corn, cilantro, parsley, and lime zest.
3. Cook for at least an hour to blend the flavors.

Nutrition: Calories: 247 kcal Protein: 11.34 g Fat: 10.27 g Carbohydrates: 32.93 g

857. Green Tea Buckwheat Soup

Preparation time: 10 minutes
Cooking time: 20 minutes
Servings: 4

Ingredients:

- 8 cups of green tea
- 2 cups of water
- ½ cup buckwheat groats
- 1 red onion, chopped
- 1 cup of seaweed, chopped
- 1 tablespoon of black sesame seeds
- ¼ cup fresh lovage, chopped
- 1 tablespoon of extra virgin olive oil
- Salt and pepper to taste

Directions:

1. Add the buckwheat and water to a large pot and bring the water to the boil. Reduce the heat, cover the pot, and simmer for 20 minutes.
2. While the buckwheat is simmering, place the green tea in a second pot and add the remaining ingredients.
3. Bring to a bowl and then reduce to a simmer and let the flavors develop while the buckwheat is cooking.
4. When the buckwheat is ready, pour broth over the top to serve.

Nutrition: Calories: 112 kcal Protein: 5.88 g Fat: 5.51 g Carbohydrates: 10.83 g

858. Parsley Spinach Chicken Stew

Preparation time: 15 minutes
Cooking time: 2 hours and 20 minutes
Servings: 6

Ingredients:

- 1 cup fresh parsley, chopped
- 3 cups spinach, rinsed and chopped
- 1 red onion, chopped
- 1 potato, cubed
- 4 skinless, boneless chicken breasts
- 6 tablespoons olive oil
- ¼ teaspoon salt
- ¼ teaspoon ground turmeric
- ¼ teaspoon black pepper
- 2 tablespoons tomato paste
- 1 cup of water
- 3 tablespoons fresh lemon juice

Directions:

1. In a medium-size frying pan, heat 4 tablespoons of the olive oil. Add the parsley and spinach and sauté until wilted, 3 – 5 minutes. Set aside.
2. Warm the other 2 tablespoons of oil in a large pot. Put the onion and sauté, occasionally stirring, until tender, 3 – 5 minutes.
3. Add on the chicken breasts and brown both sides of each breast, about 2 minutes per side.
4. Add the salt, turmeric, black pepper, fried parsley/spinach, water, and tomato paste. Bring all the ingredients to a boil and cook for 10 minutes.
5. Add the cubed potatoes. Cover and let simmer over low heat for 1 to 2 hours.
6. Add the lemon juice and put back to a boil for 10 more minutes.

Nutrition: Calories: 202 kcal Protein: 3.52 g Fat: 14.77 g Carbohydrates: 15.33 g

859. Creamy Kale And Stilton Soup

Preparation time: 10 minutes
Cooking time: 10 minutes
Servings: 4

Ingredients:

- 1 large potato
- 200g chopped kale
- 1-liter vegetable stock
- 3 tbsp. double cream
- Fresh nutmeg
- 100g Stilton Cheese

Directions:

1. In a large saucepan, placed one big peeled and diced potato and 1 liter of hot stock. Give lid, and bring to the boil and cook until potato is tender for 10 mints.
2. Add 200 g of chopped kale and 100 g of Stilton crumbled, cover, and cook for another 5 minutes.
3. Add 3 tbsp of double milk, and a generous fresh nutmeg grating. Season well, then mix half of the soup before stirring back into the unblended half.
4. Serve with some extra Crumbled Stilton on top.

Nutrition: Calories: 210 kcal Protein: 10.01 g Fat: 9.54 g Carbohydrates: 23.09 g

860. Cauliflower Soup

Preparation time: 10 minutes
Cooking time: 50 minutes
Servings: 4

Ingredients:

- 3 pounds cauliflower, florets separated
- 1 yellow onion, chopped
- 1 tablespoon coconut oil
- Black pepper to the taste
- 2 garlic cloves, minced
- 2 carrots, chopped
- 2 cups beef stock
- 1 cup of water
- ½ cup of coconut milk
- 1 teaspoon olive oil
- 2 tablespoons parsley, chopped

Directions:

1. Heat a pot with the coconut oil over medium-high heat, add carrots, onion, and garlic, stir, and cook for 5 minutes.
2. Add cauliflower, water, and stock, stir, bring to a boil, cover, and cook for 45 minutes.
3. Transfer soup to your blender and pulse well, add coconut milk, pulse well again, ladle into bowls, drizzle the olive oil over the soup, sprinkle parsley and serve for lunch.

Nutrition: Calories: 190 Cal Fat: 2 g Carbohydrates: 16 g Protein: 4 g Fiber: 4 g

861. Broccoli Soup

Preparation time: 10 minutes
Cooking time: 1 hour
Servings: 4

Ingredients:

- 2 pounds broccoli, florets separated
- 1 yellow onion, chopped
- 1 tablespoon olive oil
- Black pepper to the taste
- 1 cup celery, chopped 2 carrots, chopped
- 3 and ½ cups low-sodium chicken stock
- 1 tablespoon cilantro chopped

Directions:

1. Heat a pot with the oil over medium-high heat, add the onion, celery, and carrots, stir, and cook for 5 minutes. Add broccoli, black pepper, and stock, stir, and cook over medium heat for 1 hour.
2. Pulse using an immersion blender, add cilantro, and stir the soup
3. Heat a pot with the oil over medium-high heat, add the onion, celery, and carrots, stir, and cook for 5 minutes. Add broccoli, black pepper, and stock, stir, and cook over medium heat for 1 hour.
4. Pulse using an immersion blender, add cilantro, stir the soup again, and divide it into bowls and serve.

Nutrition: Calories: 170 Cal Fat: 2 g Carbohydrates: 10 g Protein: 9 g Fiber: 3 g

862. Shrimp Soup

Preparation time: 10 minutes
Cooking time: 15 minutes
Servings: 6

Ingredients:

- 46 ounces low-sodium chicken stock
- 3 cups shrimp, peeled and deveined
- A pinch of black pepper
- 2 tablespoons green onions, chopped
- 1 teaspoon dill, chopped

Directions:

1. Put the stock in a pot, bring it to a simmer over medium heat, add black pepper, onion, and shrimp, and stir and simmer for 8-10 minutes.
2. Add dill, stir, cook for 5 minutes more, ladle into bowls and serve.

Nutrition: Calories: 190 Cal Fat: 7 g Carbohydrates: 12 g Protein: 8 g Fiber: 3 g

863. Parmesan Tomato Soup

Preparation time: 10 minutes
Cooking time: 20 minutes
Servings: 4

Ingredients:

- ½ cup tomatoes, chopped
- 1 tablespoon tomato paste
- 1 teaspoon garlic, diced
- 2 cups beef broth
- 1 teaspoon chili pepper
- 2 oz Parmesan, grated
- 1/3 cup fresh cilantro, chopped
- 2 potatoes, chopped

Directions:

1. Mix up together tomatoes and tomato paste and transfer the mixture in the pan.
2. Add garlic and beef broth.
3. Add chopped potatoes and chili pepper.
4. Boil the ingredients for 15 minutes or until potato is soft.
5. Then blend the mixture with the help of the hand blender or in the food processor.
6. Add chopped cilantro and simmer the soup for 5 minutes.
7. Ladle the cooked soup in the serving bowls and top every bowl with Parmesan generously.

Nutrition: Calories: 148 g Fat: 3.9 g Carbohydrates: 19.8 g Protein: 9.2 g Fiber: 3.1 g

864. Meatball Soup

Preparation time: 10 minutes
Cooking time: 30 minutes
Servings: 4

Ingredients:

- 1 cup ground beef
- 1 tablespoon semolina
- ½ teaspoon salt
- 1 egg yolk
- ½ teaspoon ground black pepper
- 4 cups chicken stock
- 1 carrot, chopped
- 1 yellow onion, diced
- 1 tablespoon butter
- ½ teaspoon turmeric
- ½ teaspoon garlic powder

Directions:

1. Toss butter in the skillet and heat it until it is melted.
2. Add onion and cook it until light brown.
3. Meanwhile, pour chicken stock in the pan.
4. Add garlic powder and turmeric.
5. Bring the liquid to boil. Add chopped carrot and boil it for 10 minutes.
6. In the mixing bowl, mix up ground beef, semolina, salt, egg yolk, and ground black pepper.
7. Make the small-sized meatballs.

8. Put the meatballs in the chicken stock.
9. Add cooked onion.
10. Cook the soup for 15 minutes over the medium-low heat.

Nutrition: Calories: 143 Cal Fat: 8.8 g Carbohydrates: 7.5 g Protein: 8.8 g Fiber: 1.2 g

865. Kale And Apple Soup

Preparation time: 10 minutes
Cooking time: 25 minutes
Servings: 6

Ingredients:

- Pepper
- Salt
- 1 tbsp. Olive oil
- 2 tbsp. Chopped parsley
- 2 Chopped and cored apples
- 7 oz. Chopped fennel
- 1 lb Chopped kale

Directions:

1. Take out a big saucepan and heat the oil inside. When that is done warming up, add the fennel and the kale and cook for a bit.
2. After five minutes, the fennel will be soft. Then it is time to add in the parsley and apple. Cover this up with hot water and wait until it starts boiling.
3. Simmer the mixture for a bit. After ten minutes, you can use an immersion blender or your food processor to blend and smooth out the soup—season with a bit of pepper and salt before serving.

Nutrition: Calories: 116 kcal Protein: 5.06 g Fat: 4.16 g Carbohydrates: 18.2 g

866. Lentil Soup

Preparation time: 10 minutes
Cooking time: 50 minutes
Servings: 6

Ingredients:

- Black pepper
- Salt
- 2 tbsp. Olive oil
- 2 pints vegetable stock
- 1 tsp. Ground coriander or cilantro
- 1 tsp. Ground turmeric
- 1 tsp. ground cumin
- .5 Bird's eye chili
- 2 Chopped carrots
- 2 Chopped celery sticks
- 1 Chopped garlic cloves
- 1 Chopped red onion
- 6 oz. Lentils, red

Directions:

1. Bring a pan with oil to temperature, and when prepared, toss in onions, coating evenly, and cooking.
2. After another five minutes, it is time to add in the garlic, turmeric, cumin, coriander, chili, celery, lentils, and carrots into the pan as well and let them all cook well.
3. After five minutes here, add in the broth and allow the pot to boil. When it reaches a boil, it is time to reduce the heat and simmer it for a bit.
4. After 45 minutes of simmering, use your food processor or an immersion blender to make a smooth soup.
5. Sprinkle with some pepper and salt before serving.

Nutrition: Calories: 119 kcal Protein: 4.61 g Fat: 5.91 g Carbohydrates: 14.05 g

867. Walnut And Cauliflower Soup

Preparation time: 10 minutes
Cooking time: 25 minutes
Servings: 6

Ingredients:

- 1 tbsp. Olive oil
- .5 tsp. Turmeric
- 3.5 oz. Double cream
- 1.5 pints vegetable stock or broth
- 1 chopped red onion
- 8 Chopped walnut halves
- 1 lb. Chopped cauliflower

Directions:

1. Heat some oil inside a pan, and when it is warm, add in the red onion and cauliflower inside to make it hot. Cook four minutes, stirring constantly.
2. Introduce the broth to the pot and bring the entire mixture to a boil. Cook again for a bit, about fifteen minutes.
3. Add in the turmeric, double cream, and walnuts when this is all done. Use a food processor to process the soup to make sure it is creamy and smooth.
4. Serve into a few bowls and top with the chopped walnuts and serve.

Nutrition: Calories: 1123 kcal Protein: 27.19 g Fat: 108.44 g Carbohydrates: 30.08 g

868. Blue Cheese And Celery Soup

Preparation time: 10 minutes
Cooking time: 25 minutes
Servings: 6

Ingredients:

- 5 oz. Single cream
- 1.5 pints Chicken stock or broth
- 1 Chopped red onion
- 1 Celery head
- 1 oz. Butter
- 4 oz. Blue cheese

Directions:

1. Take out a pan and heat the butter inside of it. When the butter is melted and done, add in the celery and the onion. Cook these two vegetables until they are nice and soft.
2. When this is done, add stock or broth to the pot and let boil. When it reaches its boiling point, drop the heat, and allow to simmer for a while to cook.
3. After 15 minutes, you can add the cream and the cheese, stirring around until it is nice and melted. Let it heat up a little bit longer as well.
4. Serve the soup and eat it as soon as possible.

Nutrition: Calories: 433 kcal Protein: 54.83 g Fat: 20.1 g Carbohydrates: 5.47 g

869. Spicy Squash Soup

Preparation time: 10 minutes
Cooking time: 25 minutes
Servings: 6

Ingredients:

- 2 tbsp. Olive oil
- 1 point Vegetable broth and stock
- 1 tsp. Ground ginger
- 2 tsp. Turmeric
- 3 Garlic cloves
- 3 Chopped bird's eye chilies
- 1 Chopped red onion

- 1 Chopped butternut squash
- 5 oz. Kale

Directions:

1. Heat some oil inside the pan, and when it is ready, add in the butternut squash and onion. Cook until soft and onion is translucent.
2. Stir in the ginger, turmeric, chili, garlic, and kale into this and cook until they get nice and soft.
3. Pour in the vegetable broth or stock and bring all of this to a boil. This needs to cook together for another twenty minutes as well.
4. When that is done, use a hand blender or a food processor and process to make it nice and smooth. Serve and enjoy.

Nutrition: Calories: 118 kcal Protein: 3.31 g Fat: 5.9 g Carbohydrates: 15.1 g

870. Slow Cooked Sausage Soup With Beer

Preparation time: 15 minute
Cooking time: 8 hours
Servings: 4

Ingredients:

- ½ cup heavy cream
- 5 oz. beef sausages, sliced
- ½ cup chopped celery
- 1 chopped carrot
- 2 garlic cloves, minced
- ½ cup cream cheese
- 1 tsp red pepper flakes
- 3 oz. beer
- 3 cups beef stock
- 1 onion, diced
- 1 cup asiago cheese, grated
- 2 tbsp. chopped fresh cilantro

Directions:

1. Add beef stock, beer, sausages, carrot, onion, celery, salt, and pepper to your slow cooker and stir to combine. Close the lid and simmer for 6 hours at a low temperature. Stir in heavy cream, asiago cheese, and cream cheese and cook for 2 hours. Ladle the soup into bowls then garnish with cilantro and red pepper flakes. Serve warm.

Nutrition: Calories: 244;Net Carbs 4g; Fat 17g, Protein 5g

871. Coconut Cream Pumpkin Soup

Preparation time: 10 minute
Cooking time: 55 minutes
Servings: 4

Ingredients:

- 2 red onions, cut into wedges
- 2 garlic cloves
- 10 oz. pumpkin, cubed
- 10 oz. butternut squash, cubed
- 2 tbsp. melted butter
- 8 oz. butter
- Salt and black pepper to taste
- Juice of 1 lime
- ¾ cup mayonnaise
- 2 tbsp toasted pumpkin seeds

Directions:

1. Preheat oven to 400 F. Place onions, pumpkin, and butternut squash to a baking sheet and drizzle with melted butter. Season with salt and pepper. Roast for 30 minutes or until the veggies are golden brown and fragrant; transfer to a pot. Add in 2 cups water, bring to a boil, and cook for 15 minutes. Break the remaining butter in the pot and puree the vegetables until smooth. Stir in lime juice, and mayo. Serve garnished with toasted pumpkin seeds.

Nutrition: Calories: 643; Fat 57g; Net Carbs 9g; Protein 10g

872. Chorizo & Cauliflower Soup

Preparation time: 10 minute
Cooking time: 40 minutes
Servings: 4

Ingredients:

- 1 cauliflower head, chopped
- 1 turnip, chopped
- 3 tbsp butter
- 1 chorizo sausage, sliced
- 2 cups chicken broth
- 1 small onion, chopped
- 2 cups of water
- Salt and black pepper to taste

Directions:

1. In a pot with 2 tbsp. of butter, melt it. Stir in onion and sauté until soft and golden, 6 minutes. Add in cauliflower and turnip and cook for another 5 minutes. Pour in chicken broth. Bring to a boil and simmer for 20 minutes. Melt the remaining butter in a skillet. Put in chorizo and cook for 5 minutes. Blitz the soup with a hand blender until smooth. Adjust the seasonings. Serve topped with chorizo.

Nutrition: Calories: 251; Net Carbs 5.7g; Fat 19g, Protein 10g

873. Kale & Egg Soup

Preparation time: 5 minute
Cooking time: 35 minutes
Servings: 4

Ingredients:

- 1 tbsp. olive oil
- 2 tbsp. butter
- 1 red onion, thinly sliced
- 1 carrot, chopped
- 3 garlic cloves, finely sliced
- 4 cups kale, chopped
- 1 lettuce head, chopped
- 4 cups vegetable stock
- 1 tbsp. fresh dill
- Salt and black pepper to taste
- 4 eggs
- 1 cup grated Parmesan cheese

Directions:

1. In a saucepan with oil and butter over medium heat and sauté onion, carrot, and garlic for 4 minutes. Stir in kale and lettuce and cook for 5 minutes. Pour in vegetable stock; place to a boil. Reduce the heat and simmer for 10 minutes. With an immersion blender, puree the soup until smooth. Season with salt and pepper. Bring 1 cup of vinegared water to a boil in another saucepan. Create a whirlpool in the center using a wooden spoon. Allow water to almost settle back to normal and crack in an egg. Poach for 3 minutes, remove, and set aside in a plate. Repeat poaching the remaining eggs. Divide the soup into serving bowls. Top with poached eggs, sprinkle with dill and Parmesan cheese and serve warm.

Nutrition: Calories: 515; Net Carbs 4.5g; Fat 33g, Protein 38g

874. Tofu Goulash Soup

Preparation time: 5 minute
Cooking time: 25 minutes
Servings: 4

Ingredients:

- 8 oz. chopped butternut squash
- 1 ½ cups tofu, crumbled
- 3 tbsps. butter
- 1 white onion, chopped
- 2 garlic cloves, minced
- 1 red bell pepper
- 1 tbsps. paprika powder
- ¼ tsp red chili flakes
- Salt and black pepper to taste
- 1 ½ cups crushed tomatoes
- 3 cups vegetable broth
- 1 ½ tsp red wine vinegar
- Chopped cilantro to serve

Directions:

1. Melt butter in a casserole at medium heat and sauté onion and garlic for 3 minutes until fragrant and soft. Stir in tofu and cook for 3 minutes. Add in butternut squash, bell pepper, paprika, red chili flakes, salt, and pepper. Cook for 2 minutes. Pour in tomatoes and vegetable broth. Bring to a boil, lower the heat to simmer for 10 minutes, and mix in vinegar. Garnish with cilantro and serve.

Nutrition: Calories: 481; Fat 41.8g; Net Carbs 9g; Protein 12g

875. Ginger-Spinach Egg Benedict Soup

Preparation time: 5 minute
Cooking time: 35 minutes
Servings: 4

Ingredients:

- 2 tbsps. butter
- 1 tbsps. sesame oil
- 1 small onion, finely sliced
- 3 garlic cloves, minced
- 2 tsp ginger paste
- 2 cups baby spinach, chopped
- 2 cups chopped green beans
- 4 cups vegetable stock
- 3 tbsps. chopped cilantro
- 4 eggs

Directions:

1. Melt butter in a pot and sauté onion, garlic, and ginger for 4 minutes, stirring frequently. Stir in spinach, allowing wilting, and pour in green beans and vegetable stock. Bring to the boil and simmer for 10 minutes. Transfer the soup to a blender and puree until smooth. Bring 3 cups of vinegared water to simmer and, when hot, slide in an egg to poach for 3 minutes; remove with a perforated spoon. Repeat the steps with the remaining eggs, one at time. Divide the soup between 4 bowls and place an egg on each one, drizzle with sesame oil and cilantro, and serve.

Nutrition: Calories: 463; Net Carbs 5.8g; Fat 30g, Protein 23g

876. Tomato Soup With Parmesan Croutons

Preparation time: 10 minute
Cooking time: 1 hour and 25 minutes
Servings: 6

Ingredients:

- Parmesan Croutons:
- 3 egg whites
- 1 ¼ cups almond flour
- 2 tsp baking powder
- 5 tbsps. Psyllium husk powder
- 4 tbsps. Butter
- 4 tbsps. Grated Parmesan
- Tomato Soup
- 2 lb. fresh ripe tomatoes
- 4 cloves garlic, peeled only
- 1 small white onion, diced
- 1 red bell pepper, diced
- 3 tbsps. Olive oil
- 1 cup coconut cream
- ½ tsp dried rosemary
- ½ tsp dried oregano
- 2 tbsps. chopped fresh basil
- Salt and black pepper to taste

Directions:

1. For the parmesan croutons:
2. Set oven to 350°F. Line a baking sheet with parchment paper. In a bowl, combine almond flour, baking powder, and psyllium husk powder. Mix in the egg whites and whisk for 30 seconds until well combined but not overly mixed. Form 8 flat pieces out of the dough. Place on the baking sheet while leaving enough room between each to allow rising. Bake for 30 minutes. Remove croutons to cool and break into halves. Mix butter with Parmesan cheese and spread the mixture in the inner parts of the croutons. Bake for another 5 minutes.
3. For the tomato soup:
4. In a baking dish, add tomatoes, garlic, onion, bell pepper, and drizzle with olive oil. Roast vegetables in the oven for around 25 minutes and after broil for 4 minutes. Transfer to a blender and add in coconut cream, rosemary, oregano, salt, and pepper. Puree until smooth. Top with croutons.

Nutrition: Calories: 434; Fat 38g; Net Carbs 6g; Protein 11g

877. Power Green Soup

Preparation time: 5 minute
Cooking time: 15 minutes
Servings: 4

Ingredients:

- 3 tbsps. butter
- 1 cup spinach, coarsely
- 1 cup kale, coarsely
- 1 large avocado
- 3 ½ cups coconut cream
- 1 cup vegetable broth
- 3 tbsps. chopped mint leaves
- Juice from 1 lime
- 1 cup collard greens, chopped
- 3 garlic cloves, minced
- 3 tbsps. Cardamom powder
- 2 tbsp. toasted pistachios

Directions:

1. Set a saucepan over medium heat, then melt 2 tbsp of the butter. Put in spinach and kale and sauté for 5 minutes. Remove to a food processor. Add avocado, coconut cream, vegetable broth, mint, and lime juice and puree until smooth; reserve the soup. Reheat the saucepan with the remaining butter and add collard greens, garlic, and

cardamom powder and sauté for 4 minutes. Ladle the soup into bowls then garnish with collards and pistachios.

Nutrition: Calories: 885; Fat 80g; Net Carbs 15g; Protein 14g

878. Mixed Mushroom Soup

Preparation time: 5 minute
Cooking time: 35 minutes
Servings: 4

Ingredients:

- 5 oz. white button mushrooms, chopped
- 5 oz. cremini mushrooms, chopped
- 5 oz. shiitake mushrooms, chopped
- 1 vegetable stock cube, crushed
- 4 oz. unsalted butter
- 1 small onion, finely chopped
- 1 clove garlic, minced
- ½ lb. celery root, chopped
- ½ tsp dried rosemary
- 1 tbsp. plain vinegar
- 1 cup coconut cream
- 6 leaves basil, chopped

Directions:

1. In a saucepan pan, put the butter and melt in over medium heat. Sauté onion, garlic, mushrooms, and celery until fragrant, 6 minutes.
2. Reserve some mushrooms for garnishing. Add in rosemary, 4 cups of water, stock cube, and vinegar. Mix and bring to a boil; reduce the heat and simmer for 20 minutes. Mix in coconut cream and puree. Garnish with the reserved mushrooms and basil and serve.

Nutrition: Calories: 506; Fat 46g; Net Carbs 12g; Protein 8g

879. Broccoli & Fennel Soup

Preparation time: 5 minute
Cooking time: 25 minutes
Servings: 4

Ingredients:

- 1 fennel bulb, chopped
- 10 oz broccoli, cut into florets
- 4 cups vegetable stock
- Salt and black pepper to taste
- 1 garlic clove
- 1 cup cream cheese
- 2 tbsp butter
- ½ cup chopped fresh oregano

Directions:

1. Put fennel, broccoli, and garlic in a pot over medium heat and pour in the vegetable stock. Bring to a boil and simmer until the vegetables are soft, about 10 minutes. Season with salt and pepper. Pour in cream cheese, butter, and oregano. Puree the ingredients with an immersion blender until smooth. Serve with cheese crackers.

Nutrition: Calories: 510; Fat 44g; Net Carbs 7g; Protein 16g

880. Asiago Tomato Soup

Preparation time: 5 minute
Cooking time: 10 minutes
Servings: 4

Ingredients:

- 1 small can Tomato paste
- 1 tsp. Minced garlic
- 1 tsp. Oregano
- 1 cup Heavy whipping cream
- .25 cup Water
- Pepper and salt (as desired)
- .75 cup Asiago cheese

Directions:

1. Pour the minced garlic and tomato paste in a dutch oven and add the cream. Gently whisk.
2. As it begins to boil, blend in small amounts of cheese. Pour in the water and simmer for four to five minutes.
3. Serve with pepper as desired.

Nutrition: Calories: 302 Protein: 9 grams Net Carbohydrates: 8.75 grams Fats: 26 grams

881. No-Cook - Chilled Avocado & Mint Soup

Preparation time: 5 minute
Cooking time: 20 minutes
Servings: 5

Ingredients:

- 2 leaves Romaine lettuce
- 1 medium Ripened avocado
- 1 cup Coconut milk
- 1 tbsp. Lime juice
- 20 leaves fresh mint
- Salt (to your liking)

Directions:

1. Combine all of the fixings into a blender and mix well. (You want it thick but not puree-like.)
2. Chill in the refrigerator for 5 to 10 minutes before serving.

Nutrition: Calories: 280 Protein: 4 grams Net Carbohydrates: 4 grams Fats: 26 grams

882. Lamb Bone Broth

Preparation time: 15 minute
Cooking time: 1 day
Servings: 4

Ingredients:

- 1 lb. Lamb's bones
- 1 tbsp. Olive oil
- 1 large Onion
- 3 medium Carrots
- 3 stick Celery
- 3 Garlic cloves
- 3 Rosemary sprigs
- 5 Thyme sprigs
- Optional: Salt
- 1-3 gallons Water

Directions:

1. Dice the onion and roughly chop the celery and carrots.
2. Warm the oven to reach 390° Fahrenheit.
3. Arrange the lamb bones in a baking pan. Bake them for 30 to 40 minutes.
4. Prepare a large stockpot with oil using the medium heat setting.
5. Toss in the prepared veggies, thyme, and rosemary. Sauté for about five minutes.
6. Toss in the bones with all of the juices and fat from the pan. Sauté for another five minutes.
7. Pour in one gallon of water and simmer using the low setting. Lower the heat to low and simmer uncovered for eight to 24 hours. Add water as needed.
8. When it's ready, strain the broth using a fine mesh-type strainer. Serve it hot or chilled.

Nutrition: Calories: 52 Protein: 3 grams Net Carbohydrates: 1 gram Fats: 4 grams

883. Chinese Tofu Soup

Preparation time: 5 minute
Cooking time: 15 minutes
Servings: 2
Ingredients:

- 2 cups chicken stock
- 1 tbsp soy sauce, sugar-free
- 2 spring onions, sliced
- 1 tsp sesame oil, softened
- 2 eggs, beaten
- 1-inch piece ginger, grated
- Salt and black ground, to taste
- ½ pound extra-firm tofu, cubed
- A handful of fresh cilantro, chopped

Directions:

1. Boil in a pan over medium heat, soy sauce, chicken stock, and sesame oil. Place in eggs as you whisk to incorporate completely. Change heat to low and add salt, spring onions, black pepper, and ginger; cook for 5 minutes. Place in tofu and simmer for 1 to 2 minutes.
2. Divide into soup bowls and serve sprinkled with fresh cilantro.

Nutrition: Calories: 163; Fat: 10g, Net Carbs: 2.4g, Protein: 14.5g

884. Sausage & Turnip Soup

Preparation time: 5 minute
Cooking time: 40 minutes
Servings: 2-4
Ingredients:

- 3 turnips, chopped
- 2 celery sticks, chopped
- 2 tbsps. butter
- 1 tbsps. olive oil
- 1 pork sausage, sliced
- 2 cups vegetable broth
- ½ cup sour cream
- 3 green onions, chopped
- 2 cups of water
- Salt and black pepper, to taste

Directions:

1. Sauté the green onions in melted butter over medium heat until soft and golden, about 3-4 minutes. Add celery and turnip, and cook for another 5 minutes. Pour the vegetable broth and water over.
2. Bring to a boil, simmer covered, and cook for about 20 minutes until the vegetables are tender. Remove from heat. Puree the soup with a hand blender until smooth. Add sour cream and adjust the seasonings. Warm the olive oil in a skillet. Add the pork sausage and cook for 5 minutes. Serve the soup in deep bowls topped with the pork sausage.

Nutrition: Calories: 275, Fat: 23.1g, Net Carbs: 6.4g,Protein: 7.4g

885. Vegan Coconut Green Soup

Preparation time: 5 minute
Cooking time: 30 minutes
Servings: 2-4
Ingredients:

- 1 broccoli head, chopped
- 1 cup spinach
- 1 onion, chopped
- 1 garlic clove, minced
- ½ cup leeks
- 3 cups vegetable stock
- ½ cup of coconut milk
- 2 tbsp. coconut oil
- 1 bay leaf
- Salt and black pepper, to taste
- 2 tbsp. coconut yogurt

Directions:

1. In a large pan, put coconut oil and heat it over medium heat. Put onion, leeks, and garlic and cook for 5 minutes. Add broccoli and cook for an additional 5 minutes. Pour in the stock over and add the bay leaf. Close the lid, bring to a boil, and reduce the heat. Simmer for about 10 minutes.
2. Put spinach and cook for around 3 minutes. Discard the bay leaf and mix the soup with a hand blender. Stir in the coconut cream, salt, and black pepper. Divide among serving bowls and garnish with a swirl of coconut yogurt.

Nutrition: Calories: 272, Fat: 24.5g, Net Carbs: 4.3g, Protein: 4.5g

886. Cauliflower Cheese Soup

Preparation time: 5 minute
Cooking time: 20 minutes
Servings: 2-4
Ingredients:

- ½ head cauliflower, chopped
- 2 tbsp. coconut oil
- ½ cup leeks, chopped
- 1 celery stalk, chopped
- 1 serrano pepper, finely chopped
- 1 tsp garlic puree
- 1 ½ tbsp. flaxseed meal
- 2 cups of water
- 1½ cups of coconut milk
- 6 ounces Monterey Jack cheese, shredded
- Salt and black pepper, to taste
- Fresh parsley, chopped

Directions:

1. Place a deep medium heat, melt the coconut oil, and sauté the serrano pepper, celery, and leeks until soft, for about 5 minutes. Add in coconut milk, garlic puree, cauliflower, water, and flaxseed.
2. While covered partially, allow simmering for 10 minutes or until cooked through. Whizz with an immersion blender until smooth. Fold in the shredded cheese, and stir to ensure the cheese is completely melted and you have a homogenous mixture—season with pepper and salt to taste.
3. Divide among serving bowls, decorate with parsley, and serve while warm.

Nutrition: Calories: 312; Fat: 16g, Net Carbs: 7.1g, Protein: 13.8g

887. Sauerkraut & Corned Beef Soup

Preparation time: minute
Cooking time: 20 minutes
Servings: 2-4
Ingredients:

- 1 parsnip, chopped
- 1 onion, diced
- 3 cups beef stock
- 1 celery stalk, diced
- 1 garlic clove, minced
- 1 cup heavy cream
- ½ cup sauerkraut, shredded
- ½ pound corned beef, chopped

- 2 tbsp. lard
- ½ cup mozzarella cheese, shredded
- Salt and black pepper, to taste
- Chopped chives for garnish

Directions:

1. Melt the lard in a large pot. Add parsnip, onion, garlic, and celery, and fry for 3 minutes until tender.
2. Pour the beef stock over and stir in sauerkraut, salt, and black pepper. Bring to a boil. Reduce the heat to low, and add the corned beef. Cook for about 15 minutes, adjust the seasoning. Stir in heavy cream and cheese and cook for 1 minute. Garnish with chives to serve.

Nutrition: Calories: 463, Fat: 41.3g, Net Carbs: 5.8g, Protein: 21.2g

888. Almond Parsnip Soup With Sour Cream

Preparation time: 5 minute
Cooking time: 20 minutes
Servings: 2-4

Ingredients:

- 1 tbsp olive oil
- 1 cup onion, chopped
- 1 celery, chopped
- 2 cloves garlic, minced
- 2 turnips, peeled and chopped
- 4 cups vegetable broth
- Salt and white pepper, to taste
- ¼ cup ground almonds
- 1 cup almond milk
- 1 tbsp fresh cilantro, chopped
- 4 tsp sour cream

Directions:

1. In a pot, put oil over medium heat and sauté celery, garlic, and onion for 6 minutes. Stir in white pepper, broth, salt, and ground almonds. Boil the mixture.
2. Bring to the boil and simmer for 15 minutes. Transfer the soup to an immersion blender and puree. Serve garnished with sour cream and cilantro.

Nutrition: Calories: 125; Fat: 7.1g, Net Carbs: 7.7g, Protein: 4g

889. Wild Rice Soup

Preparation time: 10 minute
Cooking time: 50 minutes
Servings: 4

Ingredients:

- 1/2 tablespoon canola oil
- 1 1/2 cups diced yellow onion
- 1 cup diced carrot
- 1 cup diced celery
- 2 cloves garlic, minced
- 1 1/2 cups chopped kale
- 1 tablespoon minced parsley
- 2 cups low-sodium vegetable stock
- 1 teaspoon fennel seeds, crushed
- 1 teaspoon ground black pepper
- 1 cup unsalted prepared white beans -or about 1/2 of a 15.5 ounce can of white beans, rinsed and drained
- 2 cups 1 percent milk
- 1/2 cup wild rice, cooked

Directions:

1. With canola oil, sauté garlic, onion, celery, and carrots in medium-high heat. Stir in parsley, stock, spices, and kale. Bring to a boil.
2. Puree beans and milk, then add the mixture to the soup.
3. Add the rice and cook for 30 minutes.
4. Serve

Nutrition: Calories: 264; Carbs: 37g; Fats: 8g; Protein: 11g; Saturated fat: 1g; Sodium: 173mg

890. Roasted Butternut Squash Soup

Preparation time: 10 minute
Cooking time: 50 minutes
Servings: 2

Ingredients:

- 1 Butternut Squash, cut into cube pieces -or frozen, cubed Butternut Squash
- 2 tsp. Canola Oil, divided
- 1 cup Celery, diced
- 1 ½ cup Yellow Onion, diced
- 1 ½ cup Fresh Spinach
- 2 cloves Garlic, minced
- 1 cup Carrots, diced
- 3 cup low-sodium Vegetable Broth
- 1 cup Water
- 1 tsp. Sage
- ½ tsp. Nutmeg
- Black Pepper to taste

Directions:

1. Toss squash with oil.
2. Roast at 400 o for 40 minutes.
3. Puree the squash then set aside.
4. Add leftover oil to a pot and sauté vegetables until soft.
5. Add the spices, broth, water, and squash. Simmer for 10 min

Nutrition: Calories: 215; Carbs: 38g; Fats: 3g; Protein: 9g; Saturated fat: .5g; Sodium: 97mg

891. Avocado Chicken Soup

Preparation time: 15 minute
Cooking time: 6-8 hours
Servings: 6

Ingredients:

- 1-pound boneless chicken breast
- 5 cups low-sodium chicken broth
- 1 medium poblano chili chopped
- 1 medium tomato chopped
- 3 baby carrots chopped
- 1 medium onion chopped
- 2 Tablespoons garlic minced
- 1/2 medium avocado, cubed optional

Directions:

1. Combine all ingredients into the slow cooker -except for avocado
2. Cook for 6-8 hours.
3. Shred chicken and add the chopped avocado to each serving.

Nutrition: Calories: 98; Carbs: 5g; Fats: 2g; Protein: 15g; Saturated fat: 2g; Sodium: 112mg

892. Carrot Curry Soup

Preparation time: 15 minute
Cooking time: 30 minutes
Servings: 6

Ingredients:

- 1 tablespoon olive oil
- 1 teaspoon mustard seed
- 1/2 yellow onion, chopped -about 1/2 cup
- 1-pound carrots, peeled and cut into 1/2-inch pieces

- 1 tablespoon plus
- 1 teaspoon peeled and chopped fresh ginger
- 1/2 jalapeno, seeded
- 2 teaspoons curry powder
- 5 cups low-sodium chicken stock, vegetable stock or broth
- 1/4 cup chopped fresh cilantro -fresh coriander, plus leaves for garnish
- 2 tablespoons fresh lime juice
- 1/2 teaspoon salt -optional
- 3 tablespoons low-fat sour cream
- 1 grated lime zest

Directions:

1. Sauté mustard seed until they start to pop. Add the onion and saute until translucent. Mix in jalapeno, ginger, carrots, and curry powder. Cook for a few minutes. Add in 3 cups of the stock and bring to a boil. Cook until carrots are tender.
2. Pour the soup in small batches with a food processor. Stir in remaining stock.
3. Before serving, put in lime juice and cilantro. Season with salt if desired.

Nutrition: Calories: 104; Carbs: 12g; Fats: 4g; Protein: 5g; Saturated fat: 1g; Sodium: 116mg

893. Chicken And Beans Soup

Preparation time: 10 minute
Cooking time: 25 minutes
Servings: 4

Ingredients:

- 1 can -10 ounces white chunk chicken
- 2 cans -15 ounces each low-sodium white beans, drained
- 1 can -14.5 ounces low sodium diced tomatoes
- 4 cups low-sodium chicken broth
- 1 medium onion, chopped
- 1/2 medium green pepper, chopped
- 1 medium red pepper, chopped
- 2 garlic cloves, minced
- 2 teaspoons chili powder
- 1 teaspoon ground cumin
- 1 teaspoon dried oregano
- Cayenne pepper, to taste
- 8 tablespoons shredded reduced-fat Monterey Jack cheese
- 3 tablespoons chopped fresh cilantro

Directions:

1. Simmer chicken, beans, chicken broth, and tomatoes over medium heat for 10 minutes.
2. Add garlic, peppers, and onions.
3. Sauté veggies for 5 minutes.
4. Simmer for another 10 minutes after seasoning with oregano, chili powder, cumin, and cayenne.
5. Garnish with cilantro.

Nutrition: Calories: 212; Carbs: 25g; Fats: 4g; Protein: 19g; Saturated fat: 1.5g; Sodium: 241mg

894. Herbed Veggie Soup

Preparation time: 10 minute
Cooking time: 20 minutes
Servings: 4

Ingredients:

- 1 tablespoon olive oil
- 1/2 cup chopped onion
- 1/3 cup chopped celery
- 1 carrot, diced
- 1 garlic clove, minced
- 4 cups fat-free, unsalted chicken broth
- 2 large tomatoes, seeded and chopped
- 1/2 cup chopped spinach
- 1 can -16 ounces or about 1 1/2 cups canned chickpeas or red kidney beans, drained and rinsed
- 1/2 cup uncooked whole-grain small shell pasta
- 1 small zucchini, diced
- 2 tablespoons fresh basil, chopped

Directions:

1. Sauté onion, garlic, celery, and carrots in the olive oil.
2. Stir in broth, pasta, spinach, tomatoes, and beans. Bring to a boil then reduce to simmer.
3. Add zucchini and basil and cook for 5 more minutes.

Nutrition: Calories: 205; Carbs: 30; Fats: 5g; Protein: 10g; Saturated fat: 1g; Sodium: 300mg

895. Roasted Corn Soup

Preparation time: 10 minute
Cooking time: 60 minutes
Servings: 12

Ingredients:

- 4 cups corn kernels
- 1 1/2 tablespoons olive oil
- 3 cups chopped onion
- 2 cups chopped carrots
- 2 cups chopped celery
- 2 teaspoons chopped garlic
- 1/4 cup all-purpose flour
- 1 teaspoon cumin
- 6 cups vegetable stock
- 2 jalapeno peppers, minced
- 1 1/2 cups half-and-half
- 1 teaspoon salt
- 1/8 teaspoon white pepper
- 1 tablespoon chopped parsley

Directions:

1. Heat oven to 500 F. Roast corn in the oven for 8 minutes.
2. Sauté onion, carrots, garlic, and celery in medium-high heat. Reduce heat and stir in cumin, flour, and corn. Mix thoroughly.
3. Add in jalapenos and veggie stock. Let it cook for 30 minutes.
4. Stir in half and half, pepper, parsley, and salt. Serve

Nutrition: Calories: 120; Carbs: 17; Fats: 5g; Protein: 3g; Saturated fat: 2g; Sodium: 184mg

896. Sweet Potato Soup Cuban Style

Preparation time: 10 minute
Cooking time: 20 minutes
Servings: 6

Ingredients:

- 2 tablespoons extra virgin olive oil
- 1 onion, chopped
- 5 cloves of garlic, minced
- 1-pound sweet potatoes, peeled and diced
- 1 red bell pepper, chopped
- 1 cup tomatoes
- 1 bay leaf
- 1 teaspoon ground cumin
- 2 teaspoons dried oregano
- Pepper to taste

- 4 cups of water

Directions:

1. Place a heavy-bottomed pot on medium-high fire.
2. Add all ingredients and mix well.
3. Bring to a boil. Once boiling, lower fire to a simmer and cook for 15 minutes while covered.
4. Serve and enjoy.

Nutrition: Calories: 100; Carbs: 18.8g; Protein: 2.0g; Fats: 2.3g; Saturated Fat: 0.4g; Sodium: 68mg

897. Bacon Stew With Cauliflower

Preparation time: 10 minute
Cooking time: 40 minutes
Servings: 4

Ingredients:

- 1 head cauliflower, cut into florets
- 1 cup grated mozzarella
- 2 cups chicken broth
- ½ tsp garlic powder
- ½ tsp onion powder
- Salt and black pepper, to taste
- 4 garlic cloves, minced
- ¼ cup heavy cream
- 1 cup chopped bacon

Directions:

1. In a pot over medium heat, sauté bacon until crispy, about 5 minutes; reserve. Add chicken broth, cauliflower, salt, and pepper to the pot and cook for 15 minutes. Stir in heavy cream, garlic powder, mozzarella cheese, onion, and garlic powders and cook for 5 minutes. Top with bacon.

Nutrition: Calories: 380; Net Carbs 6g; Fat 25g; Protein 33g

898. Scottish Beef Stew

Preparation time: 10 minute
Cooking time: 40 minutes
Servings: 4

Ingredients:

- 1 ¼ lb. beef chuck roast, cubed
- 12 oz. sweet potatoes, cut into quarters
- 2 tbsp. lard
- 1 parsnip, chopped
- 1 onion, chopped
- Salt and black pepper to taste
- 1 ½ cups beef stock
- 2 tsp rosemary, chopped

Directions:

1. Melt lard in a pan at medium heat and cook the onion for 4 minutes. Add in the beef, season with salt and pepper, and brown on all sides for about 7-8 minutes. Add in sweet potatoes, parsnip, rosemary, and beef stock. Stir and cook on low heat for 15-20 minutes. Serve warm.

Nutrition: Calories: 445; Net Carbs 12g; Fat 18g; Protein 42g

899. Yellow Squash Duck Breast Stew

Preparation time: 15 minute
Cooking time: 40 minutes
Servings: 4

Ingredients:

- 1 pound duck breast, skin on and sliced
- 2 yellow squash, sliced
- 1 tbsp coconut oil
- 2 green onions, chopped
- 1 carrot, chopped
- 1 green bell pepper, chopped
- Salt and black pepper, to taste

Direction:

1. Set a casserole at medium heat and warm coconut oil. Sauté the duck for 3 minutes per side; reserve. Stir green onions in the saucepan for 2 minutes. Place in the yellow squash, bell pepper, carrot, salt, and pepper and cook for 10 minutes. Return the duch and cook for 10-15 minutes.

Nutrition: Calories: 433; Net Carbs 8g; Fat 21g, Protein 53g

900. Pork & Pumpkin Stew

Preparation time: 15 minute
Cooking time: 45 minutes
Servings: 6

Ingredients:

- 1 cup pumpkin puree
- 2 lb. chopped pork stew meat
- 1 tbsp. peanut butter
- 4 tbsp. chopped peanuts
- 1 garlic clove, minced
- ½ cup chopped onion
- ½ cup white wine
- 1 tbsp. olive oil
- 1 tsp lemon juice
- ¼ cup granulated sweetener
- ¼ tsp cardamom powder
- ¼ tsp allspice
- 2 cups of water
- 2 cups chicken stock

Directions:

1. Heat olive oil in a casserole at medium heat and sauté onion and garlic for 3 minutes. Add in pork and cook for 5-6 minutes. Pour in white wine and cook for 1 minute. Add in the remaining ingredients, except for the lemon juice and peanuts. Bring to a boil and cook for 5 minutes. Lower the heat and cook for around 30 minutes. Stir in the lemon juice. Serve topped with peanuts.

Nutrition: Calories: 451, Net Carbs: 4g, Fat: 33g, Protein: 27g

901. Chili Beef Stew With Cauliflower Grits

Preparation time: 15 minute
Cooking time: 55 minutes
Servings: 4

Ingredients:

- 2 tbsps. olive oil
- 2 lb. chuck roast, cubed
- 1 large yellow onion, chopped
- 3 garlic cloves, minced
- 2 large tomatoes, diced
- 1 tbsps. Rosemary
- 1 tbsps. Smoked paprika
- 2 tsp chili powder
- 2 cups beef broth
- 2 tbsps. Butter
- ½ cup walnuts, chopped
- 2 cups cauliflower rice
- 1 cup half and half
- 1 cup shredded cheddar

Directions:

1. Heat oil in a casserole at medium heat. With salt and pepper, season the beef then cook for 3 minutes. Stir in onion, garlic, and tomatoes for 5 minutes. Mix in rosemary, paprika, and chili and cook for 2 minutes. Pour

in beef broth and bring to a boil; simmer for 25 minutes. Pour in cauli rice and ½ cup water and cook for 5 minutes. Stir in half and a half and cheddar cheese for 3-4 minutes. Melt butter in a skillet and cook walnuts for 3 minutes. Transfer to a cutting board, chop and sprinkle over the stew. Serve.

Nutrition: Calories: 736; Net Carbs 7.8g; Fat 48g, Protein 63g

APPETIZER

902. Apple Cheese Wraps

Preparation time: 2 minutes
Cooking time: 0 minutes
Servings: 4

Ingredients:

- 1 granny smith apple
- 1 slice lemon
- 2 slices cheddar cheese, (cut into half)
- 2 slices deli turkey or ham, (cut into half)

Directions:

1. Cut the apples into slices with a thickness of 1/2 inch. Use a lemon wedge to rub the apple to avoid going brown.
2. Slice the cheddar cheese into slices with the width of 1/2 inch and the ham in half or in 1/4 (the ham needs to be big enough for wrapping around the apple).
3. Put on top of the deli meat with a cheese slice and an apple slice, then fold over deli meat to wrap.

Nutrition: Calories per serving: 144; Carbohydrates: 36g; Protein: 3g; Fat: 0.5g; Sugar: 2g; Sodium: 21mg; Fiber: 0.7g

903. Bacon Wrapped New Potatoes

Preparation time: 10 minutes
Cooking time: 30 minutes
Servings: 15

Ingredients:

- Small new potatoes
- Slices bacon, cut into thirds
- 1 (1 oz.) package ranch dressing mix
- Toothpicks

Directions:

1. Heat an outdoor grill on low heat and oil the grate lightly.
2. Wrap a piece of bacon on each potato and secure it using a toothpick. Add a sprinkling of powdered ranch dressing mix on the potatoes.
3. Put wrapped potatoes on the grill. Turn the potatoes a few times to ensure all sides of the bacon are cooked. It should be done in 20-25 minutes or until the bacon is crispy.

Nutrition: Calories per serving: 92;Carbohydrates: 17g; Protein: 4g; Fat: 2g;Sugar: 0.9g; Sodium: 207mg; Fiber: 0g

904. Asparagus Guacamole

Preparation time: 15 minutes
Cooking time: 1hr 15 minutes
Servings: 4

Ingredients:

- 24 spears fresh asparagus, trimmed and coarsely chopped
- 1/2 cup salsa
- 1 tbsp. chopped cilantro
- 2 cloves garlic
- Green onions, sliced

Directions:

1. In a pot, put the asparagus and pour water enough to cover it. Make it boil and let it cook for 5 minutes, until cooked and firm enough.
2. Remove the water then wash out using cold water.
3. In a blender, put the green onions, garlic, cilantro, salsa, and the asparagus, then mix until you reach the consistency you want.
4. Place inside the refrigerator to chill for 1 hour until serving time.

Nutrition: Calories per serving: 548; Carbohydrates: 64g; Protein: 5g; Fat: 2g; Sugar: 1g; Sodium: 64mg; Fiber: 3g

905. Fruit Spread

Preparation time: 15 minutes
Cooking time: 15 minutes
Servings: 20

Ingredients:

- 1 cup fat-free cottage cheese
- 1 package (8 oz.) reduced-fat cream cheese
- 1 tbsp. orange juice
- 1/2 tsp. grated orange zest
- 1/2 cup assorted dried fruit, chopped
- Toast or English muffins

Directions:

1. Set the first 4 ingredients in a food processor or blender.
2. Put cover and process until it becomes smooth.
3. Mix in fruit then spread it on English muffins or toast. Store the leftovers in the fridge.

Nutrition: Calories per serving: 44; Carbohydrates: 7g; Protein: 0.7g; Fat: 2g; Sugar: 0.5g; Sodium: 36mg; Fiber: 1g

906. Spinach Artichoke Dip

Preparation time: 10 minutes
Cooking time: 30 minutes
Servings: 5

Ingredients:

- 2 cups mayonnaise
- 2 cups grated Parmesan cheese
- 1 can (14 oz.) water-packed artichoke hearts, rinsed, drained and chopped
- 2 packages (10 oz. each) frozen chopped spinach, thawed and squeezed dry
- 2 garlic cloves, minced

Directions:

1. Mix all ingredients in a big bowl.
2. Place in a 9-inch deep-dish pie plate that is ungreased.
3. Bake without a cover for 20-25 minutes at 350 degrees or until it's thoroughly heated through. Eat warm.

Nutrition: Calories per serving: 211; Carbohydrates: 34g; Protein: 1g; Fat: 3g; Sugar: 1g; Sodium: 54mg; Fiber: 0g

907. Roasted Chickpeas

Preparation time: 10 minutes
Cooking time: 9 hours 20 minutes
Servings: 12

Ingredients:

- 1 lb. dried chickpeas (garbanzo beans)
- 2 tbsps. Olive oil
- Kosher salt to taste

Directions:

1. In a big container, put the chickpeas, pour a couple of inches of cold water to cover, and then let it stand for 8 hours to overnight.
2. Let the chickpeas drain and pat it dry.
3. Set an oven to preheat to 200°C (400°F).
4. In a bowl, toss together the salt, olive oil, and chickpeas until coated evenly, then in a single layer spread it on, in a baking tray.
5. Allow it roast in the preheated oven for about 40 minutes, mixing every 8 minutes, until the chickpeas become crisp and turn brown.

6. Toss the chickpeas with more salt and allow it to fully cool.

Nutrition: Calories per serving: 507; Carbohydrates: 48g; Protein: 0.4g; Fat: 2g; Sugar: 0.5g; Sodium: 27mg; Fiber: 0.1g

908. Mango Salsa

Preparation time: 15 minutes
Cooking time: 1hour 15 minutes
Servings: 6

Ingredients:

- Mangos - peeled, seeded, and diced
- 1 (15 oz.) can black beans
- 1 (10 oz.) can white shoepeg corn and drained
- 2 tbsps. Chopped fresh cilantro
- 1 lime, juiced
- Salt and pepper to taste

Directions:

1. Mix pepper, salt, lime juice, cilantro, corn, black beans, and diced mango in a bowl.
2. Chill for at least 1 hour; serve.

Nutrition: Calories per serving: 99; Carbohydrates: 32g; Protein: 1.7g; Fat: 2g; Sugar: 2g; Sodium: 47mg; Fiber: 0g

909. Grape Caterpillars

Preparation time: 15 minutes
Cooking time: 15 minutes
Servings: 4

Ingredients:

- 20 green grapes
- 1 tbsp. cream cheese softened
- 10 miniature semisweet chocolate chips
- Skewers

Directions:

1. Choose 5 nicest looking grapes.
2. Put on each one with 2 small dollops of cream cheese to make eyes and stick in mini chocolate chips for the pupils.
3. Thread 3-4 grapes lengthways onto a skewer, depending on your skewers' length, followed by the grape with the eyes horizontally.
4. Repeat with other grapes.

Nutrition: Calories per serving: 31; Carbohydrates: 32g; Protein: 4g; Fat: 2g; Sugar: 0.6g; Sodium: 29mg; Fiber: 1g

910. Crab Filled Deviled Eggs

Preparation time: 20 minutes
Cooking time: 20 minutes
Servings: 16

Ingredients:

- Hard-boiled large eggs
- 3 tbsps. Fat-free mayonnaise
- 2 tbsps. Lemon juice
- 2 tsp. Minced fresh tarragon
- 1 tbsp. chopped green onion
- 1/4 tsp. salt
- 1/4 tsp. hot pepper sauce
- 1/8 tsp. cayenne pepper
- 1 can (6 oz.) crabmeat, drained, flaked and cartilage removed

Directions:

1. Halve the eggs lengthwise.
2. Take out the yolks, then put aside the 4 yolks and egg whites
3. Mash the reserved yolks in a big bowl. Stir in cayenne, hot pepper sauce, salt, onion, tarragon, lemon juice, and mayonnaise.
4. Mix in crab until well blended. Pipe or stuff it into egg whites, then chill it in the fridge until ready to serve.

Nutrition: Calories 321; Carbohydrates: 23g; Protein: 2g; Fat: 1.7g; Sugar: 1g; Sodium: 103mg; Fiber: 0g

911. Cinnamon Toasties

Preparation time: 10 minutes
Cooking time: 20 minutes
Servings: 4

Ingredients:

- Slices bread
- 1/4 cup reduced-fat cream cheese
- Refrigerated butter-flavored spray
- 3 tbsps. Sugar
- 1-1/2 tsp. Ground cinnamon

Directions:

1. Use a rolling pin to flatten bread.
2. Spread half of the piece with cream cheese on one side; put remaining bread on top.
3. Slice into four squares each. Spritz butter-flavored spray on both sides.
4. Blend cinnamon and sugar in a small bowl; include bread squares and flip to cover both sides.
5. Put on an ungreased baking sheet—Bake for 8-10 minutes at 350° or until golden and puffed. Serve right away.

Nutrition: Calories per serving: 231; Carbohydrates: 42g; Protein: 0.6g; Fat: 1g; Sugar: 0.3g; Sodium: 98mg; Fiber: 1g

912. Fusion Peach Salsa

Preparation time: 5 minutes
Cooking time: 5 minutes
Servings: 4

Ingredients:

- 2 (15 oz.) cans peaches, drained and chopped
- 2 green onions with tops, thinly sliced
- 2 tsp. Chopped fresh cilantro
- 2 tbsps. Lime juice
- 1/4 tsp. Asian five-spice powder
- 2 tsp. Garlic Chile paste
- 1/8 tsp. white pepper

Directions:

1. Mix lime juice, cilantro, green onion, and peaches in a medium bowl, then combine in white pepper, garlic Chile paste, and five-spice powder.
2. Chill with a cover until serving.

Nutrition: Calories per serving: 103; Carbohydrates: 39g; Protein: 1g; Fat: 1g; Sugar: 1g; Sodium: 87mg; Fiber: 0g

913. Basil And Pesto Hummus

Preparation time: 10 minutes
Cooking time: 10 minutes
Servings: 5

Ingredients:

- 1 (16 oz.) garbanzo beans (chickpeas), drained and rinsed
- 1/2 cup basil leaves
- 1 clove garlic
- 1 tbsp. olive oil
- 1/2 tsp. balsamic vinegar
- 1/2 tsp. soy sauce
- Salt and ground black pepper to taste

Directions:

1. In a food processor, mix garlic, basil, and garbanzo beans, then pulse a few times.
2. Scrape down the sides of the processor bowl using a spatula. Pulse again while drizzling in the oil.

3. Stir in soy sauce and vinegar, and process until incorporated.
4. Sprinkle pepper and salt to season.

Nutrition: Calories per serving: 131; Carbohydrates: 56g; Protein: 0g; Fat: 0g; Sugar: 0.4g; Sodium: 22mg; Fiber: 0g

914. Sweet Potato Chips

Preparation time: 5 minutes
Cooking time: 15 minutes
Servings: 2

Ingredients:

- One sweet potato, thinly sliced
- 2 tsp. olive oil, or as needed
- Coarse sea salt

Directions:

1. Mix olive oil and sweet potato slices in a big bowl and coat by tossing.
2. Place the sweet potato slices in one layer on a big plate that's microwave-safe. Season using salt.
3. Cook until slightly browned, crisp, and dry in a microwave for 5 minutes.
4. Cool the chips on a plate then transfer to a bowl—repeat steps with leftover sweet potato slices.

Nutrition: Calories per serving: 140; Carbohydrates: 64g; Protein: 3g; Fat: 1.3g; Sugar: 2.3g; Sodium: 17mg; Fiber: 0g

915. Mango Mania Salsa

Preparation time: 30 minutes
Cooking time: 40 minutes
Servings: 24

Ingredients:

- 1 red onion, peeled and halved
- 12 mangos - peeled, seeded, and diced
- 1/2 head garlic, pressed
- 3 habanero peppers, seeded and minced
- 1 bunch fresh cilantro, chopped
- 2 tbsps. apple cider vinegar
- salt to taste

Directions:

1. Preheat outdoor grill to high heat.
2. Oil the grate lightly. Put onion onto the grill.
3. Cook until blackened slightly.
4. Dice onion. In a mixing bowl, mix apple cider, cilantro, habanero, garlic, and mango—season with salt to taste.

Nutrition: Calories per serving: 72; Carbohydrates: 34g; Protein: 3g; Fat: 2g; Sugar: 1g; Sodium: 20mg; Fiber: 1.4g

916. Crab Dip

Preparation time: 10 minutes
Cooking time: 10 minutes
Servings: 2

Ingredients:

- 3/4 cup fat-free mayonnaise
- 1/4 cup chili sauce
- 1 tbsp. lemon juice
- 1 tsp. horseradish
- 1/2 tsp. garlic powder
- 1/4 tsp. pepper
- 2 cans (6 oz. each) lump crabmeat and drained
- Assorted crackers or fresh vegetables

Directions:

1. Mix the first 6 ingredients in a small bowl, then fold in the crab.
2. Let it chill until ready to serve.
3. Serve alongside crackers.

Nutrition: Calories per serving: 54; Carbohydrates: 32g; Protein: 3g; Fat: 0.1g; Sugar: 1g; Sodium: 16mg; Fiber: 0g

917. Feta And Beet Stacked Appetizer

Preparation time: 30 minutes
Cooking time: minutes
Servings: 4-6

Ingredients:

- 2 large fresh beets
- ½ teaspoon dried lovage
- ½ cup red wine vinegar
- ¼ cup lemon juice (optional)
- ½ cup feta cheese
- ½ cup walnuts, crushed

Directions:

1. Soak the lovage in the red wine vinegar while you're preparing the rest of the appetizer.
2. Set a pot of water to a boil, cook the beets for 25 minutes, or wait until tender.
3. Cool, peel, and slice in 1/3" thick slices.
4. Place beets in a bowl with the lovage red wine vinegar and marinate 15 minutes.
5. Separate the beets from the vinegar, and add the lemon juice to the liquid.
6. Place a few beet slices on a microwave-safe dish and sprinkle them with some feta cheese and crushed walnuts. Drizzle with some of the lemon vinegar mix.
7. Top with more beet slices, and sprinkle again with feta, walnuts and lemon vinegar. Repeat until you have no more beet slices left.
8. Microwave on medium for 45 seconds to 1 minute.
9. Cool slightly before serving.

Nutrition: Calories: 108 kcal Protein: 4.34 g Fat: 8.09 g Carbohydrates: 4.89 g

918. Walnut Stuffed Bacon Wrapped Dates

Preparation time: 10-20 minutes
Cooking time: 10 minutes
Servings: 4

Ingredients:

- 1 (8 ounces) package pitted Medjool dates
- 4 ounces walnuts, halved
- 1 pound sliced bacon

Directions:

1. Preheat your broiler.
2. Slit the dates and place one walnut half inside each—wrap dates with ½ slice of bacon, using toothpicks to hold them together.
3. Broil 10 minutes, turning once, or until bacon is evenly brown and crisp.

Nutrition: Calories: 705 kcal Protein: 21.84 g Fat: 66.06 g Carbohydrates: 9.33 g

919. Herbed Tomato And Buffalo Mozzarella Appetizer

Preparation time: 10 minutes
Cooking time: 30 minutes
Servings: 4-6

Ingredients:

- 1 tablespoon parsley, minced
- ½ teaspoon dried basil
- ½ teaspoon dried lovage
- 1 tablespoon capers, drained
- 2 cloves garlic, minced

- 4 tablespoons extra virgin olive oil
- 1 ball of buffalo mozzarella cheese, sliced thinly
- 2 beefsteak tomatoes, sliced thinly
- 1 (7 ounces) jar roasted red peppers, drained
- Chili pepper flakes to taste (optional)

Directions:

1. In a medium-sized bowl, mix parsley, basil, lovage, capers, garlic, and olive oil.
2. On a large plate or serving platter, layer slices of mozzarella cheese with tomato and top with roasted red pepper slice.
3. Drizzle the herb and olive oil mixture over top of each stack. Cover and chill in the refrigerator for at least 30 minutes.
4. Sprinkle with chili flakes before serving (optional).

Nutrition: Calories: 61 kcal 3% Protein: 1.54 g Fat: 5.1 g Carbohydrates: 2.48 g Calorie breakdown

920. Roast Tomato And Parmesan Bruchetta With Capers

Preparation time: 10 minutes
Cooking time: 10-15 minutes
Servings: 4-6

Ingredients:

- 4 to 6 thick slices of whole-grain baguette, sliced on a diagonal
- 1 cup cherry tomatoes
- 2 tablespoons capers, drained
- 3 to 4 tablespoons extra-virgin olive oil
- 1 tablespoon extra, additional
- ½ teaspoon of sea salt
- 2/3 cup aged Parmesan, shaved

Directions:

1. Pre-heat oven to 400 degrees F.
2. Mix the cherry tomatoes, capers, and 3 to 4 tablespoons of olive oil and pour them into an oven-proof dish. Roast for 10 to 15 minutes.
3. When the tomatoes are roasting, toast the bread on both sides and drizzle the remaining 1 tablespoon of oil over the bread.
4. Spoon the roast tomatoes and capers over the toasted bread, salt to taste, and top with the shaved Parmesan to serve.

Nutrition: Calories: 134 kcal Protein: 7.57 g Fat: 6.78 g Carbohydrates: 11.02 g

921. Greek Stuffed Mushrooms

Preparation time: 10 minutes
Cooking time: 20 minutes
Servings: 4-5

Ingredients:

- 20 large mushrooms, washed
- 1 tablespoon extra-virgin olive oil
- 1 cup broccoli, chopped
- 1 medium red onion, diced
- 1 teaspoon garlic, minced
- ¼ cup capers
- ½ teaspoon dried oregano
- ½ teaspoon dried parsley
- 3 tablespoons feta cheese
- 1 tablespoon breadcrumbs
- Salt and pepper to taste

Directions:

1. Preheat oven to 425 degrees F.
2. Remove the stems from the mushrooms carefully and dice them.
3. Place mushroom tops in a single layer on a baking sheet, with the hole facing up, and bake for 5 minutes.
4. Warm olive oil in a pan with the diced mushrooms stems, broccoli, onion, garlic, capers, oregano, parsley, salt, and pepper. Cook for 5 – 10 minutes.
5. Add feta and breadcrumbs.
6. Stuff mushrooms with mixture and bake for 8 – 10 minutes.

Nutrition: Calories: 89 kcal Protein: 6.36 g Fat: 4.76 g Carbohydrates: 7.19 g

922. Kale Dip With Cajun Pita Chips

Preparation time: 10 minutes
Cooking time: 8-10 minutes + 1 hour cooling
Servings: 40

Ingredients:

- For the Dip:
- 2 cups sour cream
- 1 ½ cups baby kale
- ¼ cup red bell pepper, diced
- ¼ cup green onions, diced
- 1 clove garlic, minced
- 1/8 teaspoon chili pepper flakes
- For the Chips:
- 5 pita breads, halved and split open
- ½ cup extra virgin olive oil
- ½ teaspoon Cajun seasoning
- ¼ teaspoon ground cumin
- ¼ teaspoon turmeric
- Salt to taste

Directions:

1. To make the dip:
2. In a bowl, combine the sour cream, baby kale, red pepper, onions, garlic, salt, and chili pepper flakes. Cover and refrigerate for 1 hour.
3. To make the chips:
4. Preheat oven to 400°F
5. Cut each pita half into four wedges. Combine the olive oil, Cajun seasoning, cumin and turmeric and brush over the rough side of the pita wedges
6. Put on ungreased baking sheets and bake for 8-10 minutes or until chips are golden brown and crisp.
7. Serve with dip.

Nutrition: Calories: 39 kcal Protein: 0.94 g Fat: 2.58 g Carbohydrates: 2.95 g

923. Endive Leaves With Citrus Cream

Preparation time: 10 minutes
Cooking time: 20 minutes
Servings: 48-60

Ingredients:

- 4-6 heads red endive
- 8 ounces cream cheese
- 1 tablespoon shallot, finely chopped
- ¼ cup sour cream
- ¼ cup Vegannaise or mayonnaise
- Zest from one small lemon
- 1 tablespoon lemon juice
- 2 tablespoons fresh tarragon, chopped
- 2 tablespoons fresh dill, chopped,

- 2 tablespoons parsley, chopped
- 1 tablespoon green onions, finely chopped
- Anchovy paste (optional), to taste
- Salt and pepper, to taste

Directions:

1. In a medium bowl, blend all the ingredients, except the endive leaves, until smooth. Refrigerate until needed.
2. When well chilled, put the filling into a piping bag with a French tip.
3. Cut the stem end of the endive leaves and carefully peel them off the base of the head, so you have individual leaves.
4. Set the leaves in a single layer on a platter and fill with the cream from the piping bag. Alternatively, spoon the filling into a small bowl or ramekin and serve the endive leaves and crackers around it for guests.

Nutrition: Calories: 33 kcal Protein: 1.37 g Fat: 2.17 g Carbohydrates: 2.5 g

924. Avocado Deviled Eggs

Preparation time: 10 minutes
Cooking time: 5 minutes
Servings: 3

Ingredients:

- 3 eggs
- 1 avocado
- 1 tablespoon chopped chives
- 1 tablespoon freshly squeezed lime juice

Directions:

1. Peel your hard-boiled eggs, cut them in half, lengthways.
2. Take off the cooked yolk and add to a mixing bowl along with the avocado and lime juice.
3. Mash it using a fork, until you achieve the desired texture. Mix in the chopped chives.
4. Either use a spoon to the mixture back into the eggs or pipe it into the eggs with a piping bag or zip lock back.
5. Serve straight away.

Nutrition: Calories 156 Fat 5.3g Carbohydrates 3.8g Protein 3.4g

925. Spicy Roasted Nuts

Preparation time: 20 minutes
Cooking time: 15 minutes
Servings: 6

Ingredients:

- 8 oz. pecans or almonds or walnuts
- 1 tablespoon olive oil or coconut oil
- 1 teaspoon paprika powder or chili powder
- 1 teaspoon ground cumin
- 1 teaspoon salt

Directions:

1. In a frying pan, mix all the ingredients then cook on medium heat until the almonds are warmed.
2. Allow it cool and serve as a snack with a drink. Store it in a container with a lid at room temperature.

Nutrition: Calories 201 Fat 7g Carbohydrates 5g Protein 4g

926. Crab Salad Stuffed Avocado

Preparation time: 15 minutes
Cooking time: 10 minutes
Servings: 2

Ingredients:

- 4 oz. lump crab meat
- 2 tablespoons light mayonnaise
- 1 teaspoon chopped fresh chives
- ¼ cup peeled and diced cucumber
- 2 teaspoons Sriracha, plus more for drizzling
- 1 small avocado (about 4 oz. avocado when pitted and peeled)
- ½ teaspoon furikake
- 2 teaspoons gluten-free soy sauce

Directions:

1. In a medium bowl, mix mayonnaise, Sriracha, and chives.
2. Add crab meat, cucumber, and chive and gently toss.
3. Cut the avocado open, take off the pit and peel the skin or spoon the avocado out.
4. Fill the avocado halves equally with crab salad.
5. Top with furikake and mizzle with soy sauce.

Nutrition: Calories 194 Fat 13g Carbohydrates 7g Protein 12g

927. Cheddar Olives

Preparation time: 15 minutes
Cooking time: 20 minutes
Servings: 6-8

Ingredients:

- 1 8-10 jar pitted olives, either pimento-stuffed or plain
- 1 cup all-purpose flour
- 1 ½ cups shredded sharp cheddar cheese
- ¼ teaspoon freshly grated black pepper
- 4 tablespoons unsalted butter, softened

Directions:

1. Preheat oven to 400° F. Drain the olives well and dry them thoroughly with clean dish towels. Set aside.
2. Mix the cheese, flour, butter, and spices in a medium bowl and knead it within the bowl until a dough form. If the dough is still powdery and won't hold together, put some water, 1 teaspoon at a time until it does.
3. Pinch a small quantity of dough, and press it as thin as you can between your fingers to flatten. Wrap it and smoosh the dough around a dry olive. Pinch off any excess, and then roll the olive in your hands until smooth. Continue until all the olives are covered.
4. Bake for at least 15-20 minutes, or until golden brown all over. Serve immediately and enjoy!

Nutrition: Calories 195 Fat 12.2g Carbohydrates 8.1g Protein 6.9g

928. Crispy Breaded Tofu Nuggets

Preparation time: 15 minutes
Cooking time: 20 minutes
Servings: 4

Ingredients:

- 1 block extra firm tofu
- 1 cup panko bread crumbs
- 2 flax eggs let sit 5 minutes before using
- ½ cup vegetable broth
- 1 tablespoon lite soy sauce
- ½ cup all-purpose flour
- 1 ½ teaspoons paprika
- ½ teaspoon onion powder
- ½ teaspoon garlic powder
- ½ teaspoon cayenne pepper
- ¼ teaspoon salt
- ¼ teaspoon fresh ground black pepper

Directions:

1. Preheat oven to 400° F. set a line in a baking sheet with parchment paper.
2. Slice the tofu into ten squares, cut them into 5 slices along the long edge, and then cut every column in half to make squares. Gently press each slice of tofu with a paper towel to take off some of the liquid.
3. To make the marinade, mix the vegetable broth and soy sauce in a pan. Soak the tofu in the vegetable broth mixture for around 10minutes.

4. Prepare 3 bowls: 1 with the flour, 1 with panko bread crumbs and spices, and 1 with the flax eggs. Coat the tofu in the flour, flax eggs, and finally the panko.
5. Bake at 400° F on the parchment-lined baking sheet for 15 minutes. Carefully flip the tofu bites over and then bake for another 15 minutes. They're ready when golden brown and crispy. Enjoy!

Nutrition: Calories 127 Carbohydrates 23g Protein 5g

929. Rosemary Toasted Walnuts

Preparation time: 10 minutes
Cooking time: 20 minutes
Servings: 8

Ingredients:

- 2 cups raw walnuts
- 2 tablespoons fresh rosemary, finely chopped
- ¼ cup olive oil
- ½ teaspoon salt
- 1 teaspoon pepper

Directions:

1. Preheat oven to 350° F. Set a line a baking sheet with parchment paper.
2. In a bowl, mix the olive oil, rosemary, salt, and pepper.
3. Put the walnuts and toss until completely covered in olive oil mixture.
4. Bake the walnuts for about 10-15 minutes in the oven, tossing every 4-5 minutes until their golden brown. The walnuts cook fast, so be careful not to burn them. Enjoy!

Nutrition: Calories 223 Fat 23g Carbohydrates 5g Protein 4g

930. Cream Cheese Stuffed Celery

Preparation time: 15 minutes
Cooking time: 25 minutes
Servings: 12

Ingredients:

- 10 stalks celery, rinsed and dried well
- 16 oz. (2 packages) cream cheese softened to room temperature
- 1 tablespoon milk
- 1 ¼ oz. (1 packet) vegetable soup mix
- ½ cup walnut chips
- ½ cup bacon pieces, for topping

Directions:

1. Cut dried celery stalks into 3 sections each. Set aside.
2. In a bowl, using an electric mixer put cream cheese and milk. Add on dry vegetable soup mix and stir well.
3. Stuff the celery with cream cheese mixture.
4. Sprinkle with walnut chips or bacon pieces (optional). Enjoy!

Nutrition: Calories 208 Fat 18g Carbohydrates 9g Protein 5g

931. Baked Artichoke & Cilantro Pizza Dipping Sauce

Preparation time: 10 minutes
Cooking time: 28 minutes
Servings: 6

Ingredients:

- 1 – 6.5 oz. jar artichoke hearts, drained and chopped
- ½ cup pizza sauce, preferably with garlic
- 2 tablespoons fresh cilantro
- ¾ cup Parmesan cheese, grated
- 1/3 cup light mayonnaise
- Garnish:
- Fresh cilantro sprigs

Directions:

1. Heat oven to 350° F.
2. Mix all of the dip ingredients and spoon into a shallow ovenproof pan or 9-inch pie plate sprayed with non-stick cooking spray.
3. Bake 20 minutes until hot and bubbly.
4. Garnish with cilantro sprigs and serve warm. Serve with chips, nachos, bread, or veggies. Enjoy!

Nutrition: Calories 88 Fat 5g Carbohydrates 2g Protein 3g

932. Broccoli Cheddar Bites

Preparation time: 15 minutes
Cooking time: 20 minutes
Servings: 24

Ingredients:

- 1 large bunch of broccoli florets
- ½ cup, packed, torn fresh bread
- 2 eggs, lightly beaten
- ¼ cup mayonnaise
- ¼ cup grated onion
- 1 ½ teaspoon lemon zest
- 1 cup, packed, grated sharp cheddar cheese
- ¼ teaspoons freshly ground black pepper
- ½ teaspoon kosher salt

Directions:

1. Place it in 1 inch of water in a pot with a steamer basket. Bring to a boil. Put the broccoli florets.
2. Steam the broccoli florets for approximately 5 minutes, until tender. Rinse with cold water to stop the cooking. Finely chop the steamed broccoli florets. You should have 2 to 2 ½ cups.
3. Put the beaten eggs and the torn bread in a large bowl. Mix until the bread is thoroughly moistened. Put on the grated onion, mayonnaise, cheese, lemon zest, salt, and pepper. Stir in the minced broccoli.
4. Set the oven to 350° F. Coat the wells of 2 mini muffin pans with olive oil. Spread the broccoli mixture in the muffin wells.
5. Bake at 350° F for about 25 minutes or until cooked through and lightly browned on top.

Nutrition: Calories 62 Fat 4.8g Carbohydrates 3g Protein 1.7g

933. No-Bake Zucchini Roll-Ups

Preparation time: 10 minutes
Cooking time: 20 minutes
Servings: 20

Ingredients:

- 1 large zucchini
- 1 jar pepperoncini
- 1 medium carrot
- Handful mixed greens
- 1 tub guacamole
- 1 single celery stalk
- Fresh dill

Directions:

1. Using a peeler slice the zucchini in a long way on all sides to avoid the center. Make 3-4 slices on 1 side and move on to the opposite side, then the other two sides until you have around 20 slices.
2. Don't throw the middle; just add to your next skillet meal. Set aside.
3. Using the mandolin slicer, cut the carrots and celery into thin strips and set aside.
4. Finally, cut the top part off each pepperoncino and cut one side to open and clean seeds out.
5. Arranging the Roll-Ups:
6. On a flat surface, put 1 zucchini strip and then spread a dab of guacamole on one end. Put a pepperoncino on top

of the guacamole, open side up. Fill the pocket whole of the pepperoncini with guacamole. Put in 1-2 mixed green leaves, 3 strips of carrots, 1-2 pieces of celery, fresh dill, and roll it tight until the end of the zucchini.

7. Do this step until you've used all the ingredients.
8. Serve cold and refrigerate leftovers until 24 hours. The guacamole will darken after this time.

Nutrition: Calories 214 Fat 4.7g Carbohydrates 4g Protein 5g

934. Spicy Deviled Eggs

Preparation time: 15 minutes
Cooking time: 15 minutes
Servings: 24

Ingredients:

- 12 large eggs
- 1 tablespoon Sriracha sauce
- 1/3 cup mayonnaise
- 1 tablespoon Dijon mustard
- Fine chili flakes
- Fresh chives, minced
- Salt, to taste
- Freshly ground black pepper, to taste

Directions:

1. Fill enough water into a saucepan to cover eggs by an inch and bring to a full boil. Carefully lower eggs into boiling water. Allow eggs boil uncovered for about 30 seconds. Lower the heat and cover. Simmer for 11 minutes. Take boiled eggs to a bowl of ice water. When cool enough to handle, carefully break the shell apart and peel. If possible, refrigerate eggs overnight, to make them easier to cut.
2. When the eggs are cool, cut it in half lengthwise with a very sharp knife. Gently spoon yolks out into a small bowl and prepare whites on serving platter.
3. In a bowl, mash yolks into a paste using the back of a fork. Put mayonnaise, Sriracha sauce, and mustard; whisk until smooth. Season it with salt, freshly ground black pepper and more Sriracha if you like.
4. Spoon or pipe the filling into egg white halves.
5. Cover and refrigerate eggs for 2 hours or more (up to 1 day). Once chilled sprinkle generously with fine chili flakes and minced chives. Serve and enjoy!

Nutrition: Calories 53 Fat 4g Net Carbs 0.6g Protein 2 g

935. Delicious Cucumber Cups

Preparation time: 10 minute
Cooking time: 0 minutes
Servings: 24

Ingredients:

- 2 cucumbers, peeled, cut in ¾ inch slices and some of the seeds scooped out
- ½ cup sour cream
- Salt and white pepper to the taste
- 6 ounces smoked salmon, flaked
- 1/3 cup cilantro, chopped
- 2 teaspoons lime juice
- 1 tablespoon lime zest
- A pinch of cayenne pepper

Directions:

1. In a bowl, mix salmon with salt, pepper, cayenne, sour cream, lime juice, and zest and cilantro and stir well.
2. Fill each cucumber cup with this salmon mix, arrange on a platter, and serve as a keto appetizer.
3. Enjoy!

Nutrition: Calories 30, Fat 11, Fiber 1, Carbs 1, Protein 2

936. Caviar Salad

Preparation time: 6 minute
Cooking time: 0 minutes
Servings: 16

Ingredients:

- 8 eggs, hard-boiled, peeled and mashed with a fork
- 4 ounces black caviar
- 4 ounces red caviar
- Salt and black pepper to the taste
- 1 yellow onion, finely chopped
- ¾ cup mayonnaise
- Some toast baguette slices for serving

Directions:

1. In a bowl, mix mashed eggs with mayo, salt, pepper, and onion and stir well.
2. Spread eggs salad on toasted baguette slices, and top each with caviar.
3. Enjoy!

Nutrition: Calories 122 Fat 8, Fiber 1, Carbs 4, Protein 7

937. Marinated Kebabs

Preparation time: 10 minute
Cooking time: 20 minutes
Servings: 6

Ingredients:

- 1 red bell pepper, cut in chunks
- 1 green bell pepper, cut into chunks
- 1 orange bell pepper, cut into chunks
- 2 pounds sirloin steak, cut into medium cubes
- 4 garlic cloves, minced
- 1 red onion, cut into chunks
- Salt and black pepper to the taste
- 2 tablespoons Dijon mustard
- 2 and ½ tablespoons Worcestershire sauce
- ¼ cup tamari sauce
- ¼ cup lemon juice
- ½ cup olive oil

Directions:

1. In a bowl, mix Worcestershire sauce with salt, pepper, garlic, mustard, tamari, lemon juice and oil and whisk very well.
2. Add beef, bell peppers and onion chunks to this mix, toss to coat and leave aside for a few minutes.
3. Arrange bell pepper, meat cubes, and onion chunks on skewers alternating colors. Put them on your preheated grill over medium-high heat, cook for about 5 minutes on each side, and transfer to a platter and serve.
4. Enjoy!

Nutrition: Calories 246, Fat 12, Fiber 1, Carbs 4, Protein 26

938. Simple Zucchini Rolls

Preparation time: 10 minute
Cooking time: 5 minutes
Servings: 24

Ingredients:

- 2 tablespoons olive oil
- 3 zucchinis, thinly sliced
- 24 basil leaves
- 2 tablespoons mint, chopped
- 1 and 1/3 cup ricotta cheese
- Salt and black pepper to the taste
- ¼ cup basil, chopped
- Tomato sauce for serving

Directions:

1. Brush zucchini slices using olive oil, season with salt and pepper on both sides, bring them on preheated grill over medium heat temperature, cook them for about 2 minutes, flip and cook for another 2 minutes.
2. Put zucchini slices on a plate and leave aside for now.
3. In a bowl, blend ricotta with chopped basil, mint, salt, and pepper and stir well.
4. Spread over zucchini slices, divide whole basil leaves and roll, and serve as an appetizer with some tomato sauce on the side.
5. Enjoy!

Nutrition: Calories 40, Fat 3, Fiber 0.3, Carbs 1, Protein 2

939. Simple Green Crackers

Preparation time: 10 minute
Cooking time: 24 hours
Servings: 6

Ingredients:

- 2 cups flax seed, ground
- 2 cups flax seed, soaked overnight and drained
- 4 bunches kale, chopped
- 1 bunch basil, chopped
- ½ bunch celery, chopped
- 4 garlic cloves, minced
- 1/3 cup olive oil

Directions:

1. In your food processor, mix ground flaxseed with celery, kale, basil, and garlic and blend well.
2. Add oil and soaked flaxseed and blend again.
3. Spread this into a tray, cut into medium crackers, introduce in your dehydrator and dry for 24 hours at 115 degrees F, turning them halfway.
4. Arrange them on a platter and serve.
5. Enjoy!

Nutrition: Calories 100, Fat 1, Fiber 2, Carbs 1, Protein 4

940. Cheese And Pesto Terrine

Preparation time: 30 minute
Cooking time: 0 minutes
Servings: 10

Ingredients:

- ½ cup heavy cream
- 10 ounces goat cheese, crumbled
- 3 tablespoons basil pesto
- Salt and black pepper to the taste
- 5 sun-dried tomatoes, chopped
- ¼ cup pine nuts, toasted and chopped
- 1 tablespoons pine nuts, toasted and chopped

Directions:

1. In a bowl, mix goat cheese with the heavy cream, salt, and pepper and stir using your mixer.
2. Spoon half of this mix into a bowl and spread.
3. Add pesto on top and also spread.
4. Add another layer of cheese, then add sun-dried tomatoes and ¼ cup pine nuts.
5. Spread one last layer of cheese and top with 1 tablespoon pine nuts.
6. Keep in the fridge for a while, turn upside down on a plate, and serve.
7. Enjoy!

Nutrition: Calories 240, Fat 12, Fiber 3, Carbs 5, Protein 12

941. Avocado Salsa

Preparation time: 10 minute
Cooking time: 30 minutes
Servings: 4

Ingredients:

- 1 small red onion, chopped
- 2 avocados, pitted, peeled and chopped
- 3 jalapeno pepper, chopped
- Salt and black pepper to the taste
- 2 tablespoons cumin powder
- 2 tablespoons lime juice
- ½ tomato, chopped

Directions:

1. In a bowl, mix the onion with avocados, peppers, salt, black pepper, cumin, lime juice, and tomato pieces and stir well.
2. Move this to a bowl and serve with toasted baguette slices as a keto appetizer.
3. Enjoy!

Nutrition: Calories 120, Fat 2, Fiber 2, Carbs 0.4, Protein 4

942. Tasty Egg Chips

Preparation time: 5 minute
Cooking time: 10 minutes
Servings: 2

Ingredients:

- ½ tablespoon water
- 2 tablespoons parmesan, shredded
- 4 eggs whites
- Salt and black pepper to the taste

Directions:

1. In a bowl, mix egg whites with salt, pepper and water and whisk well.
2. Spoon this into a muffin pan, sprinkle cheese on top, introduce in the oven at 400 degrees F and bake for 15 minutes.
3. Transfer egg white chips to a platter and serve with a keto dip on the side.
4. Enjoy!

Nutrition: Calories 120, Fat 2, Fiber 1, Carbs 2, Protein 7

943. Chili Lime Chips

Preparation time: 10 minute
Cooking time: 20 minutes
Servings: 4

Ingredients:

- 1 cup almond flour
- Salt and black pepper to the taste
- 1 and ½ teaspoons lime zest
- 1 teaspoon lime juice
- 1 egg

Directions:

1. In a bowl, mix almond flour with lime zest, lime juice, and salt and stir.
2. Add egg and whisk well again.
3. Divide this into 4 parts, roll each into a ball and then spread well using a rolling pin.
4. Cut each into 6 triangles, place them all on a lined baking sheet, and introduce them in the oven over 350°F and bake for 20 minutes.
5. Enjoy!

Nutrition: Calories 90, Fat 1, Fiber 1, Carbs 0.6, Protein 3

944. Artichoke Dip

Preparation time: 10 minute
Cooking time: 15 minutes
Servings: 16

Ingredients:

- ¼ cup sour cream
- ¼ cup heavy cream
- ¼ cup mayonnaise

- ¼ cup shallot, chopped
- 1 tablespoon olive oil
- 2 garlic cloves, minced
- 4 ounces cream cheese
- ½ cup parmesan cheese, grated
- 1 cup mozzarella cheese, shredded
- 4 ounces feta cheese, crumbled
- 1 tablespoon balsamic vinegar
- 28 ounces canned artichoke hearts, chopped
- Salt and black pepper to the taste
- 10 ounces spinach, chopped

Directions:

1. Warm a pan with the oil over medium heat, add shallot and garlic, stir and cook for 3 minutes.
2. Put the heavy cream and cream cheese and stir.
3. Also add sour cream, parmesan, mayo, feta cheese, and mozzarella cheese, stir and reduce heat.
4. Add artichoke, spinach, salt, pepper, and vinegar, stir well, take off heat, and transfer to a bowl.
5. Serve as a tasty keto dip.
6. Enjoy!

Nutrition: Calories 144, Fat 12, Fiber 2, Carbs 5, Protein 5

945. Cauliflower Bites With Asiago Cheese

Preparation time: 10 minute
Cooking time: 35 minutes
Servings: 2
Ingredients:

- 1 ½ cups cauliflower florets
- 1 tablespoon butter, softened
- 1 egg, whisked
- Sea salt, to taste
- Ground black pepper, to taste
- 1 teaspoon Italian seasoning mix
- 1/2 cup Asiago cheese, grated

Directions:

1. Pulse the cauliflower in your food processor; now, heat the butter in a nonstick skillet and cook the cauliflower until golden.
2. Put the remaining ingredients and blend until well incorporated.
3. Form the mixture into balls and flatten them with the palm of your hand. Arrange on a tinfoil-lined baking pan—Bake in the preheated oven at 410 degrees F for 25 to 30 minutes. Serve with homemade ketchup. Bon appétit!

Nutrition: 236 Calories; 19.2g Fat; 4.5g Total Carbs; 12.3g Protein; 1.6g Fiber

946. Chunky Burger Dip

Preparation time: 10 minute
Cooking time: 1 hour and minutes
Servings: 2
Ingredients:

- 1/4 pound ground pork
- 1/4 pound ground turkey
- 1/2 red onion, chopped
- 1 garlic clove, minced
- 1 serrano pepper, chopped
- 1 bell pepper, chopped
- 2 ounces sour cream
- 1/2 cup Provolone cheese, grated
- 2 ounces tomato paste
- 1/2 teaspoon mustard
- 1/2 teaspoon dried oregano
- 1/2 teaspoon dried basil
- 1/4 teaspoon dried marjoram

Directions:

1. Put all of the ingredients needed, except for the sour cream and Provolone cheese in your slow cooker.
2. Cook for 1 hour 30 minutes at Low setting. Afterward, fold in sour cream and cheese.
3. Serve warm with celery sticks if desired. Bon appétit!

Nutrition: 423 Calories; 29g Fat; 5g Total Carbs; 32.1g Protein; 1g Fiber

947. Ranch Bacon Chips

Preparation time: 5 minute
Cooking time: 15 minutes
Servings: 12
Ingredients:

- 1 ½ pounds bacon, cut into 1-inch squares
- 1/4 cup lemon juice
- 1 teaspoon Ranch seasoning mix
- 1 tablespoon hot sauce

Directions

1. Toss the bacon squares with the lemon juice, ranch seasoning mix, and hot sauce. Arrange the bacon squares on a parchment-lined baking sheet.
2. Roast in the preheated oven at 375 degrees F approximately 10 minutes or until crisp.
3. Let it cool completely before storing. Bon appétit!

Nutrition: 232 Calories; 22.4g Fat; 0.8g Carbs; 7.1g Protein; 0g Fiber

948. Cheese And Anchovy Fat Bombs

Preparation time: 10 minute
Cooking time: 1 hour and 10 minutes
Servings: 4
Ingredients:

- 8 ounces cheddar cheese, shredded
- 6 ounces cream cheese, at room temperature
- 4 ounces canned anchovies, chopped
- 1/2 yellow onion, minced
- 1 teaspoon fresh garlic, minced
- Sea salt, to taste
- Ground black pepper, to taste

Directions:

1. Combine all of the above ingredients in a bowl. Bring the mixture in the refrigerator for 1 hour.
2. Then, shape the mixture into bite-sized balls.
3. Serve immediately.

Nutrition: 122 Calories; 8.9g Fat; 3.2g Carbs; 7.3g Protein; 0g Fiber

949. Bacon-Wrapped Shrimp

Preparation time: 5 minute
Cooking time: 15 minutes
Servings: 8
Ingredients:

- 24 medium shrimp, deveined
- 8 slices of thick-cut bacon, cut into thirds
- 1 teaspoon mustard powder
- 1 teaspoon onion powder
- 1/2 teaspoon granulated garlic
- 1/2 teaspoon red pepper flakes, crushed
- Sea salt, to taste
- Ground black pepper, to taste

Directions:

1. Preheat the oven into 400°F. Line a large-sized baking sheet with a Silpat mat or aluminum foil.
2. Wrap each shrimp with a piece of bacon; secure with a toothpick. Put the wrapped shrimp on the prepared baking sheet.
3. Sprinkle with mustard, onion powder, garlic, red pepper, salt, and black pepper.
4. Bake for at least 13 minutes or until the shrimp is thoroughly cooked. Bon appétit!

Nutrition: 119 Calories; 10.3g Fat; 0.3g Carbs; 5.7g Protein; 0g Fiber

950. Cheese And Bacon Fat Bombs

Preparation time: 5 minute
Cooking time: 1 hour
Servings: 4

Ingredients:

- 1/2 stick butter, at room temperature
- 8 ounces cottage cheese, at room temperature
- 8 ounces mozzarella cheese, crumbled
- 1 teaspoon shallot powder
- 1 teaspoon Italian seasoning blend
- 2 ounces bacon bits

Directions:

1. Mix the butter, cheese, shallot powder, and Italian seasoning blend until well combined.
2. Put the mixture in the refrigerator for 1 hour.
3. Shape the mixture into 18 balls. Roll each ball in the bacon bits until coated on all sides. Enjoy!

Nutrition: 149 Calories; 9.3g Fat; 2.2g Carbs; 13.1g Protein; 0.6g Fiber

951. Favorite Onions Rings

Preparation time: 5 minute
Cooking time: 20 minutes
Servings: 4

Ingredients:

- 1/2 cup coconut flour
- 3 eggs
- 2 tablespoons water
- 2 tablespoons double cream
- 4 ounces pork rinds
- 3 ounces parmesan cheese, grated
- 2 onions, cut into 1/2-inch thick rings

Directions:

1. Place the coconut flour in a shallow dish. In another dish, mix the eggs, water, and cream; place the pork rinds and parmesan in the third dish.
2. Dip the onion rings into the coconut flour; then, dip them into the egg mixture; lastly, roll the onion rings in the parmesan mixture. Place the coated rings on a lightly greased baking rack; bake at 420 degrees F for 13 to 16 minutes. Enjoy!

Nutrition: 322 Calories; 27.8g Fat; 5.7g Carbs; 10.1g Protein; 1g Fiber

952. Walnut Fat Bombs

Preparation time: 5 minute
Cooking time: 10 minutes + chilling time
Servings: 10

Ingredients:

- 2 tablespoons keto chocolate protein powder
- 1/4 cup Erythritol
- 5 ounces butter
- 3 ounces walnut butter
- 10 whole walnuts, halved

Directions:

1. In a sauté pan, melt the butter, protein powder, and Erythritol over a low flame; stir until smooth and well mixed.
2. Spoon the mixture into a piping bag, pipe into mini cupcake liners. Add the walnut halves to each mini cupcake.
3. Bring to your refrigerator for at least 2 hours. Bon appétit!

Nutrition: 260 Calories; 26.4g Fat; 3.2g Carbs; 4.8g Protein; 1.6g Fiber

953. Bacon Avocado Sushi

Preparation time: 5 minute
Cooking time: 15 minutes
Servings: 8

Ingredients:

- 1 teaspoon garlic paste
- 2 scallions, finely chopped
- 4 ounces cream cheese, softened
- 1 teaspoon adobo sauce
- 1 avocado, mashed
- 2 tablespoons fresh lemon juice
- 8 bacon slices
- 1 tablespoon toasted sesame seeds

Directions:

1. In a mixing bowl, thoroughly combine the garlic paste, scallions, cream cheese, adobo sauce, avocado, and fresh lemon juice.
2. Divide the mixture evenly between the bacon slices. Roll up tightly and garnish with toasted sesame seeds. Enjoy!

Nutrition: 350 Calories; 37.2g Fat; 3.4g Carbs; 1.5g Protein; 1.9g Fiber

954. Chinese Enoki Mushroom Bacon Dippers

Preparation time: 10 minute
Cooking time: 45 minutes
Servings: 5

Ingredients:

- 1/2 pound enoki mushrooms
- 5 slices bacon, cut into halves
- Dipping Sauce:
- 1/2 cup water
- 2 tablespoons sesame oil
- 2 tablespoons coconut aminos
- 1 teaspoon monk fruit powder
- 1 large clove of garlic, minced
- 1/2 teaspoon ground ginger
- 1 teaspoon Chinese five-spice powder
- Kosher salt, to taste
- Ground black pepper, to taste

Directions:

1. Wrap the mushrooms with the bacon and secure with toothpicks. Prepare on a parchment-lined baking tray and bake at 380 degrees F for 40 minutes, flipping once halfway through cooking.
2. For a while, make the sauce by whisking all ingredients in a wok or deep saucepan—Cook over medium heat up to thickened and reduced.
3. Serve the bacon dippers with the sauce on the side. Enjoy!

Nutrition: 323 Calories; 33.2g Fat; 4.4g Carbs; 1.5g Protein; 1.4g Fiber

955. Ham Cheese Egg Cups

Preparation time: 5 minute
Cooking time: 10 minutes
Servings: 9
Ingredients:

- 9 slices ham
- Coarse salt, to taste
- Ground black pepper, to taste
- 1 teaspoon jalapeno pepper, deseeded and minced
- 1/2 cup Swiss cheese, shredded
- 9 eggs

Directions:

1. Begin by preheating your oven to 390 degrees F. Lightly grease a muffin pan with cooking spray.
2. Line every cup with a slice of ham; add salt, black pepper, jalapeno, and cheese. Crack an egg into each ham cup.
3. Bake in the preheated oven for around 13 minutes or until the eggs are cooked through. Bon appétit!

Nutrition: 137 Calories; 8.6g Fat; 1.8g Carbs; 12g Protein; 0.4g Fiber

956. Taco Chicken Wings

Preparation time: 10 minute
Cooking time: 60 minutes
Servings: 5
Ingredients:

- 2 tablespoons extra-virgin olive oil
- 2 pounds of chicken wings
- 1 tablespoon whiskey
- 1 tablespoon taco seasoning mix
- 1 cup tomato sauce

Directions:

1. Preheat your oven to 410°F. Toss the chicken wings with the other ingredients until well coated.
2. Place the wings onto a rack in the baking pan. Bake in for 50 to 55 minutes in the preheated oven until a meat thermometer reads 165 degrees F.
3. Serve with dipping sauce, if desired. Enjoy!

Nutrition: 293 Calories; 12.1g Fat; 3.4g Carbs; 40.6g Protein; 0.9g Fiber

957. Ham And Avocado Stuffed Eggs

Preparation time: 5 minute
Cooking time: 20 minutes
Servings: 5
Ingredients:

- 4 large eggs
- 1/2 avocado, mashed
- 1/2 teaspoon yellow mustard
- 1 garlic clove, minced
- 2 ounces cooked ham, chopped

Directions:

1. Set the eggs in a saucepan and fill with enough water. Bring the water to a rolling boil; heat off. Cover and allow the eggs rest for about 12 minutes; let them cool.
2. Slice the eggs into halves; mix the yolks with the avocado, mustard, and garlic.
3. Dive the avocado filling among the egg whites. Top with the chopped ham. Bon appétit!

Nutrition; 128 Calories; 8.9g Fat; 2.9g Carbs; 9.2g Protein; 1.7g Fiber

958. Saucy And Spicy Spareribs

Preparation time: 10 minute
Cooking time: 2 hours and 35 minutes
Servings: 4
Ingredients:

- 2 pounds St. Louis-style spareribs
- 1 tablespoon fajita seasoning mix
- 2 cloves garlic, pressed
- 1/2 cup chicken bone broth
- 1 cup tomato sauce

Directions:

1. Toss the spareribs with the Fajita seasoning mix, garlic, chicken bone broth, and tomato sauce until well coated.
2. Arrange the spare ribs on a tinfoil-lined baking sheet.
3. Bake in the preheated oven at 260 degrees F for 2 hours and 30 minutes.
4. Place under the preheated broiler for about 8 minutes until the sauce is lightly caramelized. Bon appétit!

Nutrition: 344 Calories; 13.6g Fat; 4.9g Carbs; 49.5g Protein; 1.2g Fiber

959. Mini Stuffed Peppers

Preparation time: 5 minute
Cooking time: 15 minutes
Servings: 5
Ingredients:

- 2 teaspoons olive oil
- 1 teaspoon mustard seeds
- 5 ounces ground turkey
- Salt and ground black pepper, to taste
- 10 mini bell peppers, stems and seeds removed (cut in half, lengthwise)
- 2 ounces garlic and herb seasoned chevre goat cheese, crumbled

Directions:

1. In medium-high heat, warm the oil in a skillet. Once hot, cook mustard seeds with ground turkey until the turkey is no longer pink. Crumble with a fork. Season with salt and black pepper.
2. Lay the pepper halves cut-side-up on a parchment-lined baking sheet. Use a spoon to the meat mixture into the center of each pepper half.
3. Top each pepper with cheese. Bake at 400°F in the preheated oven for 10 minutes. Bon appétit!

Nutrition: 198 Calories; 17.2g Fat; 3g Carbs; 0.9g Fiber; 7.8g Protein;

960. Tender Ribs With Hot Sauce

Preparation time: 10 minute
Cooking time: 2 hours
Servings: 2
Ingredients:

- Ribs:
- 1 pound spare ribs
- 1 teaspoon Dijon mustard
- 1 tablespoon rice wine
- Salt and ground black pepper, to season
- 1 teaspoon garlic, pressed
- 1/2 shallot powder
- 1 teaspoon cayenne pepper
- 1/2 teaspoon ground allspice
- 1 tablespoon avocado oil
- Hot Sauce:
- 1 teaspoon Sriracha sauce
- 1 tablespoon olive oil
- 1 cup tomato sauce, sugar-free
- 1 teaspoon garlic, minced
- Salt, to season

Directions:

1. Arrange the spare ribs on a parchment-lined baking pan. Add the remaining ingredients for the ribs and toss until well coated.
2. In the preheated oven at 360°F, bake for 1 hour. Rotate the pan and roast an additional 50 to 60 minutes. Baste the ribs with the cooking liquid periodically.
3. In the meantime, whisk the sauce ingredients until well mixed. Pour the hot sauce over the ribs. Place under the broiler and broil for 7 to 9 minutes or until internal temperature reaches 145 degrees F.
4. Brush the sauce onto each rib and serve warm. Bon appétit!

Nutrition: 472 Calories; 27g Fat; 6.5g Total Carbs; 48.7g Protein; 2g Fiber

961. Taco Cups

Preparation time: 10 minute
Cooking time: 40 minutes
Servings: 30

Ingredients:

- 1 pound beef, ground
- 2 cups cheddar cheese, shredded
- ¼ cup of water
- Salt and black pepper to the taste
- 2 tablespoons cumin
- 2 tablespoons chili powder
- Pico de gallo for serving

Directions:

1. Divide spoonfuls of parmesan on a lined baking sheet, introduce in the oven at 350 degrees F, and bake for 7 minutes.
2. Leave the cheese to cool down for 1 minute, transfer them to mini cupcake molds and shape them into cups.
3. Meanwhile, in medium-high heat, heat the pan, then add beef, stir and cook until it browns.
4. Add the water, salt, pepper, cumin, and chili powder, stir and cook for 5 minutes more.
5. Divide into cheese cups, top with pico de gallo, transfer them all to a platter and serve.
6. Enjoy!

Nutrition: Calories 140, Fat 6, Fiber 0, Carbs 6, Protein 15

962. Tasty Chicken Egg Rolls

Preparation time: 2 hours and 15 minute
Cooking time: 10 minutes
Servings: 2

Ingredients:

- 4 ounces blue cheese
- 2 cups chicken, cooked and finely chopped
- Salt and black pepper to the taste
- 2 green onions, chopped
- 2 celery stalks, finely chopped
- ½ cup tomato sauce
- ½ teaspoon erythritol
- 12 egg roll wrappers
- Vegetable oil

Directions:

1. In a bowl, mix chicken meat with blue cheese, salt, pepper, green onions, celery, tomato sauce, and sweetener, stir well and keep in the fridge for 2 hours.
2. Place egg wrappers on a working surface, divide chicken mix on them, roll and seal edges.
3. Heat a pan with vegetable oil over medium-high heat, add egg rolls, cook until each side is golden.
4. Arrange on a platter and serve them.
5. Enjoy!

Nutrition: Calories 220, Fat 7, Fiber 2, Carbs 6, Protein 10

963. Halloumi Cheese Fries

Preparation time: 10 minute
Cooking time: 5 minutes
Servings: 4

Ingredients:

- 1 cup marinara sauce
- 8 ounces halloumi cheese, pat dried and sliced into fries
- 2 ounces tallow

Directions:

1. Heat a pan with the tallow over medium-high heat.
2. Add halloumi pieces, cover, cook for 2 minutes on each side and transfer to paper towels.
3. Drain excess grease, transfer them to a bowl and serve with marinara sauce on the side.
4. Enjoy!

Nutrition: Calories 200, Fat 16, Fiber 1, Carbs 1, Protein 13

964. Jalapeno Crisps

Preparation time: 10 minute
Cooking time: 25 minutes
Servings: 20

Ingredients:

- 3 tablespoons olive oil
- 5 jalapenos, sliced
- 8 ounces parmesan cheese, grated
- ½ teaspoon onion powder
- Salt and black pepper to the taste
- Tabasco sauce for serving

Directions:

1. In a bowl, mix jalapeno slices with salt, pepper, oil, and onion powder, toss it to coat and spread on a lined baking sheet.
2. Introduce in the oven at 450 degrees F and bake for 15 minutes.
3. Take jalapeno slices out of the oven, leave them to cool down.
4. In a bowl, mix pepper slices with the cheese and press well.
5. Arrange all slices on another lined baking sheet, introduce in the oven again and bake for 10 minutes more.
6. Leave jalapenos to cool down, arrange on a plate, and serve with Tabasco sauce on the side.
7. Enjoy!

Nutrition: Calories 50, Fat 3, Fiber 0.1, Carbs 0.3, Protein 2

965. Tasty Broccoli Sticks

Preparation time: 10 minute
Cooking time: 20 minutes
Servings: 20

Ingredients:

- 1 egg
- 2 cups broccoli florets
- 1/3 cup cheddar cheese, grated
- ¼ cup yellow onion, chopped
- 1/3 cup panko breadcrumbs
- 1/3 cup Italian breadcrumbs
- 2 tablespoons parsley, chopped
- A drizzle of olive oil
- Salt and black pepper to the taste

Directions:

1. Warm a pot with water over medium heat, add broccoli, steam for 1 minute, drain, chop, and put it into a bowl.

2. Add egg, cheddar cheese, panko, and Italian breadcrumbs, salt, pepper, and parsley and stir everything well.
3. Shape sticks out of this mix using your hands and places them on a baking sheet that you've greased with some olive oil.
4. Introduce in the oven at 400 degrees F and bake for 20 minutes.
5. Arrange on a platter and serve.
6. Enjoy!

Nutrition: Calories 100, Fat 4, Fiber 2, Carbs 7, Protein 7

966. Parmesan-Crusted Asparagus

Preparation time: 10 minute
Cooking time: 15 minutes
Servings: 4

Ingredients:

- 1 ounce (28 g) shaved Parmesan cheese
- 1 pound (454 g) thin asparagus spears
- 1 tablespoon extra-virgin olive oil
- Freshly ground black pepper, to taste

Directions:

1. Preheat the oven at 450°F.
2. Coat a baking pan with olive oil, then place the asparagus spears into the pan. Dust with Parmesan cheese and ground black pepper.
3. Arrange the pan in the preheated oven and cook for 12 minutes until the asparagus spears are crisp and tender, and the cheese melts.
4. Remove them from the oven. Let it cool for 1 to 2 minutes before serving.

Nutrition: Calories: 93 Total fat: 5.6g Carbs: 7g Protein: 5.3g Cholesterol: 6mg Sodium: 114 mg

967. Shrimp Skewers

Preparation time: 70 minute
Cooking time: 0 minutes
Servings: 6

Ingredients:

- 2 pounds (907 g) fresh shrimp, peeled and deveined
- 2 tablespoons red wine vinegar
- ¼ cup unsweetened tomato sauce
- 3 cloves garlic, minced
- ⅓ Cup olive oil
- 2 tablespoons fresh basil, chopped
- ½ teaspoon salt
- ¼ teaspoon cayenne pepper
- 6 skewers, soaked in water for about 30 minutes to avoid them from burning

Directions:

1. Combine the red wine vinegar, tomato sauce, garlic, and olive oil in a large bowl. Put the peeled and deveined shrimps in the bowl, and sprinkle with basil, salt, and cayenne pepper. Toss to coat well.
2. Wrap the bowl in plastic and refrigerate to marinate for at least 1 hour.
3. Discard the marinade. Thread the shrimps through the skewers, then arrange the shrimp skewers onto the preheated grill.
4. Grill for 6 minutes. Flip halfway through the cooking time or until opaque. Serve warm.

Nutrition: Calories: 273 Total fat: 14.7g Carbs: 2.8g Protein: 31g Cholesterol: 230mg Sodium: 472 mg

968. Cheesy Spinach Brownies

Preparation time: 20 minute
Cooking time: 35 minutes
Servings: 24

Ingredients:

- 1 (10-ounce / 284 g) package spinach, blanched and chopped
- 1 cup almond flour
- 1 teaspoon gluten-free baking powder
- 1 teaspoon salt
- 2 eggs, beaten
- 1 cup unsweetened almond milk
- ½ cup butter, melted
- 1 (8 ounces / 227 g) package mozzarella cheese, shredded
- 1 onion, chopped

Directions:

1. Preheat the oven at 375°F.
2. Make the brownies: Combine the flour, baking powder, and salt in a bowl. Fold in the beaten eggs, almond milk, and melted butter. Then add the spinach, cheese, and onion. Stir to combine.
3. Place the mixture into a lightly greased baking pan. Arrange the pan in the oven and bake for 30 minutes or until a toothpick put in the center of the brownies and comes out clean.
4. Remove from the oven. Allow to cool for a few minutes and slice to serve.

TIP: Blanch the spinach in a pot of boiled water for 3 minutes or until soft to reduce the concentration of the oxalic acid.

Nutrition: Calories: 92 Total fat: 6g Carbs: 5.6g Protein: 4.1g Cholesterol: 32mg Sodium: 216 mg

969. Jalapeno Pepper Stuffed With Sausage

Preparation time: 15 minute
Cooking time: 7 minutes
Servings: 12

Ingredients:

- 1 pound (454 g) large fresh jalapeño peppers, halved lengthwise and deseeded
- 1 pound (454 g) ground pork sausage
- 1 cup Parmesan cheese, shredded
- 1 (8 ounces / 227 g) package cream cheese, softened
- 1 (8 ounces / 227 g) bottle Ranch dressing (optional)

Directions:

1. Preheat the oven to 425°F.
2. Sauté the ground pork sausage in a nonstick skillet over medium-high heat for 6 minutes or lightly browned. Take to a plate lined with paper towels.
3. Combine the sautéed sausage with Parmesan cheese and cream cheese. Ladle 1 tablespoon of this mixture into each jalapeño half, then place them into a greased baking pan. You need to work in batches to avoid overcrowding. Transfer the pan into the preheated oven.
4. Bake for about 20 minutes until the jalapeño peppers are blistered, and the sausage mixture is well browned, then top them with Ranch dressing, if desired, and bake for 2 minutes more.
5. Remove from the oven. Let it cool for a 1 to 2 minutes before serving.

Nutrition: Calories: 362 Total fat: 34.3g Carbs: 4.3g Protein: 9.2g Cholesterol: 58mg Sodium: 601mg

970. Garlic Parmesan Wings

Preparation time: 15 minute
Cooking time: 50 minutes
Servings: 8

Ingredients:

- 3 lbs. chicken wings

- 1 ½ Tbsp. baking powder
- Salt and pepper
- ¼ cup salted butter
- 4 cloves garlic minced
- 2 tsp. dried parsley
- Pinch red pepper flakes
- ½ ounce grated Parmesan about ½ cup
- Fresh chopped rosemary or parsley

Directions:

1. Preheat oven to 250 degrees F.
2. Set a baking rack in a baking sheet lined with foil, brush the rack with oil to prevent the chicken from sticking.
3. Pat wings dry and put in a plastic bag.
4. Add the baking powder, salt, and pepper and seal the bag, shake to coat.
5. Bring the wings in a single layer on the prepared baking rack and bake in the lower third of the oven for at least 30 minutes.
6. Increase oven temperature to 425 degrees F and move the baking sheet to the upper third of the oven, continue to bake for 20 to 30 minutes, until crispy, then transfer to a large bowl.
7. In the meantime, in a saucepan or microwaveable pot, melt the butter.
8. Add the garlic, parsley, and pepper flakes, pour over the chicken wings and sprinkle with the Parmesan, tossing well to coat, sprinkle with chopped parsley, and sprinkle with additional salt and pepper to taste.
9. Serve immediately with your favorite dipping sauce.

Nutrition: Calories: 386 Total Fat: 28.15g Protein: 30.62g Net Carbs: 1.30g

JUICES AND DRINK

971. Green Juice

Preparation time: 3 minutes
Cooking time: 5 minutes
Serving: 1

Ingredients:

- 75 grams Kale
- 30 grams Arugula
- 2 stalks Celery
- 5 grams Parsley
- Half Green apple
- .5 teaspoon Matcha tea powder

Directions:

1. Push all of the ingredients except for the matcha and lemon through an electric juicer. Once the juicer has done its job, squeeze the lemon juice into the green juice by hand or using hand-powered citrus juices.
2. Pour one-quarter of the juice into a glass, add in the matcha tea powder, and whisk until no tea clumps remain. Stir in the remaining green juice and drink straight away or store in the fridge for up to twenty-four hours before serving.

Nutrition: Calories: 228 kcal Protein: 11.24 g Fat: 7.36 g Carbohydrates: 34.12 g

972. Golden Milk

Preparation time: 3 minutes
Cooking time: 5 minutes
Servings: 2

Ingredients:

- 3 cups Soy milk, unsweetened
- 1 Black pinch pepper, ground
- .25 teaspoon Ginger, ground
- 1.5 teaspoons Turmeric, ground
- 1 Cinnamon stick, whole
- 1 tablespoon Coconut oil
- 2 tablespoons Date sugar

Directions:

1. Stir all of the golden milk ingredients into a small saucepan and whisk to combine it over medium heat. Allow it to warm, while stirring frequently, but don't let it boil. This will take about four minutes.
2. Turn the heat off and taste the golden milk, adjusting it to your taste. Serve warm.

Nutrition: Calories: 728 kcal Protein: 30.14 g Fat: 43.82 g Carbohydrates: 55.53 g

973. Strawberry Apple Cider Detox Drink

Preparation time: 3 minutes
Cooking time: 0 minutes
Servings: 2

Ingredients:

- 3 cups Water
- 1 tablespoon Lemon juice
- 1 tablespoon Apple cider vinegar
- .25 cup Strawberries
- 1 tablespoon Honey

Directions:

1. Mix all of the ingredients in a high-speed blender, with or without ice, until smooth.
2. Divide between two serving glasses and enjoy cold.

Nutrition: Calories: 164 kcal Protein: 6.76 g Fat: 6.21 g Carbohydrates: 21.26 g

974. Cleansing Cranberry Lemon Juice Drink

Preparation time: 3 minutes
Cooking time: minutes
Servings 2

Ingredients:

- 1.5 cups Cranberry juice, 100% pure and organic
- 1.5 cups Water
- .25 cup Orange juice
- 2 tablespoons Lemon juice
- 2 tablespoons Honey

Directions:

1. Add ingredients into a glass jar or pitcher and stir until combined. Chill in the fridge and serve cold.

Nutrition: Calories: 452 kcal Protein: 7.06 g Fat: 6.59 g Carbohydrates: 95.21 g

975. Ginger Turmeric Wellness Shots

Preparation time: 0 minutes
Cooking time: 5 minutes
Servings: 5

Ingredients:

- 4 inches Turmeric root
- 4 inches Ginger root
- 2 Oranges, peeled
- 2 Lemons, peeled
- .125 teaspoon Cayenne pepper
- .125 teaspoon Black pepper, ground
- .75 cup Water
- .5 teaspoon extra virgin olive oil

Directions:

1. Pour the water into a boil. Once bubbling, add in the turmeric root and reduce the heat to a medium, allowing it to simmer for seven to eight minutes. Remove from the heat of the stove and take out the turmeric root, setting it aside. Pour the turmeric liquid into a container and let it chill in the fridge until cool.
2. While the turmeric liquid cools, run the ginger root, boiled turmeric root, oranges, and lemons, through your juicer.
3. Stir the turmeric liquid, seasonings, and oil into the prepared juice.
4. Enjoy a shot of this every morning. The leftover shots can keep in the fridge for two to three days.

Nutrition: Calories: 113 kcal Protein: 6.81 g Fat: 7.3 g Carbohydrates: 6.99 g

976. Iced Matcha Latte

Preparation time: 0 minutes
Cooking time: 3 minutes
Servings: 1

Ingredients:

- 2 teaspoons Matcha powder
- 1 cup Soy milk, unsweetened
- 1.5 tablespoons Hot water
- 2 teaspoons Honey

Directions:

1. Add the matcha and hot water to a bowl and whisk it until it is thoroughly combined without clumps. Ideally, you want to use a bamboo matcha whisk in a zigzag and circular formation.
2. In a glass over ice cubes, add the soy milk and honey, stirring to combine. Slowly pour the matcha mixture over the top of the latte, lightly stirring it with a spoon. Serve immediately before the ice melts.

Nutrition: Calories 290 kcal Protein: 14.63 g Fat: 14.09 g Carbohydrates: 27.08 g

977. Hot Matcha Latte

Preparation time: 0 minutes
Cooking time: 5 minutes
Servings: 1

Ingredients:

- 1.25 teaspoon Matcha powder –
- .25 teaspoon Maca root powder, optional
- 1 tablespoon Hot water
- 1 tablespoon Maple syrup
- 1.5 cups Soy milk, unsweetened

Directions:

1. Into a large mug, add the matcha powder, Maca root, maple syrup, and hot water. Using a matcha bamboo whisk or standard kitchen whisk stir the ingredients together gently until the matcha and Maca have dissolved into the liquid. While I recommend using the matcha bamboo whisk, you can do whatever you have on hand.
2. Heat your soy milk, either in the microwave, on the stove, or with a steaming/frothing pitcher. While heating in the microwave is a quick option, I recommend using a steaming/frothing pitcher if you have one, or at the very least, heating it on the stove. By heating on the stove, you can use a whisk or a hand-held frothier to get the desired classic froth lattes usually have.
3. Pour the hot soy milk into the mug with the matcha, lightly stirring it to ensure the soy milk and matcha mixture have combined. Enjoy while hot.

Nutrition: Calories: 379 kcal Protein: 18.69 g Fat: 18.07 g Carbohydrates: 35.88 g

978. Classic Latte With Cinnamon

Preparation time: 0 minutes
Cooking time: 5 minutes
Servings: 1

Ingredients:

- 2 ounces Espresso
- 10 ounces Soy milk, unsweetened
- 1 teaspoon Date sugar
- .25 teaspoon Cinnamon, ground

Directions:

1. Heat your soy milk, either in the microwave, on the stove, or with a steaming/frothing pitcher. While heating in the microwave is a quick option, I recommend using a steaming/frothing pitcher if you have one, or at the very least, heating it on the stove. By heating on the stove, you can use a whisk or a hand-held frothier to get the desired classic froth lattes usually have.
2. If your soy milk has developed a froth from whisking or using a frothier, then stir in the date sugar and cinnamon. However, if your soy milk hasn't developed a froth, add the soy milk sugar, and cinnamon into a blender. Blend it for a minute, until it develops a dense froth.
3. Add your espresso to a mug and slowly pour the frothed milk over the top. Enjoy while warm.

Nutrition: Calories: 272 kcal Protein: 15.43 g Fat: 15.44 g Carbohydrates: 17.56 g

979. Cold Brew Caramel Frappuccino

Preparation time: 0 minutes
Cooking time: 10 minutes
Servings: 2

Ingredients:

- 2 cups Soy milk, unsweetened
- 2 cups coarsely ground dark coffee
- 4 cups of Filtered water
- 3 tablespoons Hot water
- 7 Pitted dates
- .25 teaspoon Sea salt

Directions:

1. Pour the unsweetened soy milk into an ice cube tray and freeze it overnight. Once frozen, use the cubes immediately or transfer them to a storage container so that they don't pick up flavors from the freezer.
2. Prepare the cold brew coffee overnight, as well. To do this, add the ground coffee and four cups of filtered water to a pitcher. Give the cold brew coffee a good stir, cover with a lid, and refrigerate overnight. The following day, strain the coffee through a fine-mesh sieve or a coffee filter to remove the beans.
3. Pulse the pitted dates and sea salt with the hot water in a blender. You want to pulse until it forms a thick and smooth paste. Clean the sides of the blender with a spatula as needed. While this recipe calls for three tablespoons of hot water, you only want to use as much water as necessary. Therefore, slowly add the water, adding as much as is needed to blend the dates into a smooth paste.
4. To prepare a single Frappuccino, add half of the cold brew coffee, soy milk cubes, and date caramel until it forms a creamy drink. Serve!

Nutrition: Calories: 260 kcal Protein: 11.5 g Fat: 11.11 g Carbohydrates: 30.31 g

980. Matcha Green Juice

Preparation time: 10 minutes
Cooking time: 0 minutes
Servings: 2

Ingredients:

- 5 ounces fresh kale
- 2 ounces fresh arugula
- ¼ cup fresh parsley
- 4 celery stalks
- 1 green apple, cored and chopped
- 1 (1-inch) piece fresh ginger, peeled
- 1 lemon, peeled
- ½ teaspoon matcha green tea

Directions:

1. Add all ingredients into a juicer and extract the juice according to the manufacturer's method.
2. Pour into 2 glasses and serve immediately.

Nutrition: Calories 113 Fat 0.6 g Carbs 26.71 g Protein 3.8 g

981. Refreshing Watermelon Juice

Preparation time: 2 minutes
Cooking time: 2 minutes
Serving: 1

Ingredients:

- 20g Young kale leaves (stalks removed)
- ½ Cucumber (peeled, seeds removed and roughly chopped)
- 250g Watermelon chunks

- 250g Mint leaves

Directions:

1. Bring all the ingredients needed in a blender or juicer. Blend and enjoy.

Nutrition: Calories: 76 Total Fat: 0 g Total Carbohydrates: 17 g Protein: 1 g

982. Green Juice With Green Apple And Kiwi

Preparation time: 10 minutes
Cooking time: 0 minutes
Servings: 2

Ingredients:

- 1 green apple
- 2 kiwis
- 1 celery stalk, chopped
- ½ a lime
- ½ tablespoon organic honey
- A pinch of pink Himalayan salt
- ½ teaspoon of turmeric spice.

Directions:

1. Put all the above-listed ingredients into a blender.
2. Blend thoroughly, then fill into a glass cup and drink up.

Nutrition: Calories: 222 kcal Protein: 7.26 g Fat: 6.46 g Carbohydrates: 37.15 g

983. Vanilla Matcha

Preparation time: 0 minutes
Cooking time: 10 minutes
Servings: 2

Ingredients:

- ½ teaspoon of Matcha green powder
- Vanilla pod seeds

Directions:

1. Pour of water in a kettle and allow to boil. Then remove from heat and pour into a measuring jug, about a 100ml. Pour out the boiled water (50ml) into a bowl and then warm. Add the vanilla pod seeds and the half teaspoon of matcha into the measuring jug containing the other half of the boiled water. Whisk thoroughly with a whisk stick until it becomes lump-free, slightly bubbling, and smooth. Pour the reserved warm water in the bowel into the prepared Matcha tea mixture. And then Serve.

Nutrition: Calories: 41 kcal Protein: 3.21 g Fat: 3.03 g Carbohydrates: 0.03 g

984. Turmeric Tea

Preparation time: 0 minutes
Cooking time: 5 minutes
Servings: 2

Ingredients:

- 3 heaped teaspoons of grinded turmeric
- 1 zest pared orange
- Honey with lemon slices
- 1 tablespoon of freshly grated ginger.

Directions:

1. Gather the spices and pared orange into a teapot filled with the boiling water and allow contents to fuse with water for up to 5 minutes.
2. Filter chaff with a sieve and pour it into two serving cups.

Nutrition: Calories: 63 kcal Protein: 3.77 g Fat: 3.26 g Carbohydrates: 5.21 g

985. Celery Juice

Preparation time: 10 minutes
Cooking time: 0 minutes
Servings: 2

Ingredients:

- 8 celery stalks with leaves
- 2 tablespoons fresh ginger, peeled
- 1 lemon, peeled
- ½ cup of filtered water
- Pinch of salt

Directions:

1. Place all the ingredients needed in a blender and pulse until well combined.
2. Through a fine mesh strainer, strain the juice and transfer into 2 glasses.
3. Serve immediately.

Nutrition: Calories 32 Fat 0.5 g Carbs 6.5 g Protein 1 g

986. Kale & Orange Juice

Preparation time: 10 minutes
Cooking time: 0 minutes
Servings: 2

Ingredients:

- 5 large oranges, peeled and sectioned
- 2 bunches fresh kale

Directions:

1. Add all ingredients into a juicer and extract the juice according to the manufacturer's Directions:
2. Pour into 2 glasses and serve immediately.

Nutrition: Calories 315 Fat 0.6 g Carbs 75.1 g Protein 10.3 g

987. Apple & Cucumber Juice

Preparation time: 10 minutes
Cooking time: 0 minutes
Servings: 2

Ingredients:

- 3 large apples, cored and sliced
- 2 large cucumbers, sliced
- 4 celery stalks
- 1 (1-inch) piece fresh ginger, peeled
- 1 lemon, peeled

Directions:

1. Add all ingredients into a juicer and extract the juice according to the manufacturer's directions.
2. Pour into 2 glasses and serve immediately.

Nutrition: Calories 230 Fat 1.1 g Carbs 59.5 g Protein 3.3 g

988. Lemony Green Juice

Preparation time: 10 minutes
Cooking time: 0 minutes
Servings: 2

Ingredients:

- 2 large green apples, cored and sliced
- 4 cups fresh kale leaves
- 4 tablespoons fresh parsley leaves
- 1 tablespoon fresh ginger, peeled
- 1 lemon, peeled
- ½ cup of filtered water
- Pinch of salt

Directions:

1. Place all the ingredients needed in a blender and pulse until well combined.
2. Through a fine mesh strainer, strain the juice and transfer into 2 glasses.
3. Serve immediately.

Nutrition: Calories 196 Fat 0.6 g Carbs 47.9 g Protein 5.2 g

989. Cinnamon And Turmeric Latte

Preparation time: 7minute
Cooking time: 0 minutes
Servings: 4

Ingredients:

- 3 cups almond milk
- ⅓ Tsp cinnamon powder
- 1 cup brewed coffee
- ½ tsp turmeric powder
- 1 ½ tsp erythritol
- Cinnamon sticks to garnish

Directions:

1. In the blender, add the almond milk, cinnamon powder, coffee, turmeric, and erythritol. Blend the ingredients at medium speed for 45 seconds and pour the mixture into a saucepan.
2. Set the pan over low heat and heat through for 5 minutes; do not boil. Keep swirling the pan to prevent boiling. Turn the heat off, and serve in latte cups, with a cinnamon stick in each one.

Nutrition: Calories: 132, Fat 12g, Net Carbs 0.3g, Protein 3.9g

990. Creamy Coconut Kiwi Drink

Preparation time: 3 minute
Cooking time: 0 minutes
Servings: 3

Ingredients:

- 5 kiwis, pulp scooped
- 2 tbsp erythritol
- 2 cups unsweetened coconut milk
- 2 cups coconut cream
- 7 ice cubes
- Mint leaves to garnish

Directions:

1. In a blender, process the kiwis, erythritol, milk, cream, and ice cubes until smooth, about 3 minutes. Pour into four serving glasses, garnish with mint leaves, and serve.

Nutrition: Calories: 351, Fat 28g, Net Carbs 9.7g, Protein 16g

991. Vanilla Bean Frappuccino

Preparation time: 6 minute
Cooking time: 0 minutes
Servings: 4

Ingredients:

- 3 cups unsweetened vanilla almond milk, chilled
- 2 tsp swerve
- 1 ½ cups heavy cream, cold
- 1 vanilla bean
- ¼ tsp xanthan gum
- Unsweetened chocolate shavings to garnish

Directions:

1. Combine the almond milk, swerve, heavy cream, vanilla bean, and xanthan gum in the blender and process on high speed for 1 minute until smooth. Pour into tall shake glasses, sprinkle with chocolate shavings, and serve immediately.

Nutrition: Calories: 193, Fat 14g, Net Carbs 6g, Protein 15g

992. Lychee And Coconut Lassi

Preparation time: 28minute + cooling time
Cooking time: minutes
Servings: 4

Ingredients:

- 2 cups lychee pulp, seeded
- 2 ½ cups of coconut milk
- 4 tsp swerve
- 2 limes, zested and juiced
- 1 ½ cups plain yogurt
- 1 lemongrass, white part only, crushed
- Toasted coconut shavings for garnish

Directions:

1. In a saucepan, add the lychee pulp, coconut milk, swerve, lemongrass, and lime zest. Stir and bring to boil on medium heat for 2 minutes, stirring continually. Then reduce the heat, and simmer for 1 minute. Turn the heat off and let the mixture sit for 15 minutes.
2. Remove the lemongrass and pour the mixture into a smoothie maker or a blender, add the yogurt and lime juice, and process the ingredients until smooth, for about 60 seconds. Pour into a jug and refrigerate for 2 hours until cold; stir. Serve garnished with coconut shavings.

Nutrition: Calories: 285, Fat 26.1g, Net Carbs 1.5g, Protein 5.3g

993. Blackcurrant Iced Tea

Preparation time: 8 minute
Cooking time: 0 minutes
Servings: 4

Ingredients:

- 6 unflavored tea bags
- 2 cups of water
- ½ cup sugar-free blackcurrant extract
- Swerve to taste
- Ice cubes for serving
- Lemon slices to garnish, cut on the side

Directions:

1. Pour the ice cubes in a pitcher and place it in the fridge.
2. Bring the water to boil in a saucepan over medium heat for 3 minutes and turn it off. Stir in the sugar to dissolve and steep the tea bags in the water for 2 minutes.
3. Remove the bags after and let the tea cool down. Stir in the blackcurrant extract until well incorporated, remove the pitcher from the fridge, and pour the mixture over the ice cubes.
4. Let sit for 3 minutes to cool and after, pour the mixture into tall glasses. Add some more ice cubes, place the lemon slices on the rim of the glasses, and serve the tea cold.

Nutrition: Calories: 22, Fat 0g, Net Carbs 5g, Protein 0g

994. Strawberry Vanilla Shake

Preparation time: 2 minute
Cooking time: 0 minutes
Servings: 4

Ingredients:

- 2 cups strawberries, stemmed and halved
- 12 strawberries to garnish
- ½ cup cold unsweetened almond milk
- 2/3 tsp vanilla extract
- ½ cup heavy whipping cream
- 2 tbsps. Swerve

Directions:

1. Process the strawberries, milk, vanilla extract, whipping cream, and swerve in a large blender for 2 minutes; work in two batches if needed. The shake should be frosty.
2. Pour into glasses, stick in straws, garnish with strawberry halves, and serve.

Nutrition: Calories: 285, Fat 22.6g, Net Carbs 3.1g, Protein 16g

995. Mint Chocolate Protein Shake

Preparation time: 4 minute
Cooking time: 0 minutes
Servings: 4

Ingredients:

- 3 cups flax milk, chilled
- 3 tsp unsweetened cocoa powder
- 1 avocado, pitted, peeled, sliced
- 1 cup coconut milk, chilled

- 3 mint leaves + extra to garnish
- 3 tbsp erythritol
- 1 tbsp low carb Protein powder
- Whipping cream for topping

Directions:

1. Combine the milk, cocoa powder, avocado, coconut milk, mint leaves, erythritol, and protein powder into a blender, and blend for 1 minute until smooth.
2. Pour into serving glasses, lightly add some whipping cream on top, and garnish with mint leaves.

Nutrition: Calories: 191, Fat 14.5g, Net Carbs 4g, Protein 15g

996. Almond Milk Hot Chocolate

Preparation time: 7 minute
Cooking time: 0 minutes
Servings: 4

Ingredients:

- 3 cups almond milk
- 4 tbsps. Unsweetened cocoa powder
- 2 tbsps. Swerve
- 3 tbsps. Almond butter
- Finely chopped almonds to garnish

Directions:

1. In a saucepan, put the almond milk, cocoa powder, and swerve. Stir the mixture until the sugar dissolves. Set the pan over low to heat through for 5 minutes, without boiling.
2. Swirl the mix occasionally. Turn the heat off and stir in the almond butter to be incorporated. Put the hot chocolate into mugs and sprinkle with chopped almonds. Serve hot.

Nutrition: Calories: 225, Fat 21.5g, Net Carbs 0.6g, Protein 4.5g

997. Berry Merry

Preparation time: 6 minute
Cooking time: 0 minutes
Servings: 4

Ingredients:

- 1 ½ cups blackberries
- 1 cup strawberries + extra for garnishing
- 1 cup blueberries
- 2 small beets, peeled and chopped
- 2/3 cup ice cubes
- 1 lime, juiced

Directions:

1. For the extra strawberries for garnishing, make a single deep cut on their sides; set aside.
2. Add the blackberries, strawberries, blueberries, beet, and ice into the smoothie maker and blend the ingredients at high speed until smooth and frothy, for about 60 seconds.
3. Add the lime juice, and puree further for 30 seconds. Pour the drink into tall smoothie glasses, fix the reserved strawberries on each glass rim, stick a straw in, and immediately serve the drink.

Nutrition: Calories: 83, Fat 3g, Net Carbs 8g, Protein 2.7g

998. Strawberry And Basil Lemonade

Preparation time: 3 minute
Cooking time: 0 minutes
Servings: 4

Ingredients:

- 4 cups of water
- 12 strawberries, leaves removed
- 1 cup fresh lemon juice
- ⅓ cup fresh basil
- ¾ cup swerve
- Crushed Ice
- Halved strawberries to garnish
- Basil leaves to garnish

Directions:

1. Spoon some ice into 4 serving glasses and set aside. In a pitcher, add the water, strawberries, lemon juice, basil, and swerve. Insert the blender and process the ingredients for 30 seconds.
2. The mixture should be pink, and the basil finely chopped. Adjust the taste and add the ice in the glasses. Drop 2 strawberry halves and some basil in each glass and serve immediately.

Nutrition: Calories: 66, Fat 0.1g, Net Carbs 5.8g, Protein 0.7g

999. Bulletproof Coffee

Preparation time: 5 minute
Cooking time: 0 minutes
Servings: 1

Ingredients:

- 2 tbsp. Ghee/butter
- 1.5 cups hot coffee
- 2 tbsp. MCT oil powder

Directions:

1. Prepare and pour the hot coffee into your blender.
2. Add in the powder and ghee/butter. Blend until frothy.
3. Serve in a large mug.

Nutrition: Calories: 463 Protein: 1 gram Net Carbohydrates: 0 grams Fats: 51 grams

1000. Butter Coffee

Preparation time: 6 minute
Cooking time: 0 minutes
Servings: 1

Ingredients:

- 2 tbsp. Coffee
- 1 cup Water
- 1 tbsp. Grass-fed butter
- 1 tbsp. Coconut oil
- Useful: Turkish coffee pot or a regular pot

Directions:

1. Prepare your coffee base on your taste. Simmer ground coffee in water for five minutes and strain it into the cup.
2. Pour the coffee into a high-speed blender (for example - NutriBullet). Add the coconut, oil, and butter. Mix for about ten seconds.
3. Pour it into a mug. Add cinnamon or whipped cream and serve.

Nutrition: Calories: 230 Protein: 0 grams Net Carbohydrates: 0 grams Fats: 25 grams

1001. Chocolate Milkshake

Preparation time: 5 minute
Cooking time: 0 minutes
Servings: 1

Ingredients:

- .5 cup Heavy cream/Full-fat coconut milk
- Half of 1 medium Avocado
- 1-2 tbsp. Cacao powder, as desired
- .5 tsp. Vanilla extract
- 1 pinch pink Himalayan salt/your preference
- 2-4 tbsp. Erythritol or sweetener of choice, as desired
- .5 cup Ice cubes, as needed
- Water (as required)
- Optional Additions:
- Hemp hearts

- Ground chia seeds
- MCT oil
- Mint extract/another favorite

Directions:

1. Toss/pour in all of the fixings, omitting the ice for now (coconut milk, avocado, cacao powder, vanilla extract, salt, sweetener, and add-ins of choice into a blender (high-speed is recommended).
2. Blend the fixings until smooth, using a bit of water as needed.
3. Add in ice and blend until thickened and creamy. Serve immediately.

Nutrition: Calories: 303 Protein: 3 grams Net Carbohydrates: 5.25 grams Fats: 31 grams

1002. Shamrock Shake

Preparation time: 5 minute
Cooking time: 0 minutes
Servings: 1

Ingredients:

- 2 cups Spinach or less- to taste, more if preferred
- . 25 cup fresh mint leaves
- .25 cup Vanilla protein powder of choice
- .5 cup Mashed avocado/full-fat canned coconut milk
- 1 cup non-dairy milk of choice or Ice cubes (2 cups for a thicker drink)

Directions:

1. Prepare a high-speed blender with all of the fixings.
2. Loosely pack the spinach and mint to measure.
3. Pulse the mixture in the blender until it's creamy smooth.

Nutrition: Calories: 352 Protein: 25 grams Net Carbohydrates: 5 grams Fats: 25 grams

30 DAY MEAL PLAN

Day	Breakfast	Lunch	Dinner	Snacks
1	Sirt Muesli	Colorful Vegetable Noodles	Asian King Prawn Stir-Fry with Buckwheat Noodles	Pizza Kale Chips
2	Date and Walnut Porridge	May beet Salad with Cucumber	Fragrant Asian Hotspot	Honey Chili Nuts
3	Smoked Salmon Omelette	Vegan Raw Meatballs	Prawn Arrabiata	Tofu Guacamelo
4	Avocado Toast with Egg	Spinach and Feta Quiche	Greek Fish	Iced Cranberry Tea
5	Berry Oat Breakfast Cobbler	Spicy Sweet Potato Soup	Courgette and Tomato Stew	Baked Root Veg Crips
6	Grapefruit & Celery Blast	Turmeric Baked Salmon	Fresh Saag Paneer	Corndog Muffins
7	Fresh Fruit Pizza	Horsedish Flaked Salmon Fillet and Kale	Cajun Stake and Veg Rice jar	Kale Pesto Hummus
8	Breakfast Quesadillas with Bacon, Egg and Cheese	Miso Caramelized Tofu	Minted Lamb with a couscous Salad	Buckwheat Crackers
9	Classic French Toast	Sirt Super Salad	Salmon Salad and Fresh Mint	Mata Protein Bites
10	Cherry Tomatoes Red Pesto Porridge	Chili Con Carne	Coronation Chicken Salad with Cheese	Cucumber and Radish Salad
11	Blue Hawaii Smoothie	Tofu and Shiitake Mushroom Soup	Tofu with Cauliflower	Tacos and Cauliflower Beans Mole and Sour Cream
12	Sweet Potato Hash	Fusilli with Walnut Pesto	Mussels in Red Wine Sauce	Cauliflower Nachos
13	Pea Protein Sandwich	Tuna and Kale	Ginger Prawn Stir-Fry	Cardamom Granola Bars
14	Cranberry and Kale Crush	Rosemary Endives	Honey Chili Squash	Peanut Energy Bars
15	Green Tea Smoothie	Citrus Salmon	Light Tuna and Bread Salad	Turmeric Roasted Nuts
16	Thai Nut Mix	Red Cabbage and Apple Salad	Tempeh Vegan Chili	Snow Flakes
17	Buckwheat Pancakes	Chickpea and Blueberry Salad	Courgette Tortillas	Pumpkin Brownies
18	Tomato Rellenos	Choc Processor Granola	Braised Pork Belly and Avocado Skewer	Celery and Raisins Snack Salad
19	Miso Spinach Toast	Steak and Mushroom Noodles	Smothered Green Beans	Coconut Cream Tart
20	Apple Avocado Smoothie	Kale, Edamame and Tofu Curry	Matcha Green Tea Salmon	Oatmeal Raisin Cookies
21	Arugula Linguine	Grilled Salmon	Thai Red Curry	Hearty Almond Crackers
22	Breakfast Crepes	Lemon and Garlic Chili Chicken	Vegetarian Lasagna-Smarter with Seitan and Spinach	Tortilla Chips and Fresh Salsa
23	Breakfast Turkey Skillet	Shrimp and Pineapple Salsa	Pesto Salmon Pasta Noodles	Turmeric Apple Chips
24	Fruit and Nut Porridge	Butternut Pumpkin with Buckwheat	Risotto with Broccoli and Chili Pepper	Olive Tapenade
25	Parsley Smoothie	Sesame Chicken Salad	Sweet and Sour Onions	Frozen Chocolate Grapes
26	Green Omelet	Coconut Shrimp Curry	Sri-Lanka-style Sweet Potato Curry	Coconut Brownie Bite
27	Mango, Celery and Ginger Smoothie	Braised Carrots Puy Lentils	Beef Burritos	Raw Vegan Chocolate Pie
28	Strawberry and Citrus Blend	Roasted Turkey with Vegetables	Slow-Cooked Lemon Chicken	Edamame Hummus
29	Cobb Salad	Glazed Flank Steak	Shrimp Chowder	Parmesan Cracker
30	Chilaquiles with Gochujang	Mexican Bell Pepper Filled with Egg	Beef Stroganoff French Bread Toast	Chocolate Shots

CONCLUSION

I have walked hand-in-hand as we examined the science behind the Sirt diet, its weight-loss potential, and it's amazing health benefits. It's understandable to worry if a new diet being popularized is just a fad with nothing to back it up. But the truth is that sirtuins and polyphenols have a very real and scientifically proven effect on human health and weight loss. This has been shown in countless official scientific studies and journals. You can trust that the Sirt diet works, as many people have experienced a profound change from the plan. Give phases one and two a try, just once, and you are sure to see results. If you can commit to trying it out for just those few weeks, then you can feel confident in either maintaining the plan through including sirtfoods in your regular diet. You might even repeat phases one and two for increased weight loss.

There are many uses and health benefits of Sirtfoods. Whether you are enjoying dark chocolate and wine or tofu and eggplant, you will find that you can enjoy these delicious ingredients in any meal or snack. We will be exploring the many health benefits these ingredients have to offer, along with some practical ways you can include them in your daily life. As you already know, Sirtfoods promote weight loss and weight management, so we will skip over these benefits and look toward other health benefits that they offer.

We explored the science of sirtuins and polyphenols, and how they work hand-in-hand with caloric restriction to form an effective, healthy, and safe weight loss plan. Not only that, but you also learned that by increasing your dietary intake of polyphenols, you could decrease your risk of cancer! We will be taking the science a bit further to explore some of the most common health-related concerns and how by increasing your consumption of Sirtfoods, you can fight back against them. Of course, I am not promising that the Sirt diet will heal you or that it is a miracle. But unbiased scientific studies have proven that they are health benefits that can be experienced. Some people may experience these benefits to a higher degree than others; either way, you will find your health benefits from increasing your Sirtfood consumption.

The creators of the Sirt diet, two dietitians from the UK, formed these specific coined the term 'sirtfood' and combined it into a single diet specifically to target weight loss. This was done after research found that sirtfoods are high in sirtuins, a type of protein found not only within certain foods but also in the human body. These proteins have a powerful effect on weight loss, metabolism, inflammation, and the body's natural aging process. The result is that you can lose more weight while retaining muscle and health.

While the diet had previously helped many people, it was still relatively unheard of by most individuals. The standard plan following the Sirt diet consists of two phases lasting a length of a week each. This can help people lose weight quickly when needed, such as if they are trying to get their high cholesterol or blood pressure down before a date set by their doctor or lose a certain number of pounds to their dream wedding dress or tux. However, there is another method of the Sirt diet. You can also follow for slower and more sustained weight loss. This version is ideal for the people who can take a little more time for weight loss that is just as effective yet more sustainable. Whichever version of the Sirt diet you plan to choose, the traditional or the innovative. You can attain the success you desire, whether you want to lose weight or boost your health.

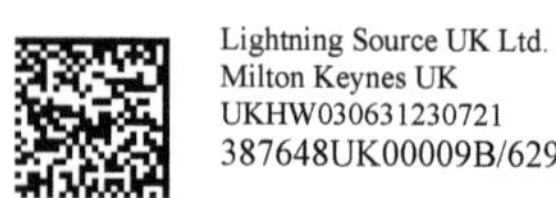

Lightning Source UK Ltd.
Milton Keynes UK
UKHW030631230721
387648UK00009B/629

9 781801 787482